INTERPRETING SCIENCE

UNDERSTANDING THE UNIVERSE

by

FRANKLIN B. CARROLL

HEAD, DEPARTMENT OF SCIENCE
FRANKFORD HIGH SCHOOL
PHILADELPHIA

FRANK A. REXFORD

EDUCATIONAL DIRECTOR, MUSEUM OF THE
CITY OF NEW YORK

AND

HENRY T. WEED

HEAD OF THE SCIENCE DEPARTMENT
GIRLS' COMMERCIAL HIGH SCHOOL
BROOKLYN, NEW YORK

Book Three

THE JOHN C. WINSTON COMPANY
CHICAGO   PHILADELPHIA   TORONTO
ATLANTA   LOS ANGELES   DALLAS

FOREWORD

Many minds, youthful or mature, want always to know causes—why the radio speaks or whence the wind comes and whither it goes. Those in this fortunate state of curiosity are led to examine new facts and old, to search for additional information, to evaluate facts. They are directed to the framing of hypotheses, to testing them by experiment and observation, then to provisional acceptance or amendment. Finally they are led to comparison, to generalization, to the concept of law.

The graveyard of once-credited scientific theories and axioms and the mistakes of pupils serve to educate no less than do brilliant explorations. Pupils are led to see that the generalizations that seem adequate at one stage of investigation are often inadequate in the light of new-found facts. Revision or abandonment of old for new is necessary as science advances. Science is shown as always tentative. The science of one age will often not do for the next. The achievements of scientists in the past are shown in relation to those of later date. It is hoped that pupils will decide for themselves that science can advance only a short distance on the road toward eternal truth.

Not accumulation of memorized facts and principles but habituation to the scientific attitude toward common experience, as well as toward the strange and new, is the better goal of general science. Respect for facts and their interpretation, an attitude of open-mindedness, a willingness to accept the tentative explanation when facts warrant and to suspend judgment when explanation cannot be reached— these are habits to be established by the study of science. Difficult to test, the establishment of such attitude has too often been left to faith and hope. This text reminds pupils through their study that they must face all problems with open minds.

The facts and principles of the science course are abundantly developed. Pupils will be familiar with them by the end of the course. But the open-minded zeal to know and to apply scientific processes to a changing world will enable them to learn from the newspaper, the magazine, the museum, the scientific report, and the daily experience. The approach to study is common experience; yet the pupil is not limited to the science of everyday problems. The unfamiliar and the distant are as fascinating to younger minds as to older. The sublime measures of space are as essential to an appreciation of man's efforts as is the science of the kitchen sink. The open places will unfold to the pupil their fascinating problems of life. Here also he will learn something of earth's past as well as man's adaptation to its features and forces.

To avoid interruption of the story, experiments, except where used in the development of the thought, are placed at the ends of the chapters. Lack of facilities and necessities of school organization often prevent the introduction of the experiment at the dramatic moment. Therefore, when experimental results are desired in the unfolding of an explanation, discussion of an experiment is incorporated in the text. For teachers who use the experiment as the point of departure in a study, detailed direction to the pupil is provided. Study may begin with the experiments assembled at the close of the chapter. Discussion of findings in the text will serve for verification or amendment of the pupil's own findings.

The connecting thread of the various problems is the study of energy. The text presents energy as manifested in natural phenomena, in man's struggle against the forces of nature, in his study of their causes and conditions, and their ultimate control in the performance of his work. Life is presented as a complex of energy transformations. The adaptation of living things to their environment is their adjustment of activity and structure to make use of supplies of energy and material. Reciprocally, their activity is determined by the supplies of energy that they can tap. Man's intentional adaptation to his environment is developed as the control of energy as well as of material.

The varying ability of pupils is recognized through the text. Questions raised by boys and girls in the class often carry the discussion beyond the grasp of some members either because of their lack of factual knowledge or their limitations in ability. It is essential that the questioner be satisfied as far as may be and be stimulated to further inquiry. Material and appropriate experiments beyond the "minimum essentials" are included in the text and indicated as optional or are inclosed in brackets. At the ends of units are questions to think out and further suggestions for investigation and experiment. Experience has shown that most pupils enjoy matching their abilities and knowledge of facts with challenging questions. Smaller, though considerable, numbers are sufficiently intrigued to pursue individual investigation in library, field, and home. Recognition of such individual effort is highly stimulating to investigator as well as to the class. This book presents general science as the interpreter of environment, as parent of the open mind, as guide to tested thought and reasoned conclusions. It seeks to develop the challenger of tradition, the foe of wishful thinking. In the lightning changes of a changing world it aims to develop a habitual reliance on open-minded study of established facts.

The authors and publishers desire to make grateful acknowledgment to the following teachers for critical reading of the manuscript: Miss Elmira Lodor, Head of the Department of Science, William Penn High School, Philadelphia; Dr. R. Foster Stevens, Head of the Department of of Science, Girard College, Philadelphia; A. J. Souba, Principal, Junior High School, Chisholm, Minn.; Arthur W. Lowe, Instructor in Physics, Frankford High School, Philadelphia.

TABLE OF CONTENTS

CONTENTS

PAGE

LIST OF EXPERIMENTS

ACKNOWLEDGMENTS

(Numbers following names refer to pages in the text)

Grateful acknowledgment is made to the following individuals and organizations for their kind permission to use the illustrative material to be found in this book:

American Bridge Co., 177, 178
American Forestry Assn., 594
American Medical Assn., 546, 547
American Museum of Natural History, 6, 105
American Poultry Journal, 411
American Red Cross, 527
Atchison, Topeka, and Santa Fe Ry. Co., 89
Autofyrstop Co., 54

Bailey, Alfred M., Chicago Academy of Sciences, 257, 640, 641
Baltimore & Ohio R. R., 176
Barber Asphalt Co., 175
Bausch & Lomb Optical Co., 530, 661, 669, 691
Belding Bros. & Co., 463
Bethlehem Steel Co., 183
Bureau of Animal Industry, 449
Bureau of Biological Survey, 573
Bureau of Chemistry and Soils, 425
Bureau of Entomology, 441, 550
Bureau of Entomology and Plant Quarantine, 565
Bureau of Plant Industry, 5, 378, 395, 396, 398, 399, 416, 417, 435, 440, 461
Bureau of Reclamation, 9
Busch-Sulzer Bros.—Diesel Engine Co., 170

Calif. Packing Corp., 600
Calif. Toll Bridge Authority, C. H. Purcell, Chief Engineer, 36
Canada Steamship Lines, 231
Canadian National Railways, 587
Caterpillar Tractor Co., 423, 574
Chicago Apparatus Co., 189, 683
Cleveland Pneumatic Tool Co., 34
Collins, Inc., Warren E., 27

Deere, John, 443
Denoyer-Geppert Co., 512, 514
Denver & Rio Grande Western R. R. Co., 8, 176, 599
Eastman Kodak Co., 274, 275
Elco Tool and Screw Corp., 155
Field Museum of Natural History, 1, 614, 646
Fire Engineering, 50
Fischer Musical Instrument Co., Inc., Carl, 244
Gatchell & Manning, Inc., Fig. 267
General Biological Supply House, 562
General Electric Co., 209, 329, 337, 342
General Motors, 168
Geologic Survey, Commonwealth of Pa., 581, 582, 583, 584, 590
Geologic Survey, Department of Interior, Washington, D. C., 433, 584, 587, 591, 592, 596, 597, 601
Grant, Heber, J., Pres., Church of Jesus Christ of Latter Day Saints, 233
Hamburg - American Line — North German Lloyd, 180
Haussman, Otto G., 281
Hudson River Day Line, 179
Ingersoll-Rand Co., 33
International Harvester Co., 442, 443
International Salt Co., Inc., 104
Lakeview Ponds, 7
Lincoln Electric Co., 77
Loomis, B. F., National Park Service, 593
Lowell Observatory, 659, 660
McKiernan-Terry Corp., 159

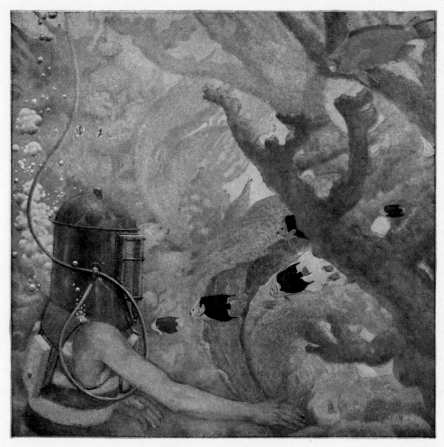

A Bahaman Coral Garden

The bottom of the sea calls the scientist. Here Dr. Roy Waldo Miner is studying life amid the coral reefs of the Bahamas. Creatures there are strange to us because their surroundings are strange to us. Yet man through the study of nature's laws has devised means of living for a time below the sea. On page 66, Figure 65, you will see an apparatus in which another scientist has descended over a half mile to study the ocean's life where it is totally dark.

Fig. 1. Men of the Old Stone Age had learned to use fire and to wrap the skins of animals about them. With clothing, weapons, and fire, the control of nature was under way.

INTRODUCTION

LEARNING WHAT SURROUNDS US

Try to imagine yourself living in the Old Stone Age. You sleep in a cave on a bearskin or a pile of branches and dead grass. You cover yourself with another skin—if you have it. In the morning, if there is a piece of bear meat, wild ox, or pony left over from the previous day, you rub together two sticks to kindle a fire to roast it. If there is no meat left, you just do not eat. You do not bother to wash. Sanitation is unkown to you, besides you have nothing to carry water in except perhaps a skin, and no vessel in which to heat it.

Early in the morning the men take up stone hammers, clubs, or poles hacked to a point with a sharp flint and hardened in a fire. They go out to hunt. If they are successful, the family eat. If they find no game, it is merely another hungry day, and you are used to them. While the men are

Text included in brackets ([ ]) comprises topics required in certain courses of study.

(1)

away, the women and children search the river edge for mussels and crawfish or they dig in the earth with sticks for roots. The older women use sharp stones to scrape away the flesh

from the skins of slain animals. Scraping skins and chipping stone implements are the only industries. The style in clothes is fur —a bearskin thrown over the shoulder, nothing more. When the weather is warm, no clothing is worn. There is no thread; sewing has not been invented. When game becomes too scarce to supply food and fur, the family take up their stone hammers, pointed staves, and skins and trudge away to another hunting ground.

Fig. 2. The city is a man-made environment. Science and industry have changed all nature except the weather.

At least it is a simple matter to move.

Now put yourself on a modern, "progressive" farm. Machinery plows, sows, reaps, and threshes. It chops and mixes food for the stock and milks the cows. Machinery cools the milk and hauls it to market. From factories and stores it brings back food supplies, prepared elsewhere by machinery; also clothing, household goods, and more machinery. Electricity lights house and barns and runs household and farm machinery. Radio brings crops reports, news of the world, and entertainment. In the fields, garden, and orchard are plants and animals that cave men never saw.

Once again, put yourself in a modern city apartment or dwelling. Winter and wet weather do not exist indoors. In the hasty run from home to office, factory, or movie theater, heated vehicles may take you from one building to another. All about you are the products of man's hand and brain. From grapefruit, bananas, and coffee at breakfast—fruits of the distant warm parts of the earth—to the printed paper at office and school or the steel at the mill, everything has been made or brought by machinery. Check over the things that you meet in the course of a day. If you live in the city, it is doubtful if you find a single thing as nature left it.

Nature's gifts. What has changed man from the slave of nature to its master? Has nature become more bountiful and kindly disposed toward man since the Old Stone Age? Not at all. Man has created his modern comforts and conveniences by developing and changing the things about him. Learning the laws of nature, he has been able to use nature's supplies and to apply its powers to his own advantage.

Fig. 3.   On the modern farm, plant and animal life is largely under the control of science.

Nature supplies the bare necessities of life. There is air to supply oxygen, which is needed by living things from man to microbes, by plants as well as animals. There is water, which no living things can do without. There is heat, equally necessary for life. There is light, which, as we shall see, is the power that makes all our food. There is soil, necessary for the production of food of those that tread the land. All these necessities lie about us. The sum of all things that make up our surroundings we call our *environment*.

Fitting the environment. The necessities of life are not equally abundant in every environment. In the depth of the sea there is an abundance of water but a dearth of free air and light. In the desert the situation is reversed. In the icy regions of the poles and on the mountain tops, the necessary heat and water are too scarce for most plants and animals. In the artificial environment of the city many people suffer from the dearth of sunshine and open air. Most living

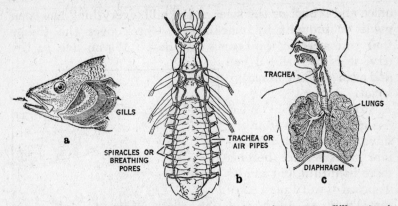

Fig. 4. (a, b, c) Animals are adapted to their environment. Gills extract oxygen from the water. Lungs of large land animals extract oxygen from the air. Branching tubes carry air through the bodies of insects.

creatures find the best conditions of life in lands of abundant rainfall and sunshine.

All living creatures from man to worms and bacteria must fit into their environment. A fish, a crab, or an oyster must get its oxygen from water. Lungs would never do, but gills of various sorts have developed. Travel through the water is a very different problem from travel on the land. The seal, a very distant relative of the dog, is descended from ancestors that took to the sea for food and safety. Seals' legs and dogs' legs have developed in very different environments, but for the same purpose of getting about (Fig. 5). A creature must have a body adapted to its environment, or it dies.

Plants, no less than animals, are adapted to live each in

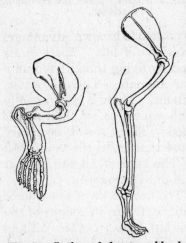

Fig. 5. Seals and dogs are blood relatives, but are adapted to different environments. The seal's leg is a broad, short flipper for paddling in the water. The dog runs on his toes and on legs that give speed.

its own particular environment (Figs. 13 and 14). The desert plant is built to hold water and its thick "hide" and compact form reduce evaporation (Fig. 6). On the contrary, a tree in the pasture spreads its branches wide and high to catch the sun (Fig. 8). The seaweed, with a flexible stem, floats with the waves where a tree would be dashed to pieces.

Changing the environment. You have perhaps seen a piece of ground left bare by a steam shovel later invaded by weeds and then by grass. The weeds and grass do not leave the ground as they found it. If crops had been planted in the bare soil left by the steam shovel, they probably would have died. But after generations of weeds and grass have lived and died, topsoil is formed again and crops can grow. Plants and animals modify their surroundings (Fig. 7). Plants growing in a pool often make great changes in the pool

Fig. 6. Plants are adapted to their environment. The thick skin of the cactus reduces evaporation and the bulky stem stores water. Giant Cereus, Sonora Desert, Mexico.

in the course of a year or two, or even in the course of a summer (Fig. 9). Small lakes may be entirely filled and converted into land by plants. You may have seen the changes wrought by the inhabitants of an anthill or of a prairie-dog

Fig. 7. Animals change their environment. Beavers have made a pond by building a dam of branches and mud across a stream.

town. In many ways plants and animals, like men, change their environment.

The swiftest changes in environment wrought by living things are those by man. The cave man, it is true, made little more change than did the bears and other dwellers of the caves. Perhaps he hacked down a few small trees with his stone axes; he broke stones to make his implements; he reduced for a time the number of those animals that he hunted about his cave. Beyond these changes he did little to alter the wilderness about him, but he had begun to learn to

Fig. 8. The spreading branches are the tree's adaptation to catch the sunlight with its leaves.

Fig. 9. Plants change their environment. Plants here are filling a pond.

do things in ways that were to bring vast changes in the days of his successors. He had learned to use the stone hammer to slay a cave bear, bigger and mightier than he. He had learned to protect his naked body with the bear's thick skin. More momentous still, he had learned to make and to use fire. Man's control over his environment had begun (Fig. 11).

From such small beginnings man's power has grown until he has now changed the face of the earth (Fig. 12). Forests that covered the eastern half of the United States a century or two ago are replaced by farms and great cities. Similar changes passed over Europe and Asia centuries earlier.

Fig. 10. Bears have adapted their habits to environment. This bear is getting his dinner from the garbage barrel. Rainier National Park.

Fig. 11. Indians of the Southwest adapted themselves to their environment by seeking safety in the cliffs. They changed their cliff environment as you see. Mesa Verde National Park.

Man, like other animals and many plants, often finds that he is unable to live amidst the changes he has wrought. Destructive lumbering and poor farming have made thousands of acres barren. However, unlike more lowly creatures, man in modern civilization seeks to turn back the tide of destruction and to restore the land to uses that will profit him. Modern governments are using science to save and restore a gift of nature that man cannot do without—the land.

Learning how nature acts. Stone Age man watched the cave bear and learned to slay him as he emerged from his narrow lair within the cave. He learned to select the kind of stone that broke with a sharp edge and that had sufficient strength and weight for a weapon. He learned to shape the ax and to bind it to the haft with the sinews of the animals he ate. He studied his environment, living and nonliving. Thus man's power over nature has grown because he has learned nature's secrets.

Fig. 12.   Man has changed the desert environment into a garden by
irrigation and planting.

The scientist today studies his environment with the same
five senses that the cave man used.   He has no other means
of learning what lies about him.   But he has learned to make
new things visible and audible.   There are waves of energy
coming to us from the depths of space that do not affect our
eyes, ears, or other organs of sense.   But the instruments of
science change the wave motions to other wave motions that
we can perceive—as sounds or gleams of light or streaks and
spots on a photographic plate.   Though the organs of the
body have scarcely changed since cave-man days, our knowledge has changed.   Man has builded on the discoveries of
man.   He has learned to search for the causes of nature's acts.

Little more than a hundred years ago an old woman was
hanged because a young woman died after the "Old Witch"
passed the door.   Less than a year before this page was
written, a farmer threw a horse collar at a black cat that
entered the stable, and next day the horse died.   The farmer
sought a "witch doctor" to learn how to make amends to the
black cat so that no more "bad luck" would come to him.

Fig. 13. The skunk cabbage lives in moist woods. Compare its leaves with the ragweed, Figure. 14.

Did the young woman die because the old woman passed the door? Did the horse die because the farmer threw the horse collar at the black cat?

We say that the old farmer and they who hanged the "witch" were superstitious. Like the rest of mankind, they sought to find the causes of events. But like many other men and women, they failed to distinguish a happening that follows an event merely by chance, from a happening that is really caused by a preceding event. They did not distinguish sequence (following) from cause and effect. Science is never satisfied until it has shown by repeated observation or controlled experiment that one event actually causes the second.

Proof by experiment. Suppose a new malady spreads among cattle until hundreds sicken and die. We may guess

Fig. 14.   The ragweed lives in sunny fields.

at the cause.   What we guess depends
upon what we know of similar events.
If we know nothing of disease germs,
we may guess that the gods are pun-
ishing us, or we may blame it on a
witch.   If we are familiar with disease germs, we may guess that the
misfortune is due to germs.

The scientist first observes carefully the course of the
disease, its beginning, the appearance of the animals, their
action, feeding, temperature, all the indications of disease—
the *symptoms*, as the doctor says.   Then he searches the
bodies of sick and dead animals for disease germs.   If he
finds some that he suspects, he may guess that they cause the
disease.   In scientific language, instead of saying he guesses,
we say that he forms a hypothesis.

When he finds suspicious germs in sick and dead animals,
has he proved that they cause the disease?   No.   He must

perform a controlled experiment. He must inject the germs into healthy animals and produce the disease. Even then he has not proved his guess or hypothesis to be correct. He must again find the germs in the animal that he injected. These steps in proving the cause of a disease were worked out by the great German bacteriologist, Dr. Robert Koch (1843–1910), one of the founders of modern scientific medicine.

An experiment of Pasteur. A certain experiment performed by the great Frenchman Pasteur (1822–1895), another of the founders of modern medicine, shows us what a controlled experiment should be. In many parts of Europe a terrible malady known as *splenic fever* (fever of the spleen), or *anthrax*, was sweeping away cattle, horses, sheep, and sometimes men and women. At an earlier time 60,000 people had died in one outbreak before the disease had stopped. The germs of the disease had been found, and Pasteur sought to show that the disease could be prevented by vaccination. His vaccine for the prevention of the disease was a mixture of the living germs that had been weakened by growing at high temperatures.

A large group of scientific men and others gathered to see Pasteur answer by an experiment the question, "Will vaccination by these weakened germs prevent splenic fever?" The experiment lasted twenty-eight days. Fifty sheep were chosen for the experiment. Twenty-five sheep were vaccinated. The rest were not vaccinated. The vaccination consisted in injecting the weakened germs under the skin. Twelve days later the vaccinated animals received a second vaccination. Two weeks later all fifty sheep were injected with the strong living germs that cause the disease. Four days afterward all the unvaccinated sheep had died of splenic fever and the vaccinated sheep were alive and healthy. The bodies of the dead sheep were opened and the germs of splenic fever were found.

What is a controlled experiment? A controlled experiment is an attempt to find whether your guess or hypothesis is correct. Do the bacteria cause the disease? Can a certain vaccine prevent a certain disease? Will a current of electricity decompose water?   Does salt water freeze at the same temperature as fresh water?

An experiment to prove or dispose a hypothesis gives the answer to a question.   You must frame such a question before you perform the experiment.   If you cannot form a simple question, you are not ready to perform such an experiment.

The second step is to perform the experiment.   It must be simple; you must attempt to answer only one question at a time.   To prove a hypothesis there must be no doubt of the answer.   Pasteur found, for example, that after the bacteria were injected into the animal's body, it became sick or it did not become sick.

Planning the experiment involves selecting suitable material with which to work.   This is often a very difficult part of the experiment.   Sometimes an experiment is delayed for years until suitable material is found.   In Pasteur's experiment with vaccination against splenic fever the following material was required: sheep, weakened germs, strong germs, hypodermic syringes for injection, thermometers for taking the temperature of the sheep, sheep pens, feed, etc.

Sometimes in medicine it is very difficult to get the material for the experiment.   You would not care to test pneumonia germs by giving them to a healthy person.   Fortunately, pneumonia germs affect mice.   Mice are part of the material for pneumonia experiments.   In 1910 only man was known to harbor yellow fever germs.   What could be used to study the disease?   Dr. Walter Reed and his fellow workers of the United States Army could not use lower animals to find the answer to their question, "Does a certain kind of mosquito carry yellow fever?"   On page 548 you may read of the brave men who offered themselves as material for the experiment and how the question was answered by illness and death.

After obtaining suitable experimental material, the next step is to perform the experiment and record the results.

The final step in experiment is to decide whether the results give an answer that cannot be doubted, and what that answer is.

3

Experiments in this course. The experiments that are outlined for this course in science follow these steps:

1. *Question:* What is the experiment to determine?
2. *Materials:* What materials are needed to perform the experiment?
3. *Method or directions:* What is to be done to perform the experiment?
4. *Results:* What happened in the experiment?
5. *Conclusion:* From what you saw, what answer can you give to the question?
6. *Applications:* What similar questions can you answer by using these results and conclusions?

Now perform Experiment 1. Then make a report of it in your notebook. Write down the six steps. Some of them are to be copied directly. Others can be completed only after you have performed the experiment. Under the heading *Directions*, add a drawing of the apparatus to your account of the procedure.

EXPERIMENT 1

Question: Does a quart of milk weigh the same amount as a quart of water?

Materials: A one-quart milk bottle, empty; platform balance; weights; a quart of milk; a quart of water.

Directions: Fill the empty milk bottle to the top with water. Weigh it accurately, and note the weight. Empty the bottle. Dry it. Fill the same milk bottle with milk to the top. Weigh it.

Results: Record the weight of the bottle filled with water, and the weight of the bottle filled with milk.

Conclusion: Answer the question.

QUESTIONS TO THINK OUT

1. Before the coming of the white man, how did the Eskimo fit into his environment? How did he obtain food, clothing, fuel, shelter? Of what did he make weapons, tools, fishhooks and lines, thread, needles? How did he make fire?

2. Contrast the uses of environment made by the Eskimo and the native Bushman of the South African desert.

3. Similarly, contrast the life of the Indian before your region was settled with that of the present population. What region supplied the Indian and the present population with the necessities of life? What

changes in environment and in control of environment have made possible the present population of the United States?

4. List some "mysteries of nature" that you would like to have explained. List some common occurrences that you would like to have explained; for example, why the radio speaks; why many trees shed their leaves in the fall and many do not; why living fish can be frozen in ice without apparent injury.

5. Devise and then perform an experiment to answer the following question: Will a boat ride higher in fresh water or in salt water? Write a report as in Experiment 1.

UNIT ONE

THE AIR: HOW IT CONTROLS US AND HOW WE CONTROL IT

We cannot get away from air and remain alive. It is a necessary part of our environment. We live in the midst of an ocean of air as fish live in the sea. Air penetrates the caves and the soil and even the water of lakes and of the sea. Man has never been able to change the atmosphere as he has changed the land. At most he has polluted the air above his cities and "conditioned" the air in his buildings and trains.

Yet study of the composition and behavior of the air has enabled man to press it into service to do his work. Packing air into closed vessels has given power to operate such things as car brakes, submarines, and torpedoes. Study of air pressure has enabled man to fly on the wings of the wind to the uttermost parts of the earth. Removal of air from closed vessels has given us such useful things as vacuum bottles, electric lamps, and radio tubes. The vacuum created by the removal of air has enabled the scientist to carry on experiments that would be impossible in the air, experiments that have given us the X ray and have taught much about what *matter* is, and what the earth and the stars are made of.

In this unit we shall study the extent and composition of the air that surrounds us, and we shall learn something about how air supports life and how living things alter it. We shall learn some of the science that has enabled man to put air to work in machines, and we shall see how some of those machines work. Then we shall study the control of that great activity *oxidation* which makes life the great producer and fire the great destroyer.

(16)

CHAPTER I

THE PRESSURE OF AIR

Air takes up room. Because you cannot see nor smell nor taste air, you may think of it as so much empty space, but a few simple experiments will make you think differently. Turn a tumbler upside down and push it, mouth down, into a pan of water. You cannot force the water to fill the glass to the upturned bottom. Air in the glass holds it back. This shows that air occupies space.

Air is heavy. Did you ever pick up an inflated automobile tire? Did it weigh the same as it did when flat? If you have had no experience with automobile tires, you may be able to perform the following experiment. Weigh an empty basket ball. Then pump it full of air until it is hard and weigh it again.

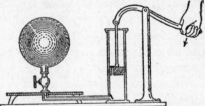

Fig. 15. Air pump and flask. To show that air has weight, weigh the flask, pump out the air, and weigh again.

You will find that air has considerable weight.

With an air pump you can reverse the last experiment. Weigh a flask. Then pump the air out and weigh it again (Fig. 15).

By such experiments we learn that twelve cubic feet of air at sea level weigh about a pound. At that rate an ordinary dwelling room holds two or three hundred pounds of air.

Air is matter. The scientist defines matter as anything that occupies space and has weight. From the first two paragraphs of this chapter you have learned that air does both. Therefore, air is matter. Matter may be in any of three forms: gas, liquid, or solid. Under certain conditions

(17)

some things may assume any of these forms: water vapor, water, or ice, or solid or molten metal. Air, too, may be either a gas or a liquid. Liquid air is produced by subjecting air under pressure to intense cold.

Fig. 16. A drinking fountain for chickens. The pressure of the air on the water in the saucer holds the water in the reservoir.

Air has a crushing weight. A simple experiment that you can perform either in a laboratory or on the back lot will show you its power. You need little apparatus, just a gallon oil can and a stopper and something with which to hold the can over a fire. Pour an inch of water into the can and boil the water for two or three minutes after the steam has begun to come out. Take the can off the fire and cork it tightly. Let it cool. If you are in a hurry, pour cold water over it. Soon the can is crushed in as if an invisible giant were squeezing it between his hands.

What crushed in the sides of the can? Steam drove the air out. When the can cooled, the steam inside condensed again, leaving a partial vacuum (emptiness). The pressure of the air outside bent the sides inward.

The fruit-can lid that you cannot unscrew is held down by the same force. The fruit is canned hot with little or no air remaining in the jar. When it cools, the air pushes down on the jar with a force of over 70 pounds on a lid $2\frac{1}{2}$ inches in diameter. If you pull out the rubber ring on one side, admitting air to equalize the pressure, you can easily unscrew the top.

Air is always pressing. Fill a test tube with water; close it with your thumb and insert the closed end into a basin of water; then remove your thumb, holding the tube upright. The water stays in the test tube because air is pressing down in the outer vessel while it cannot press down on the top of the water in the test tube. A sanitary drinking fountain for the poultry yard is made on the model of the last arrangement. Chickens have a way of getting their dirty feet in a pan of drinking water (Fig. 16). The sanitary fountain stops the fouling of the water.

Fill a tumbler with water and cover the top with a piece of wet, soft cardboard. Hold the cardboard in place with your hand and invert the tumbler; then remove your hand. Again air pressure supports the weight of the water.

Measuring air pressure. How much weight will the air support?

You can measure the air pressure with a *barometer*—a very easy thing to make and a very valuable scientific instrument. Proceed as you did with the test tube inverted in a basin of water. If you were to use water in the inverted tube, you would need to use so long a tube that you could not conveniently perform the experiment in a room. Mercury, therefore, which is more than 13 times as heavy as water, is generally used.

Use a tube closed at one end and not less than 36 inches long. The diameter is not important, except that a large tube uses a great deal of mercury. Fill the tube with mercury and invert it in a dish of mercury (Fig. 17). Such a tube of mercury is called a *column* of mercury. Unless you are in the mountains, the mercury will fall in the tube until the column is about 30 inches high. If you used water instead of mercury in making a barometer, the column of water would be about 34 feet high. If the top surface of the column of mercury or water has an area of 1 square inch, the column will weigh about 15 pounds. The pressure of the air is therefore 15 pounds to a square inch. For convenience we say that atmosphere pressure is 30 inches of mercury, or 15 pounds.

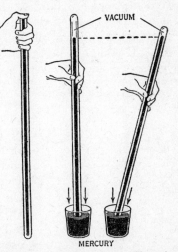

Fig. 17. A barometer. The air pressure on the mercury in the bowl determines the height of the column in the tube.

Fig. 18.   Mount Everest (left) and Makalu.   On the top of Mount Everest the barometer stands at less than 10 inches.   The lack of oxygen due to reduced air is one difficulty in climbing high mountains.

This experiment was first tried by Torricelli, an Italian scientist who lived in the sixteenth century.   The tube is therefore often called a *Torricellian tube,* and the space above the mercury a *Torricellian vacuum.*

If you get rid of some of the air that is pressing on the free mercury in the dish, the height of the mercury column will fall.   You can do this with an air pump by putting the barometer under a tall bell jar and pumping out some of the **air.**   If you have no tall bell jar, you can show the same thing as in Figure. 19.

Fig. 19.   Air is sucked out of the bottle and the barometer falls with the reduced air pressure.

When Pascal, the French scientist, had Torricelli's mercurial barometer carried up a mountain, the column of mercury gradually fell.   The air thins so rapidly above the earth's surface that the mercury falls about 1 inch for every 1000 feet ascent. On the top of Mount Everest (Fig. 18) it stands at about 9 inches.   The fall is so regular that barometers are used to measure the altitude above sea level.

A mercurial barometer is awkward to carry, but an *aneroid barometer*

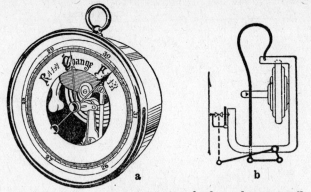

Fig. 20.   a, the aneroid barometer; b shows how a small
in-or-out motion of the box of the aneroid is magnified, producing an extended motion of the pointer.

may be carried in the pocket.   An aneroid (meaning *without
liquid*), instead of having a column of mercury with a Torricellian vacuum above it, has a metal box with a partial
vacuum.   With increased air pressure the sides of the box
tend to bend in, and with decreased outside pressure they tend
to bulge out.   An indicator measures the change (Fig. 20).

Aneroids are so delicately made that they will indicate a
difference between the floor and a table top.   Made to measure
altitude, they are often called *altimeters* (Fig. 21).

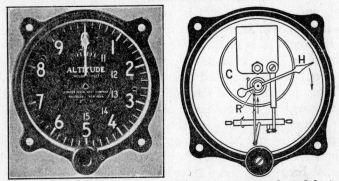

Fig. 21.   The altimeter is really an aneroid barometer graduated for height
instead of pressure.   As the airplane climbs, the air pressure on the sealed
box C decreases, and the box expands.   By means of levers and a fine
chain wound around the drum R, this motion is transmitted to the hand H.

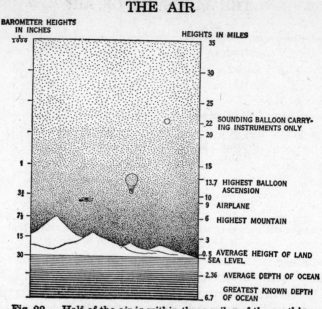

Fig. 22. Half of the air is within three miles of the earth's surface. It thins rapidly with ascent.

How air pressure affects us. Although the air extends upward over 400 miles above the earth, it is very rare at the upper levels and denser at the lower levels. In fact, three fourths of the air is pressed down within 6 miles of sea level, and more than half is within 3 miles (Fig. 22). Thus the atmosphere is mostly compressed into a small layer at the bottom. It is in this bottom layer at sea level that the pressure is 15 pounds to the square inch. Most people on the earth are accustomed to live at about that pressure.

When people from the lower lands go up into the high mountains, they sometimes get "mountain sickness," due to the thinner air. One of the difficulties of climbing high mountains is the thinness of the air and the consequent difficulty of getting enough oxygen. A little exertion brings labored breathing and a laboring heart. Aviators on altitude flights and sometimes mountain climbers going to great heights carry tanks of oxygen to make up the deficiency of thin air.

Not only the quantity of oxygen but also the actual **pressure** affects our bodies. At sea level 360 pounds press down on your hand when you hold your arm out to the side. You

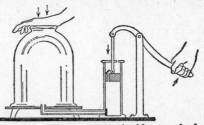

can easily calculate it. If your hand is 4 x 6 inches, it will have 24 square inches on top; at 15 pounds to the square inch, the pressure would be 360 pounds. It takes a strong man to hold up 360 pounds with both arms. How are you able to do it? The air below your hand is pressing up with the same force as the air above presses down.

Fig. 23. The pressure inside our bodies equals that of the atmosphere. When air is pumped from the bell jar, the internal pressure of the body forces the flesh to bulge into the top of the jar.

If you put your hand on the open top of the bell jar of an air pump and pump out some of the air underneath your hand, you will find that your hand is tightly pressed to the bell jar. If you remove most of the air from underneath your hand, the pressure becomes painful (Fig. 23).

Ten tons press in on your body (15 pounds × 1500, the number of square inches on the surface of the body). Why are you not crushed to death by this immense weight?

Air presses into all sorts of places. You can show that it penetrates the soil. Partly fill a glass with soil, and then pour water into the glass until it stands a little above the soil. You will see the air bubble out. If the air did not penetrate the soil, crops, helpful bacteria, insects, worms, and many other little creatures that inhabit the

Fig. 24. To show that soil contains air. When water is poured in a tumbler containing soil, air bubbles rise from the soil.

soil could not live there. In a later chapter you will learn how valuable these small plants and animals are to the farmer.

Air penetrates water. If you warm a glass of water very gently, you can see air bubbles arise. You probably have noticed that when a glass of cool water is left standing in a warm room, tiny bubbles of air form inside the glass. A hundred quarts of water at ordinary temperature will take up about two quarts of air.

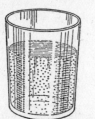

Fig. 25. Water contains air. When a cool glass of water stands in a warm room, bubbles of air collect on the glass.

Air under atmospheric pressure penetrates your body, not only to the lungs but to the blood vessels, muscles, and microscopic cells. As the pressure is equal inward and outward, you feel no pressure at all. If for any reason the pressure becomes very unequal, you become painfully aware that pressure exists.

In sea diving it is necessary to fill the diving suit with air at a pressure equal to the pressure of the deep water, let us say 45 pounds to the square inch. If the diver has been down for some time, his body is saturated with air at this pressure. If he were suddenly pulled to the top of the water, the outward pressure of the air in his body would be 45 pounds, while the pressure of the air around his body would be only 15 pounds. This would be likely to cause some of the symptons of "caisson disease"—severe pain in the joints (the "bends"), deafness, paralysis, or even death. To avoid such injury, the diver is raised only short distances at a time so that the pressure in his suit may be slowly changed.

EXPERIMENT 2

Question: Does air occupy space?

Materials: An empty tumbler; a bucket of water.

Directions: Invert the tumbler and press it down evenly to the bottom of the bucket.

Result: State in a sentence how high the water rises in the tumbler.

Conclusion: Account for your result. Answer the question.

EXPERIMENT 3

Question: Does air have weight?

Materials: A football; a metal clamp or a cord to tie the neck of the football; a pump to fill the football; a balance; a set of weights or some sand.

Directions: Pump air into the football until it is hard. Put the clamp on the neck of the ball. Put the football on one pan of the balance. Weight the other pan with weights or sand until the beam is horizontal. Then open the clamp and let the air out of the football.

Results: What happens to the balance when you let the air out of the football?

Conclusion: Account for your results. Answer the question.

EXPERIMENT 4

Perform the experiment described on page 18 showing that air can crush a tin can. Write a report of the experiment in your notebook in the regular form.

EXPERIMENT 5

Make a barometer as described on page 19. Record your experiment in your notebook. Leave the barometer in position and report the height of the column of mercury every day for two weeks.

A QUESTION TO THINK OUT

How does this type of coffee maker work?

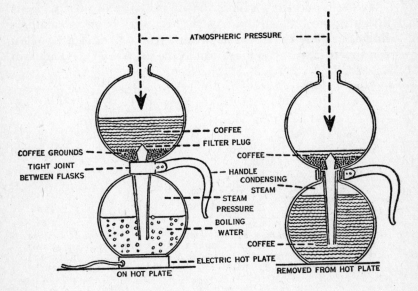

CHAPTER II

WORKING THE AIR

Air pressure at work. "Sucking soda through a straw" uses air pressure. When you put a straw in your mouth and draw through it, you reduce the pressure in the straw. If the free end of the straw is in the air, atmospheric pressure forces more air into the straw. If the free end is in a glass of soda, the air pressing upon the soda in the glass forces the liquid through the straw into your mouth.

When you squeeze the bulb of a *medicine dropper*, and then release it with the tip of the tube under water, air pushes the liquid into the dropper.

In a *vacuum cleaner* a whirling fan drives air into the dust bag, reducing the pressure at the nozzle. The outside air rushes in through the nozzle carrying the dust with it (Fig. 26).

To get liquid from a heavy bottle in the laboratory without lifting it, we often use a *siphon* (Fig. 27). This is simply a rubber or glass tube bent as in the figure. We fill the siphon and invert it with the short arm in the vessel and the long arm

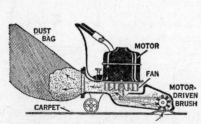

Fig. 26. Air pressure carries dust into the vacuum sweeper. The fan reduces the pressure inside so that the outside air will rush in.

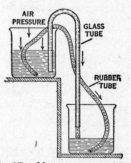

Fig. 27. Air pressure enables the siphon to carry water over a hill. What reduces the pressure in the long arm?

Fig. 28. The respirator produces artificial respiration. The patient is placed inside of the cylinder with head outside, resting on the piece of canvas.

outside as shown. The greater weight of the water in the long arm starts the water flowing out. The outflow of water tends to reduce the pressure in the siphon. The pressure of air in the upper dish forces the water up the short tube, over the bend, and into the longer tube. Siphons are convenient for emptying large tanks. A siphon is sometimes used in a water system to carry water over a small hill, but it cannot raise water more than 34 feet.

We get our *breath* by air pressure. The lungs hang in a boxlike chamber formed by the walls of the chest. The ribs and the breastbone support the side walls, and a great curved muscle, called the *diaphragm*, forms the floor. The windpipe or *trachea* leads to the outside air. When we breathe in, the diaphragm flattens and lowers the bottom of the box. At the same time muscles pull the ribs upward and outward. This increases the size of the chest box, or thorax, and thus diminishes the air pressure inside. Air then rushes in until the inside and the outside pressures are equalized. Thus when we inhale (breathe in), we do not draw air into the lungs, but air pressure forces air into them. When we exhale (breathe out), the thorax is contracted by the rising diaphragm and relaxing ribs. This contraction compresses the air in the lungs and forces it out through the windpipe. When the muscles fail to work in asphyxiation, due to gas or water in the lungs or to paralysis of certain diseases, we imitate the natural expansion and contraction of the chest by artificial respiration (Fig. 28). (See p. 526.) In Figure 29 there is a piece of apparatus which illustrates the action of the lungs.

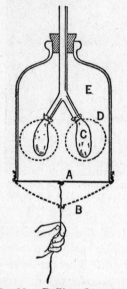

Fig. 29. Pulling the rubber A to the position B diminishes the air pressure in E, causing the balloon C to expand to D. This illustrates the expansion of lungs when the diaphragm is lowered and ribs are raised.

How water pumps use air pressure. If you ever pump water at the well, you use air pressure to raise the water. When you push down on the pump handle, you raise a piston inside the barrel of the pump (Fig. 30). Raising the piston reduces the pressure and the air in the well forces the water farther up the pump barrel. A valve prevents it from flowing back into the well (Fig. 31). When the pump handle is lifted and the piston lowered, the water in this barrel passes through valves in the piston to the space above. When the piston is raised again, this water flows from the nozzle of the pump. This kind of pump is called a *lift pump*. Atmospheric pressure cannot raise the water more than 34 feet, and, owing to leakage in the pump, it is usually not worth while to try to raise it more than 28 feet.

To raise water to greater height, a *force pump* may be used (Fig. 32). The force pump, also, depends upon air pressure to lift the water into the barrel; but the height to which water can be raised above the barrel depends upon the force that can be put on the piston. Of course the barrel should not be more than 28 feet above the water.

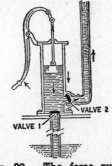

Why balloons rise. Atmospheric pressure forces balloons upward in the air. They are filled with a gas that is lighter than air. The air lifts them just as water in a basin lifts a cork. In a vacuum the balloons would not rise. They rise only because of the buoyancy (upward force) of the air.

Illuminating gas from a house gas stove may be used in toy balloons. Hydrogen gas, the lightest substance known, is often used in balloons, but it is a

Fig. 30. By pushing down the pump handle, the boy raises the piston inside the pump and water is lifted until it flows out of the pump.

dangerous explosive when mixed with oxygen. Helium gas is almost as light and will not explode. It is the gas that floats the great dirigibles, such as floated the *Macon*. This gas is so valuable that a law prohibits its exportation from the United States.

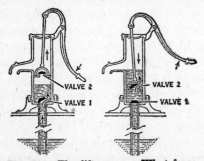

Fig. 31. The lift pump. What force raises the water from the well to the pump? Why doesn't it flow back again? What force sends the water out of the nozzle?

Fig. 32. The force pump. What force raises the water into the pump? What force sends it out through the nozzle?

Fig. 33. The airship *Macon*. The gas helium supported this ship. Wrecked and lost in the Pacific, February 12, 1935.

Fire balloons use heated air as light gas. They have open bottoms where fires are kindled (Fig. 34). As the air inside is heated, it expands and is, therefore, lighter than the air outside.

As a balloon rises, it reaches thinner and thinner air. As it reaches regions of reduced air pressure, the gas inside the balloon expands and becomes still lighter. Finally it reaches an altitude where it is as heavy as the air about it. Then it can rise no farther.

Balloons carrying instruments have risen more than 20 miles. The greatest height reached by man is 13.7 miles (72,395 feet), attained in 1935 in South Dakota by Captain Orville Anderson and A. W. Stevens of the United States Army. To protect them from the low pressure of these great altitudes, the men were sealed in a metal sphere (Fig. 35).

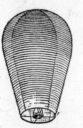

Fig. 34. A fire balloon. As a fire at the open lower end heats the air inside the balloon, the heavier, colder air outside lifts the balloon.

Airplanes. Differences in air pressure due to motion of the airplane and of the air keep the airplane flying. The wings of the plane are set at an angle as shown in Figure 36.

Fig. 35. The gondola of a stratosphere balloon. Sealed air-tight in this sphere these men rose 13.7 miles. Air pressure was then about 1 inch. Liquid oxygen and nitrogen evaporating from tanks supplied air for breathing. Sodium hydroxide absorbed the carbon dioxide breathed out by the men.

Fig. 36. Airplanes became successful after the Wright brothers learned the science of air pressure on the planes.

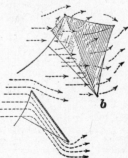

Fig. 37 (a). Difference of air pressure on the upper and lower surfaces of the wings keeps the airplane afloat. (b) Where is the higher pressure and the reduced pressure on the kite?

The propeller draws the plane forward as a screw through wood or as a screw propeller drives a ship through the water. The propeller also drives air backward under the wings.

There is an upward pressure on the wing as long as the plane is going forward, and a reduced pressure on top of the wings. The air tends to slide off the top. The difference in pressure due to the motion keeps the airplane afloat (Fig. 37). The greater the tilt of the wing the greater the lift but the slower the speed.

Parachute. When the aviator jumps, his parachute uses air pressure to land him safely on the earth. If you drop a stiff piece of paper edgewise, it

Fig. 38. How does air pressure help the aviator to land safely with his parachute?

falls rapidly. If you drop it flat surface down, it falls slowly. It then must push the air from under it, and the resistance of the air retards it.

A parachute is a great umbrella-shaped cloth with cords from the edges leading to a belt around the aviator's body.

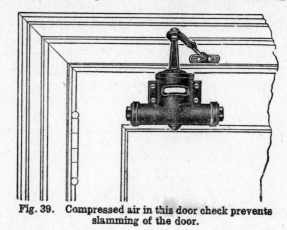

Fig. 39.   Compressed air in this door check prevents slamming of the door.

Fig. 40. Compressed air drives the riveting hammer.

The aviator carries the parachute carefully wrapped and fastened to his body. If he is forced to jump, he pulls a cord that opens the parachute pack. The resistance of the air opens the cloth umbrella. He floats down slowly because the air under the cloth is pushed slowly away (Fig. 38).

Using compressed air. Air particles can be packed tightly together, and when the pressure is released, they will instantly separate again. The scientist says that air is compressible and elastic. Therefore, we can put it to work in many ways. The air in an inflated automobile or bicycle tire by its elasticity relieves the vibration we should feel if we were riding on a hard rim. Some door checks that prevent the bang of doors depend on air compression. The door as it closes pushes a piston into a cylinder, compressing the air, which escapes slowly through a small hole (Fig. 39).

In air brakes on trains, street cars, and heavy busses, a pump compresses the air in a tank. To apply the brakes, the operator, by opening a valve, admits the compressed air into a chamber where it drives down a piston. The piston clamps the brake shoe against the wheels. Doors on subway trains are shut in a similar manner.

Compressed air drives the riveting machines that make such a racket on the new skyscrapers and bridges (Fig. 40). It drives the drill that digs up hard pavements and the drills that make holes in quarries and mines (Fig. 41).

The customers' cash payments in a department store are sometimes placed in a hollow cylinder which is inserted in a pneumatic tube (Fig. 42). A fan pumps the air from the tube, and the incoming air carries the cylinder along to the central office. Mail tubes are operated in some of the big cities by a similar system (Fig. 43).

Fig. 41. Drilling steel by compressed air.

Compressed air is used in water control. The submarine dives by admitting water into the ballast chambers, and rises by forcing it out with compressed air (Fig. 44).

In building great bridges, foundations must often be sunk through water and mud to bed rock. The *caisson* is a structure that allows man to do this work on the bottom of the river. It is a steel chamber into which air is driven until the water is forced out the bottom (Fig. 45). Men can then work in the compressed air on the bottom of the river. Compressed air is similarly used in a bell-shaped vessel which is lowered to receive men from a sunken submarine.

Fig. 42. Difference in air pressure in the tubes in front and behind the cash carrier sends the receptacle with the cash to the cashier.

Fig. 43. Air pressure carries the cylinders of mail through pneumatic (air) tubes under the street from station to station. New York General Post Office.

Fig. 44. The submarine dives by admitting water into its water chambers. It rises by driving out the water with compressed air. U. S. Submarine *Nautilus*.

Sand blasts driven by compressed air smooth down cast iron and clean the outside of city buildings. Sprays to fight insects and fungi are thrown on plants by air compressed either by hand or by motor. Automobiles and buildings are painted in the same manner. The atomizer works on the same principle (Fig. 46).

Fig. 45. A huge caisson used in building the great bridge, 8¼ miles long, from San Francisco across the bay to Oakland.

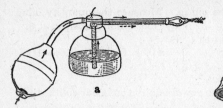

Fig. 46 (a, b, c). How does air pressure operate these articles: atomizer, force cup, nonskid tire?

EXPERIMENT 6

Question: How much air is in a football?

Materials: A football; bicycle pump; bent glass tube; deep pan; a card; a graduated cylinder or a quart milk bottle.

Method: Fill the football with water and measure the quantity of water with the graduated cylinder or quart bottle.

Pump the football full of air until it bounces easily.

Fill the cylinder or bottle with water; cover with card, invert it in a pan of water.

Measure the quantity of air in the football as follows: Insert one end of the bent tube in the neck of the ball and put the other end under the edge of the cylinder. (See Fig. 47.) Allow air to drive out the water in the cylinder. Check it as soon as the cylinder is empty. Repeat.

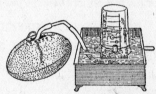

Results: Record the quantity of water in the football. Record the quantity of air. Draw a diagram of the apparatus.

Fig. 47. How to measure the volume of air in a football.

Conclusion: How do you account for the fact that the football holds more air than water? We say that air is compressible and elastic. How does the experiment show these facts?

Application: List the devices you can think of that depend upon the compressibility and elasticity of air.

EXPERIMENT 7

Question: How does a caisson work?

Materials: A glass funnel; a rubber tube to fit over funnel tube; a bicycle pump; a pan of water.

Method: Attach tube to funnel and pump to tube. Sink the funnel in the pan of water. Pump air into funnel until the water is driven out. You will need to pinch the rubber tube tightly during the upstroke of the pump to keep the air in the funnel.

Pinch the tube and remove the pump. Measure the quantity of air in the funnel as you measured the air in the football in Experiment 6.

Draw a diagram of the apparatus.

Results: Record the quantity of air in the funnel. Record the quantity of water in the funnel.

Conclusion: Answer the question.

Application: What value has this power of air been in our civilization?

EXPERIMENT 8

Question: How can I make a model parachute?

Materials: Large handkerchief; a string; a stone.

Directions: Tie a three-foot length of string to each of the four corners of a large strong handkerchief. Tie the stone to the other end of the strings. Be careful to see that all the strings are of the same length so that the stone will hang under the center of the cloth. Crumple stone, strings, and handkerchief into a ball. Throw it high into the air. As it comes down, it will unfold and sail gracefully and slowly to the earth.

Diagram: Show the parachute descending.

Conclusion: Why does the parachute go up so fast and come down so slowly?

Practical application: What commercial use is made of parachutes?

A QUESTION TO THINK OUT

Why did the stratosphere balloon (pages 30, 31) change shape as it rose?

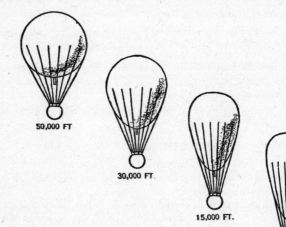

50,000 FT

30,000 FT

15,000 FT.

CHAPTER III

WHAT AIR IS

Lively air. We have seen that air is not so thin and empty as it looks, and now we shall see that air is not at all a simple substance. It is a mixture of substances. Chemists have been discovering one substance after another in air for one hundred fifty years. The first of these discoveries was made by an English clergyman and scientist, Joseph Priestley (1733–1804), who left England because of his religious views and lived for a time in Pennsylvania. Priestley heated a red powder, now known as *mercuric oxide,* and obtained a new gas. He called it "perfect air" and "active air." A candle burned in it with unusual brilliancy. A mouse placed in a jar of it was unusually active and "happy." When Priestley took a whiff of it, he found it very exhilarating. The French chemist Lavoisier (1743–94) later named the gas *oxygen.*

Oxygen is hungry for other things, or as the chemist says, it is "active," readily uniting with other substances. We can easily prepare oxygen in the laboratory as in Experiment 9. If we lower a glowing splinter into a jar of oxygen, the splinter bursts into flame. Sulphur and phosphorus burn in it with an exceedingly brilliant light. A bit of charcoal, first heated to redness, then lowered into oxygen, bursts into flame. Even iron picture wire, if heated and treated with a little sulphur to set it on fire, burns with a brilliant light.

Where things go when they burn. When iron and charcoal burn, what becomes of them? We are in the habit of saying that wood and coal just burn up, and we dismiss the subject as if that were the end of it. It is the end of the wood and of the coal, but not the end of the substances of which they are composed. Scientists have been saying for

(39)

a hundred years that matter is never created or destroyed. This is the law of *conservation of matter* (or indestructibility of matter). Lavoisier showed by weighing accurately substances before burning, and weighing all the new substances formed by burning, that there is no loss of matter when substances burn. Indeed, substances seem to gain in weight because of the addition of oxygen of the air.

The reason we often think that wood or charcoal burns away to nothing, or almost nothing, is that we do not see a large part of the new things that are formed by the burning. We can easily show that a new substance is formed when we burn charcoal in a jar of oxygen. If we put some clear limewater in the jar in which the charcoal has been burned, and shake it, the limewater becomes milky. The substance that turns limewater milky is *carbon dioxide*. Hence we conclude that there must have been some carbon dioxide in the jar. Charcoal is largely the element carbon, which also is a large part of coal. When charcoal burns, oxygen unites with the carbon to form the new substance, carbon dioxide. The syllable *di-* means two. The name then means that the substance is one atom of carbon and two atoms of oxygen. The chemist abbreviates it CO_2.

You are probably familiar with carbon dioxide, as it is the gas that makes soda water fizz and froth. It can be solidified and then forms *dry ice*. This solid carbon dioxide is extremely cold—110° F.—very much colder than ice. "Dry ice" is supplanting ice for many uses, for packing ice cream, for cooling refrigerator cars and refrigerators in ships. It has the great advantage that it leaves no water when it melts. Sometimes you may have a container cooled with dry ice in which to carry ice cream from the store or take it on a picnic. When you remove the ice cream, leave the dry ice in the container and keep the container right side up. Lower a lighted match into the container. If CO_2 is still there, the match is extinguished. Shake some limewater into the container and watch it turn milky. One caution: do not pick up the "dry ice" with your fingers. It is so cold that it quickly kills flesh and leaves a painful frostbite.

If you pour a little limewater into a pint jar and shake it vigorously, the limewater will turn milky slowly, showing that there is some CO_2 in the air. It is an extremely small amount, however, three one-hundredths of one per cent.

Other oxides. Now let us return to the other substances we burned in oxygen. Each of them united with oxygen and formed an oxide—phosphorus oxide, sulphur oxide, iron oxide. You could also burn the gas hydrogen and form hydrogen oxide, a substance with which you are familiar. You ordinarily call it *water*. Oxygen unites so easily with many other elements that oxides are very common. The soil contains many oxygen compounds. Our bodies contain more oxygen than any other element, the oxygen united with other elements to form compounds.

Oxygen will unite with many substances without burning with flame and heat. If we throw a piece of iron in the back yard, oxygen unites with it and forms the familiar brown substance, iron rust, or iron oxide. Oxygen unites with the oil in paint and forms the coat that sticks to the wood. We say that the paint dries, but more accurately the oil of the paint oxidizes. Oxygen unites with the bits of garbage that picnickers leave on other people's land, but unfortunately the oxidation of the garbage goes on very slowly. The leaves that fall in the woods and the dead branches that are not more rapidly destroyed by bacteria and fungi are slowly oxidized by the oxygen of the air.

Living things *burn* food. Bacteria and fungi draw their nourishment from the dead things of the woods, and then oxidize the food. Living things, animal and plant, oxidize their food. The oxygen we take into our lungs is carried to the cells in our bodies, where it unites with the food which has also been brought to the cells.

Food contains a large percentage of carbon and hydrogen. When the food is oxidized, these elements unite with the oxygen to form carbon dioxide, CO_2, and water, H_2O. These oxides are waste products that must be cast out of the bodies. Water is given out through the lungs, skin, and kidneys. Carbon dioxide passes off through the lungs. You can easily show that carbon dioxide comes from the lungs by blowing through a tube into limewater.

Oxidation supplies the energy of life. It supplies the heat of the body, the power that moves us about, the power that sends the blood through the body, the energy that keeps up all the variety of cell activities that make up life. All these activities are due to the energy of slow burning—so slow that there is no flame, although there is heat as long as life lasts.

Oxidation in industry. Our homes and our factories, our trains, steamships, and airplanes are warmed or driven almost entirely by oxidation. Some energy, it is true, is due to electric dynamos driven by water power, but most of our electric energy comes from power plants run by steam. Coal, oil, or its refined product gasoline, the gas of our homes, and wood furnish the compounds that are oxidized.

Carbon and hydrogen are the two commonest elements in fuels. It is their union with oxygen that is largely responsible for the heat of combustion (burning). The waste gases from furnaces contain large quantities of carbon dioxide and water as well as oxides of other elements present in the fuels. You can show the presence of water by lowering a kettle of cool water into the flame of a gas burner. Water in the flame will condense for a short time on the bottom of the kettle.

Explosions. When there is an abundant supply of oxygen and an abundant supply of something that will oxidize rapidly, look out. If the vapor from gasoline is mixed with air, everything is set for an explosion. A spark will start the oxidation that produces gases which expand tremendously in the fraction of a second. That sudden, enormous expansion of gases is the explosion. Gunpowder contains potassium nitrate, which supplies abundant oxygen, and powdered charcoal and sulphur, which oxidize rapidly. Nitroglycerine used in dynamite, TNT used in shells, and nitrocellulose used in smokeless power produce extremely rapid oxidation and release gases that expand violently.

How much oxygen in the air. Although air furnishes the oxygen for life and industry, only one fifth of the air is oxygen. You can easily show this by burning a bit of phosphorus in a jar of air inverted over a dish of water as in Figure 48. When the fire goes out, the water has risen one fifth of the way up the jar. Experiment 13 shows how iron filings may be used in a similar demonstration.

Nitrogen. The gas that remains when the oxygen is taken out of the air is nearly all nitrogen. It is quite the opposite of oxygen in disposition. It is hard to make it do anything. It will not unite with things of its own free will. To get it out of the air requires great plants, such as that at Muscle Shoals on the Tennessee

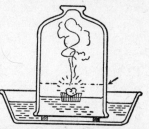

Fig. 48. When phosphorus has burned in a jar of air, the water rises to fill ⅕ of the jar. How does this show that ⅕ of the air is oxygen?

River, that cost millions of dollars to erect. Then, by the aid of electricity, nitrogen can be made to unite with other elements to form nitrogen compounds.

All living things, including ourselves, contain a large part of nitrogen. Our flesh is largely a mixture of nitrogen compounds called *proteins*. Proteins must form part of our foods. We get our proteins chiefly from animal food, to a lesser amount from vegetables. Animals get their proteins from plants. Our crop plants make them from nitrogen compounds in the soil.

Strangely enough, although we live in air, four fifths of which is nitrogen, neither our bodies nor our animals nor our crop plants can take the nitrogen out of the air. Only very lowly plants, chiefly certain kinds of bacteria, can absorb the nitrogen of the air and make it into nitrogen compounds. All the other living things of the earth owe a debt to those lowly plants for the nitrogen of which they are built. Some of the bacteria live on the roots of clover. When we drink the milk of a cow fed on clover hay, we owe thanks to the lowly bacteria. When we eat the beef or the pork from cattle and hogs that fed on the corn grown in a soil previously enriched by a clover crop, we owe more thanks to the bacteria.

The lazy gases. You know those brilliant and peculiar red lights that hold your gaze on an electric sign. Those lights are made by passing an electric current through a tube filled with the gas *neon*. The way neon lights penetrate fog makes them valuable in aviation and in water navigation. The hypnotizing blue tubes of the electric signs are filled with *argon*. Both these gases are in the air in minute quantities. There are several other rare gases in the air. You need remember only one more, *helium*, the gas that floats giant dirigibles, such as the *Macon*. Helium for airships, however, is not obtained from the air but from natural gas, chiefly in Texas. We call the gases *lazy*, or *inert*, because they will not unite with other elements. That is why they are valuable. They do not burn up in lamps or explode in balloons.

Water in the air. When clothes dry on the clothesline or when a wet road dries, the water goes into the air. It evaporates or becomes vapor. Water is constantly evaporating from lakes and oceans. We shall see later that the amount of water vapor in the air depends upon the temperature. Warmer air can hold more than cool air. When air is cooled, some of the water vapor condenses again to drops of water.

You have seen a water pitcher "sweat" on the outside. That "sweat" did not come through the pitcher from the water inside. The cool pitcher condensed some of the water vapor in the warm air of the room. Those who wear eyeglasses have had a similar experience when they came into a warm room on a cold winter day. The chilled eyeglasses collect a mist by condensing moisture of the warm air.

When the grass cools off at night, water vapor in the air condenses on it as *dew*. When the vapor condenses as tiny drops that float in the air, it forms *fog* or *clouds*. Sometimes so much vapor condenses that it falls as *rain* or *snow*. We shall study the process in the unit on Weather.

EXPERIMENT 9 (TEACHER DEMONSTRATION)

Question: How can I prepare oxygen? What can I learn about it?
Materials: A flask; a two-hole stopper; a thistle tube; a delivery tube

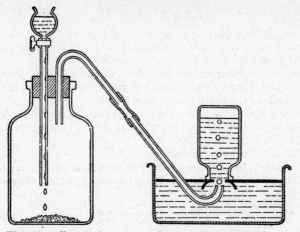

Fig. 49. Generating oxygen from sodium dioxide. Be careful to allow the water to enter drop by drop.

(glass tubing and rubber tubing); a pneumatic trough or flat dish of water, charcoal; potassium chlorate; sodium dioxide; sulphur; phosphorus; magnesium; and steel wool.

Directions and results: (*a*) Put one-half inch of potassium chlorate into a test tube. Holding the test tube with a test-tube holder, heat until the potassium chlorate melts. Then drop in a small piece of charcoal. 1. What evidence have you that oxygen was given off?

(*b*) Set up the sodium dioxide generator, add water, and collect five bottles of oxygen by displacement of water (Fig. 49). 2. What is the physical state of oxygen (solid, liquid, or gas)? 3. What are the color, odor, and taste of oxygen?

(*c*) Place a glowing splint in a bottle of oxygen. 4. What is the result and what does it show you about chemical activity of oxygen?

(*d*) Put a small piece of sulphur in an iron spoon and set fire to the sulphur by directing a Bunsen burner flame downward on it. Lower the burning sulphur into a bottle of oxygen. 5. Note how the sulphur burns in air and in the oxygen.

(*e*) Repeat, using red phosphorus, magnesium, charcoal, and steel wool instead of sulphur. 6. In each case state whether the action is more violent in air or in oxygen.

Diagram: Show the generator and collection of gas.

Conclusion: State two ways of making oxygen in the laboratory. Describe oxygen and tell how it acts. State in general terms what is formed when oxygen combines with other elements. What do we call the process?

5

EXPERIMENT 10

Question: Does oxidation go on in living things?

Materials: A living fish; limewater; a battery jar or other jar; a piece of glass tubing; a test tube or tumbler.

Directions: (a) Pour an inch of limewater into a battery jar. Transfer the fish to it for a few minutes, until you notice a change in the limewater. Remove the fish again to pure water.

(b) Pour a little limewater into the test tube or tumbler. Take the glass tube in your mouth and breathe out through the limewater.

(c) Perform Experiment 111.

Results: State result of each step.

Conclusion: What evidence have you seen that oxidation goes on in living things? Now perform Experiment 11 which shows further evidence.

EXPERIMENT 11

Question: What further evidence can I find of oxidation in living things?

Materials: A clinical (doctor's) thermometer or a small thermometer that can be placed in the mouth; a laboratory thermometer; materials for Experiment 111.

Directions: (a) Take the temperature of the room. If you have a clinical thermometer, shake down the mercury in the thermometer without jarring and breaking the thermometer. Then take your temperature by placing the thermometer under your tongue and allowing it to remain two or three minutes. If you have no clinical thermometer, use a laboratory thermometer and have a classmate read it without removing it from your mouth.

(b) Pack the sprouted peas loosely in the flask or thermos bottle until about half full. Insert the stopper bearing the thermometer. Allow to stand for two or three hours or until next day. Then read the temperature of the sprouted seeds.

Results: Record the temperature of the room and that of the human body and of sprouting seeds.

Conclusion: Answer the question.

EXPERIMENT 12

Question: How can I prepare carbon dioxide? What can I learn about it?

Materials: Flask; delivery tube; thistle tube; dry ice; candles; tumblers; limewater; pieces of marble; hydrochloric acid.

Directions: (a) Set up a generator as shown in Figure 50. Place a lump of dry ice (solid carbon dioxide) in a flask. Insert a fine jet in the end of the delivery tube. Half fill a test tube with limewater, and put

the end of the delivery tube into the limewater.   **1.** What evidence
have you that the dry ice is vaporizing?   2. How do you know that a gas
given off by the dry ice is carbon dioxide?

(*b*) Put a drop of hydrochloric acid on
a lump of marble.   Notice that the combination fizzes (effervesces).

(*c*) Arrange a generator, as shown in
Figure 51.   Fill it quarter full with small
pieces of marble.   Add *dilute* hydrochloric
acid through the thistle tube and collect
the gas given off by displacement of water.
Collect four 6-oz. bottles of the gas.   Use
one bottle to determine the color, taste,
and odor of the gas.   Add limewater to a
second bottle and shake. 3. What happens to the limewater?

Fig. 50.   Generating carbon
dioxide from dry ice.

(*d*) Light a taper and thrust it into a
third bottle.   4. What happens and why?

(*e*) Put one-half inch of limewater in the
bottom of a 4-oz. bottle.   Hold the fourth
bottle of carbon dioxide with the mouth of
the bottle upward.   See if you can pour
some of the gas that it contains into the
bottle containing the limewater.   You cannot see that you are pouring gas, but you
can go through the motions.   Shake the
bottle containing the limewater.   5. What
happens, and what does this prove concerning the weight of carbon dioxide?

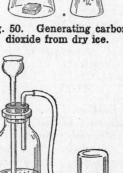

Fig. 51.   Generating carbon
dioxide by action of hydrochloric acid on marble.

Diagram: Show the carbon dioxide generators in action.

Conclusion: How may carbon dioxide be prepared?   What are its
color, odor, weight?   Will it burn?   What does it do to the fire?   How
can you show that carbon dioxide is present?

Practical application: Effervescent drinks fizz because they contain
large quantities of dissolved carbon dioxide.   One type of fire extinguisher generates carbon dioxide.

EXPERIMENT 13

Question: How can I find the percentage of oxygen in the air?

Materials: Large test tube; fine iron filings; tumbler of water.

Directions: (*a*) Fill an 8 x 1 test tube with water and then empty it.
Pour a few iron filings into the test tube and roll them around until the
wet sides of the test tube are well coated.   Put the test tube mouth

down into the tumbler of water. Label it, and put it aside for two days.
1. At the end of that time note what has happened.

(b) Raise the test tube until the level of the water inside and outside is the same. 2. What proportion of air has disappeared?

(c) Gently place your thumb over the end of the test tube under water and bring it right side up, without admitting air into it. Thrust a spark into the gas in the test tube. 3. Why does the spark go out? 4. How has the iron changed in color? 5. What has settled in the bottom of the test tube? 6. How far has the water risen in the test tube?

Diagram: A titled and labeled diagram showing the experiment in operation is required.

Conclusion: 7. Why did the water rise in the test tube? 8. What has become of the oxygen of the air? 9. What is the new substance that is formed from the iron filings? 10. What is the gas that is left in the test tube? 11. Answer the question.

EXPERIMENT 14

Question: Does air contain water vapor? How can I illustrate the formation of dew?

Materials: Polished metal cup or a glass tumbler; ice; cool water.

Directions: Fill a tumbler or polished metal cup an eighth full of cool water. Put a large lump of ice in the water and place on the outside window ledge. Then stir the water until you notice a mist beginning to form on the outside of the cup.

How do you explain the fact that sometimes mist does not form and the experiment fails?

Diagram: A titled and labeled drawing of the apparatus in use is required.

Conclusion: State how this proves that air contains dissolved water, and how it illustrates the formation of dew.

Practical application: Is dew more likely to form on a hilltop or a valley?

NOTE: It is necessary to put the metal cup outside the window because the humidity (dissolved water vapor) in the room is often so low that dew will not form.

CHAPTER IV

PREVENTING OXIDATION

Preventing slow oxidation. If you have ever dropped your knife in the grass and found it several months later, you know how oxidation has ruined the blade. Wood is usually painted or varnished to keep away the air and thus prevent slow oxidation and ward off the attacks of bacteria and fungi that cause decay. Metals are painted or coated with another metal that does not readily oxidize. The red paint on iron bridges and iron fences is an oxide of lead, called *red lead*, that sticks to the iron and prevents oxidation of the iron. The radiator shell of an automobile is plated with nickel or chromium. The galvanized pail in the kitchen is iron covered with zinc. Slow oxidation is prevented by covering the surface of the object so that air cannot reach it.

Spontaneous combustion. One form of slow oxidation causes a real fire hazard. Paint is linseed or other oil with the addition of coloring matter. We mentioned in the last chapter that "drying" of paint is really oxidation of the oil. If the painter wipes his brush on a rag and then for the sake of neatness puts the rag in a pasteboard box and shoves the box in the corner of a closet, a fire is likely to occur. As the linseed oil on the rag oxidizes, heat is produced. This heat cannot readily escape from the box, and the temperature of the rag is raised. The hotter the rag the faster the oil oxidizes, and the faster the oil oxidizes the hotter the rag becomes. In a few days the rag reaches its kindling temperature and the papers report a mysterious fire.

This spontaneous combustion (burning of its own accord) may occur in many substances. Formerly coal dust from soft coal carried in ships sometimes would oxidize and spon-

(49)

Fig. 52. Four or five hundred million dollars are lost each year in the United States through uncontrolled oxidation of this kind.

taneous combustion would set the ship afire. Today steamers carrying soft coal place thermometers in the coal. A marked rise of temperature indicates slow oxidation and precautions are immediately taken to prevent fire.

Fire losses. Oxidation not only runs the world but destroys much of it. Forest fires destroy immense numbers of trees and cause even greater damage through loss of soil and water supply. Fires in homes and factories destroy property and lives. Fire losses in the United States reach the enormous total of four or five hundred million dollars a year. Practically all of this loss is preventable (Fig. 52).

Most fires are caused by carelessness. A smoker tosses a lighted match or a cigarette among some dry leaves in the forest, in a scrap basket in the office, or on some oily rags in the shop. In a few minutes there is a devastating forest fire or a factory goes up in smoke, with the possible loss of many lives. An electric iron is left on the ironing board with the current turned on. In a short time an apartment house is on fire. No matter how careful we may be ourselves, an accident or carelessness of a neighbor may put our property in danger.

Preventing fires. Stop fires before they start. Keep oily rags in covered iron cans or burn them at once. Do not pour kerosene into the stove or furnace to start the fire. Dry paper and dry wood are just as efficient, less smoky, and far safer. See that every electric switch is turned off when you have finished with the current. See that every smoker crushes out every cigarette and every cigar stump and every lighted match. Do not allow a lighted stump to be thrown from the window of an auto or a railroad car. In the woods soak your camp fire with water before you leave it. Train yourself to break every match before you throw it away. You will not break a lighted match.

What starts fires. No fires can start without three things: (1) something to burn; (2) oxygen to support combustion; (3) heat enough to start the union.

We have spoken of the first two; let us examine the third. All things are not equally hungry for oxygen. In starting a fire in the stove, you ignite paper or thin shavings, then heavier wood, then when the wood is roaring, you add coal. Phosphorus is so greedy for oxygen that it is stored in the laboratory under water. If a piece of phosphorus dries out in the air, it takes fire. Iron, on the contrary, must be heated to a very high temperature before it ignites even in pure oxygen. Each substance has its own *kindling* temperature.

Preparation against fire. Think in advance just what you would do in case of fire. What is the location of the nearest fire-alarm box, and how would you send in an alarm? How would you use the telephone to send in an alarm? Where is the fire escape in your home, school, hotel, or theater? If it should be shut off by fire, what other exit could you use? If your neglected picnic fire spreads into the woods, what should you do? Knowing the answers to such questions as these may save your life and the lives of others. If you know, you are less likely to "lose your head."

What to do in case of fire. When fires first start, they are often readily extinguished. It is better to pull down a blazing curtain than to run out and call the fire department. A few cupfuls of water thrown on a small fire will often stop it. Remember the first and main rule in an emergency. Keep cool. Remember next that smoke rises, therefore by crawling on hands and knees you may escape from a smoke-filled room when the smoke would suffocate you if you stood up. A wet towel or a handkerchief over the nose helps.

In school the fire drill is of grave importance. Should a panic start in a school, there would be loss of life. Therefore we have fire drills. If we all know exactly what to do and how to do it, there will be no loss of life. In fire drills do your utmost to live up to all the rules and see that your comrades do the same.

Should your clothes catch fire, remember that air is necessary for combustion. Throw yourself down on the floor and draw a rug, coat, or blanket around you, thus smothering the fire. If you remain standing, the flames will naturally rise, will envelop your head and you may inhale them. If you lie flat on the floor, this will not happen. *Do not run.* Running fans the flames and will surely result in your being badly burned. If possible, tear off your burning clothing, but in any case keep the flames away from your face and do not inhale them.

Burns. A burn may be either superficial, causing only a slight injury, or it may actually destroy tissue, which is a serious matter. A slight burn is best treated by keeping air from it. Covering it with mineral oil does this. A somewhat better method is to use carron oil, which is prepared by shaking together equal volumes of limewater and linseed or olive oil. Pour plenty of this on the burn. There are excellent ointments prepared for burns, and one should ask one's doctor or druggist to suggest one of these and keep a tube ready for an emergency. A deep burn may be treated in this way until the doctor comes, but such burns always require medical attention.

Vaseline (petroleum jelly) or a mineral oil may be used if carron oil or other prepared remedy is not at hand. Petroleum

Fig. 53. Do you know why water puts out fire? Several reasons are given in the text at the bottom of this page.

products are better dressings for burns than either butter or baking soda and are usually just as handy.

Never put a *dry* cloth on a burn. The cloth will stick and when removed, will bring the skin with it. Always soak the cloth in oil before using it to bandage a burn, and never tie it tightly. The cloth should be used only as a cover for the injured part.

Fire extinguishers. Water puts out a fire for four reasons: (1) It keeps oxygen from the burning material. (2) It cools the burning substance below its kindling point. (3) To change water to steam requires heat and much of this heat must come from the burning substance, thus cooling it below its kindling point. (4) It produces steam which acts as a blanket and shuts off the supply of oxygen (Fig. 53).

Fig. 54. This fire extinguisher throws a stream of carbon tetrachloride on the fire when the handle is pumped out and in.

There are two common fire extinguishers suitable for home use. One is a small container having a pump worked up and down by a handle (Fig. 54). A fine stream of liquid is forced out of a hole in the bottom of the container. The liquid is carbon tetrachloride, a heavy liquid that easily changes into a noncombustible (nonburning) gas. Pumping a stream of this liquid at the base of the fire extinguishes it because the gas produced makes a blanket that keeps the oxygen away and so prevents burning.

In one form of fire extinguisher the carbon tetrachloride is contained in a sealed glass bottle. The bottle is thrown into the fire and broken. The gas immediately formed extinguishes the fire (Fig. 55).

Fig. 55. This fire extinguisher is a bottle of carbon tetrachloride which is crashed at the edge of the fire or contents sprinkled on the fire.

Another type of fire extinguisher is a copper tank with a solution of sodium bicarbonate (baking soda). In the upper part of the tank is a bottle of sulphuric acid (Fig. 56). A rubber tube ending in a small nozzle is attached to the top. When the tank is inverted, the acid and the bicarbonate mix. A chemical change takes place and carbon dioxide is set free. This creates pressure in the tank and a mixture of the gas and water is driven through the nozzle. The fire may be extinguished by directing this jet against it. A chemical engine used by many fire departments for small fires uses a similar device.

Foam is sometimes used in fire fighting. A solution of sodium bicarbonate containing an extract of licorice root is mixed with a solution of aluminum sulphate as the solutions pour from the nozzle of the apparatus upon the fire. The aluminum and licorice form a tough film which becomes a foam filled with bubbles of carbon dioxide. The foam covers the fire and shuts out the oxygen; so extinguishing it. Foam methods are especially valuable in fighting oil fires. Never throw water on an oil or gasoline fire. Oil and gasoline are lighter than water. They float away on the top of the water, burning as they go and so spreading the fire. Throw sand or dirt on an oil fire or use a fire extinguisher charged with carbon tetrachloride.

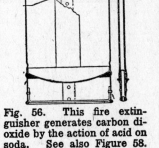

EXPERIMENT 15

Question: How can I show the different kindling temperatures of phosphorus, sulphur, wood, and coal?

Materials: A four-armed cross of sheet copper; ring-stand burner; phosphorus; sulphur; wood; and coal.

Directions: Support the copper cross on a ring stand. Place one of the substances at the end of each arm and heat the middle by the Bunsen burner, taking care to place it so that each arm is equally heated. Note the order in which the substances catch fire.

Fig. 56. This fire extinguisher generates carbon dioxide by the action of acid on soda. See also Figure 58.

Diagram: A titled and labeled diagram showing the apparatus in operation is required.

Conclusion: State which substance has the lowest kindling temperature. Name the others in the order in which they burn.

Practical application: A match consists of a stick soaked in paraffin to make it damp proof. The top of the stick is tipped with a mixture of some oxidizing agent (substance which readily gives off oxygen), as potassium chlorate, glue, powdered glass, and a compound of phosphorus. When we strike the match, friction between the powdered glass and the striking surface gives heat. The phosphorus compound is heated to its kindling temperature.

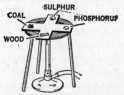

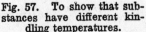

Fig. 57. To show that substances have different kindling temperatures.

The oxidizing agent gives oxygen to support the combustion. The phosphorus burns, the wood is heated to its kindling temperature. and the match burns. In a safety match the mixture is divided, the head of the match having all the substances except the phosphorus compounds, which is placed on the box. What is the advantage of a safety match? How do we make use of kindling temperature in building a coal fire in stoves?

A burning match thrust into a pail of kerosene is extinguished, while a pail of kerosene thrown on a large bonfire results in a tremendous fire. Why?

NOTE: The experiment of thrusting a burning match into a pail of kerosene is not advised. There is danger.

Wood burns readily, yet a bag of sawdust emptied on a small fire extinguishes it. Why?

EXPERIMENT 16 (TEACHER DEMONSTRATION)

Question: How can I make a model fire extinguisher?

Materials· Sulphuric acid; sodium bicarbonate (baking soda or saleratus); vial; an 8-oz. bottle fitted with delivery tube.

Directions: Half fill the bottle with a solution of baking soda. Half fill the small vial with diluted sulphuric acid and carefully lower it

into the bottle so that it floats on the solution of baking soda. Cork the bottle with a rubber stopper and delivery tube. The end of the glass delivery tube is drawn out into a fine jet. It is safer to tie the cork on tightly, for pressure of gas sometimes blows out the cork.

Invert the bottle. The acid and the bicarbonate will mix, and carbon dioxide gas will be set free. This causes a pressure inside the bottle and forces the gas and liquid out through the fine jet. Light a few crumpled papers, place them in a tin pan, and direct the stream of liquid at the fire. Why is the fire extinguished?

Fig. 58. A model fire extinguisher. The small bottle containing dilute acid floats in baking soda solution. To operate, turn upside down.

Avoid getting the liquid on your clothes, as it will leave a stain.

Diagram: A titled and labeled diagram showing the apparatus in use is required.

Conclusion: Answer the question.

Practical application: The model you made is similar to the large extinguishers used commercially. They are cheap and efficient.

QUESTIONS TO THINK OUT

1. How many pounds of air are in your classroom?
2. Do you weigh more or less because of air pressure?
3. Make a magic shower bath with a tin can and a piece of cheesecloth. Punch a hole in one end of the tin can, such that you can close

it with your finger, and cover the other end with the cheesecloth. Close the hole with the finger. Fill the can with water and invert it. Why does not the water run out? Raise the finger. Why does the water run out?

4. Why is it not necessary to carry the barometer out of doors to make a reading?

5. How high would the mercury stand in a barometer if the tube were three inches in diameter?

6. If you placed a bottle of milk and a glass on a table, could you fill the glass with a siphon? Could you empty the bottle?

7. If a boat lying high on the beach were filled with water, could you siphon the water out? If the boat were in the water, could you siphon the water out?

8. Pour some kerosene into half a tumbler of water. What happens? Why? Would a lift pump raise kerosene to the same height as water?

9. If air pressure in a tire is 35 pounds before a blowout, what is it afterwards? If the pressure were 35 pounds at sea level, how would the tire seem when you drove to the top of a high mountain?

10. Why does water gurgle and bubble out of a bottle instead of flowing out smoothly as it does from a pitcher?

11. Why is it difficult to get condensed milk out of a can with only one hole punched in the top? What is the remedy?

12. Why are the ends of a can of tomatoes usually somewhat dented in? What would bulging ends indicate? Why is there a hissing sound when you pierce the top of the can with a can opener?

13. What holds the rubber cup with the coat hanger or the glare shield on the window of an automobile?

14. Why can you not raise water more than 34 feet with a siphon?

15. How can you get gasoline out of an auto tank?

16. If you started a siphon on the platform of an air pump and then covered the tank with a bell jar and exhausted the air, what would happen? Why?

17. The moon has no atmosphere. How would a balloon act there?

18. If you boil water thoroughly, cool it, and then put fish into it, the fish will probably spend most of the time at the top of the water. Why?

19. Would air have the same pressure at the bottom of a mine a mile deep as at the top?

20. Climbers in high mountains sometimes suffer with nosebleed. Why?

21. Why does a football bounce?

22. Where is the atmosphere?

23. If nitrogen were burned in oxygen, would carbon dioxide be produced?

24. Should you expect carbon dioxide to burn in pure oxygen? Explain.

25. A well cleaner lowers a lighted lantern into a well before descending. If the lantern goes out, he does not descend. What gas is in the well to extinguish the lantern? Why does it stay there?

26. Why do spectacles sometimes become covered with mist when the wearer enters a room?

27. Why does a fire smoke when first started? Why does a camp fire blaze up when you poke it?

28. Why does a lamp smoke when turned too high? Why do shavings catch fire more readily than heavy wood?

29. Do you suppose a mouse would live longer in a jar of pure oxygen than in air?

30. Could nitrogen be used for filling balloons?

31. What gas of the air goes into the fire in greatest quantities? What gas does most of the work in keeping the fire burning?

32. Certain bacteria, such as those that cause lockjaw (tetanus), live deeply buried in the flesh. Where do they get oxygen?

33. Although our bodies cannot take nitrogen from the air, the nitrogen is of great benefit to us. How?

34. Often the wash on the clothesline dries very slowly on a hot day. Why?

35. Why does the oiling of tools prevent rust?

36. Why is coal dust more likely to ignite spontaneously than coal in the bin?

37. If you saw a child running with its clothes afire, what should you do?

38. If the pupil next to you stumbled and fell in a fire drill, what should you do?

39. Make a list of all the fire hazards in your house and school. Decide how each could be removed.

UNIT TWO

WATER: HOW SCIENCE HAS FORCED IT TO SERVE

"Plant a stick in the desert, water it, and it will grow to be a tree," so say the Arabs. Irrigated deserts produce orchards, fields, and flower gardens. When the spring rains come, the desert is clothed with flowers. Water is a second part of our environment, necessary for life. Sixty-five per cent of our bodies is water. The body must get it from the surroundings.

Early man lived where there was water. He had no means of bringing it to him. When he had invented pottery, he had a means of carrying water a short distance and storing it. Then, too, he could boil roots and seeds that he or his wives and daughters had gathered in swamps and forests, and also the meat of the bear which he and his sons had killed. The ancient Romans built great, beautiful stone aqueducts that brought pure water to their cities. Modern man brings water through huge pipes hundreds of miles over deserts, through mountains, and under rivers. Our demands for water have grown with civilization. We need it not only for drinking and for washing, but also for manufacturing, for power, for heating, and for a variety of other uses.

Water, the giver of life, has been also the bearer of death. Plagues of typhoid fever and cholera, water-borne plagues, have made cities dreaded by country dwellers. Malaria and yellow fever have stricken city and country dwellers alike in the low regions. Science is gaining control of these diseases.

Oceans and lakes were barriers to the wanderings of early man. Modern transportation, the product of science, has made the oceans the great pathways of the earth.

Water science was studied two thousand years ago by **Archimedes of Sicily.** Today it is still a subject of scientific study. The scientist is still learning more about how water is put together and how it behaves. He writes his discoveries in laws of science which describe its action. Understanding the laws of its action enable him to control water, to put it to work.

In this unit we shall study what water is and its laws of action. We shall study the operation of these laws in our homes and out of doors, in the forces of nature and in developing power for our machines. We shall see the laws in operation when water supports our great ships and our submarines. We shall study how cities and nations provide pure water in the vast quantities needed in modern life—water free from disease. We shall see how water is treated chemically when it is necessary to make it suitable for household and industrial uses.

CHAPTER V

SOME WATER SCIENCE

When water boils. It takes longer to boil potatoes at Denver than at Chicago, not because Chicago is a fast city but because Denver is a mile high. Water boils at 212° F. (100° C.) at sea level. Atmospheric pressure at sea level is 15 pounds to the square inch, but with increased altitude it becomes less. As the pressure decreases, the boiling point decreases. At Denver water boils at about 202° F. Potatoes must be boiled longer to cook them at 202° F. The lower the pressure the lower the boiling point, and the higher the pressure the higher the boiling point. In steam boilers increased pressure raises the boiling point far above 212° F., in some cases to 400° F.

The pressure cooker. If you live in the high mountains or have a summer home there, you can beat nature by raising the boiling point within the cooking pot. When a vessel containing boiling water is entirely inclosed, the pressure of the confined steam increases and the temperature of the boiling water rises. This principle is used in the pressure cooker. Food that is cooked in a pressure cooker will be cooked at a higher temperature than in an open pot. The food to be cooked is placed in the cooker and the lid is screwed on (Fig. 59). A steam-pressure gauge indicates the pressure and a thermometer shows the temperature of the confined food. A safety valve automatically opens before the pressure becomes too great.

Even at sea level pressure cookers save fuel because the cooking time is reduced. The foods are softened and sterilized to a degree impossible at the lower temperatures employed in ordinary cooking. A pressure cooker called an *autoclave* is used in hospitals and laboratories for sterilizing instruments and surgical dressings and for cooking foods and heating liquids.

Waterless cookers are really types of pressure cookers that use the water which is contained in meats and vegetables. They are efficient and reliable but do not attain the high pressures of the pressure cooker.

Why steam has power. Water, like other substances, expands upon heating (Exp. 61). The expansion continues regularly from a few degrees above freezing up to 212° F. (100° C.), the boiling point. At that point, as liquid water changes to steam, it suddenly expands enormously. It is the pressure due to this expansion that gives steam its power.

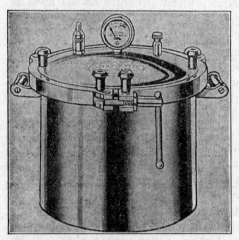

Fig. 59. A pressure cooker. Increased steam pressure in the air-tight pot raises the boiling temperature.

Why a pond freezes from the top. Did you ever wonder why a pond does not freeze first at the bottom instead of at the top? Water has a very peculiar trick upon cooling. Like other substances, water at ordinary temperatures contracts on cooling. As it contracts, each cubic inch contains more water and is therefore heavier. Because it is heavier, it sinks. The contraction continues down to about 39° F. (4° C.). At that temperature water performs the peculiar trick. It expands if it is cooled further. Therefore it becomes lighter and rises to the top of the pond. The expansion continues on down to 32° F. (0° C.), at which point water freezes (Exp. 157). At the freezing point, therefore, the lightest water is at the top of the pond.

The hot-water boiler. Water is lighter (less dense) when warm, and heavier (denser) when cool. We recognize this fact in heating water for household use. The supply of hot water in the home is usually obtained from a storage tank. The water is heated by a stove or in a pipe coil of an independent gas or oil heater (Fig. 60). Very often the coil is placed in the fire box of a furnace. In all cases the principle is the same. Water coming from the bottom of the tank is made to pass through a pipe or coil or a water jacket. When the water is heated, it expands, becomes lighter, and is pushed up by the colder, heavier water. The hot water is thus transferred to the top of the boiler where it remains until it is drawn off.

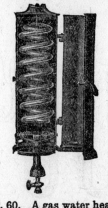

Fig. 60. A gas water heater. Water is heated in the copper coil.

In the instantaneous gas heater, the gas is automatically turned on and lighted by a pilot light when the faucet is opened. Heat of the burning fuel heats the water in a copper coil.

Water pressure. If you have carried a bucket of water up several flights of stairs, you know that it is heavy. A cubic foot of water weighs 62.4 pounds (at 39° F., 4° C.). It is clear that this weight will cause pressure, and a pressure of 62.4 pounds a square foot is a valuable force that can be put to work.

The weight of water also must be reckoned with when water is stored to be used. The water contained in a tank exerts a considerable pressure on the bottom and sides of the tank.

Fig. 61. A manometer.

This is shown in our next experiment. For this we need a pressure gauge called a *manometer* (Fig. 61).

Half fill a U-tube with water colored with red ink. Cork one end of the tube with a stopper having a hole in it. Put a short, bent glass tube through the hole. Attach a rubber tube to the glass tube. Note that the water stands at the same level in both arms of the U-tube. A rubber band around the U-tube serves to mark the position of the water. Blow through the rubber tube, thus increasing the pressure on the water. Notice that the levels of the water in the two arms change. Blowing gently causes only a slight change, while blowing hard causes a much greater change in level. This device is a crude manometer with which we can measure small pressures. (Fig. 62).

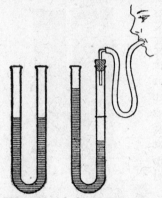

Fig. 62. A homemade manometer or pressure gauge. Explain the change of level in the figure on the right.

Tie a piece of thin rubber (rubber dam) over the end of a funnel and then connect the end of the funnel with the rubber tube from the manometer. Immerse the funnel in a tall battery jar filled with water (Fig. 63). Notice that as you push the funnel down into the water the pressure shown on the manometer increases. If a depth of 3 inches causes a certain water pressure, a depth of 6 inches will cause twice the pressure. Evidently water pressure depends on the depth.

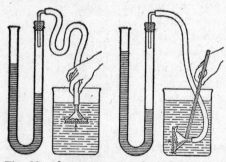

Fig. 63. Apparatus to study pressure of water at varying depths and in varying directions.

At a depth of 1 foot water exerts a pressure of 62.4 pounds on a square foot. A depth of 100 feet will give a pressure of 6240 pounds a square foot. Therefore, dams are thicker

Fig. 64. Dams must be thicker at the bottom because water pressure increases with depth. Building the Kensico Dam for the New York City water system.

at the bottom than at the top (Fig. 64). The suggestion is sometimes made that submarines might be used to recover treasures from ships sunk in water a mile or more deep. Why is this impossible? (Fig. 65.)

Turn the funnel sideways, so that the rubber dam stands vertical. Find the pressure on the rubber when its center is 3 inches, and when its center is 6 inches, below the surface. Note that again the pressure depends on the depth below the surface. At 6 inches below the pressure is twice what it is at 3 inches below.

Put the funnel 6 inches under the surface and determine the pressure. Keeping the center of the rubber 6 inches under the surface, turn the funnel in various directions. You will find that the pressure always remains the same—that is, at any one point *the pressure is the same in all directions.*

Why things float. When you were swimming, did you ever pick up a big stone from the bottom of the pool? If you did, you found it came up easily enough, but suddenly got

Fig. 65. The bathysphere. Sealed in this steel sphere, Dr. William Beebe descended about a half mile into the ocean to study living things. The steel sphere supports the pressure of the water. Electric lights illuminated the dark water.

heavy when you tried to take it out of the water. You have noticed that a cork floats in water and that a piece of iron sinks. Have you ever wondered why a great steel ship floats and a small steel nail sinks?

A few simple experiments will help to explain *buoyancy,* the tendency to float. Weigh a small stone or, better, a cube of marble. Write down the weight as *weight in air.* Then tie a string to the marble, lower it into a glass of water, and with a spring balance weigh it immersed in water. Write down the *weight in water.* You find that it weighs less in water. When the marble is lowered into the water, it pushes the water aside to make room for itself. The water tries to push back. It pushes on all six faces of the cube. The pressure on the four side faces is equal. The upward pressure on the bottom, however, is greater than the downward pressure on the top because the bottom is lower in the water and water pressure increases with the depth. The difference between the upward pressure of the water and the downward pressure is the lifting or buoyant force.

Now, by experiment, measure the force or weight of the water that is pushed aside by the marble. Fill a glass brimful of water and set the glass in a pan. Then lower the block of marble into the glass, saving the water that is displaced by the marble and overflows into the pan (Fig. 66). Weigh this displaced water. Compare this weight with the weight lost by the stone when you weighed it in water. The loss of the weight in water equals the weight of the water displaced. This is a very important principle. It was discovered twenty centuries ago by Archimedes. The *principle of Archimedes* may be stated thus: "A body immersed in a liquid loses a weight equal to the weight of the liquid displaced." Perhaps an easier way to remember it is: "The loss of weight in a liquid equals the weight of the liquid displaced." The architects who design our great ships today use the principle of Archimedes.

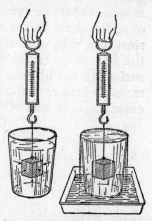

Fig. 66. Experiment to learn how much weight a body loses in water. Study the arrows in the left figure and tell why a body loses weight.

To understand why steel ships float, try an experiment on the water displaced by a floating body. Weigh a small block of wood. Again fill the glass brimful of water and set it in the pan. Gently lower the block of wood into the glass of water and weigh the water displaced as you did before. The weight of the floating block of wood equals the weight of the water displaced. Look back at your record of the experiment with the block of marble. The marble weighed more than the water displaced. When the object weighs more than the water displaced, it sinks. When the object weighs the same as the water displaced, the water holds it up. Make sure that you remember this principle of floating bodies: a floating body displaces its weight of liquid.

The secret of floating a steel ship lies in designing a ship so that it will displace a large amount of water. The larger the quantity of water displaced, the greater the buoyancy. You can illustrate with a piece of tin foil folded into the shape of a boat. Such a tin-foil boat floats, but if you roll the same piece of tin foil into a tight ball, it sinks. The tin-foil boat presents greater surface to the water and displaces more water. A naval architect designs a ship so that it will displace a weight of water equal to the weight of the ship and cargo. If the steel of a ship were all in a compact mass, it would sink as the ball of tin foil sinks. The ship as built exposes greater surface to the upward pressure of the water. If a steel ship rams an iceberg and a hole is punched in its hull, water will enter the hull and will press the ship downward. The increased downward pressure sinks the ship. Punch a hole in the tin-foil boat and see what happens.

Fig. 67. Cartesian diver shows how a submarine dives. When you press on the rubber cover, the water rises in the small bottle. Why? When you release the pressure, the bottle rises. Why?

When a submarine dives, the same principles are illustrated. Water is admitted into compartments in the hull. The submarine then weighs more than the water it displaces, and therefore sinks. To bring it to the surface the water is driven out by compressed air. Its weight, thus decreased, is less than the water displaced and it rises. You can illustrate the diving and rising of a submarine by a Cartesian diver (Fig. 67). A vial partially filled with water is inverted in a bottle or cylinder partially filled with water. A piece of rubber dam or inner tube is tied over the top of the cylinder. Pressure on the rubber forces water into the diver and it sinks. The entrance of the water compresses the air in the diver. Releasing the pressure on the rubber allows the compressed air in the diver to force down the water. Its weight is reduced and it rises.

What water is. Water looks like a simple substance, but it is not so simple as it looks. If an electric current is passed through water in the apparatus shown in Figure 68, little bubbles will arise in each tube. The water gradually disappears. At the end of the experiment gas has replaced the water. One arm of the tube contains, however, twice as much gas as the other. We can show by tests that the larger quantity of gas is hydrogen, and that the smaller quantity is oxygen. This experiment shows that water is composed of hydrogen and oxygen, and that when it is decomposed we obtain a volume of hydrogen twice as great as the volume of oxygen.

Electrolysis of water, as just described, is one of the two chief ways of obtaining the oxygen so much in demand both in hospitals and in industry.

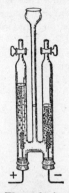

Fig. 68. Electrolysis of water. When an electric current passes through the water, oxygen collects in the left tube and hydrogen in the right. How much more hydrogen than oxygen?

Experiment 17 (Optional)

To show that the boiling point rises with increased pressure. Arrange apparatus as in Figure 69. Bring the water to the boiling point without inserting the stopper. Read temperature. Insert the stopper and bring the water to a boil. Care is needed. The pressure may blow the mercury from the tube. Note the evidence of increased pressure and the temperature of boiling.

Experiment 18 (Optional)

To show that the boiling point falls with decreased pressure. Boil a flask half full of water. When the steam has driven out the air, remove the flask from the fire and then cork the flask. Condense the steam by cooling the flask under a stream of cold water. The pressure will be reduced. Note what happens to the water in the flask.

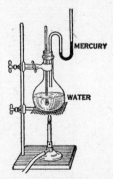

Fig. 69. Experiment to show that the boiling point rises with increased pressure.

LATER EXPERIMENTS

To show that water expands upon heating, see Experiment 61, page 201.

To show that when water changes to steam, it expands and produces pressure, see Experiment 56, page 171.

To show that water expands upon freezing, see Experiment 157, page 603.

To show how hot water rises in the heating plant, see Experiment 72, page 222.

A QUESTION TO THINK OUT

What makes a coffee percolator work?

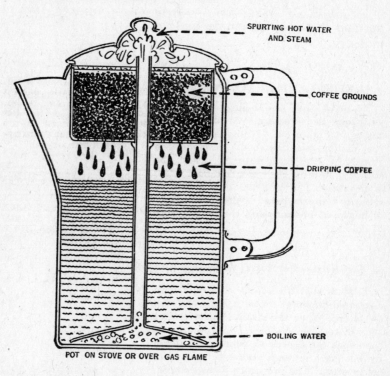

SPURTING HOT WATER AND STEAM

COFFEE GROUNDS

DRIPPING COFFEE

BOILING WATER

POT ON STOVE OR OVER GAS FLAME

CHAPTER VI

PUTTING WATER TO WORK

Water wheels. Have you ever played around a quaint old water wheel in a brook? Have you ever gazed in wonder and perhaps bewilderment at the giant machinery of the power plant of a great modern dam? The early settlers set up their mills to grind their corn beside many a little stream in our eastern country. They led the water to the mill and dropped it upon the wheel or led the water under the wheel to turn it (Fig. 70). The mill wheels turned the machinery directly. Modern hydroelectric plants change the energy of falling water into electrical energy, which is more easily controlled and can be transmitted long distances across country to cities and factories.

The great hydroelectric plants today harness the falling water by means of water turbines. The turbine is an improved type of water wheel with curved blades (Fig. 71). This wheel is entirely inclosed in a case, and the water is fed to it from a height through a large, wide tube called the *penstock*. Turbines are sometimes so efficient that they utilize 90 per cent of the energy of the falling water. The revolving shaft of the turbine turns the dynamo, and electrical energy is produced by the force of the falling water. (Fig. 74.)

 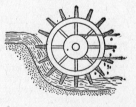

Fig. 70. How the old-time water wheels worked. The overshot, undershot, and breast wheels.

(71)

Fig. 71.   A turbine for a large hydroelectric plant.

Muscle Shoals hydroelectric plant.   Muscle Shoals is a series of rapids in the Tennessee River in Alabama.   Until recently, Muscle Shoals was chiefly known to the world as a serious obstruction to navigation on an ordinarily deep and navigable river.   In descending Muscle Shoals, the river falls 132 feet in 37 miles, a fall nearly equal to that at Niagara, which is 160 feet (Fig. 73).

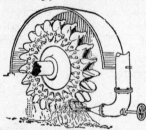

Fig. 72.   The Pelton water wheel.   These wheels are used when a comparatively small supply of available water can be delivered under great pressure, or "head." The water thus acquires great velocity when directed against the cup-shaped blades on the rim of the wheel.

The Wilson Dam is the most important of the several dams that have been erected at Muscle Shoals.   The dam itself is almost a mile long, and the pool above created by the dam, Wilson Lake, is 17 miles long and has an average width of $\frac{3}{4}$ of a mile.   It covers the rocks and shoals with deep water, making this part

Fig. 73. Wilson Dam at Muscle Shoals, Alabama, on the Tennessee River.

of the river navigable. The Wheeler Dam at the head of Wilson Lake will create a lake extending 80 miles upstream.

To prevent alternating flood and low water at different seasons, it has been proposed to dam the headwaters in the mountains, producing immense reservoirs in rainy seasons. The water would then be let out in seasons of drought for water power. Extensive forests on the mountains and the upper courses of the river will aid in regulating the supply by holding rain water and feeding it more slowly to the rivers.

In times of war the electric power of Muscle Shoals may be used to manufacture nitrates to be used in the making of explosives. In time of peace these nitrates may be combined with phosphates in near-by beds to make fertilizers for farm

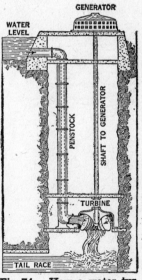

Fig. 74. How a water turbine is arranged.

lands. The production of cheap fertilizers for restoring the productiveness of worn-out lands has become one of the most important problems in the United States today.

The electric power of the plant can be carried to Birmingham, Memphis, Nashville, and Chattanooga, and to a large number of smaller cities. Railroads crossing the Appalachian Mountains can be supplied with power derived from Muscle Shoals.

EXPERIMENT 19

Question: How does a dam increase water pressure?

Materials: A tin can; a tripod or a box to set it on; a large pan.

Method: With a small nail punch three very small holes in the side of the can, one above another, an inch apart. Whittle wooden plugs to fit the holes. Fill the can with water. Remove plugs one at a time and measure distance from the base that each stream reaches.

Results: Record horizontal distance from base that each stream reached.

Conclusion: What determines the force of the water?

The tremendous power generated by Boulder Dam may be judged by the gush of water from the flume.

CHAPTER VII

SAFE AND SUFFICIENT WATER

A city's water supply. Water pressure is used to supply water to our homes. New York City and Los Angeles are two cities that draw their water from land much higher than the city. In consequence, the water pressure forces the water through pipes and out of the faucets in the homes of these cities. Since water will rise to the level from which it comes, water flows from the faucets because they are not so high as the water reservoir in the mountains. This type of water supply system is called the *gravity water system*.

In 1843 the city of New York dammed the Croton River a few miles above its junction with the Hudson, thus making an artificial lake (reservoir) that held about one billion gallons of water. This water was taken to the city through a pipe (aqueduct) more than 40 miles long.

Soon the water supply from the Croton River became inadequate for the needs of the city, and a larger dam was built. Even this did not give enough water, and the city bought 900 square miles in the Catskills. This large area of ground over which streams and brooks drain into a reservoir is called a *watershed*. Great care is taken to prevent the watershed from becoming a source of impure water. People are not allowed to live on the shed, and every effort is made to keep the surface of the ground clean.

By means of *dams* the water supply of this region is stored in huge *reservoirs* and the water pressure increased. The water then flows from Ashokan Reservoir to the city through the Catskill aqueduct on the west side of the Hudson (Fig. 75). This tunnel can deliver a half billion gallons of water a day. The aqueduct, 92 miles long, crosses under the Hudson River near Poughkeepsie, through a tunnel drilled in solid

Fig. 75.   The Ashokan Dam on the Catskill Mountains forms a huge
reservoir.

rock.   It was necessary to drill down 1100 feet before solid
rock capable of resisting the water pressure was found.

On the east side of the Hudson the water from the old
Croton Reservoir mixes with the Catskill water in the Catskill aqueduct.   From the aqueduct the water passes to
storage reservoirs such as Kensico or Hill View.   From
these storage reservoirs it is distributed through large pipes
(water mains), then through smaller pipes (street mains), and
finally into the buildings of New York.   Along the pipes in
the buildings are water faucets, each containing a hole that
can be opened or closed by turning a handle.

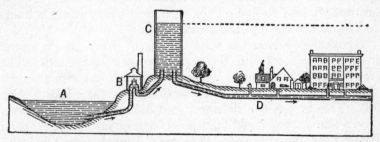

Fig. 76.   Pumping water-supply system.   A, reservoir; B, pumping
station; C, standpipe; D, water main.

Pumping systems of water supply. Cities and towns that draw their water from a source below their own level use a pumping system. The water may be pumped directly into the water mains or it may be pumped into standpipes or reservoirs located at high levels from which it flows down again to the houses (Fig. 76). Often there is a combination of direct pumping and standpipes. During hours of low demand the pumps fill the standpipes. During hours of average use the pumps supply the demand directly. In emergencies, as during a great fire, the standpipes help to supply the demand.

Even where the gravity system is used it is often supplemented by pumps. The Empire State Building in New York is so high that gravity alone would not force

Fig. 77. A giant pipe seven feet in diameter brings safe water over mountain and canyon to Los Angeles.

water to the upper stories. A pump is placed in the basement and water is pumped into the tank on the roof. This furnishes an abundant water supply for the building. Many school buildings, apartment houses, and office buildings contain such water tanks on the roof. This is necessary when the building stands on high ground and uses large amounts of water.

Making water safe. Several diseases, such as typhoid, cholera, dysentery, and enteritis, are spread by means of contaminated water. Before the discovery of the part that

7

Fig. 78. A settling basin in a water-supply system.

water plays in transmitting disease, terrible epidemics of
water-borne diseases were frequent.   Now the water of our
great cities is safer than that from village wells.

To secure a pure and adequate supply, many cities have
bought large areas of land forming the watershed of their
supply.   Los Angeles, Denver, and many other cities like
New York draw their supply from watersheds in the mountains where the land is guarded from pollution (Fig. 77).
The cities along the Great Lakes generally draw their supply
from the lakes (Fig. 79).   Formerly this supply was badly
contaminated by sewage.   Chicago dug a drainage canal
which carries sewage into the Illinois River and then to the
Mississippi.   Other cities have located their water intakes
so that the lake currents carry away the contaminated
water.   The "cribs" for the intake are at least two miles

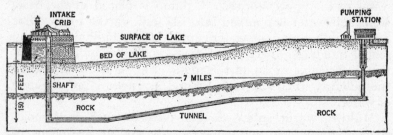

Fig. 79.   Great Lake cities draw their water from the lake two miles or more
from shore.   Note the tunnel through solid rock beneath the lake.

Fig. 80. Aërating the water to improve the taste after treating with chlorine.

from shore. Philadelphia and St. Louis draw their supply of water from rivers.

Whatever the source, provision is made for purification, and constant tests for purity safeguard the supply. Muddy water is led into great settling basins (Fig. 78). Then it is led to other reservoirs where exposure to sun and air destroys bacteria. Alum is sometimes added. Alum forms little flakes which, in settling, carry down fine mud and many other impurities. The water then is filtered through sand. Sand filters remove many impurities, including most forms of harmful bacteria. To destroy any remaining bacteria, liquid chlorine or a compound of chlorine is added. To improve the taste, the water is often forced through a spray to permit it to absorb air (Fig. 80).

Water supply for the country house. On the farm the water supply is usually from a well or spring. When we dig below the surface, we find that the soil is moist. If we go far enough, we reach a level at which water seeps into the hole

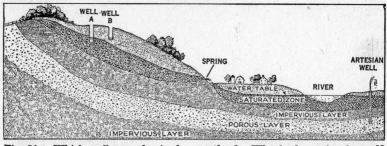

Fig. 81. Which well goes dry in dry weather? Why is the spring formed? Will the river go dry? Where does the rain fall that supplies the artesian well?

we have dug. In dry weather this level may be a little deeper than in wet weather. For a permanent supply, the well must go below the water level in dry weather. This level of ground water is called the *water table* (Fig. 81). Where the water comes to the surface at the edge of a hill, a spring or a swamp may be formed (Fig. 81).

Running water in the house may be obtained by piping from a spring at a higher level, or by pumping from a well by use of a pump or by a pressure system as shown in Figures 81 and 84.

Contrary to a common belief, wells and springs are very likely to contain contaminated water (Figs. 82 and 83). The typhoid rate in cities often rises in the fall when summer

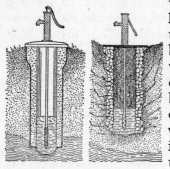

Fig. 82. Why is the well on the left, which is lined with concrete, safer than the well on the right?

vacationists return; some of them have contracted the disease on their vacation trips and bring it back home with them. An easy way to make sure of safe water in camp and summer cottage is to boil it for 10 minutes. One drop of tincture of iodine in a quart of water will kill typhoid germs, but iodine may be dangerous poison to some persons, if this quantity is exceeded. Many persons before traveling for the summer are vaccinated against typhoid fever.

Fig. 83. Why is the water supply on this farm unsafe?

Sewage disposal. The great danger to a safe water supply is sewage. Turned into a stream or lake, it endangers communities toward which it drifts. Modern sewage disposal consists in destroying the solids and the harmful bacteria, and then allowing the water to escape into the ground or into streams (Fig. 83). A cesspool, sometimes still used in villages and in the country, is simply a large pit 10 feet deep or more, lined with stones and covered. The solids are partially liquefied by bacteria and the water seeps off through the soil. Such a cesspool always involves danger of contamination of springs or wells. The cesspool should be more than 50 feet from the well and drain away from it. One can never be certain, however, of the movement of underground water.

An improvement on the cesspool is the septic tank, shown in Figure 85. The septic tank is built of steel or concrete and retains the sewage until there is more

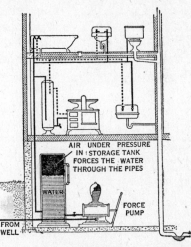

AIR UNDER PRESSURE IN STORAGE TANK FORCES THE WATER THROUGH THE PIPES

WATER

FORCE PUMP

FROM WELL

Fig. 84. Plan of water-pressure system in a house.

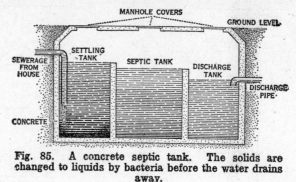

Fig. 85. A concrete septic tank. The solids are changed to liquids by bacteria before the water drains away.

opportunity for liquefaction of solids. City sewage-disposal plants are modified septic tanks. The sewage may be first pumped through aëration sprays from which it trickles over stones. Sun, oxygen, and bacteria attack the solids and some of the harmful bacteria. Septic tanks where bacteria that live without air destroy other bacteria often follow the aëration basins. Settling basins followed by sand filters remove practically all the remaining objectionable substances. Some solids always collect in the basins, forming "sludge" which must be removed from time to time. Sludge has some little value as fertilizer for farm lands, but on the whole is not very satisfactory. Its disposal is not yet satisfactorily accomplished.

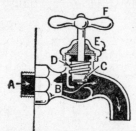

Fig. 86. A compression faucet. A, water supply pipe; B, opening through which water passes; C, fiber washer held in place by screw (a leaky faucet can usually be corrected by replacing the washer); D, the plunger which opens and closes the faucet; E, cap which holds the plunger in place; F, handle which opens and closes faucet.

Stopping water waste in the home. A faucet constantly dripping is an expensive waste of water. A leak or drip from a faucet usually comes from the fact that the fiber washer closing the hole is worn. It can easily be repaired. Turn off the water at the house cock, unscrew the top of the faucet, and replace the washer with a new one. Ten minutes of time will save dollars' worth of water in a year.

Examine Figures 86 and 87 which show the construction of two common types of faucet.

We are likely to think of water as free. In reality it costs large sums of money. In 1933, for example, New York spent $44,000,000 in maintaining and distributing its water supply. Wasting water is clearly wasting our own and other people's money.

A leak in the flush tank over a water-closet is usually due to a faulty rubber ball that forms the outlet valve from the tank. A new ball can be bought for a few cents in a hardware store and installed in a few minutes. Figure 88 shows how the tank and bowl work.

Saving the nation's water supply. Few of us give a thought to what would happen if our supply of water failed us, yet in certain years, month has succeeded month with little or no rain. Crops and pasture grass disappear. Livestock is shipped away or slaughtered. Occasionally a series of two or three dry years follow one another. The water level underground falls gradually lower. Springs and wells go dry. Rivers and lakes dwindle and the smaller streams disappear. Farmers, villagers, and townspeople suffer first from failing water supply, then the city dwellers are warned to reduce their consumption of water.

On the other hand, floods sometimes sweep river valleys, over-

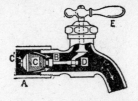

Fig. 87. A Fuller faucet. A, water supply pipe; B, opening through which water passes; C, rubber washer held in place by nut C′ (a leaky faucet usually can be repaired by replacing this washer); D, the eccentric, attached to the handle E, which opens and closes the faucet.

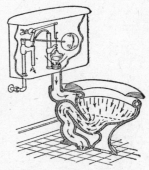

Fig. 88. A flush tank and bowl. Examine the tank in your bathroom. A turn of the handle pulls the plug and floods the bowl. The plug falls with the water and closes the pipe. The large metal ball on the right floats up with the incoming water and shuts off the supply. The dotted line marks the level of water that stands in the bowl. The upward turn of the drain pipe forms a trap to exclude gases from the drain.

Fig. 89a.　Embankments are often used to keep a stream in its natural banks.　Dams in the upper courses of the stream and forests on the hills reduce the danger from flood and from low water.　Water not under control is destructive.　Flood waters of the Ohio, at Cincinnati, Ohio.

Fig. 89b.　Forests and lakes in the mountains reduce floods and store water that may be used in droughts.　Heart Lake and Mount McIntyre, Adirondack Mountains, New York.

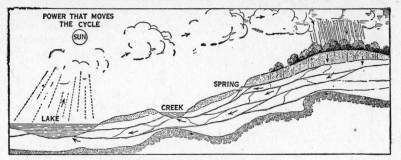

Fig. 90. The water cycle in nature.

whelming towns and cities, destroying farm lands and live stock, carrying away bridges, railroads, and factories (Fig. 89a). Both drought and flood are destructive, and both may be partially controlled.

Most of the rain that falls on a bare hillside quickly runs off, but much of that which falls on a forested hillside is absorbed in the spongy forest floor. Actual measurements have shown that 28 times as much rain runs off a bare hillside as off a forested hillside. An important step in controlling our water supply is to see to it that hillsides too steep to be farmed profitably are covered with forests (see p. 453). Forests save water for us (Fig. 89b). Some of the water absorbed by the forest floor is taken up by the trees and passed into the air, but a greater part sinks into the ground to come to the surface again in springs and lake beds. Such ground water coming to the surface maintains the permanent flow of streams and the permanent level of lakes (Fig. 90). A second important step in preventing both flood and dearth of water is the erection of dams in the upper courses of streams, in which water may be dammed up, or *impounded*, and stored. Such dams reduce the rush of flood water down the valley and save it for distribution in dry seasons.

EXPERIMENT 20

Question: How can I illustrate the gravity system of water supply?
Materials: Bottles, tubes, and faucets arranged as in diagram. Colored water is used to show the movement better.

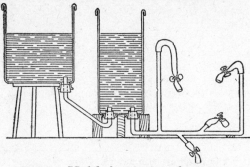

Fig. 91.　Model of a water-supply system.

Directions: A bottle represents the reservoir. From the bottom of this, a pipe (the aqueduct) leads to a smaller bottle (storage reservoir). From the bottom of this a pipe (water main) leads to a number of smaller pipes (house pipes). At the end of the house pipes, faucets are placed at different levels.

Notice that the water flows with the most force from the lowest faucet. Notice that one faucet is above the level of the water in the storage reservoir, and that water will not flow from it. Notice that the level of the water in the highest pipe and the level of the water in the storage reservoir are the same (water seeks its own level).

Diagram: A titled and labeled drawing of the apparatus in use is required. A drawing showing an ideal gravity pumping system is required.

Conclusion: Explain the system by which a city distributes water to our homes.

Practical application: Which is better, a gravity or a pumping system? Why? Why does New York not rely upon wells for its water supply?

Fig. 92.　How to fold filter paper (Experiment 21).

EXPERIMENT 21

Question: How can I make dirty water clean?

Materials: Funnel and support; beakers; lamp chimney; clean sand; filter paper; mud; salt.

Directions: (a) Drop some mud in a beaker of water and stir. Tie a piece of cheesecloth over the bottom of the lamp chimney, and then fill the chimney with sand. Fold the filter paper into a cone and place in the funnel. Pour some of the dirty water into the filter paper and

some into the lamp chimney. Catch the
filtrate, or the water that drips out the
bottom, in beakers.

(b) Dissolve some salt in a clean beaker
of water. Set up a *clean* funnel and filter
paper. Pour the salt water into the filter.
Taste the filtrate.

Results: (a) Is the filtrate clear or
muddy?

(b) Does the filter remove dissolved
salt?

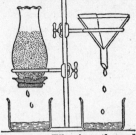

Fig. 93. Filtering through sand and paper.

Conclusion: What sort of material may
be removed by filters? Is filtered water
necessarily pure? What cannot be removed by filtering? Is clear,
colorless water always pure water? Answer the question of the
experiment.

EXPERIMENT 22

Question: How do cities make their water supply safe?

Materials: A culture of Paramecium or other microscopic animals
(see page 370); microscope, slide, and cover glass; medicine dropper;
a bit of filter paper or paper towel; dilute solution of chloride of lime.

Directions: Put a drop of the culture of microscopic animals on the
slide and examine under the microscope.

Later put a drop of the chloride of lime at one edge of the cover glass.
Touch the filter paper or towel to the opposite edge. Water will be
drawn from under the cover glass and the chloride solution will flow in
to replace it.

NOTE: Chloride of lime is not used in city systems, but for our
purpose is more convenient than liquid chlorine.

Results: What happened to the living things when the chloride
solution reached them?

Conclusion: How may bacteria be destroyed in a water system?

CHAPTER VIII

THE CHEMICAL PURITY OF WATER

Hard water. Sometimes, when you have tried to wash your hands with soap and water, you have found it difficult to make suds. At first you got just a greasy scum on your hands. If you kept at it, however, you finally worked up a lather. Some waters produce a cleansing lather very easily and some do not. Those that do are called *soft;* those that do not are called *hard.* In washing clothes, hard water adds considerably to the work, to the quantity of soap, and hence to the cost of washing. In laundries hard water may add so much to the expense that profits are seriously reduced. It pays then to install apparatus to soften the water. Even in homes the added expense of hard water in the course of a year makes the use of water softeners profitable. We shall see why water is hard and how the condition may be corrected.

Why water becomes hard. When water sinks into the soil, it dissolves some of the rocks and minerals and becomes in consequence impure chemically. Water that contains a considerable amount of minerals, especially of lime compounds, is called hard water.

Water containing carbon dioxide dissolves some minerals more readily than does pure water. Carbon dioxide is a very common compound. It is breathed out by living things, both animals and plants, including those minute plants, fungi, and bacteria which cause the decay of organic matter. Many living things, both plants and animals, make their home in the soil and constantly add carbon dioxide to it. Carbon dioxide is always present in the air. When it rains, some carbon dioxide dissolves in the rain water, forming a weak acid, carbonic acid.

(88)

Fig. 94. Water containing carbon dioxide dissolved the limestone forming the cave. Water dripping from the roof deposited the stalactites hanging from above and built up the stalagmites rising from the floor. Carlsbad Caverns, New Mexico.

Rain water and soil water are solutions of an acid and therefore can dissolve some things that are not easily affected by pure water. For example, marble or limestone is easily soluble in carbonic acid. When the water containing dissolved carbonic acid sinks into the ground and chances to meet limestone, the rock dissolves and may form a cave (Fig. 94). The water itself is made hard.

Such a solution of limestone (calcium carbonate) and carbon dioxide, as we have been discussing, occurs naturally in sea water. It is from this source that oysters, clams, and corals obtain the limestone from which they build their shells.

If you look inside your teakettle, you may see a deposit that looks like, and is, stone. It has come from the water used to fill the kettle. In a few sections of our country this will not be so. The water in those sections is so soft that on evaporation it leaves no residue. You can easily test your home water. Pour a teaspoonful in the cover of a tin can, put it over a flame, and evaporate the water. The amount of residue remaining after the water is evaporated shows how much dissolved mineral matter is in the water.

When hard water is used in boilers, the dissolved minerals are deposited as *boiler scale* on the inside of the boiler. Because this scale is a very poor conductor of heat, the engineer has to burn much more coal than he should to heat the boiler water. The same thing is true in your home. A teakettle covered on the inside with scale takes a long time to heat.

Softening water. If hard water containing dissolved limestone is heated, carbon dioxide gas will be driven off. There will then be nothing to keep the limestone dissolved. It will then come out of solution, and the water will no longer be hard. Since this kind of hard water can be made soft by heating, we name it *temporary hard water*.

You will better understand what has been said about hard water if you will perform the following experiment:

Generate carbon dioxide in a flask as in Experiment 12. From this flask run a tube ending in a small hole to a second flask containing limewater (Fig. 50). As the carbon is generated, it passes into the second flask and bubbles through the limewater. At first the limewater turns milky. Finely divided limestone (calcium carbonate) appears as a precipitate. (A precipitate is a solid formed in a liquid.) As the action continues, this precipitate will dissolve and form an artificial temporary hard water. It is not necessary to wait until all of the limestone has dissolved. After a while you can filter the liquid. The filtrate (the part that runs through the filter paper) will be clear.

Put some of the artificial hard water in a test tube and heat it. You will see bubbles of carbon dioxide being driven off. The water will turn cloudy, owing to the precipitation of limestone. To the cloudy liquid add a few drops of hydrochloric acid. You will see the limestone dissolve and the water will once more be clear. Limestone and marble are soluble in many acids. Nature uses carbonic acid. In the laboratory we ordinarily use hydrochloric acid because it is a stronger acid and acts faster.

Permanent hard water contains dissolved substances (chiefly calcium sulphate) which are not destroyed by heating, and therefore the water must be softened by chemical means. Permanent hard water is a poor name, for it may easily be softened.

Prepare an artificial hard water by adding 10 grams of calcium chloride to a liter of water. Add to a test tube half full of this hard water a few drops of a strong soap solution and shake it. You will see that the water does not lather but that a curd forms. The soap has been used up, not in doing its proper work of making something clean, but in softening water. Continue adding soap until finally, on shaking, a lather forms. The hard water is now soft and the amount of soap that you have used to soften the water represents waste. Repeat the experiment, first adding washing soda to the hard water. You will find that washing soda may be used to soften hard water. Since washing soda is cheaper than soap, laundries sometimes soften hard water by treating it with soda. Borax also softens water.

Water can be softened in another way that is used commercially. If the hard water is passed over a mineral called a *zeolite*, or *permutite* (which is an artificial zeolite), a chemical change takes place and the water is made soft. If a solution of salt is now passed over the exhausted zeolite, it is regenerated or made fit for use again. This process is moderately cheap, and has the advantage that the hardening substances are really taken from the water. After the process is installed, salt is the only chemical used.

Distilled water. Water may be freed of all the dissolved minerals by distillation. On boiling, water evaporates as steam. The minerals remain. When the steam is condensed by cooling, we have distilled water. Of natural waters, only rain water compares with it in purity. Rain water is naturally distilled water, but contains gases dissolved from the atmosphere. Figure 95 shows a glass still often used in the laboratory.

Distilled water, if carefully prepared and stored in clean containers, is pure, and free from all dissolved minerals and bacteria. It is, of course, too expensive for a city supply, but on shipboard sea water is often distilled to furnish the ship's supply of pure water.

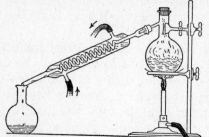

Fig. 95. A glass still. Cool water circulating through the outer tube, Liebig condenser, cools the inner tube, causing the steam to condense to water.

Distilled water is used in the laboratory whenever chemically pure water is needed. It is added to automobile and other electric batteries, because natural waters contain minerals that will neutralize the battery acid and cause deposits that interfere with the battery action.

EXPERIMENT 23

Question: How can you soften water?

NOTE: Water that produces suds upon shaking with soap may be considered soft; water that does not, hard.

Materials: Test tubes; test-tube supports; Bunsen burner; rain water or distilled water; tap or well water; limewater; salt solution; washing soda; soap shavings.

Directions: Label test tubes 1, 2, 2a, 3, 3a, 4, 4a.

In 1 put distilled or rain water; in 2 and 2a put tap water or well water; in 3 and 3a limewater; in 4 and 4a salt solution.

To 1, 2, 3, and 4 add a little soap shavings, cover each tube with the thumb, and shake it violently. In the table under "Results," indicate, by writing *yes* or *no*, which formed suds.

To 2a, 3a, and 4a add soap shavings; heat, shake, and record results.

To those that did not produce suds add washing soda, again shake and record results.

Results: Record your results by writing "yes" or "no" in a table or chart prepared as follows:

	DISTILLED WATER	TAP WATER	LIME-WATER	SALT SOLUTION
Suds upon shaking....	....	....	....	....
Suds upon heating....	....	....	....	....
Suds upon addition of washing soda.......	....	....	....	....

Conclusions: Which of your specimens of water were hard at the beginning of the experiment?

What treatment made each soft?

What treatment should your tap or well water receive to make it soft?

Application: What is the advantage of softening hard water before using it to wash?

Country people often save rain water in cisterns or rain barrels. Why is rain water superior to tap or well water?

What chemicals do you suppose are added to hard-water soap?

EXPERIMENT 24

Question: How can I prepare distilled water?

Materials: Desk apparatus; distilling flask; Liebig condenser; copper sulphate; salt; thermometer.

Directions and results: (a) Half fill the distilling flask with water. Add a teaspoonful of salt and enough copper sulphate to color the water distinctly. These are added to give a decidedly impure water. Set up the apparatus and see that a slow stream of water is passing through the condenser. Boil the water in the flask gently, and watch what happens. Collect the distillate in a small beaker. What is its color?

(b) Taste the distilled water. Is it salty?

(c) Put a little of the water containing salt and copper sulphate in an evaporating dish and boil till all the water is gone. What remains?

Diagram: Show the still in operation.

Conclusion: Distillation frees water of ——.

NOTE: Liebig was a great German chemist. The Liebig condenser was named for him.

Practical applications: 1. How can you distinguish spring water that is perfectly clear from distilled water? 2. What commercial use is made of distillation? 3. How could distillation help in a supply of drinking water aboard ship? 4. When a teakettle boils dry, you often find a deposit left in the kettle. How did it get there?

QUESTIONS TO THINK OUT

1. The moon has no atmosphere. Would the boiling temperature of water on the moon be higher or lower on this account?

2. Recall what you learned about air pressure and tell whether a lift pump would raise water to the same height in New Orleans and in Denver.

3. Sometimes when you turn on the cold water faucet in your home you get spurts of hot water and steam accompanied by a rumbling and pounding in the pipes and boiler. Study the diagram of the hot-water system and decide what the trouble is and how it may be remedied.

4. Is it easier to float with your lungs full of air or after you have exhaled part of the air? Why?

8

5. Why is it difficult to dive deep?

6. A diver's suit has shoes heavily weighted with lead. Why?

7. Will a piece of marble weigh the same in fresh water as in salt water? Reason it out and then find out by experiment.

8. If a football were filled with water instead of air, would it bounce?

9. Hydrogen peroxide (H_2O_2) loses its antiseptic strength upon long standing in your home medicine closet because it gives up half its oxygen. What substance does it then change into?

10. Why does water flow downhill?

11. Suppose a small stream were flowing down a valley. How could its effective power be increased?

12. Water motors may be attached to the faucet to run small machines. How does the water in the pipe get its power?

13. Examine a water-power project in your region—either a small plant on an estate or a mill or a large commercial plant. Report briefly, as was done for the Muscle Shoals project.

14. Study your city water supply.

(a) Where is the source of supply?

(b) What provision is made to insure a supply in dry seasons?

(c) How is clear water obtained?

(d) How is safe water insured?

(e) What is the plan for sewage disposal?

15. In a famous park in one of our great cities, springs were closed to public use. What is the chief danger to park springs?

16. Make a survey of the water supply and drainage at a country home or farm. Note the arrangement of water supply, barnyards, toilets, etc. What possibilities are there for contamination?

17. If you know of a place where you would like to spend the summer camping, plan a sanitary camp. Sketch a small map showing hills and hollows, streams, woods, other camps and houses, water supply, etc. Indicate the location of plants for disposal of sewage and other wastes. How should you make certain that the water was safe?

18. Examine a public picnic ground and report on the water supply, toilets, waste disposal, and other necessary features for sanitation.

19. What has your State done to preserve the water supply?

20. If water evaporated from a muddy pond, would the water vapor be pure or impure?

21. If you filtered muddy water, would it be fit to drink?

22. Would distillation of hard water soften it? Would filtration soften it?

23. The water flowing from fresh-water bogs is often slightly acid. Would soap make a free lather in it? Prove by an experiment.

24. If you distilled muddy water, should you obtain clear water? water fit to drink?

25. Why do you suppose the sea is not so limy as it is salty?

UNIT THREE

WHAT THINGS ARE MADE OF: MATTER

The chemist has made silklike dresses and neckties from waste wood. He has made gorgeous dyes and substances sweeter than sugar from foul-smelling coal tar. The chemist governs the production of innumerable things of our daily environment, from steel and concrete and paper and ink to candy and medicines. His control is due to his knowledge of what things are made of, how they are put together in nature, and how the elements act when he takes them apart.

The universe contains a vast variety of things, yet chemists now believe that there are only 92 simple substances, or elements, and that every substance we know is either one of these few elements, or a combination of two or more of them. Only in the last few years have the last of the 92 been detected, yet before the last few were found in the laboratory, the scientist had foretold what they would be like and how they would act.

We say that all things are made of *matter*. But what is matter? In this unit we shall see what the scientist means by *matter*. We shall study some of the elements that make up the matter of our everyday life, our surroundings, and our bodies. We shall see how they unite to form other substances.

Then we shall make a short study of how we measure matter. The scientist and the engineer must measure— measure accurately. Building a great bridge, a skyscraper, or an ocean liner would be a sorry failure without the most accurate and minute calculations.

Did you ever wonder where our measures came from? What is a foot? Who taught us to measure in miles? Why do scientists use the metric system? We shall see. How is the correct length of a yard determined?

Chapter IX

WHAT MATTER IS

Stuff. What is your shadow made of? Your shadow is undoubtedly a "thing," but you cannot roll it up like a paper doll, and put it in your pocket. Both your shadow and a paper doll are "things"; but wherein do they differ? You might say that the doll is "real stuff," that it has "substance." The scientist calls such "real stuff" *matter*. To him matter means one thing and nothing else: *Matter is that which occupies space and has weight.* Anything that fulfils this definition is matter; anything that does not, is not matter. Tell which of these things are matter: electricity, light, air, water, iron, your hand, your breath, your thought.

What matter is like. What is amber like? What is paper like? What is matter like? When you ask such questions, you are trying to find out how a thing resembles or differs from other things. In scientific language you are asking, "What are its *properties*?"

The paper you are looking at is white, it can be written or printed upon, and it tears easily. It will burn, forming carbon dioxide and water, and it leaves an ash. It turns yellow with age, but can be bleached white. The properties listed in the first sentence of this paragraph are different in kind from those in the second and third sentences. The properties in the first sentence are those you tell by your senses; they are *physical properties*. The properties in the second and third sentences are the result of combination with other things; they are *chemical properties*.

When we try to tell what something is like most of us are very careless and indefinite. Our hearer, in consequence, generally has a very hazy idea of what we have in mind. If we say that amber is hard, brown stuff that looks somewhat

like celluloid or glass, our hearer may be excused if he mistakes
a lump of resin or a horehound tablet for a piece of amber.
Such descriptions will not do in science. We must describe a
thing exactly—that is, in such a way that our hearer will
recognize it when he finds it, and mistake nothing else for it.
To make sure of such exactness, scientists use terms which
mean one thing and nothing else. Whenever you see such a
term in a science book, you will know it always means exactly
the same.

Here are some of the terms scientists use in naming the
special properties or qualities of matter. You need not
commit them to memory; they are listed merely to show you
how the scientist tries to be definite in his description.

Hardness—the ability to resist scratching.

Brittleness—the ease with which a substance breaks.

Tenacity—the ability to resist being torn.

Malleability—the capability of being pressed or beaten
into sheets.

Elasticity—the ability to regain original shape after
distortion.

How much matter in a cubic inch. You know that a
cubic inch of iron weighs more than a cubic inch of wood.
The cubic inch of iron has more matter in it. It is denser.
The quantity of matter in a cubic inch or a cubic centimeter
is called its *density*. You can find how much matter there is
in a piece of iron by dividing its weight by its volume. You
thus find how much a cubic inch weighs.

* [Scientists and engineers usually judge the density of a
substance by comparing its weight with the weight of water.
This is its specific gravity. When we say that the specific
gravity of iron is 7, we mean that iron is 7 times as heavy as
water. You can easily find the specific gravity of a piece of
iron or other similar substance. You know that if you sink
a piece of iron in water, it will displace its volume of water.
You know further from your study of buoyancy, that when
you weigh a piece of iron in water, it loses weight. Its loss of
weight is equal to the weight of the water it displaces; that
is, its loss of weight is equal to the weight of a volume of

---

* Text included in brackets ([ ]) comprises topics required in certain courses of study↓

water equal to the volume of iron. Then we can find the specific gravity of iron by dividing its weight in air by its loss of weight in water.]

Matter changes in form. You know that ice is matter. When it melts, it is matter. When the water boils away to steam, it is still matter. Iron may be changed in the same way, although a very high temperature is necessary. Oxygen may become a liquid and then a solid, but it takes a very low temperature. Through all these changes of state, matter still remains matter.

Everyone knows in a general way what is meant by solid, liquid, and gas, yet it is not easy to give satisfactory definitions of these terms. As good a way as any is to think of how each behaves when placed in a box. The solid will keep its original shape and volume. The liquid will flow over the bottom and take the shape of the box, but keep its original volume. The gas will fill the box, keeping neither its original shape nor volume, but taking the shape and volume of the box. Thus it is clear that although matter behaves differently in some ways in the three states, in all three it occupies space and may be weighed. Therefore, the scientist says that *solid*, *liquid*, and *gas* are the three states of matter.

Elements, compounds, and mixtures. Is paper one "thing" or several? If we examine closely the different forms of matter, the "things" about us, we find that it is often possible to pull apart a particular form of matter or to separate it into simple substances. If we char paper, we can get from it (1) a black substance called *charcoal* or *carbon;* and (2) *water*. The water in turn can be separated into two gases called *hydrogen* and *oxygen*. Paper, then, is made up of at least three different substances—carbon, hydrogen, and oxygen.

If we try to break up carbon into simpler substances, we fail. No one has been able to get anything except carbon from carbon. Substances that have not been broken up into simpler substances are called *elements*. Carbon, oxygen, hydrogen, iron, gold, lead, silver are elements. Of the ninety-two elements many are rare and commercially unimportant. We shall have occasion to speak of only a few.

Some important elements are listed in the following table, with the melting point and boiling point of each in degrees centigrade.

Element	Melting Point	Boiling Point
Aluminum	660° C	1,800° C
Argon	−190°	−185°
Arsenic	....	450°
Bromine	−7°	63°
Calcium	810°	....
Carbon (Graphite)	....	3,600°
Chlorine	−102°	−34°
Chromium	1,515°	2,200°
Copper	1,083°	2,100°
Fluorine	−223°	−187°
Gold	1,094°	2,500°
Hydrogen	−257°	−253°
Iodine	113°	184°
Iron (Wrought)	1,530°	2,450°
Lead	327°	1,525°
Magnesium	650°	1,100°
Manganese	1,250°	2,000°
Mercury	−38.9°	357°
Nickel	1,432°	......
Nitrogen	−214°	−196°
Oxygen	−218°	−183°
Phosphorus (White)	44°	287°
Platinum	1,755°	3,910°
Potassium	62.5°	720°
Radium	960°	1,140°
Silver	960°	1,955°
Sodium	97.5°	742°
Sulphur $\{\ \alpha$	115°	444°
β	120°	444°
Tin	232°	1,600°
Tungsten	3,350°	5,830°
Zinc	419°	930°

Elements combine to form *compounds*. If you heat a mixture of carbon and oxygen, they combine, and a new substance called *carbon dioxide* is formed. We call substances formed by the combination of elements *compounds*. Sugar, starch, iron rust, white of egg, and water all are compounds.

If we put some oxygen and hydrogen into a bottle and shake them together, no real change takes place. Every particle of oxygen and hydrogen retains its own separate existence. The bottle contains a *mixture* of oxygen and hydrogen. Now touch a match to the bottle. An explosion occurs and a mist forms inside the bottle. We have forced the two elements to combine and a new compound, *water*, has been formed. When we caused the oxygen and the hydrogen to combine, we formed a compound.

In a *mixture*, the substances present may be mixed in any proportion. In a compound, the elements are always present in the same proportion. Water has been analyzed (taken apart) thousands of times. No one has ever found water which does not contain two parts of hydrogen and one part oxygen by volume. *The composition of every pure chemical compound is always the same.* This statement is known as the *law of definite proportions*.

Brass looks like a compound or an element. If, however, we analyze thirty different pieces of brass, we find not only that every piece is made up of copper and zinc, but that the proportions of the two may vary between quite wide limits. If brass were a compound, it would always contain exactly the same proportion of copper and zinc. Since the percentage of copper varies, brass is not a compound but a mixture. Such mixtures of metals are called *alloys*.

Solutions. When we add sugar to coffee or cocoa and stir it, the solid sugar disappears. Every drop is made sweet, therefore the sugar has been distributed throughout the liquid. If we let it stand, no further change takes place. Each drop remains sweet as before. We have made a *solution*. Solutions are common in our homes. Tea and lemonade are solutions. When beets are boiled in water, the water becomes red. The coloring matter of the beets is dissolved in the water. If we think of the work that goes on in the kitchen, we can think of many solutions.

We may define a solution as *a uniform mixture of two or more substances that do not separate even on long standing*. We speak of the material used to dissolve something as a *solvent*, while the thing dissolved we call a *solute*. The result we call a solution. Make sure that you know the meaning of these terms, for we shall use them many times.

Alcohol is a very good solvent. It dissolves many substances. In the old-fashioned drug store, with its even rows of bottles on the shelves instead of "package goods," did you ever notice how many bottles had labels beginning with "Tr"? At least you have heard of "tincture of iodine." A tincture is a solution in alcohol. Many of the solutions used in medicine are tinctures. Vanilla extract is a solution of vanilla bean in alcohol. Probably there is a bottle of perfume in your home. If so, it is a solution of one or more flower extracts in alcohol. Shellac and varnish dissolve in alcohol. That is why alcohol dropped on the table destroys the varnish. Alcohol dissolves some kinds of spots from your clothes, but carbon tetrachloride is a better solvent for spots.

Water is a better solvent than alcohol. It dissolves more substances than any other liquid. For this reason natural waters are never chemically pure. They have always become solutions by dissolving substances out of the course along which they flow. Chemically pure water is obtained by distillation (page 91).

When you dissolve a little sugar in a cup of water, you make a *dilute*, or *weak*, solution. When you add a considerable quantity of sugar to your weak solution, you have a *strong*, or *concentrated*, solution. If you continue to add sugar, there comes a time when not all of the sugar will dissolve, even on long shaking. You now have a *saturated* solution. If you warm your saturated solution, more of the sugar will dissolve. In saying that a solution is saturated, you must always give the temperature. You must say, for example, "A solution of sugar, saturated at 70° F."

When a hot saturated solution cools, the liquid can no longer contain so much dissolved substance. Some is deposited. The cool solution is still saturated, but its capacity is less. Also when some of the liquid evaporates, the dissolved substance is deposited, but the remaining solution is saturated. Did you ever notice crystals of sugar around the top of a jam

Fig. 96. Muddy water is a suspension of mud. The mud may be removed by filtering or allowing it to settle.

jar, or salt on a bucket of salt fish? You sometimes find salt on paper in which butter is wrapped. The salt that was added to the butter was carried out by water contained in the butter, and left behind as the water evaporated.

[Certain substances, such as "hypo" used by photographers, do not behave as simply as sugar or salt in solution. When a hot, saturated solution of hypo is cooled, hypo is not immediately deposited. Such a solution is said to be *supersaturated*. It holds more hypo than is needed to saturate it at the lower temperature. Supersaturated solutions are very unstable (easily unbalanced). Dropping a crystal of hypo into the supersaturated solution, or even shaking it, will cause depositing of the excess hypo.]

Other solutions. The word *solution* does not apply to solutions of solids in liquids only. Soda water is a solution of a gas, carbon dioxide, in water. The carbon dioxide is forced in under pressure. When the pressure is released, the carbon dioxide bubbles out. The greater the pressure the more gas will be dissolved by a liquid.

Liquids also dissolve in gases. The air of your science classroom contains dissolved water vapor. The higher the temperature, the more water vapor it can dissolve. Chilling the air throws the water out of solution as with dew or rain. The metal iron can dissolve large quantities of gas. Solids, liquids, and gases can dissolve in solids, liquids, and gases.

Muddy water and muddy coffee. Muddy water is not a solution, because if left standing the mud settles (separates). We can also filter the mud out by letting the muddy water run through filter paper. The mud is not dissolved in the water. Fine particles of mud are floating throughout the fluid. Such a mixture of fine particles supported in the body of a fluid is called a *suspension* (Fig. 96). The particles settle upon long standing. Coffee should be a solution, but often a fine muddy sediment settles in the bottom of the cup. Such coffee is both a solution and a suspension.

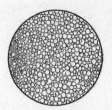

Fig. 97. Cream is an emulsion containing microscopic droplets of fat.

Grease and cold water. You cannot wash grease off your hands with cold water. Let us see why. Shake oil and water together. They mix, but if left standing, the mixture separates. Now add a little gum acacia (gum arabic) and shake again. The oil and the water mix, and on standing, the mixture does not separate. Such a mixture of two liquids is an *emulsion*. Soap makes an emulsion with the grease on your hands and the cold water. Then the grease washes off. Cream is an emulsion of butterfat (Fig. 97). Cold cream is a thick emulsion. Such emulsions often break down on their own accord. Anything that destroys the *emulsifying agent* will also break the emulsion. At the seashore, have you ever tried to wash your hands with salt water and soap? You get a greasy scum of dirt on your hands. The soap will not do its work because the salt breaks down the emulsion.

Crystals. Dissolve some salt and some sugar in separate dishes of water. Then evaporate the water in each over a slow flame until it dries up. Examine the salt that you have recovered under a magnifying glass. You will find that the small particles are not simply irregular masses, but they have a regular shape. Each little particle is a cube (Fig. 98). Sugar particles have a somewhat similar shape but they are not exactly cubes. Such natural regular forms are called *crystals*.

Many minerals exist as crystals, or can be crystallized. Often these crystal forms give us an easy way of identifying minerals. Quartz (rock crystal) is a common mineral. It is hard, often colorless, and has been mistaken for diamonds.

Quartz, however, is crystallized in six-sided prisms, topped with six-sided pyramids. These prisms and pyramids are clearly shown by the crystals in Figure 99. Diamonds

never crystallize in this form. A quick look at the two crystals tells us at once which is the diamond.

Water in compounds. Crystals often contain water. If you heat a crystal of copper sulphate, or bluestone, in a test tube the copper sulphate becomes white powder and moisture collects on the outer end of the tube. This is water of crystallization. On

Fig. 98.   Crystals of rock salt. Salt crystals usually assume a cubical form.

allowing the white copper sulphate to stand exposed to the air, it again absorbs water and turns blue. Some substances absorb water enough from the air to dissolve them. (Such substances are said to be *deliquescent*.)   Calcium chloride, which absorbs moisture from the air, is therefore sometimes spread upon the road to lay the dust. Many other substances absorb water. Crackers exposed to the air become limp. Candy becomes sticky in damp weather. Salt "cakes" in the shaker.

Other substances, like washing soda, lose water when exposed to the air. (Such substances are said to be *efflorescent*.)

What matter is built of.   If we dissolve sugar in a cup of water, every drop of the solution is sweet. A grain of the dye methyl violet as large as a pinhead will color a pail of water. We can explain how the solid becomes evenly distributed through the liquid by supposing that the solid as well as the liquid is made up of minute particles. In solution the particles of the components become mingled together. If we mix 1 pint of water with 1 pint of alcohol, we should expect to find 1 quart of mixture. Instead, we get only 1.9 pints. No weight is lost, but the volume is diminished. To explain the spreading of the dye or sugar and the loss of 'volume of the alcohol and water, we must understand how matter is built, as the scientist explains it today.

To explain the action of matter, the scientist supposes that all matter, although to the eye it may seem solid and continuous like a piece of iron or cheese, is made up of very fine particles. A block of iron greatly magnified might be compared to a box of marbles. The minute particles of matter are called *molecules*. It

Fig. 99. Crystals of quartz. Notice the pyramidal forms with their sharp edges.

must be remembered that we have not actually seen molecules. They are much too small to be seen even with a powerful microscope. The size of a molecule is about one three-hundred-millionth of an inch. A molecule is the smallest particle of a substance that can exist and still remain the same substance. If a molecule were divided, we should no longer have the same substance. Thus the smallest particle of water that can exist is a molecule of water. If the molecule of water is divided, we get two *atoms* of hydrogen and one *atom* of oxygen. An atom is the smallest particle of an element that can combine with other atoms and form molecules.

The contraction in volume when alcohol and water are mixed is explained by supposing the molecules of one substance are smaller than those of the other. The smaller kind sifts in among the larger kind as sugar sifts in among peas.

Now let us account for the spreading of the crystal of dye in the bucket of water. It is supposed that molecules are in motion even in solids. When we drop a crystal of dye into water, the molecules of dye move about among the molecules of water until they are evenly distributed.

When water is heated, the molecules move more violently. Molecule bumps against molecule. The molecules are driven farther apart. The volume is increased. With continued heating, the motion of the molecules becomes so violent that the water molecules fly away as vapor, gas, or steam. We shall learn something more about the motion of molecules when we study heat.

EXPERIMENT 25

Question: What are two general properties of matter?

Materials: A graduated cylinder; a balance and weights; a small stone.

Directions: (a) Weigh and record the weight of the cylinder in the table under Results.

(b) Fill with water to the 50 c.c. mark. Again weigh and record the weight.

(c) Weigh a small stone and record.

(d) Lower the stone gently into the cylinder of water. Read and record the increased volume.

Results: Weight of cylinder:

Weight of cylinder with 50 c.c. of water:

Weight of 50 c.c. of water:

Weight of stone:

Volume of water:

Volume of water and stone:

Volume of stone.

Conclusion: If you try similar experiments with a great variety of things, you will find that matter always has the two general properties that you measured above. Answer the question at the beginning of the experiment.

EXPERIMENT 26 (OPTIONAL)

Question: How can I recognize some common substances by studying their characteristic physical and chemical properties?

Materials: Desk apparatus; copper penny; window glass; wood; gasoline; water.

Directions and observations: (a) Examine the copper penny and answer the following questions. Use complete sentences, and number your answers to correspond to the questions. 1. What is the color, luster, and weight (heavy or light) of copper compared with aluminum? (We call the peculiar shine of metals "metallic luster.") 2. What is the action of air upon copper? 3. Is copper malleable? How do you know? 4. How could you distinguish copper from iron?

(b) Examine the piece of window glass. 5. Give its physical properties. 6. Both window glass and ice are brittle and transparent. How should you distinguish them?

(c) Examine the piece of wood.   7. Give four physical properties and one chemical property of wood.   8. How should you distinguish wood from glass?   9. How should you distinguish gasoline from water?

Conclusion: How are different substances distinguished?   1. Name two substances that can be distinguished by smell.   2. Name two substances that can be distinguished by color.   3. Name two substances that can be distinguished by touch.   4. Name two substances that can be distinguished by sight.   5. Name two substances that can be distinguished by weight.   6. Name two substances that can be distinguished by taste.

EXPERIMENT 27 (OPTIONAL)

Particular kinds of matter have special properties.   On page 97 are listed some of these special properties.   Examine a number of different substances and determine their special properties.   Find names for those properties not listed.   Most organic matter (compounds produced by plants and animals, organisms) burns readily.   Try various kinds of paper, sugar, coal, flour by holding them in a flame with forceps or by heating on an iron plate.   Burning, however, is not a test for organic matter, as some inorganic matter also burns, sulphur, for example; and some organic matter does not burn, as carbon dioxide.

EXPERIMENT 28

Question: What is formed when mercuric oxide is heated?

Materials: Desk apparatus; mercuric oxide; ignition test tube; Syracuse watch glass; hand magnifier.

WARNING.—Mercury dissolves gold and silver.   Keep jewelry away from it.   Mercury fumes are poisonous.

Directions and results: Place one c.c. of mercuric oxide in an ignition test tube and heat.   Ignition test tubes are thick and require careful heating to avoid breakage.   After the powder has changed color, place a glowing splint (spark) in the tube.   1. What happens to the spark?   What must have been given off?

Should nothing happen, heat the tube more intensely and try the spark test again.   2. Through the magnifying glass, examine the deposit that collects on the cooler part of the tube.   Pour the contents of the tube into a Syracuse watch glass.   The little globules are mercury. This illustrates one type of chemical change, *simple decomposition.*

Conclusion: Answer the question.   1. Name two elements which compose the red powder.   2. What is an oxide?   3. Define simple decomposition.

EXPERIMENT 29

Question: How can I distinguish a mixture from a compound?

Materials: Six c.c. of powdered sulphur; 4 c.c. of fine iron filings;

two pieces of paper; bar magnet; 6-inch test tube; asbestos board; sheet iron 2 inches square; Bunsen burner; water.

Directions and results: (*a*) Mix the sulphur and iron filings. 1. Can you distinguish iron and sulphur by eye?

(*b*) Spread a thin layer of the mixture on a paper. Pass a magnet over it. 2. What happens?

(*c*) Put a pinch of the mixture in half a test tube of water. Cover with thumb and shake. 3. What collects at bottom and at top?

(*d*) Place 1 c.c. of the mixture in a test tube and 5 c.c. of carbon tetrachloride. Shake. Filter through the dry filter paper into a watch glass. Place the watch glass outside the window until the liquid evaporates. 4. What remains on the filter paper? 5. What remains on the watch glass?

(*e*) Heat a small part of the mixture of sulphur and iron filings on sheet iron until all action stops. Allow it to cool. 6. Compare with original mixture as to color, appearance.

(*f*) Crush the heated material to a powder. Test with the magnet. 7. Result?

(*g*) Put a portion in a test tube of water as above. 8. Result?

Conclusions: Which procedure did not change the original substances? Which procedure resulted in a new chemical compound?

EXPERIMENT 30

Question: What is meant by solution?

Materials: Desk apparatus; powdered copper sulphate; mustard spoon.

Directions and results: (*a*) Pour an inch of water into a test tube. Add a mustard spoonful of powdered copper sulphate (blue vitriol). Copper sulphate instead of sugar is used because it is blue and so shows solution by coloring the water. Shake the test tube. 1. Describe what happens.

(*b*) Add two more mustard spoonfuls of copper sulphate, and shake as before. 2. How has the solution changed? What word is used to denote such a solution?

(*c*) Add *three* more spoonfuls of copper sulphate and shake. 3. What results? What kind of solution have you now?

(*d*) Warm the water in the test tube and shake as before. 4. Result?

(*e*) Add *four* more spoonfuls of copper sulphate and boil. 5. Note result.

(*f*) Pour off the clear, boiling hot, saturated solution into a test tube and cool by letting cold water run over the test tube. 6. Tell what results.

Conclusion: 1. Explain how you would prepare cold solutions of washing soda in three strengths: dilute, strong, and saturated. 2. How does temperature affect the solvent (dissolving) action of a liquid?

When speaking of a saturated solution, why must you mention the temperature?

Practical application: Chemists use solution as a means of purification. How should you obtain pure sugar from a mixture of sugar and sand?

EXPERIMENT 31 (OPTIONAL)

Problem: To distinguish a suspension from a solution.

Make a suspension by stirring a little mud in a glass of water. Pour half of the muddy water into a second glass and set the glass aside where it will not be disturbed until the next day. Filter half through a filter paper that has been already wet with clear water (Fig. 92).

Compare your results with those obtained with a glass of water in Experiment 30, in which you put a spoonful of copper sulphate into a little water. Which is the solution and which is the suspension?

EXPERIMENT 32 (OPTIONAL)

Question: How can I prepare an emulsion?

Materials: Desk apparatus; glycostearin; vaseline; paraffin wax; mineral oil; any perfume.

Directions: (a) Cold creams are emulsions of either animal or mineral fats in water, usually with a small amount of added perfume. In order to prepare cold cream, it is necessary to have something to keep the fat evenly distributed throughout the water. Substances of this kind are called *emulsifying agents.* In the cold cream which we will make, we shall use diglycol stearate, a very close relative of beef fat, as the emulsifying agent.

(b) Weigh into a small beaker:

glycostearin	$5\frac{1}{2}$ grams
vaseline	4 "
paraffin wax	3 "
mineral oil	$7\frac{1}{2}$ "

Into a second small beaker, pour 25 grams of water. Heat both beakers over a water bath to a temperature of 170° F. Be very careful that the mixture of fats is not heated above that temperature. When fats and water have reached the desired temperature, pour the water slowly into the mixture of oils with constant stirring. Stir thoroughly for a short time and then allow to stand until air bubbles have disappeared.

(c) Allow the cold cream to stand until it has reached a temperature of about 120° F., then add a few drops of any perfume and stir again. Pour into small jars. Cover jars as soon as possible, and allow them to stand until the next day. The following day you will find that you have prepared an excellent and inexpensive cold cream.

(d) If the consistency of the cold cream that you make does not suit

9

you, you can make it harder by increasing the proportion of paraffin wax, or softer by increasing the proportion of mineral oil.

Diagram: None required.

Conclusion: Answer the question.

Practical application: The formula given above is similar to that used in preparing one of the well-known commercial cold creams. It is not necessary to use the fats specified. Almond oil may be substituted for mineral oil and lard for vaseline, and other similar changes made. Sometimes the cream turns out to be grainy. A grainy consistency is due to insufficient stirring or to mixing at too low a temperature.

EXPERIMENT 33

Question: How can I prepare crystals?

Materials: Tumbler; sugar; string; water.

Directions: (a) Prepare a tumblerful of a warm saturated solution of sugar. Pour the solution into a tumbler and put it in a warm place where it will not be disturbed. Attach the string so that one end will hang down in the tumbler. The rough surface of the string will give the sugar crystals something to which to cling.

(b) In a few days examine the string. You will probably find it covered with small crystals of sugar. As the water evaporates, these crystals will grow larger. You have made rock candy.

(c) If you wish, you can substitute alum, copper sulphate, potassium bichromate, or any of many other chemicals for the sugar. It makes an interesting exercise for members of the class to prepare different crystals.

Diagram: Show the sugar crystals on the string.

Conclusion: What are crystals? Answer the question.

Practical application: Many minerals can be identified by the form in which they crystallize. Many substances do not crystallize. Examine starch under the microscope and you will see that it consists of rounded irregular bodies that are not crystals. Such substances are called *amorphous* (without definite shape).

EXPERIMENT 34

Question: What happens to lye and washing soda upon exposure to the air?

Materials: Two watch glasses; two test tubes; Bunsen burner; washing soda; lye (potassium hydroxide).

Directions and results: (a) Heat gently in the test tube a small piece of washing soda, holding the mouth of the test tube pointing slightly downward. Note what is deposited on the cooler parts of the test tube.

(b) Place on the watch glasses a small piece of washing soda and a small piece of lye. (*Caution:* Do not remove the lye from the bottle

until ready to use, and immediately cork the bottle.   Do not handle
the lye with your fingers; use forceps or a piece of paper.)   Set the
watch glasses aside, observe at the end of an hour and again at the
end of two days.

Results: Record the results in a table.

Conclusion: Answer the questions.   Use the terms explained on
page 104 to describe the behavior of the two substances.

EXPERIMENT 35 (OPTIONAL)

Heat copper sulphate in a test tube.   Write the report of the experiment, using the appropriate term for the behavior of the substance.

EXPERIMENT 36

Question: How can I show the minute particles that make up
matter?

1. That they are very small;
2. That they are in motion;
3. That they do not fill all the space they seem to?

Materials: Desk apparatus; any aniline dye; copper sulphate; glass
measuring tube; colored alcohol.

Directions: (a) Put a piece, as large as the head of a pin, of some
aniline dye, such as methyl violet, in a quart of water.   Stir well.
Notice that every drop of the water becomes colored.   1. How do you
account for the water becoming colored?

(b) Put a piece of copper sulphate at the bottom of a test tube.
Fill the test tube with water and allow it to stand undisturbed during
the class period.   At the end of the period examine it.   2. What
evidence have you that the particles of solids are in motion?

(c) Half fill a long measuring tube (eudiometer tube) with water.
Carefully pour colored alcohol on top of the water.   Avoid mixing the
alcohol with the water.   Color is used only to show that the alcohol
floats on the water.   Put a rubber band around the tube at the top of
the alcohol.   Cork the tube and invert several times until the alcohol
and water are well mixed.   Note the level of the mixed liquids, as
shown by the band.   3. The tube was corked so that nothing could
get in or out.   How then do you account for the decreased volume of
the liquid?

Diagram: None is required.

Conclusion: From this experiment, what do you conclude about the
way matter is built?

Chapter X

SOME COMMON ELEMENTS AND COMPOUNDS

The element hydrogen. In addition to being a constituent of water, which forms 66 per cent of our bodies, hydrogen is a constituent of our very flesh, for it occurs in proteins and fats which make up our flesh (see pages 473 and 474). It is a constituent of all our foods unless we wish to call common salt a food. This gives an idea of the important part hydrogen plays in the world.

You can easily generate some hydrogen by the action of hydrochloric or other acid on zinc. (Experiment 37, Fig. 100.) You can collect test tubes full of hydrogen by holding the delivery tube under the inverted test tubes. You cannot see the hydrogen, smell it, or taste it. How do you know that the tube contains it? When you bring the tube close to a flame, there is a slight explosion and you may see a faint blue flame running up the tube. If the tube is partly filled, there is a louder explosion. If you start with a perfectly dry test tube, you will probably find a little moisture on the sides of the tube after the explosion

After the generator has been working well for some time, you will be able to light the gas escaping at the end of the delivery tube. Hydrogen will burn with a faint bluish flame. If you hold a cold plate in the flame, you will find a deposit of moisture on the plate. We have learned that burning, or combustion, is oxidation, or the union of other matter with oxygen. Burning hydrogen makes water. You must not try this experiment until the generator has been working for some time and all the air is driven out of the tube, or there may be a violent explosion that will scatter glass, acid, and zinc. Oxygen and hydrogen make an explosive mixture. Its explosive nature makes the use of hydrogen dangerous in balloons, although its extreme lightness—it is the lightest of all substances—makes it the best gas for lifting balloons.

Carbon. You have met the element carbon in your study of carbon dioxide. It is a very important element to us. The largest part of the dry weight of our bodies is carbon. Carbon is the black stuff of coal. A soft form of carbon is graphite, which, mixed with fine clay, forms the "lead" of pencils. The slipperiness of graphite makes it a valuable lubricant. Its blackness accounts for its use in stove polish. The diamond is a hard form of carbon. Its exceeding hardness makes it useful in cutting other substances. Diamond drills are studded with diamonds, and saws studded with diamonds are used to cut marble. Carbon from bones (animal charcoal) makes a valuable filter for clearing coloring matter from sugar and other solutions. In the iron industry carbon in the form of coke, obtained by driving off the gas from coal, is mixed with limestone to free iron from its ore.

Carbon is a part of many familiar compounds—sugar, starch, washing soda (sodium carbonate), baking soda (sodium bicarbonate), the calcium carbide used in generating acetylene for acetylene lights, alcohol, and carborundum for grinding. It is one of the principal elements of fuels. If you lower a plate into a candle or gas flame, the plate will be coated with lampblack or carbon. Smoky flames are due to the unburned carbon in them. Carbon causes the yellow gas flame. If you open the holes at the bottom of the Bunsen burner so that there is plenty of oxygen to unite with carbon, the Bunsen flame is blue. Carbon collects in the cylinders of automobile engines when the combustion (burning) is so poor that the carbon is not all burned.

You have learned that the combustion or burning of carbon and of hydrogen in our bodies generates the energy that keeps us alive. You know of the respiratory organs designed by nature to rid the body of the resulting carbon dioxide. No person or animal can live in an atmosphere containing a large proportion of carbon dioxide. In certain valleys, such as Death Gulch and Poison Valley, Java, carbon dioxide lies in the valleys in such quantity that persons or animals attempting to cross the valley are smothered to death. "Choke damp" that occurs in coal mines, especially after fires or explosions, is carbon dioxide.

When carbon burns with insufficient oxygen to form carbon dioxide (CO_2), it forms carbon monoxide (CO). This is an exceedingly dangerous gas. It is poisonous and stealthy. Since it is colorless, odorless, and tasteless, one does not know of its presence. It is formed by incomplete combustion in automobile motors; hence one should never stay in a closed garage with the engine running. Coal and gas stoves sometimes give off carbon monoxide. The blue flame that you see in a coal fire is carbon monoxide burning to become carbon dioxide.

Chlorine and its compounds. In purifying water for our cities, chlorine is often used. It destroys bacteria and other living things. Perhaps you have read of its use in the World War to destroy human lives. It is a choking, irritating, greenish yellow gas. We seldom use the gas because it is more conveniently handled as a liquid or in one of its compounds. It is easily liquefied and is added to water supplies in liquid form when necessary. A compound of chlorine, called *Dakin's solution* (sodium hypochlorite), is used for disinfecting wounds. Javelle water (a solution of potassium hypochlorite and calcium hypochlorite) is used also for disinfecting, but is more irritating to the flesh. Both solutions may be used in small quantities to make water safe for drinking. Chloride of lime is a familiar disinfectant for toilets and other "rougher" uses. Potassium chlorate is sometimes used in throat tablets to kill the germs of sore throat. Sal ammoniac (ammonium chloride) we shall use in our study of electricity to make electric battery cells.

In laboratories and in industry, hydrochloric acid, a compound of hydrogen and chlorine, is an exceedingly important chemical. You will use it many times in your study of science. Common table salt is sodium chloride, a compound of the metal sodium with chlorine. Chloride of lime and other chlorine compounds are used for bleaching. Ink eradicators bleach out the ink with such compounds.

Organic and inorganic matter. Years ago, scientists called all compounds made in the bodies of living things *organic*. Living things, plants and animals, are called *organisms*. Humus, the part of the soil made up of decaying plants, is organic. The blue dye called indigo was organic because it was made by the indigo plant. Chemists finally succeeded in making this compound in the laboratory. They made not an imitation but real indigo. Evidently it was impossible to call indigo organic when it was made by living nature and inorganic when it was made in the laboratory. It was known that the compounds made by living nature contained the element carbon. We therefore changed our definition and now define organic compounds as *compounds containing carbon*. Starch is organic because it is a carbon compound. Water is inorganic because it contains no carbon. Plants and animals are composed of carbon compounds and are therefore organic. *Inorganic substances are substances that contain no carbon.* Most rocks, water, iron rust are inorganic.

We know that carbon burns, so we should expect all organic matter to burn, since it is made up of carbon compounds. We know that many organic compounds, such as wood, straw, and meat, do burn (or, scientifically speaking, are combustible). You must remember, however, that when a carbon compound burns (combines with oxygen), a new carbon compound is formed, and this new carbon compound, although it is organic, may not burn because it is really an ash (oxide). Carbon dioxide, for example, does not burn. It is not true, therefore, that all organic compounds will burn.

EXPERIMENT 37 (TEACHER DEMONSTRATION)

Question: How can hydrogen be prepared? What can I learn about it by experiment?

Materials: Generator, as shown in figure; trough or flat dish for collecting hydrogen; 4 bottles or test tubes; 4 glass plates for covers; zinc; sulphuric acid.

Directions and results: (a) Move the lighted Bunsen burner 4 feet away. Put the zinc into the generator and cover it with water. See that the thistle tube reaches below the surface of the water in the generator. Pour concentrated sulphuric acid into the thistle tube.

1. What evidence do you see of chemical action? Hold the delivery tube under water in the trough to show that gas is being delivered.

(b) Hold a bottle with mouth down over the delivery tube for a minute or two. Then carry the bottle holding the mouth down to the flame. 2. What happens? A "pop" or slight explosion shows that there is a mixture of hydrogen and oxygen present.

(c) Repeat the operation until there is no explosion. Then you may consider that hydrogen but no oxygen is coming from the generator. Note that the mixture of hydrogen and oxygen is explosive and may be dangerous. 3. What color is the hydrogen flame?

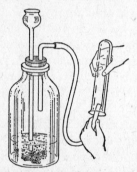

Fig. 100. Generating and collecting hydrogen.

(d) Fill four bottles with hydrogen as shown in Fig. 100. Cover each with a plate of glass, and stand it with mouth down. 4. What are the color, odor, taste of hydrogen?

(e) Try pouring a bottle of hydrogen into an empty bottle. You will see nothing, but go through the motions. Then bring the second bottle to the flame. 5. Is there any evidence that the hydrogen went into the second bottle?

(f) Try pouring a bottle full of hydrogen upward into an inverted bottle. Holding the second bottle with mouth down, carry it to the flame. 6. Is there any evidence that hydrogen went upward into the inverted bottle? 7. What do operations (e) and (f) show about the weight of hydrogen compared with that of air?

Diagram: Show the generator and the method of collection. Show operations (e) and (f).

Conclusion: Answer the question.

Application: Why has hydrogen been used to fill balloons? Why is it dangerous in aircraft?

EXPERIMENT 38

Problem: To become acquainted with carbon.

Materials: One piece each of hard coal, soft coal, coke, charcoal, lead from a pencil, wood splint; a little cornstarch; sugar; pair of forceps; evaporating dish or other white dish; three test tubes; Bunsen burner.

Directions and results: (a) With the forceps hold in the Bunsen flame pieces of coal, coke, pencil lead.

Under heading, *Results*, draw up a table reporting: ease of burning, and presence of smoke or gas, flame, and ash.

(b) Put sugar and starch into test tubes and heat each until no more smoke is given off. 1. What is the black substance remaining?

(c) Light the wood splint and lower over it the white dish. 2. What is deposited on the dish?

(d) Close the air hole at the base of the Bunsen burner. Lower the white dish into the yellow flame. 3. What is deposited? 4. Where did it come from?

Conclusions: What is the appearance of carbon? Is the element common or uncommon about us? Does carbon burn?

Application: If an automobile engine leaves a deposit of carbon, is it efficient (that is, does it get all the heat and power out of the fuel)?

EXPERIMENT 39 (OPTIONAL)

Question: How can I make ink eradicator?

Materials: A large beaker or a pint jar; two smaller beakers; chloride of lime; washing soda (sodium carbonate); hot water; 10 per cent solution of hydrochloric acid.

Directions: (a) Pour the hot water into the large beaker. Stir in the chloride of lime. Then stir in the washing soda. Allow to settle and pour off the clear liquid into a beaker. Make the dilute acid in the other beaker by pouring 10 c.c. of hydrochloric acid into 90 c.c. of water. Do not pour the water into the acid, or the action may be so violent as to throw the acid out.

(b) Write on a piece of paper with ink. Blot. With a glass rod rub some of the solution from the first beaker on the writing. Then with the rod rub some of the dilute acid solution over it. Note what happens.

Conclusion: Answer the question.

CHAPTER XI

SOUR, BITTER, AND SALTY STUFFS

What an acid is. You know what is meant by sour. A lemon is sour. Vinegar is sour. This sour taste is characteristic of a class of chemical compounds that we name *acids*. The German name for acid is *sourstuff*. Lemons contain citric acid. Vinegar contains acetic acid. Cranberries, tomatoes, and fruits in general owe their tart taste to various acids that they contain. You know much about the properties of some of these acids, even if you do not know their chemical names. You know that such acids are *sour* and that they *corrode* (eat away metals). If you stew tomatoes in an aluminum pan you get a beautifully clean pan because the acid in the tomatoes has eaten away the surface. A drop of strong acid eats a hole in your clothes or burns your skin.

In the chemical laboratory we do not like to taste unknown substances, lest they be poisonous. We use instead some chemical test. When we put a little dilute hydrochloric acid and a small strip of metal, as magnesium or zinc, into a test tube, the metal starts to dissolve and a gas is given off. This gas is hydrogen. The acid contains hydrogen and when zinc is added, the zinc replaces or drives out the hydrogen. This action gives the definition of an acid. An acid is a substance which contains hydrogen that may be replaced by a metal.]

What a base is. A second kind of chemical compound having properties opposite to those of acids is known as a *base* or an *alkali*. You are familiar with a base in the form of ammonia water or, as chemists call it, ammonium hydroxide. Sodium hydroxide is another common base used in the laboratory, as lye is sometimes used in the kitchen sink. Potash lye, or potassium hydroxide, is still another common base.

The fresh mortar between the bricks in a wall contains another base, slaked lime or calcium hydroxide. Bases are called *hydroxides* because they contain hydrogen and oxygen (OH).

Bases are bitter to the taste, and they feel soapy because they destroy the outer layer of the skin. Do not handle lye or other strong bases with the bare hands, and do not try the experiment of tasting them. Bases destroy animal fibers; therefore blankets or other wool or silk cloth should not be washed in water containing lye or other strong bases.

Neutralization. Did you ever take baking soda or soda mint when your stomach was not feeling right? It sometimes brings quick relief. Milk of magnesia (magnesium hydroxide) acts similarly. The glands of the stomach manufacture hydrochloric acid to assist in the digestion of food. Sometimes the glands get out of order and pour in too much acid. Soda and milk of magnesia destroy the excess acid. They are used, therefore, for a tooth wash in "acid mouths."

When an acid and a base are mixed, heat is given off and this heat is an evidence that a chemical change has occurred. If we mix an acid and a base in just the right proportions, we find that neither acid nor base is left over. The hydrogen of the acid combines with the hydrogen and oxygen of the base and forms water. The metal of the base combines with the other elements of the acid to form a salt. Copper sulphate or bluestone is a salt. Common table salt (sodium chloride) is another illustration. We call the combining of an acid and a base *neutralization*. A neutral substance is formed.

A word of caution in handling acids and bases. You would no doubt decide if you spilled acid on your hand to pour on a base, and if you spilled a base, to pour on acid. But an excess of either poured on will burn, for both acids and bases destroy flesh. The best thing to do is to hold your hand immediately under the faucet and let water run on it. This dilutes and washes off the substance. If neutralization is attempted, it should be with dilute solutions.

It is said that the poison of a bee sting, which is alkaline (containing a base), may be neutralized with vinegar or other

weak acid. Wasp stings are acid and may be relieved by
soda. Generally, however, if you grin and bear it until you
find the remedy for the sting, there is then no need to use it.

Litmus, the detective. A certain lichen, one of those
crushy little gray plants you sometimes see growing on bare
rocks, gives a blue dye named *litmus.* Shake up two or three
lumps of litmus in a flask of water. The litmus will dissolve
and you will obtain a blue solution. Put about an inch of
this in each of several test tubes. Add to one test tube a
drop of lemon juice. Shake, and you will see the litmus
turn red. Repeat this, using various other acids, as vinegar,
tomato juice, cranberry juice, and hydrochloric acid. In
every case the blue dye turns red. This gives us a test for
acids. If we wish to know whether an unknown liquid contains an acid, add a drop of the liquid to a little litmus and
see whether the litmus turns red.

To a tumbler of blue litmus solution, add just enough
acid, drop by drop, to turn it red. Pour about an inch of
the red litmus into each of several test tubes. To one test
tube add a drop of ammonia water that you know to be a
base. The red litmus will turn blue. To the other test
tubes add potassium hydroxide, sodium hydroxide, or any
other base that your laboratory affords. In every case you
will see that the red litmus turns blue. Red litmus then
gives a test by means of which you can detect the presence
of a base.

Many substances, for example, salt, do not affect either
red or blue litmus. We say of such substances that they are
neutral.

It is not always convenient to use litmus in solution.
Instead we prepare strong solutions of red and blue litmus
and soak filter paper in these solutions. On drying this
paper, we have litmus paper. This paper is used to detect
the presence of acids and bases. Just as we used the solution,
with red and blue litmus paper, test the *reaction,* as we call
it, of the fruits and vegetables in your kitchen.

It is possible to prepare a neutral violet litmus. This will
turn red with acids and blue with bases. Practically, we do

not use it.   The air of the laboratory is almost always
slightly acid, and even though our paper may be neutral when
we prepare it, it is usually red when it is dry.   Many other
substances may be used instead of litmus as *indicators* of
acidity.   Phenolphtha-
lein, often used in the
laboratory, is red in a
basic solution and color-
less in an acid solution.

Marble, a salt.
Many fine Roman ruins
have been destroyed by
peasants of later cen-
turies who carried away
the marble to burn for
lime.   In limestone re-
gions of our country you
often find old limekilns
where limestone was
burned with wood to get
lime to spread upon
"sour" or acid lands
(Fig. 101).

You can easily make
lime from limestone or
marble.   Both are cal-
cium carbonate, a salt
of carbonic acid with the
metal calcium.   If you
heat the limestone or
marble, a gas is driven
off.   If you let this gas
bubble through lime-
water, the limewater
becomes milky, showing
that the gas carbon di-
oxide is present.   The
limestone   on   heating

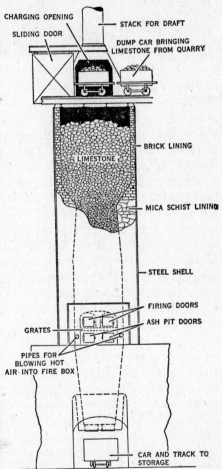

Fig. 101. A commercial limekiln. Limekilns
are located at the quarries so that cars may
be run to the top of the kiln and the limestone
may be dumped directly into it.

Fig. 102. Muddy Mountain borax deposits, California.

crumbles to a fine white powder. This powder is quicklime (calcium oxide). If water is poured on quicklime, it becomes slaked lime (calcium hydroxide). If the lime dissolves in the water, it becomes lime water (also calcium hydroxide). If quicklime is exposed to the air, it absorbs water and carbon dioxide, and becomes air-slaked lime.

Lime mixed with sand and water forms mortar. In making lime, the carbon dioxide was driven off from the limestone (calcium carbonate). When mortar is made, the lime again absorbs carbon dioxide from the air and forms limestone. Mortar that has hardened is, therefore, really limestone. The shining white plaster on the wall is another salt of calcium, called *plaster of Paris* (calcium sulphate).

Salts of earth and ocean. The ocean is salty with many kinds of salts in addition to table salt. The rocks of the earth contain salts of numerous acids. Acids and bases formed in rock or soil are certain to neutralize one another sooner or later. Soluble salts are carried away by streams to the ocean. Through the ages as water evaporates from the oceans, the salts are left behind. Therefore, the sea water yields several kinds of salts upon evaporation. The salt lakes are salted as is the sea. They are without outlets and lose water only by evaporation. When salt lakes dry up in the course of ages, they leave salt plains behind. Borax, formerly hauled from Death Valley, California, and sodium nitrate, sent as fertilizer from the desert of Chile, are such beds of salt (Fig. 102). Potash fertilizer imported from Germany is from great beds of potassium salts. Table salt is

Fig. 103. Preparing salt by evaporating sea water, Malabon, Philippine Islands.

prepared in some parts of the world by evaporating sea water (Fig. 103). In New York State water is pumped down wells to beds of salt below the surface. When it has dissolved the salt, it is pumped up again and evaporated.

Chemical shorthand. Stenographers have a method of writing sentences in shorthand that saves much time. In the same way, chemists have agreed upon a chemical code. Instead of writing "one atom of hydrogen," we write the symbol H. One atom of oxygen is O.

We combine these symbols in writing molecules. You have learned that one molecule of water contains two atoms of hydrogen and one atom of oxygen. Instead of writing this out, it is much more simple to write H_2O. The 2 written after the H shows that there are two atoms of hydrogen. Sugar is $C_{12} H_{22} O_{11}$. This means that one molecule of sugar contains 12 atoms of carbon, 22 atoms of hydrogen, and 11 atoms of oxygen. If we wish to write 4 molecules of sugar, we place a 4 in front of the formula for sugar, and write $4 C_{12}H_{22}O_{11}$.

Chemical changes are easily expressed by writing these formulas. If we put sodium hydroxide and hydrochloric acid together in proper proportions, water and sodium chloride (common salt) will be formed. How much simpler it is to write:

$$NaOH \quad + \quad HCl \quad \rightarrow \quad H_2O \ + \quad NaCL$$
sodium hydroxide   hydrochloric acid   water   common salt

The names of compounds tell the chemists something of their composition. Thus *-ate* at the end of a word denotes oxygen; *-ite* denotes less oxygen. Thus sodium sulph*ate* contains sodium, sulphur, and oxygen, and sodium sulph*ite* contains the same three elements with less oxygen. The suffix *-ide* tells that there are two substances only in the compound. Thus sodium chlor*ide* (common salt) is composed of sodium and chlorine.

Making soap. A common chemical compound is soap. This is made by combining soda lye (sodium hydroxide) or potash lye (potassium hydroxide) with a fat. The result is soap and glycerine. In colonial days wood ashes, which contain potash, were saved from the fireplaces. From this potash combined with fats the housewife made her own supply of soft soap, for potash soaps do not form hard cakes. If lye and fat are mixed in just the right proportions, neither will be left over. If we use too much lye, the excess lye will make the soap very hard on our hands. If we use too much fat, the excess fat will make the soap greasy. The manufacturers rely upon chemists and chemical analysis to tell them just what proportions should be used to obtain a perfect product. Industrially, the fat and the lye are mixed together and heated in kettles until the combination is complete. Dyes and perfumes are often added. Then salt is added. Soap is insoluble in salt solution. The soap rises to the top as a soap curd. The curd is taken off, dried, cut up into cakes, and sold. Perfumes or substances with strong medicinal odors, such as carbolic acid, are sometimes used to conceal the odor of inferior materials, as well as for the legitimate purpose of making the soap more attractive or giving it remedial properties. It is doubtful, however, if enough antiseptic solution is added to the soap to improve the mild antiseptic quality of pure soap.

Washing compounds. Perhaps you use in your kitchen some of the innumerable washing compounds that are on the market. These all have the property of cleaning greasy pans easily. From your knowledge of how soap is made, you can understand why they act in this way. They are not pure soap, but contain an extra amount of soda lye or washing soda which is a similar compound. When you put some into a greasy pan, you are really combining the fat with a base and forming additional soap. You need not buy these washing compounds; you can make a very satisfactory one at home. Cut a cake of laundry soap into small pieces. Add twice as much water as you have soap, and heat. The mixture on cooling will form a thick soap jelly. This soap jelly can be used instead of ordinary soap. If while it is heating you add $\frac{1}{5}$ as much washing soda (sodium carbonate) as you have soap and then cool, you will have a washing compound. Put a little of this into a greasy frying pan. It will clean the grease out and save scrubbing the pan.

Try sometime the effect of adding a little ammonia water to the water with which you wash your windows. You will be surprised to see how bright and shining the glass will become. This is because you are combining a base with the oil deposit that forms on the window, leaving the glass really clean. The disadvantage of all such washing compounds is that they are very hard on the hands. They take the oil from the skin, leaving it dry and likely to crack.

How things change. After you have worn a coat for a while, you notice that the nap has worn off, perhaps a button is loose, the thread is worn, and the lining torn. Every molecule of the original coat may still exist, but not in its former position. We call such changes as these *physical changes*. When you break an egg and beat it, you have, seemingly, an altogether different substance. There certainly is no physical similarity between the beaten egg and the egg as it was in the shell. Yet, in this case, also, we have a physical change. Every molecule of the original egg still exists, but the positions have been changed. If you break a match stick in two, you again have a physical change.

When you burn wood, you have a change of a different kind. The wood no longer exists. The molecules of wood have been destroyed. They are replaced by a white ash and invisible gas that has floated off into the air. This is an example of a *chemical change*. We may then define a physical change

10

as a change in which no new molecules are formed, and a chemical change as a change in which new molecules are formed.

Tell to which class the following belong: the rusting of iron, the baking of bread, the boiling of water, the rotting of wood, burning a match, the decay of leaves, the rotting of an apple.

EXPERIMENT 40

Question: How can I detect an acid?

Materials: Three beakers; hydrochloric acid; tartaric acid; vinegar; strips of red and of blue litmus paper; some pieces of mossy zinc.

Directions: (a) Pour about 15 c.c. of water in each beaker. Add about 15 c.c. of hydrochloric acid to one beaker, of tartaric acid to the second, and of vinegar (acetic acid) to the third.

(b) Wet the tip of the finger in each beaker and touch it to the tip of the tongue. What is the taste of each?

(c) Place the ends of blue litmus and of the red litmus in each beaker. Note color change.

(d) Place a piece of zinc in each beaker. Note what occurs.

Result: Record your observations in a table.

Conclusion: Answer the question.

EXPERIMENT 41

Question: How can I detect a base?

Materials: Three beakers; a piece of potassium hydroxide; ammonia; limewater; strips of red and of blue litmus paper.

Directions: (a) Pour about 30 c.c. of water into each beaker. Add to one a piece of potassium hydroxide about ½ inch long; to a second 20 c.c. of ammonia; to the third 20 c.c. of limewater. Caution: Do not touch the potassium hydroxide stick with your fingers. Use forceps.

(b) Taste each with the tip of the finger.

(c) Rub a little between the tip of the thumb and finger. How does each feel?

(d) Test each with the end of a strip of red, then of blue, litmus paper.

Results: Record results for each substance in a table under the headings taste, feel, litmus test.

Conclusion: Answer question.

EXPERIMENT 42

Question: How can I neutralize hydrochloric acid and how can I determine what is formed?

Materials: Hydrochloric acid; sodium hydroxide; litmus paper; 2 medicine droppers; glass rod; 2 beakers; evaporating dish.

Directions: (*a*) Medicine droppers are a convenient means of adding small quantities of liquid to a solution. Measure out 1 c.c. of acid in one dropper and paste around the tube a small piece of red paper to mark the quantity. Do the same with a second dropper, using blue paper for alkali (base).

(*b*) Place 10 c.c. of dilute hydrochloric acid in a small evaporating dish and add a piece of litmus paper half an inch square. Add sodium hydroxide solution until, after vigorous stirring with your glass stirring rod, the litmus paper turns blue. This shows that your solution is now slightly alkaline. Add acid, drop by drop, until the litmus turns slowly red. Your solution is now very faintly acid. The addition of one drop of the base will turn the litmus to a violet color. Put fresh pieces of both red and blue litmus into the solution. If you have exactly neutralized it, each paper should retain its color. You will probably find that a slow change in color takes place, as it is very difficult, with your apparatus, to reach an exactly neutral point.

(*c*) Pour into one large beaker all of the neutral solution obtained by the members of the class. Filter, evaporate, and set aside to crystallize. The next day, examine the residue. Taste it, and you will find that it is salt. (After tasting any substance in the laboratory, always spit out the tasted substance, for you never know what impurities have been introduced into the solution.)

Conclusion: When an acid and a base are combined, what do we call the process? What new substance is formed? What is meant by an *indicator*?

Practical application: Chemists rely upon indicators to determine the reactions of substances. Acids and bases are bought and sold at prices depending upon the real amount of acid or base present, which can be determined by neutralizing the substance. The chemist uses an indicator to determine when neutralization has been reached.

NOTE: Many dyes are indicators. Bring from home a number of colored cloths. Put a drop of acid and a drop of a base upon these cloth materials. You will find that in many cases the dye used is an indicator.

EXPERIMENT 43 (HOME)

With litmus paper test the reaction of materials found in your kitchen—washing soda, ammonia water, meat, fruits, potato, coffee, etc. Record your results in the table below.

MATERIALS TESTED	REACTION (acid, alkaline, or neutral)
....	....
....	....
....	....

What is the general reaction of meats?_____

What is the general reaction of fruits?_____

What is the general reaction of vegetables?_____

If you wish to do so, you can prepare your own indicator by boiling a few leaves of red cabbage in a small quantity of water. Use the colored liquid obtained. If you do this, record the colors below:

Red cabbage in acid solution is_____

Red cabbage in alkaline solution is_____

Red cabbage in neutral solution is_____

EXPERIMENT 44 (OPTIONAL)

Question: How can I make lime from limestone?

Materials: A piece of limestone about ½ cm. in diameter; strip of red litmus paper; piece of wire about 6 inches long; forceps; ring stand; evaporating dish; beaker; Bunsen burner; 6-inch test tube; glass tubing.

Directions: (a) Moisten the litmus paper and test the limestone.

(b) Twist one end of the wire around the limestone, and support it from the upper ring of the stand. Place the evaporating dish on the lower ring about 2 inches below the limestone. Heat the limestone holding the Bunsen burner in the hand. Quicklime (calcium oxide) will form.

(c) Place the crumbled limestone in the evaporating dish. Add water. Limewater (calcium hydroxide) is formed. Test with litmus paper.

(d) Pour the limewater into a test tube. Blow through the glass tube into the test tube of limewater. Note change.

Results: Record the results in each step of the experiment.

Conclusion: Answer the question. Is limestone a base? Is limewater a base?

EXPERIMENT 45

Question: How can I make a small quantity of soap?

Materials: A fat or an oil, as palm or coconut oil; sodium hydroxide (lye); alcohol; evaporating dish; desk apparatus.

Theory: When a fat and sodium hydroxide are heated together, they combine. A soap is formed and glycerine is left. This action is slow because fats do not dissolve in water, and therefore it is difficult to mix the fat and the lye. To shorten the operation, we add alcohol. Since both lye and fat are soluble in alcohol, it is now possible to mix them, and the chemical change goes on rapidly. Remember that the alcohol is used in this experiment only as a solvent to hasten the chemical change. Commercially it is not used because of the expense.

Directions: (*a*) Place in a small evaporating dish 10 c.c. of sodium hydroxide solution, 2 c.c. of any fat or oil, preferably coconut oil, and 5 c.c. of denatured alcohol. Support the dish on your ring stand. Have ready a square of asbestos that will completely cover the evaporating dish. Heat the dish very gently over a Bunsen burner, stirring all the while with a wooden splint. It usually happens that the dish is heated too hot, and the alcohol catches fire. If this happens, remove the burner and put the asbestos over the dish. This cuts off the supply of air and the flame goes out. Wait until the dish cools and then start heating again, more gently.

(*b*) When the mixture has become pasty, turn off the heat and examine the mixture. It is soap, mixed probably with an excess of lye and glycerine. Shake a little in a test tube half filled with water. It will lather, showing that it is soap. Wash your hands, using a little of the soap you have made. If you have a small cut on your hands, it will probably sting. This shows that your soap has an excess of lye in it. Sometimes your hands will feel greasy after you have washed them. This shows that your soap has an excess of fat. Commercially, the quantities of fat and lye used are so adjusted that when the action is over, neither substance is left.

Conclusion: Answer the question.

Practical application: Soap is made commercially in this way, except that no alcohol is used.

EXPERIMENT 46

Question: How can I make a washing compound?

Materials: Washing soda (sodium carbonate); soap.

Directions: Cut a small cake of any pure soap into small pieces. Place the pieces of soap in a pan with a pint of water. Heat, stirring constantly to prevent burning, until the soap has dissolved. Add a tablespoonful of washing soda. Stir until you have a uniform mixture. Place this in a pint fruit jar. As it cools, it will form a thick jelly.

The next time your mother has a greasy pan to clean, place a tablespoonful of the jelly in the pan, add three times the quantity of hot water, and scrub the pan, using a brush. You will find that the grease is quickly "cut"; that is, it will combine with the washing soda to form a soap, and the pan will be washed clean.

Conclusion: 1. Why was the washing soda added? 2. Answer the question.

NOTE: Washing soda is hard on your hands. Therefore, do not keep your hands in this washing compound longer than necessary.

You may also clean your greasy pans by using ammonia. Ammonia is an alkali similar in its chemical action to sodium hydroxide. Add a small quantity of ammonia to the water in which you are washing the pans. The ammonia combines with some of the fat to form a soap, and assists in forming an emulsion with the remaining fat. You will find that the addition of the ammonia has lightened your work.

Some science of paint. The chemist makes our paints. Paint is an oil in which is a pigment or coloring matter, and to which is added a "thinner" and a "drier." The chief pigment is white lead (lead carbonate), made by the action of the fumes of acetic acid on lead. Other white pigments may be used in addition or instead of white lead, for example, zinc oxide and titanium oxide. To secure paints of other color than white, other pigments are added. The browns, yellows, and reds are often "earth pigments," that is, minerals obtained from the earth, chiefly compounds of iron. Black paints are colored with carbon. Other colors such as blues, greens, and reds are produced by the chemist. Often "extenders" are added to increase the quantity of paint cheaply, chalk, silica, and marble dust. They are adulterants although, in some instances, it is claimed that they increase the life of the paint.

The best oil is linseed made from the seed of flax. It oxidizes or "dries" to a hard resistant surface. In cheap paints fish oil is added to the linseed oil. The oil in the paint is a vehicle to carry the pigment and on oxidiation furnishes the protective surface.

The "thinner" added to the oil makes it flow more easily. Turpentine is the most common. Driers increase the rapidity of drying and help in producing a hard, resistant surface. They are produced by heating certain minerals (lead, manganese, or cobalt) in oils and rosin and then dissolving in turpentine, benzene, or other solvent. Oil varnishes are made by heating gums and resins in oil.

Paint, varnish, and lacquer save the surface from oxidation and from bacteria and fungi which cause rotting.

CHAPTER XII

MEASURING THINGS IN SCIENCE

How measures began. When the English in the days of Henry II wanted to measure the length of an object, they compared it with the length of their king's foot. Our foot measure was originally the length of a man's foot. The Romans, in measuring distance, paced it off. They gave us the *mile*. *Mile* is from Latin *mille* (a thousand) *passuum* (of paces). Small objects were weighed by comparing them with a grain of wheat. That gave us the weight of one grain.

With that sort of history, there is little wonder that we have a jumble of figures in our measures: 12 inches, one foot; 3 feet, one yard; 5½ yards, one rod; 320 rods, one mile. Our weights are equally irregular: 27 $\frac{11}{32}$ grains, one dram; 16 drams, one ounce; 16 ounces, one pound; 2000 pounds, or sometimes 2240 pounds, one ton. It is similar with our other measures.

The metric system. In 1789 the French began a revolution that rid them of their old form of government and of a great many old customs. Among the reforms was the setting up of a new and orderly system of weights and measures. They set up the *metric system* of measurements, which is now used by almost all civilized countries and by scientists throughout the world. They took as their unit of measure one ten-millionth of the supposed distance from the Equator to the Pole. This they called the *meter*, which means measure. Larger units are successively ten times as large, and smaller units are one tenth as large. That arrangement simplifies the arithmetic of measuring. To multiply by 10 you move the decimal point one place to the right. $25 \times 10 = 250$. To divide by 10 you move the decimal point one place to the left. $25 \div 10 = 2.5$. You can learn to use the metric system in 5 minutes.

TABLE OF METRIC MEASURES

TABLE OF METRIC MEASURES

10 millimeters (mm.) make 1 centimeter (cm.).
10 centimeters make 1 decimeter (dm.).
10 decimeters make 1 meter (m.).
10 meters make 1 dekameter (Dm.).
10 dekameters make 1 hectometer (Hm.).
10 hectometers make 1 kilometer (Km.).

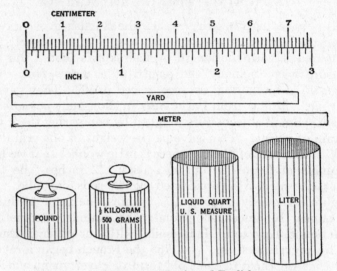

Fig. 104. Comparison of Metric and English measures.

COMPARISON OF METRIC AND ENGLISH MEASURES.

1 millimeter =	0.039 inch	1 liter	= 1.057 quarts
1 centimeter =	0.394 inch	1 gram	= 0.035 ounce
1 meter	= 39.37 inches	1 kilogram	= 2.205 pounds
1 kilometer	= 0.621 mile		

The metric system derives its other measures from its unit of length. A liter is (approximately) the volume of a cube whose side is $\frac{1}{10}$ of a meter. A gram is (approximately) the weight of water contained in a cube whose edge is $\frac{1}{100}$ of a meter.

Getting measures exact. Try an experiment. Measure the length of this book with a metric ruler, estimating in tenths the fractions smaller than the smallest divisions on the ruler. Write down your measurement, but do not show it to anyone. Now ask five of your classmates separately to measure the length without showing results. Then compare results. In all probability they are not the same. Which one is right? Perhaps no one's.

If you are measuring the parts for a machine and are wrong $\frac{1}{1000}$ of an inch, the machine may not work properly. If you are measuring your purchases at a store and your measurements do not agree with those of the storekeeper, you may have an argument. If you are measuring the boundary of a country and your measurement is inaccurate, there may be a war.

Now suppose you are making a meter stick or a yardstick, how can you tell how long to make it? No doubt you will get another meter stick or yardstick and try to make the new one the same length. But you have just found that it is exceedingly difficult to measure accurately. If several people have made meter sticks, they are probably not all exactly the same length. What shall be used as the standard?

The nations, centuries ago, discovered that it was important to have fixed standards that could be used for measuring. The old English took the king's foot as the standard measure of length; but when the king passed away, what was the correct foot?

It is a rather difficult task to remeasure the earth to get a correct meter. To establish standards that can be used more easily and exactly, laws in the various countries have defined units of length as the length of certain metal bars that are safely kept.

A yard is the distance measured at 60° F. between two lines on two gold plugs set in a bronze bar kept at Westminster, London. A meter is the distance measured at the temperature of melting ice between two lines on a platinum-iridium bar kept at Sevres, France, by an International Commission. Copies of this meter bar are kept in various countries.

The United States Bureau of Standards determines our standards. Besides the measures of length, weight, and volume, the Bureau of Standards passes upon many other measures, for example, the units of diphtheria antitoxin. Following are some quantities for which science and industry need units of measurement; see if you know what unit is used for each before you look it up on the page referred to; temperature, page 195; heat, page 198; power, page 141; work page 141; electricity, pages 315–317; light intensity, page 262; radio wave length, page 347.

EXPERIMENT 47

Question: How accurately can I measure?

Materials: A metal or cardboard pattern, somewhat like the diagram; an English metric rule (a rule for measuring both inches and centimeters).

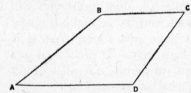

Directions: Copy the number of the pattern. Measure each side of the pattern, estimating to tenths of a millimeter. Add the four sides to get the perimeter (sum of the sides). Repeat this operation five times, trying to allow time to forget your previous measurements.

Fig. 105.   A pattern to measure.

Add the five measurements, and divide by five to find the average.

Results: Record your measurements in a table.

Number of pattern:	SIDE AB	SIDE BC	SIDE CD	SIDE DA	PERIMETER
First reading........	....	....	....	....	....
Second reading......	....	....	....	....	....
Third reading.......	....	....	....	....	....
Fourth reading......	....	....	....	....	....
Fifth reading.......	....	....	....	....	....
Sum of readings....	....	....	....	....	....
Average............	....	....	....	....	....

Compare your measurements with a list of measurements kept by the teacher.

Conclusion: Are your results persistently too large or persistently too small? How much? Does averaging the results of several readings give greater accuracy?

EXPERIMENT 48

Question: How can I measure the volume of an irregular stone?

Materials: A graduated cylinder; a small stone or other irregular object.

Directions: Pour water into the cylinder until it is half full. Read the volume of water, estimating to a tenth of a cubic centimeter. In making this reading have your eye on the same level as the surface of the water. You will notice that the surface curves down in the center of the cylinder. This curved surface is called the *meniscus.* Take the reading at the bottom of this curve. See diagram.

Lower the stone gently into the water. Read the volume again.

Results: Record your readings in a table.

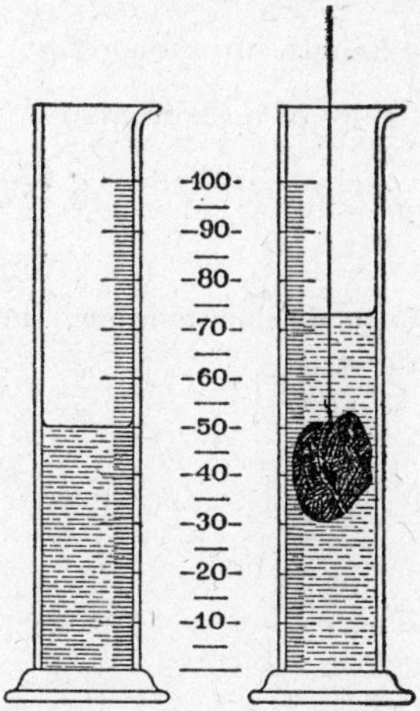

Fig. 106. How to measure the volume of an irregular solid.

Volume of water without stone ....

Volume of water with submerged stone ....

Volume of stone ....

Conclusion: Answer the question.

EXPERIMENT 49

Question: How long is an inch in the metric system?

Materials: English and metric rules; a card; your notebook; your textbook.

Directions: Measure the length, in inches and in centimeters (1) of a card, (2) of a leaf in your textbook, (3) of a leaf of your notebook. Record, add, and divide the sum in inches into the sum in centimeters.

Results:

	INCHES	CENTIMETERS
Length of card............		
Length of leaf of textbook..		
Length of notebook........		
Sum of measurements......		

Number of centimeters in an inch   ....

ADDITIONAL EXPERIMENTS

In similar manner, determine the metric equivalent of a pound; a quart.

UNIT FOUR

THE POWER TO DO THINGS: ENERGY

Animals get things done by jaw and claw and muscle. Primitive man used his good arm and his sturdy back. When he learned to swing a club and use it as a pry, he gained more power. He had invented a simple machine. Later, men improved upon the machines of those who had gone before. Modern man does his great work by machinery. Power from other sources has largely replaced that of the good right arm. With power machinery man has changed the face of the earth. He has made a new world—a world of machinery—and this world has become a part of his environment. This new part of his environment determines many of his activities. Machinery runs our lives.

The cave man's power lay in his muscular energy. It is the same energy that sends the blood coursing through the vessels and expels the air from the lungs—the energy of life. Lower animals display the same energy. Plants, too, live by the expenditure of energy. The great tree builds itself to towering heights and raises water to its very top. The tiny moss, though less spectacular, does its measure of work each day it lives. Just to stay alive requires energy. When energy deserts the living body, it dies.

The energy of nature is not confined to life. The volcanic outburst, the earthquake, the waves, and the hurricane often make vast displays of energy, to the consternation and dread of man. Forces, silently and unnoticed except by the scientist, are rearing continents with their mountain chains and lowering them again beneath the sea.

Beyond the earth, also, energy is constantly producing change. Meteors flash, comets move into our view and move away again. The planets travel through their courses. The astronomer sees new stars blaze out in the blackness of space. All these occurrences are displays of energy. The rotation of the earth, bringing sunrise and sunset; the yearly journey around the sun, bringing the seasons; the waxing and waning of the moon are due to energy.

Light, by which we learn of stars too far away to count in millions of miles, is a form of energy. Sound, heat, electricity, the waves that carry messages from the arctic explorer to our snug living rooms and pleasant theaters are forms of energy. Indeed the scientist cannot think of matter, of things, of existence of any kind without the association of energy. The activity of man and of the universe is a display of energy.

In the units which follow we shall study the science of various forms of energy. We shall see how scientific study has enabled man to live on the same earth as the lowly animals, yet live in a different world, a world of his own creation. Modern man to a large extent has made his own environment. He has made it by controlling the energy that surrounds all plants and animals, the energy of the earth, the sun, and the distant heavens. Science that he has created has given man the powers of creation.

In the present unit we shall study something of the nature of energy and how we measure it. Then we shall study how man has put it to his service by the use of machines. We shall try to understand how machines have enabled him to do his work with greater ease and speed. We shall study some of the simple machines that we use every day, some as simple as spoons and scissors. Then we shall see how energy from other sources has been used to replace muscular power, how engines use power to drive other machines, how science builds railroads, roads, and bridges for our machines of transportation.

Finally in this unit we shall see how metal, the material of modern machines, is obtained from the rocks and made into machines by other machines.

Chapter XIII

ENERGY AND WORK

Ability to work. Air can do things. It can crush cans by its pressure. When in motion as wind, it can uproot mighty trees. It can keep us alive or it can burn down our house. We call this ability to do things *energy*. *Energy is the capacity to do work.*

Two kinds of energy. Throw a ball upward to a boy leaning out of a second-story window. When you throw it, you give it energy of motion. If you are careless, the moving ball may break a windowpane. It can do this because you have given the ball energy.

When we have learned the exact meaning of a scientific idea, it saves much time and many words to name our ideas. Let us call this energy of motion *kinetic* (moving) *energy*. The ball you threw upward had kinetic energy as long as it had motion.

The boy in the window catches the ball (Fig. 107). It is now motionless. It has no kinetic energy. The energy that you originally gave to the ball, however, is still stored up in

Fig. 107. The moving ball has kinetic energy.

The ball at the second story window has potential energy.

it as *energy of position*.   If the ball is dropped, it will fall to the ground, exchanging its energy of position for energy of motion.   Let us call this energy of position *potential* (possible) *energy*.

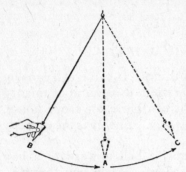

The pendulum gives a very good illustration of both kinds of energy.   Draw the pendulum bob to one side *B* and release it (Fig. 108).   The bob will move faster and faster until at the middle point *A* of the swing its energy is all kinetic.   It then rises to the point *C* on the opposite side where for an instant it is motionless.   Its energy is now all potential.   In this way the energy of the bob is trans-

Fig. 108.   When has the pendulum potential energy and when kinetic energy?

formed in each swing from potential to kinetic, and back to potential.

Where we get energy.   We cannot create energy.   We must always get it somewhere; but having found it, we can change it into many forms.   Thus we may find water on a mountain side.   High up it has potential (possible) energy. It falls and turns a wheel.   The energy is changed in falling to energy of motion, and this energy is utilized to turn the water wheel.   The water wheel runs a dynamo, and the energy becomes electrical energy.   It is led through a wire to a motor and becomes again energy of motion, or is turned into an electric toaster and becomes heat energy, or into a lamp and becomes heat and then light energy.

Most of the energy of industry comes from burning coal, which gives heat energy.   We do not create energy by burning.   Coal is the remains of plants from past ages.   The plants grew when sunlight fell upon them.   In a way which we shall study later, the sun's energy enabled the plants to build up chemical compounds, such as starch and then wood. When we burn wood, the sun's energy is given out again as heat.   The energy was stored in the chemical compounds of the wood.   In that stored condition we say that it is chemical energy.   When the wood or coal burns, the chemical energy is changed to heat energy.

In all this series of transformations, energy is neither gained nor lost, but has merely changed its form.   We express all these facts in *the law of conservation of energy: energy can neither be created nor destroyed.*

What is work?   You will probably say the word *work* means *labor*.   In science, however, this word has a special meaning that differs somewhat from the common idea.   In science, work is defined as the effect of a force in moving a body upon which the force acts.   Work always implies motion.   If you push against a heavy wall, you are laboring, but you are doing no work, for there is no motion.   The columns supporting a heavy building are doing no work, for there is no motion.

Measuring work.   When you lift a pound weight 1 foot, you have done a certain amount of work.   It makes no difference how slowly or how rapidly you do this work, the amount remains the same.   If you lift 2 pounds 3 feet, you will have done 6 times the work.   Our unit of work is the foot pound. *A foot pound is the amount of work done in lifting 1 pound 1 foot.*   To find the foot pounds of work done, multiply the pounds lifted by the vertical distance in feet that the weight is raised.

If your classroom is 40 feet from the ground and you weigh 100 pounds, you will have done $40 \times 100 = 4000$ foot pounds of work in lifting your body from the sidewalk to the room. Of course the work done need not be lifting.   If you push a box over the floor for the distance of 3 feet, using a force of 2 pounds all the way, you do 2×3 foot pounds of work. Work is always force multiplied by distance.   The motion may be in any direction.   The work done is compared to that required to lift 1 pound 1 foot.

Horse power.   In industry we are interested not only in how much is done but in how much time it takes to do it. When we include the idea of the time it takes to do work, we are thinking of *power*.   Long ago James Watt, a Scotchman who was one of the first men to put steam to work by means of the steam engine, tried to measure the amount of work horses could do in a given time. He estimated that a horse, working steadily, could lift 33,000 pounds 1 foot in 1 minute. This he called *1 horse power*, often abbreviated to h.p. If, then, the motor of an elevator has 10 h.p., it can lift 330,000 pounds 1 foot in 1 minute. This is, of course, the same thing as lifting 3300 pounds 100 feet in 1 minute. As long as the product of the pounds and feet equals 330,000 and the work is done in 1 minute, we have a horse power of 10.

Suppose you ran as fast as you could from the sidewalk to your classroom. Suppose it took you a minute and a third. In the paragraph on work you calculated that in making this trip you did 4000 foot pounds of work. If you do it in $1\frac{1}{3}$ minutes, you are doing 3000 foot pounds a minute. The horse power that your action displays would be found by making the calculation $\dfrac{3,000}{33,000}$; that is, $\frac{1}{11}$ horse power.

Measuring energy. Since energy is the power to do work, we measure it by measuring the foot pounds of work that the energy can do. The storage battery in your automobile has potential energy. If the battery can be used to lift 5 pounds 70 feet, it has $5 \times 70 = 350$ foot pounds of potential energy. The more rapidly a body moves, the more foot pounds of work it can do, and the more kinetic energy it possesses. A rifle bullet moves very rapidly. It has great kinetic energy. If it strikes a steel plate, this energy is changed into heat energy, and enough heat may be set free to melt the bullet. No matter in what form energy appears, we can measure it by the foot pounds of work it can do.

Definition of terms. Make sure that you know the meaning of the terms that the scientist uses when he talks of energy and what it does. Energy is the capacity to do work. Work is done only when a force moves a body through space. A force is a push or pull that moves a body or tends to move it. There can be no work without a force, but a force does work only when it moves a body. Power is the rate of doing work.

Chapter XIV

THE SIMPLEST MACHINE

What this machine is. If you ever have pushed a stick under a rock and pried up the rock, you have used a simple machine. If you have rolled a plank on a roller, skated on roller skates, pulled down a roller towel, or pushed a baby carriage, you have used another simple machine. The bewildering complex of machinery in an airplane or an automobile is but the combination of a number of just such simple machines. Each particular part has only one simple act to perform.

The simplest machine is illustrated by the crowbar which is used to pry up weights, the seesaw, and the oar of a boat. These are all illustrations of the *lever*. Very often when you cannot budge a heavy rock by pushing and pulling, you can move it very easily with a pry, or a lever, such as a crowbar. Let us see why.

Fig. 109. Note the position of the fulcrum in relation to the length of the rule.

Balance a 2-foot rule on a pencil (Fig. 109). The support on which the rule balances we call the *fulcrum*. Note the point where you must place the fulcrum in order to balance the rule. If the rule is of the same size throughout, it will balance when the fulcrum is beneath the 12-inch mark.

Put a 4-ounce weight on one end of the rule and an 8-ounce weight on the other end. The rule no longer balances. Leaving the fulcrum at the center of the rule, place the

4-ounce weight at one end and the 8-ounce weight halfway in from the other end. Now 4 ounces balances 8 ounces. Let us see how it is possible. The 4-ounce weight is 12 inches from the fulcrum; the 8-ounce weight is 6 inches from the fulcrum. Multiply 4 by 12, and 8 by 6. Notice that the two products are the same: $4 \times 12 = 8 \times 6$. Our simple machine, the lever, enables the 4-ounce weight to balance the 8-ounce weight.

Now pull down the end of the rule carrying the 8-ounce weight until it touches the table. Measure the distance that the 4-ounce weight is from the table. Then pull down the 4-ounce weight and measure the distance that the 8-ounce weight travels. You will find by this experiment that the 4-ounce weight travels twice the distance that the 8-ounce weight travels.

When we use a lever to move a big rock, we really gain no energy. We merely exchange moving a small weight a long distance for moving a heavy weight a short distance. In this way a lever may be used to lift a stone that is too heavy to be lifted directly (Fig. 110). To accomplish this a small effort continued through a long distance produces the same result as a great effort continued through a short distance.

Law of the lever. Let us state these facts as a law of science. Let us call the weight that we wish to move the *resistance* (R) and the weight that we use to move it the *effort* (E). The effort multiplied by its distance, D, from the fulcrum will always equal the resistance multiplied by its distance, D' (called D *prime*), from the fulcrum. To represent this mathematically we say $E \times D = R \times D'$.

Let us consider a lever from another point of view. Resistance multiplied by the distance it moves will always equal the effort multiplied by the distance that it moves. Now let us put this in mathematical form. If we represent the distance the effort moves by d and the distance the resistance moves by d', then $E \times d = R \times d'$.

Solving problems. When an engineer needs machinery to move rocks and gravel, he must know how heavy and how strong his machines must be. He then has a problem somewhat like the following. Let us suppose a boy who is able to exert an effort of 50 pounds wishes to move a boulder weighing 550 pounds. He has a crowbar 48 inches long. Can he move the stone? Use the Law of the Lever. Suppose he places a smaller stone as a fulcrum at such a distance from the larger boulder that 4 inches of the crowbar will be at one side of the fulcrum and 44 inches of the crowbar at the other side of the fulcrum. The resistance arm is 4 inches and the effort arm is 44 inches. Their ratio will be 1:11. The ratio of the effort and resistance will then be

Fig. 110. A crowbar is a lever.

1:11. A downward push of 50 pounds by the boy will balance the stone weighing 550 pounds.

By placing the fulcrum closer to the boulder so as to make the resistance arm still shorter, it would be possible to lift an even heavier boulder, but remember that the boy has actually gained no energy. He has only exchanged moving a small weight a long distance for moving a heavy weight a short distance. In pushing down his end of the lever 11 inches, the boy has raised the stone only 1 inch.

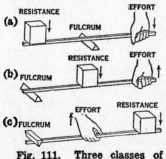

Fig. 111. Three classes of levers: (a) First class, (b) Second class, (c) Third class.

Every boy is familiar with the seesaw. If a large boy at one end of the seesaw balances a small boy at the other end, the sawhorse (fulcrum) on which the plank balances must be nearer to the larger boy. Suppose you work out such a problem for yourself.

One boy weighs 100 pounds and is seated 4 feet from the fulcrum. The other boy weighs 60 pounds. How far from the fulcrum must he be placed in order that the seesaw may

balance? In this discussion we have omitted any consideration of the weight of the lever itself. In physics you will learn how this affects your results.

Fig. 112.   A seesaw is a lever.

Some common use of levers. Why does a pair of shears for cutting tin have long handles and short blades, and your mother's scissors have short handles and long blades (Fig. 114)? It is difficult to cut sheet metal with ordinary scissors because the resistance arm is too long. In tin shears, or shears for cutting sheet metal, we make the handles (effort arms) long, and the cutting blades (resistance arms) short. Applying a small effort through a long distance enables us to overcome the larger resistance necessary to cut the metal (Fig. 114). A pair of shears for cutting paper has short effort arms and long resistance arms, giving increased speed where little effort is required.

Levers in your bodies. Your own forearm is a lever. The muscle of your upper arm (biceps) is attached at one end to your shoulder and at the other end to your forearm, near the elbow. When you contract this muscle, you are using the bones of your forearm as a lever. The elbow acts as the fulcrum. The distance from the elbow joint to the point where the muscle is attached to the bone is the effort arm, and the distance from the elbow joint to the weight is the resistance arm. The shorter you make this resistance arm, the heavier the weight that you can lift. If

Fig. 113.   **The wheelbarrow is a lever.**

you will hang two heavy packs of books by a strap over your arm (Fig. 115), you will find that by moving the strap close to the elbow you can lift the weights, while if you move the weights to the end of your fingers, you will either be unable to lift them, or, at best, will lift them only by a very considerable effort.

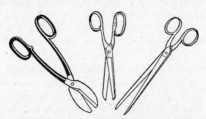 

Fig. 114. Simple machines. Why have the tin shears short blades and the paper shears long blades?

Fig. 115. The arm is a lever.

EXPERIMENT 50

Question: What is the Law of the Lever?

Materials: A small piece of wood for use as a fulcrum; a 2-foot rule; weights of 16, 8, and 4 ounces.

Directions: (a) Place the rule on the fulcrum and slide it along until it just balances. You will find that the 12-inch mark is just over the fulcrum.

(b) Place the center of the 8-ounce weight (call this weight the effort *E*) just over the 2-inch mark on the rule. Slide the 16-ounce weight along the rule on the opposite side of the fulcrum until the rule just balances. (Call the 16-ounce weight the resistance *R*). You will find that *R* must be placed just over the 17-inch mark. Calculate the distance of *E* and *R* from the fulcrum. Record all your results in the table. Call the distance of *E* from the fulcrum, *D*. Call the distance of *R* from the fulcrum, *D'*. Write the following table in your notebook.

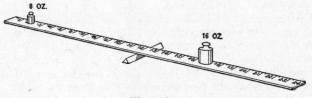

Fig. 116.

Table.—To make the rule balance when the 8-ounce weight *E* was .... inches from the fulcrum, I had to put the 16-ounce weight *R* .... inches from the fulcrum.   *E* = ... ounces. *D* = ... inches.   *R* = ... ounces.   *D′* = ... inches.

(*c*) Multiply *E* by *D*.   Multiply *R* by *D′*.   Notice that you obtain the same result in both cases.   This fact is always true and is known as the *law of the lever*.

(*d*) To confirm your result, place the 4-ounce weight 10 inches from the fulcrum and, using the law you have just found, calculate where you must put the 8-ounce weight to balance the lever.   Place the 8-ounce weight on the calculated position and see that the lever really does balance.

In this experiment, pay no attention to the weight of the rule.   It is also difficult to place the weights exactly over the proper marks.   For these reasons your results may not be exact.   If you repeat them a number of times and take the average of the results, you will find that the law is true.   The better your apparatus and the more care you use in carrying out the directions, the more nearly you will accurately illustrate the law.

Diagram: Show the rule balanced on the fulcrum and two weights in position.   Be sure to mark weights and distances properly.

Conclusion: Answer the question.

Practical application: 1. To move a heavy stone, using a heavy bar as a lever, should the fulcrum be placed near your hand or near the stone?   Why?   2. Explain how an ordinary equal-arm balance illustrates the law of the lever.

EXPERIMENT 51

Question: I learned that energy can neither be created nor destroyed. With a lever, I can lift a 16-ounce weight, using only an 8-ounce effort. Does this not contradict what I learned about energy?

Materials: A 2-foot rule; a 1-foot rule; weights of 8 and 16 ounces; a fulcrum.

Directions: (*a*) Put the 2-foot rule on the fulcrum, the 8-ounce weight (call this weight *E*) at one end and the 16-ounce weight (call this weight *R*) at the other end.   Slide the rule along on the fulcrum until it balances.

(*b*) Taking care to avoid changing the position of the lever on the fulcrum, press the end carrying the 8-ounce weight *E* to the table. Measure the distance the 16-ounce weight *R* is from the table.   Record the result in the table.

(*c*) Press the end carrying the 16-ounce weight *R* to the table. Measure the distance the 8-ounce weight *E* is from the table.   Write and fill in the following table in your notebook.

TABLE

The rule balanced when the fulcrum was at the .... inch mark.

When E is at the table level, R is .... inches from the table.

When R is at the table level, E is .... inches from the table.

The weight E (8 oz.) therefore moves .... inches while the weight R (16 oz.) is moving .... inches.

(d) Multiply E by the distance it moves. Multiply R by the distance it moves. Your results should be the same, showing that the law of energy has not been proved untrue. What you have gained by being able to move a large weight with a small one, you have lost by having to move the smaller weight a longer distance. This is always true in machines. We can get nothing more out of the machine than we put in, but we can exchange moving a large resistance a short distance for moving a small effort a large distance.

Diagram: Show the arrangement of the lever and weights.

Conclusion: Answer the question, and explain how your answer is arrived at.

Practical application: A cheat made a balance having the fulcrum so placed that one arm A of the balance was 7 inches long and the other arm B was only 5 inches long. When he bought, he placed the goods on one pan, and when he sold, he placed the goods on the other pan. 1. Did he use pan A or B for goods to be sold? If you wish to do so, you may calculate just how much he cheated, for you will see that a 7-pound weight in pan B will just balance a 5-pound weight in pan A. 2. If you bought 10 pounds of butter (real weight) at 50 cents a pound, what did the butter seem to weigh in the dishonest scales, and what was the overcharge?

In the case above, the difference in the length of the arms is so great that you would notice it. If the difference is made small, you might not notice it, but the grocer or the butcher would be giving short weight all the time. To prevent this, balances are tested by the government and sealed. That is, they are stamped to certify that they give an honest weight. Look at the next scale that you see and find the mark of the sealer.

CHAPTER XV

OTHER SIMPLE MACHINES

Pulleys. Have you ever helped to hoist sail? (Fig. 117.) If not, perhaps you have watched the ropes run through the pulleys on a derrick (Fig. 118). One man with a block and tackle once pulled an automobile out of a ditch after six men failed to push it out with their shoulders.

Pulleys and gear wheels are really modified levers. The science of these machines is easy to understand if you have grasped the principle of the lever.

A pulley is a grooved wheel (called the sheave) supported in such a way that the wheel can turn freely. A rope passes over the groove as shown in Figure 119a. Two or three pulley wheels may be mounted in the same block, so that by using two pulleys, one can make such an arrangement as shown in Figure 121a. With a pulley one can lift a body by pulling downward, an easier job than pulling upward, because you can let your weight do the work. In changing the direction of pull, by means of a pulley as in Figure 120b, you neither gain nor lose energy. If the resistance is lifted 1 foot, the effort will go down 1 foot, and to lift a 100-pound weight will require a pull of 100 pounds.

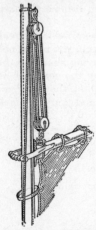

Fig. 117. Pulleys hoist sail.

With several pulleys arranged as in Figure 121a you can lift heavier weights by smaller effort. If you will look at Figure 121b, you will see that when the effort *E* is pulled down 2 feet, each rope (*A* and *B*) will be shortened 1 foot, and the weight *R* will be lifted 1 foot. Here we have an advantage similar to that gained by the use of a lever.

(150)

Fig. 118. The steam shovel is a combination of simple machines. How many can you name?

Moving the effort 2 feet moves the resistance only 1 foot. An effort of 50 pounds can overcome a resistance of 100 pounds, but the resistance will move only one half the distance that the effort moves. Imagine that in Figure 121b the rope E is pulled 4 feet. How much will each of the ropes supporting the weight be shortened? What effort will be required to lift the 100-pound weight?

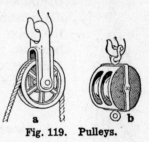

Fig. 119. Pulleys.

When you wish to lift a heavy weight with a moderate effort, you may use two pulleys as in Figure 121a. In this case, you will see that there are 6 ropes between the 2 pulleys, all of which are shortened when the weight is lifted. If then the rope marked "effort" E is pulled down 6 feet, each of these 6 ropes will be shortened 1 foot. The distance that the effort moves is 6 and the distance that the resistance moves is 1, and an effort of 50 pounds can overcome a resistance 6 times as great, or 300 pounds.

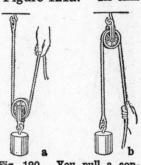

Fig. 120. You pull a convenient direction.

Mechanical advantage. In the last case of the pulleys, you found that an effort of 1 would lift a resistance of 6. This ratio between *R* (resistance) and *E* (effort) is called the *mechanical advantage* of the machine. Thus the mechanical advantage of this arrangement of pulleys is described as 6 divided by 1, or 6.

Efficiency. If you will try in the laboratory the actual arrangement of two pulleys, as shown in Figure 121b, you will find a difference between theory and practice. In theory a weight of 6 ounces should be lifted by an effort of 1 ounce. In practice you will find that a weight of 6 ounces will require somewhat more than an effort of 1 ounce, because the effort must not only lift the resistance but must turn the wheel (sheave) in the pulley, must bend the rope around the pulley, and must overcome other mechanical deficiencies in the apparatus. The more flexible the rope, the less effort will be required to bend it. The smoother and more polished the bearings on which the pulley wheel (sheave) turns, the less effort will be required to turn it. The more nearly perfect the pulley, the less the loss.

Suppose you find that if you use a very stiff rope and pulleys with very rusty bearings, it actually requires an effort of 60 pounds to lift a 300-pound weight. In theory an effort of 50 pounds would lift the weight. In practice you find that for every 50 pounds of useful effort, it is necessary to expend about 10 pounds of wasted effort. If you polished the bearings a little and used a somewhat more flexible rope, you might be able to get your effort down to 55 pounds. In this case you would have only 5 pounds of wasted effort. The nearer your actual effort comes to the theoretical effort, the less is the wasted effort and the more

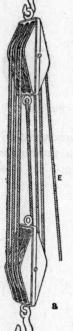
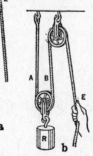

Fig. 121. You save effort.

efficient the machine. Calling the effort that is put into a machine 100 and the work that is taken out of the machine 60, the efficiency of the machine will be 60 divided by 100, or 60 per cent. The efficiency of the toy motors run by a dry battery may be as low as 15 per cent, while the efficiency of a large electric motor may rise to 96 per cent. The higher the efficiency, the less energy the machine wastes and the better it is.

Fig. 122. The windlass—a wheel and axle.

Wheel and axle. Figure 122 shows another simple machine, which you have probably seen used to lift a bucket of water from a well. It is called a *windlass*. It is really a modification of a lever. When the handle (A) has made one complete turn, the rope will have wound around the cylinder (B) one turn. If the circumference of the circle made by the handle measures 6 feet and the length of the rope wound on the cylinder is 1 foot, then the effort has moved 6 while the resistance moves 1. An effort of 10 pounds applied on the handle of such a windlass will overcome a resistance of 60 pounds, or will lift a bucket of water weighing 60 pounds from the well. Here, again, we are neglecting in this discussion the effort necessary to turn the cylinder in its bearings and to bend the rope around the cylinder. Practically, therefore, the mechanical advantage of the wheel and axle is always somewhat less than you might expect it to be; or, to put it another way, the efficiency of the wheel and axle is always less than 100 per cent.

A ship's capstan is another good example of the wheel and axle (Fig. 123). It consists of an upright, revolving drum that can be pushed around with the capstan bars placed in the openings of the drum. The longer the capstan bar, the greater

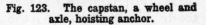

Fig. 123. The capstan, a wheel and axle, hoisting anchor.

the resistance that can be overcome, but also the longer the distance that a sailor pushing the bar must walk. Such a device used with 4 or 6 capstan bars can lift a heavy anchor.

Fig. 124.   On an inclined plane, a man can roll up a barrel too heavy to lift.

The steering wheel of an automobile is another case of levers and wheel and axle. The driver's hands supply the effort, while the friction of the tire on the road offers the chief resistance. Examine carefully this device on your automobile and you can readily trace the action of the different parts involved.

Skids, or the inclined plane.   It often happens that a truckman wishes to load into his truck a barrel that is too heavy for him to lift. To do this he uses an inclined plane. The truckman places two long poles reaching from the back of his truck to the ground. He then rolls the heavy barrel up these poles (Fig. 124). If the end of his truck is 3 feet from the ground, he must lift the barrel 3 feet, but if his poles (skids) are 6 feet long, he rolls the barrel over a distance of 6 feet. By using the skids, he exerts a smaller effort over a longer distance instead of the greater effort over the short distance of the direct lift. If the barrel weighs 200 pounds and is lifted 3 feet, resistance times the distance moved will be 600. If the skids are 6 feet long, the distance through which the effort moves will be 6 feet, and the effort itself must equal 100 pounds. The longer the skids, the smaller the effort to roll the barrel into the truck, but also the greater the distance through which the truckman must roll the barrel.

The screw. The screw jack used to raise an automobile is a familiar machine. The screw is an inclined plane, wound around a cylinder. When you give a screw one complete turn, you have driven the screw into the wood a distance equal to the distance between two of the grooves on the screw (Fig. 125). Theoretically, by making the distance between the grooves small and the head of the screw large, it is possible to secure a very great mechanical advantage. However, the friction of the screw turning in the wood or metal is so

Fig. 125.   A screw is an inclined plane.

great that its efficiency is very small. You are, of course, familiar with the uses of the wood screw and the use of machine bolts in the automobile. The finer the thread, the greater the mechanical advantage of the screw but also the more likely the thread is to strip.

Friction. You are familiar with friction; but just what is it? No matter how smooth two metal surfaces may seem to be, if you examine them under the microscope, you will find that the surface of the metal is, in reality, rough. In Figure 126 two polished metal blades are shown and a highly magnified view of a section of the blades, showing that they are rough. To slide one of these blades over the other requires that the hills and valleys of one blade be pushed over the hills and valleys of the other. Evidently the rougher the blade, the higher the hills will be, and the more effort will be required to push one surface over the other. This resistance to motion is called *friction*. The smoother the surface, the less the friction. The roughness of the surfaces in contact is an important cause of friction. When you study physics, you will learn additional causes much more difficult to understand.

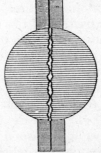

Fig. 126.   Two surfaces magnified.   What is a cause of friction?

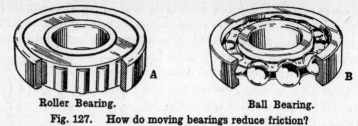

Roller Bearing.   Ball Bearing.
Fig. 127.   How do moving bearings reduce friction?

If a drop of oil is put between the two surfaces, the oil will fill up the depressions; and the upper surface will really rest on a film of oil, so there will be greatly diminished friction. Rolling friction is less than sliding friction, and for this reason roller bearings (Fig. 127a) are used in many machines. A still more efficient bearing is the ball bearing (Fig. 127b) used in bicycles, automobiles and many other machines. The next time you are in a garage, ask the mechanic to show you some of the many ball bearings used in automobiles.

Friction a friend.   Although we are constantly struggling to reduce friction in machinery, we should have an awkward time if we banished friction from the earth. When ice and water reduce the friction of your shoes on the walk, it is awkward if not dangerous. Athletes wear spikes in their shoes to increase the friction between their shoes and the ground. When wet ice or oil on the street reduces the friction of automobile tires, there may be a skid and a crash. Indeed, it is friction of tire with street surface that makes it possible for an automobile to go along the street. It is the friction of the driving wheel on the rail that makes it possible for a locomotive to pull a train (Fig. 142). If the rail is covered with ice or oil, the driving wheel slips, and it is difficult for the engineer to get up speed until he has put sand on the track to increase the friction. Friction of the nail or screw in the wood holds a box together. Friction of the brake on the wheel stops the speeding car. Like many other things, friction is a friend or an enemy, depending on where the friction occurs.

Starting and stopping. Did you ever help to push a stalled automobile? It was hard to get it started, but once started, it moved along without a great deal of effort. If you have not had that experience, perhaps you have noticed the same thing in riding a bicycle or you have started a barrel rolling or a box sliding or have pulled a wagon carrying a little sister or brother. You know that an automobile is started in low gear because the low gear has more power. You have seen a locomotive make a great fuss in getting started. All these examples show something that is constantly opposing the efforts of machines and men. There is a constant tendency of a body at rest to remain at rest unless acted upon by an outside force. This tendency is called *inertia*.

Moving things also have inertia. It is the inertia of a moving automobile that makes brakes necessary. It is the inertia that smashes the car against a pole if the driver does not put his foot on the brake in time. It is the inertia of the batted ball that carries it smashing through a window-pane.

Inertia is the tendency of a body at rest to remain at rest, and of a body in motion to continue moving without changing the direction or speed of motion, unless acted on by an outside force.

A speeding car is harder to stop than a slow car. A fast ball is more difficult to stop than a slow one. When you are driving a car, riding a bicycle, or skating, it is more difficult to turn a sharp corner when you are going fast than when you are going slowly.

Weight, too, increases the difficulty of starting, stopping, and changing direction. With an outstretched hand you can stop a toy wagon, but not an automobile going at exactly the same speed.

Speed and weight together determine how much force we need to stop, to start, or to change motion. A little more scientifically we say that the quantity of motion or *momentum* is due to weight and velocity (speed). We calculate the momentum by multiplying the weight by the velocity.

12

Of course people were aware of these things in a general way a long while before there was any true science, but we have learned to use them in the construction of great machines only since they have been expressed in the simple and exact statements of laws of science.   The laws of motion, some of which we have been discussing, were first stated by one of the greatest scientists of all time, an Englishman, Sir Isaac Newton (1642–1727).   The start of modern science was in a large measure due to his clear thinking.   You will find other discoveries of Newton as you proceed in your study of science.

How machines help.   Friction, weight, and inertia make work hard.   Machines are man's means of overcoming them. A lever enables a man to overcome the weight of a heavy rock.   Roller bearings and wheels help to overcome friction and inertia.

Machines also make use of friction, weight, and inertia. The weight of a locomotive gives the friction with the track necessary for the use of its power.   The momentum of a falling body drives piles (Fig. 128).   The inertia of moving machinery gives a smooth ride instead of a jerky one as one cylinder of an automobile fires after another.   So the engineer, who uses the findings of the scientist to build machinery, balances one force of nature against another.

Each simple machine does one or more things better than we could do them without the machine.   (1) A machine may enable us to do a great amount of work with reduced effort, as when we pry up a heavy rock with a lever.   (2) It may increase speed, as when a large cogwheel turns a small cogwheel, or it may reduce the speed as when a little cogwheel turns a big one.   (3) It may enable us to exert a force in a more convenient direction, as a pulley to haul up a bale of hay or a steering wheel to turn an automobile.   (4) It may do the work more accurately, as when a compass draws a circle.

EXPERIMENT 52

Question: What is the advantage of arranging pulleys in various ways?

Materials: Single-, double-, and triple-sheaved pulley blocks; stout flexible cord; a pound weight; a delicate spring balance reading to fractions of an ounce.

Fig. 128. The pile driver does its work by momentum of a falling weight.

Directions: (*a*) Mount a single pulley as shown in Fig. 129A. Pass a cord over the groove in the sheave (wheel). Tie a pound weight to one end of the cord, and the spring balance to the other end. Pull the cord down by means of the spring balance until you raise the weight from the table. 1. For every inch of the cord that you pull down after the weight has been raised, how many inches do you raise the weight? 2. Read the spring balance. What effort was required to lift the pound weight? 3. What is the only thing that this particular arrangement of a pulley does? 4. What is the advantage of this arrangement?

(*b*) Mount a single pulley as shown in Fig. 129B. Pass a cord over the groove in the sheave. Tie a pound weight to one end of the pulley. Attach the spring balance to the free end of the cord. Raise the spring

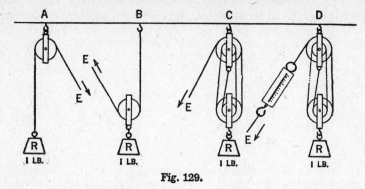

Fig. 129.

balance until the weight is raised from the table.　1. For every inch of cord that passes through the pulley, how many inches do you raise the weight?　2. What effort was required to raise the pound weight? 3. What is the advantage of this pulley arrangement?

(c) Mount two double pulleys as shown in Fig. 129C.　Pass the cord around the sheaves and hang the weight on the pulley as shown. Pull down on the cord until you raise the weight.　1. For every inch of cord that passes through the pulley, how many inches is the weight raised?　2. What is the advantage of this pulley arrangement?

(d) Using the same arrangement of pulleys as in (c), attach the spring balance to the loose end of the cord as shown in Fig. 129D.　Pull the spring balance until you have lifted the weight from the table.　Read the balance.　1. How many ounces of effort are required to overcome the resistance of 1 pound (16 ounces)?　Remember the law of the lever and that this law applies generally to machines.　2. From your answer to question (c) 1, how should you expect the spring balance to read? 3. How near does it come to this reading?　4. What might be one cause of any difference?

Diagram: Show the different arrangement of the pulleys.

Conclusion: Answer the question.

Practical application: You wish to raise a barrel weighing 150 pounds. The greatest effort that you can exert is 25 pounds.　Draw an arrangement of pulleys showing how you could raise the barrel to a higher level.

Pulleys are often used in construction work.　The next time you pass a building that is being erected, see how many examples you can find of their use.

EXPERIMENT 53

Problem: Show an easy way to put a barrel on a truck.

Material: A board 32 inches long and 5 or 6 inches wide;　pile of books 16 inches high;　a toy car;　weights to fill the car;　cord;　spring balance.

Directions: (*a*) Load the car so that it weighs 1 or 2 pounds. Attach the balance and lift the car vertically. Record this weight in table under results as the effort required to raise vertically (Fig. 130a).

(*b*) Place one end of the board on the pile of books 16 inches high. Attach balance to car and pull car up the incline (Fig. 130b). Record the effort in the table.

(*c*) Lower the end of the board so that its height is ¼ its length. Again pull up the car and record the effort.

(*d*) Again reduce the height to ⅛ the length. Record the effort to pull the car. Fill in the results on a table like the following:

Results: TABLE

Effort required to lift vertically ....

Effort when height is ½ length ....

Effort when height is ¼ length ....

Effort when height is ⅛ length ....

Conclusion: 1. Along which inclined plane would the car have to travel farthest to reach a given height? 2. The ascent of which plane required the least effort?

Practical application: 1. If a man had to roll barrels upon a truck, should he use long or short skids? 2. If two men were rolling each barrel, could the skids be shorter or must they be longer? 3. Why is it easier to walk up a gently sloping ramp than it is to walk up a flight of stairs, when both land you at the same level?

In factories and in loading trucks, skids are often used. When skids are used, the barrel is rolled a greater distance than if it is lifted vertically, but the effort required to move the barrel is less. This makes it possible for one man to do work that otherwise would require the labor of several men, and this is often a convenience.

Ramps are used to make the motion of crowds easier, as in railroad stations.

How do engineers who build railroads make use of inclined planes in the road beds? how do highway engineers?

A wedge used to split wood is an inclined plane. How does the angle of the wedge effect: (1) ease of driving; (2) speed of splitting?

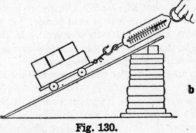

Fig. 130.

EXPERIMENT 54

Question: 1. What is the relation between an inclined plane and a screw? 2. Of what use is a screw jack?

Materials: Two triangular pieces of paper which represent inclined planes. Both are 2 inches high, one is 4 and the other is 8 inches long; a wooden rod 6 inches long and ½ inch in diameter; a large machine bolt having a coarse thread with nut; a screw jack.

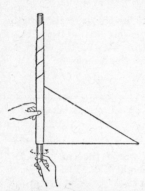

Fig. 131. Shows how a sheet of paper wound around a rod illustrates the principle of the screw.

Directions: (*a*) Starting at the wide end of the paper, wrap the 8-inch long triangular piece of paper around one end of the wooden rod. Fasten the end by pasting it down. You will see that the slanting edge of the paper, which represents an inclined plane, now forms a spiral around the rod. (See Fig. 131.) To make the spiral more distinct, outline it with a blue pencil. Compare the blue outline with the machine bolt and you will see that by winding up the inclined plane you have changed it into a spiral, and that this spiral represents the thread (cut-out portion) of a screw. We call the distance between two threads (the distance between two of the blue marks) the *pitch* of the screw. Examine the machine screw nut, and you will see a thread cut around the hole which goes through it.

(*b*) Wrap the 4-inch-long piece of paper around the middle of the wooden rod just as you did the 8-inch piece. Fasten the end and outline the spiral. Compare the two spirals. You will see that the pitch (the distance between two threads) of the second screw is greater than that of the first.

(*c*) Compare the spirals you have made with the thread of the machine bolt. You will see that they are similar. If you wish, you can file out the spiral that you have marked, and thus change the inclined plane into a real screw. A screw, then, is really an inclined plane wound up into a spiral. If the rod on which you wound the paper had tapered, you would have made a spiral that would represent an ordinary tapered wood screw.

Put the edge of your finger nail into one of the threads of the machine bolt. Turn the bolt. Notice that giving the bolt one completed turn has moved your finger nail forward the distance between two threads. The coarser the thread, the farther your finger nail will move. The coarser the thread of a screw, the harder it is to turn.

(*d*) Both of the triangular papers that you used were 2 inches high. They represented two inclined planes, one 4 and the other 8 inches long. 1. If equal weights were being pulled up these two inclined planes, on which one would the greater effort be required? 2. Which, then, of the two screws that you made would require the greater effort to turn

If it were being used in a screw jack to raise a weight? 3. Why is the thread on machine screws sometimes made fine and sometimes made coarse?

(e) Place on the head of a screw jack as heavy a weight as you can lift. Give the screw several turns. Why does it require less effort to turn the screw jack than it did to lift the weight upon its head?

Diagram: Show the two triangular pieces of paper, and the papers wound around the rod; the machine bolt and nut; the screw jack.

Conclusion: Answer questions 1 and 2.

Practical application: The finer the thread of a screw, the easier it is to turn the screw and the less distance the screw will advance. Why have automobile bolts a finer thread than a stove bolt?

Screw jacks are used whenever tremendous weights have to be lifted, as in lifting a building that is to be moved. Examine the construction of the jack which is used to lift your automobile, and be ready to discuss it in class.

EXPERIMENT 55

Question: What makes an automobile skid?

Materials: A block of wood 2 × 2 × 6 inches, having two sides rough and two sides smooth; a wooden plank 8 inches by 2 feet, one side of which is smooth and the other side rough; a spring balance showing ounces; nails and hammer.

Directions: (a) Drive a tack into the end of the block of wood and tie to the tack a string about a foot long. Tie the other end of the string to the spring balance. Put the plank, rough side up, on the table and put on it the wood block, rough side down. This brings the two rough sides together. Put a pound weight on the block and then pull on the spring balance hard enough to move the block along the plank slowly. Read the spring balance. Try this twice, and each time take the reading of the spring balance. In your notebook make a table like the one below and record your readings in it.

TABLE	1	2	AVER-AGE
Reading with rough sides in contact.....	....	....	....
Reading with smooth sides in contact....	....	....	....

(b) Turn the plank smooth side up and put the wood block on it smooth side down. Put the pound weight on the block. All things are now just as they were, except that the smooth surfaces are together instead of the rough surfaces. Again pull the block slowly along the plank. Try twice and record your readings in your table. Complete the table.

We call the resistance to the motion of the block *friction*.   1. Is friction greater when rough or when smooth surfaces are in contact?

It is the friction between the road and the rubber tires of an automobile that holds the automobile on the road.   When it rains, the city streets are covered with a slime of oil and mud.   When this happens, automobiles are likely to skid.   2. Explain why this is true.

Diagram: Show the block being drawn along.

Conclusion: Answer the question.

Practical application: What holds a nail in wood? What would happen to wooden boxes held together with nails if friction should cease to exist?

CHAPTER XVI

THE ENGINE

The steam engine. The cave man no doubt used a **lever** and an inclined plane. Men of the New Stone Age had invented wheels (Fig. 132). Here were all the simple elements of modern machines, for modern machines are but intricate complexes of levers, wheels, and planes. As time went on, water wheels were devised to supply power for machines. Yet machinery made relatively little advance until man discovered how to harness steam and put it to work. It was not until James Watt (1736–1819), a Scottish engineer, made the first really practical steam engine, that the great substitution of mechanical power for man power became possible.

The actual mechanism of a steam engine may be rather complicated, but the principle is simple. The round cylinder has, sliding back and forth in it, a tightly fitting piston (Fig. 134). A device called a *slide valve* is so arranged that steam can be admitted to either side of the piston. Examine Figure 134. Steam is passing from the boiler through a pipe into the cylinder to the left of the piston as is shown by the arrows. The pressure of this steam will push the piston to the right. Any

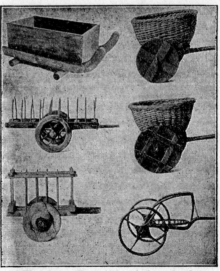

Fig. 132. Evolution of the wheel.

gas on the right side of the piston will pass out through passages as indicated by the arrows.   When the piston has moved as far to the right as is possible, the slide valve is

moved automatically, reversing the position of the valves of the engine. Steam will now be admitted to the right of the piston.   The piston will be pushed to the left and the waste steam on the left side of the piston will escape. This to-and-fro motion of the piston is the source of power.

Usually it is necessary to convert this to-and-fro motion (called *rectilinear* because the piston moves in a straight line) into a rotary motion. This is accomplished by

Fig. 133.   Cave man used a machine, but his muscles supplied the power.

the device shown in Figure 135.   If you will look at this figure and imagine the rod being pushed back and forth, you will see that the final effect will be to make the wheel *rotate*. A treadle sewing machine or a grindstone illustrates such a device in actual use.

As the piston moves back and forth, the steam on one side

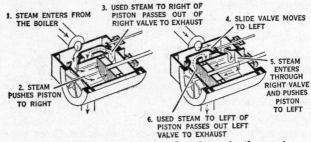

1. STEAM ENTERS FROM THE BOILER

3. USED STEAM TO RIGHT OF PISTON PASSES OUT OF RIGHT VALVE TO EXHAUST

4. SLIDE VALVE MOVES TO LEFT

2. STEAM PUSHES PISTON TO RIGHT

5. STEAM ENTERS THROUGH RIGHT VALVE AND PUSHES PISTON TO LEFT

6. USED STEAM TO LEFT OF PISTON PASSES OUT LEFT VALVE TO EXHAUST

Fig. 134.   How steam drives the piston in the engine.

of the piston is pushing the piston along. The steam on the other side is resisting this push. To avoid the loss due to this resistance, the steam is condensed after it has done its work, thus relieving the pressure and making the engine more powerful.

In building operations, a small steam engine is often used as a source of power for hoisting the building materials. When you have the opportunity, examine one and you will be able to learn more of its actual operation.

Fig. 135. How a steam engine changes to-and-fro motion to rotary motion.

Steam turbine. Another method of applying the energy of compressed steam is found in the steam turbine. This has the advantage that it generates a rotary motion directly. Steam from jets (Fig. 136) is made to strike small buckets on the rim of a wheel. The energy of the expanding steam forces this wheel to rotate and gives a source of power. Many of the large power units used in modern electric plants use steam turbines.

Putting explosions to work. A gasoline engine, as in the automobile, is driven by a succession of explosions. Put a *very few* drops of gasoline in an empty can, shake the can for a moment, stand back and bring a match to its

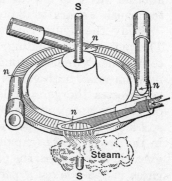

Fig. 136. A steam turbine. Steam from the nozzle *n* strikes the blades on the wheel.

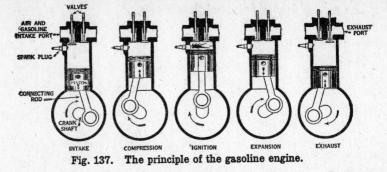

Fig. 137.   The principle of the gasoline engine.

mouth. This must be done with great care. There will be an explosion. The gasoline vaporizes and mixes with the air in the can. When you bring the match to this mixture, the vaporized gasoline burns very rapidly. The hot gases expand with tremendous rapidity, producing the explosion. This fact—that mixtures of inflammable substances and air can produce an explosion—is the basis of the gasoline engine used so extensively in automobiles. The principle of such an engine is simple, although the actual mechanism, when you examine the engine of an automobile, may seem to be complex.

In Figure 137 the principle of the gasoline engine is illustrated. It consists of a cylinder, a tightly fitting piston moving in its cylinder, a valve to admit the explosive mixture, another valve to let out the burned gases, and a spark plug to furnish a spark to ignite the explosive mixture.

Study the figure carefully. Begin with the *intake stroke*. The piston is descending, and the gas and air mixture is entering the cylinder through the intake valve. In the *compression stroke* both valves are closed, and the piston rises and compresses the gas. When the gas is compressed, *ignition* occurs by an electric spark between the two points of the spark plug. The hot gases expand and drive down the piston in the *power stroke* (expansion in the diagram). Finally the exhaust valve opens, the piston rises and forces out the burned gases in the *exhaust stroke*.

Since there are four distinct actions in such an engine, it is known as a *four-cycle engine*. Of the four strokes, only one is a power stroke. As a result, the action of such an engine is irregular. Early automobiles had a one-cylinder gas engine. When running at low speed, these cars were decidedly uncomfortable. There would be a sudden jerk as the power stroke pushed the car ahead and then a lull during the other three strokes. To avoid this, modern cars have at least four cylinders. The explosions in these cylinders are so arranged that one of the four is always delivering a power stroke. By using six, eight, or twelve cylinders, the power strokes can be made to overlap and a smooth flow of power results. The next time you are in an automobile garage, examine an engine that has been taken out of a car for repairs. If you will disregard all of the mechanism that is necessary to cause the valves to open and close, the spark plugs to function, etc., you will have no difficulty in seeing that, fundamentally, such engines are nothing but the cylinders, valves, and spark plugs that have just been described.

The explosive mixture is prepared for the cylinders in the *carburetor*. Gasoline rises through a nozzle in the carburetor in a fine spray and changes to vapor. Air drawn into the carburetor mixes with the gasoline vapor. The gasoline vapor and air form the explosive mixture that passes into the cylinders (Fig 138).

The electric current necessary for the spark plug is provided by a storage battery and an induction coil. Space cannot be taken here to discuss all these matters, but a study of a car in the repair shop, together with the friendly help of a mechanic, will teach you how they operate.

The Diesel engine. When a gas is compressed, it becomes very hot. Suppose that in a gas engine no gasoline is used, but during the admission stroke only air is admitted. During the compression stroke, this air, because of its compression, will become very hot. If, now, a drop of fuel oil is forced into

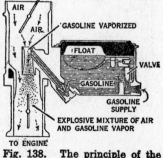
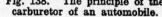

Fig. 138. The principle of the carburetor of an automobile.

Fig. 139.   A large Diesel engine.

this hot air, the fuel oil will burn and the power stroke will develop just as it did when the mixture of gasoline and air was compressed.   Engines forcing fuel oil into the hot air instead of using an explosive mixture of gasoline and air are called Diesel engines.   They have certain advantages.   The fuel is cheap and the complications of electrical ignition are

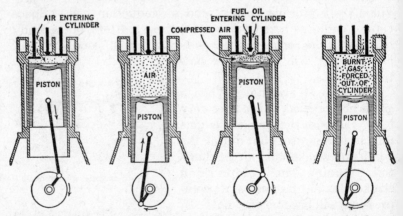

Fig. 140.   How a Diesel engine works.   Explain what is shown in each figure.

done away with. They are often used in large ships, and they have even been tried out in an experimental way for use in airplanes.

EXPERIMENT 56

Question: What makes steam engines go?

Materials: Test tube; cork to fit; Bunsen burner.

Directions: Put a half inch of water in the test tube, put in the cork firmly but not tightly. With a test-tube holder hold the corked tube over the flame at arm's length with the cork pointing away from you and others.

Result: What happens?

Conclusion: What makes it happen? How is this force put to practical use?

CHAPTER XVII

TRANSPORTATION

Transportation in modern life. Perhaps you sat down
this morning to a breakfast table made in Detroit, set with
chinaware made in Czechoslovakia. Perhaps there was grapefruit from Florida or California, cereal from the Middle West,
coffee from Brazil sweetened with sugar from Cuba, Louisiana, or Colorado, an egg seasoned with pepper from Asia, and
perhaps you ate the breakfast with an eye on a clock made in
Germany. Even milk for the coffee and cereal may have
come hundreds of miles in refrigerator cars.

Modern civilization is largely dependent on transportation.
Throughout the history of mankind, culture and efficiency,
as well as comfort and pleasure, have increased with the improvement of transportation. It has made possible great
cities and fine suburban homes. It has put modern machinery
on the farms and made possible the production of enormous
supplies of grain, milk, and meat. It has released the individual from making many necessities which he could not make
well and permitted him to devote himself to the one thing he
could do well. By enabling us to travel and by bringing to
us the creations of distant people, it has changed us from
old-fashioned folk interested only in our immediate neighbors to a people eager for news from Germany, China,
and India. Our profits from farm and factory are intimately bound up with the happenings on the other side of
the earth.

Transportation is a great modern industry. It employs
millions of people in the construction and operation of its
machines in building and maintaining roads and bridges, and
in handling freight and passengers. Though roads and automobiles take care of a large part of present-day transportation,

(172)

Fig. 141. A modern streamlined train. The train is so constructed that it encounters a minimum of air resistance. This makes possible greater speed, economy of fuel, and greater comfort for passengers.

Fig. 142. The driving wheels of a locomotive. Where are the driving bars attached to the wheels?

13

and air travel is steadily improving, railroads and steamships carry the largest part of goods and passengers. We have studied how power is harnessed by means of engines. We shall now study how engines move vehicles.

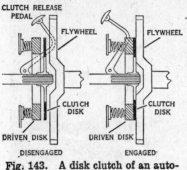
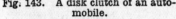

Fig. 143. A disk clutch of an automobile.

The locomotive. George Stephenson (1781–1848), an English engineer, building on earlier discoveries, was the inventor of the steam locomotive, which consists essentially of two steam engines, one on each side near the front. In each of these engines a piston is driven forward and backward. The piston in turn drives a bar, attached as shown, just outside the center of the big driving wheels. (For steam engine, see page 165.)

The automobile. The gasoline engine drives the automobile with a more complex transfer of power. The automobile engine has very little power when just starting. Therefore, it must start running without connection with the driving wheels. After the engine has started, a clutch connects the engine with the wheels (Fig. 143). In setting the vehicle into motion, also, more power is needed than after it is under way.

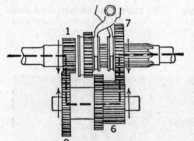

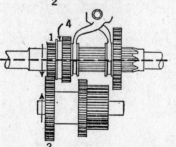

Fig. 144. Low gear and high gear in the automobile. Trace out the transmission of power through the gears in low gear.

after it is under way. The low gear gives greater power (Fig. 144). After the machine is moving, the higher gears are used.

The engine of an automobile being in the front and the driving wheels in the rear, the power is carried to the driving wheels by means of a long shaft running to the rear of the car. Here a set of gears changes the direction of the motion of the shaft so that it may be applied to the wheels (Fig. 145).

Good roads. Good automobiles are of small value without good roads. The Romans studied road construction and built superior roads, but they progressed very little in the development of vehicles. Modern road engineering is an important branch of science, and building roads is an important industry. Figure 146 shows the general principles of construction in modern hard-

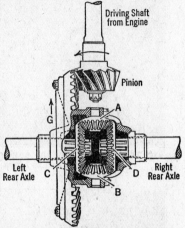

Fig. 145. The differential in the rear of the automobile.

surface roads. The engineer has studied the behavior of vehicles at varying speeds on both roads and railroads. Figure 147 shows how curves are banked to allow machines to round them without undue loss of speed. Roads are straightened; hills are cut down, and hollows are filled to allow machines to maintain their speed with safety. In railroads the grade must be very gentle, at most a rise of two feet in one hundred

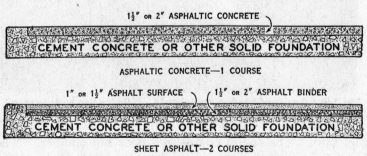

Fig. 146. A cross-section of a modern road.

Fig. 147. Notice how the engine is tilted to one side as it rounds the curve banked to allow the train to keep up speed.

Fig. 148. A railroad needs a gentle grade. Note the two engines even on this grade.

(Fig. 148). The steam engine is a poor hill climber. The electric motor and the automobile are much better on hills.

Fig. 149. A suspension bridge of grass rope in Tibet.

Bridge construction. The building of bridges has grown slowly through the ages (Fig. 149). The simplest bridge is supported by uprights (Fig. 150). This is sufficient for small bridges that may be built of wood or steel. Figure 151 shows how braces in the form of triangles increase the strength. Figure 152 shows how the arch supports the weight. Concrete now often replaces stone. For larger bridges, cantilever or suspension construction is used to support the great weight of steel (Fig. 153).

Fig. 150. A deck plate girder bridge, Eagle River, Colorado.

Fig. 151. A truss span bridge over the Ohio River. Note that the trusses form a series of triangles.

Fig. 152. A stone arch bridge, Perkiomen Creek, Pennsylvania.

Fig. 153. A modern suspension bridge, the Mid-Hudson Bridge, Poughkeepsie, New York.

Fig. 154. A modern paddle wheel steamboat on the Hudson.

Water transportation. Muscle and wind power have given place to steam in moving the world's commerce. John Fitch had a steamboat propelled by paddle plying on the Delaware after the Revolution (Fig. 155). Robert Fulton invented the steamboat propelled by paddle wheels. In shallow water paddle wheels are still used (Fig. 154). In 1836 Ericsson invented the screw propeller, which became the basis of modern ocean transportation (Fig. 156). We have already studied why a great steel ship floats, and later we shall study how a mariner finds his way across the pathless sea.

Air transportation. The gas engine has made possible rapid transportation through the air. We have studied why an airplane and a gas-filled airship stay in the air. The airplane became a practical machine after the experiments of Orville and Wilbur Wright, who solved the problem of air pressure on the planes. The principles are explained in the unit on air. Scientific study is constantly improving carrying power, speed, and safety. The lone cavalier of World War I, 1918, is replaced by squadrons of speedy and terrible engines of destruction. More lovely to contemplate, in time of peace oceans are spanned on regular schedule and

Fig. 155. How was John Fitch's steamboat propelled?

the far places of the northern wilderness formerly reached only by weeks of travel by canoe or dog sledge are now matters of a few hours' flight.

Fig. 156. Screw propellers drive the great ships. Compare with the size of the men.

Photo by Ralph Morgan

For business or pleasure the airplane is a favorite means of travel.

CHAPTER XVIII

GETTING AND WORKING METALS

Metals and ores. We should have but few machines without metals. Our automobiles, our trains, our steamships—our whole machine age depends on metal. In addition to machinery, we use innumerable things of metal each day, from pins, needles, and tin cans to bridges and skyscrapers. Jewelry, lighting fixtures, electric wires, water pipes, buckets, and works of art are made of metal. You could easily write a long list of articles of metal that are important for our safety, comfort, and advancement in civilization.

A few metals, such as copper, platinum, and gold, are sometimes found free, but most metals occur in nature combined with other substances in the form of ores. If the metal is combined with sulphur or carbon, the ore is *roasted*, or heated in the air to oxidize it. The sulphur or carbon burns or combines with the oxygen of the air. Iron is mostly found in nature combined with oxygen in the form of an oxide, or with sulphur in the form of a sulphide.

Iron is freed from its ore by the process known as *smelting*. This process is carried on in the blast furnace (Fig. 157). The blast furnace is charged with limestone, coke, and ore. The coke is then ignited. Hot air is blown in from below. The heat of the burning coke drives carbon dioxide from the limestone, and the lime so produced unites with the impurities of the ore. The lime and impurities form *slag*, which is a waste product. The molten iron sinks through the liquid slag and is drawn off from the bottom of the furnace cylinder. Then it is run into molds of size convenient for shipping or storing, and is called *pig iron*. Sometimes the iron, instead of being cast into pigs, is converted directly into steel without being allowed to cool and solidify.

(181)

Making steel. To make steel, impurities still remaining in the pig iron are oxidized by blowing air through the molten iron. Figure 158 shows the Bessemer converter, in which the process is carried on. Various kinds of steel are made by mixing it while molten with other elements, such as carbon, tungsten, vanadium, and chromium.

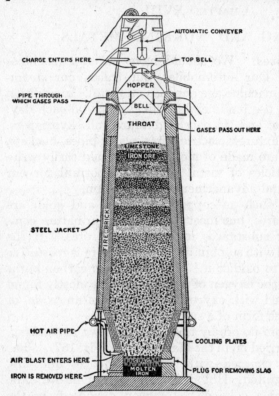

AUTOMATIC CONVEYER

CHARGE ENTERS HERE

TOP BELL

HOPPER

PIPE THROUGH WHICH GASES PASS

BELL

THROAT

GASES PASS OUT HERE

LIMESTONE
IRON ORE

STEEL JACKET

FIRE BRICK

HOT AIR PIPE

COOLING PLATES

AIR BLAST ENTERS HERE

MOLTEN IRON

IRON IS REMOVED HERE

PLUG FOR REMOVING SLAG

Fig. 157. Section of a blast furnace. Everything that goes into it comes out as gas, molten iron, or molten slag (waste). The fire is kept burning by a blast of hot air. The automatic conveyor dumps measured quantities of materials into the hopper. When the bell is lowered, they drop into the furnace, which will make 700 tons of iron a day.

Working steel. Heated iron and steel are hammered or rolled into sheets or bars, and molten steel is cast in molds. Tool steel is tempered by heating and plunging into water. Steel for certain purposes is also tempered in baths of molten solder, oils, or solutions of salts. In the erection of bridges and buildings, steel girders are riveted together.

Red-hot rivets are inserted in holes in the girders, and a bar is held against one end while a hammer, driven by compressed air, flattens the other end. As the bolt cools, it contracts and draws the girders tightly together. In

Fig. 158.   A Bessemer converter changing iron into steel.

Fig. 159.   Welding steel with an electric arc.

newer constructions bolts are sometimes inserted and hammered cold.

Steel is sometimes welded together by the heat of an electric arc, sometimes by using burning gases, especially a mixture of oxygen and acetylene (Fig. 159). The heated parts melt and fuse together as one piece of steel. On the other hand, it is possible to cut a bar of steel into two pieces by melting it at the place where the cut is desired, with an oxy-acetylene flame. The jet of acetylene burning in oxygen gives an intensively hot flame which eats through steel very rapidly. Holes are quickly bored in steel plates, and thick armor plate may be cut by the same means.

EXPERIMENT 57

Question: How is metal separated from the ore?
Materials: Lead oxide; a block of charcoal; blowpipe; Bunsen burner.
Directions: Make a little hollow in the block of charcoal and place in it a little lead oxide. With the blowpipe blow the flame against the oxide.

Results: Describe the changes undergone by the lead oxide. What finally remains?

Conclusion: What chemical changes take place in the ore as the flame is blown against it?

Application: This represents one method by which ores are reduced and pure metals obtained. What ores are reduced in this manner?

Fig. 160.

QUESTIONS TO THINK OUT

1. How could you show that a stone on a housetop has energy? Old-time clocks used such energy instead of the energy stored in a coiled spring. Can you think out how it might be done?

2. How many foot pounds of work do you perform in walking from the street floor to the level of your classroom?

3. How many horse power does it take to get you to your bedroom at night?

4. How can you get a fence post out of a hole with the least effort?

5. Devise an experiment to show whether it requires a greater effort to lift a pile of books directly or to pry them up with a lever.

6. Suppose you had a blow-out on a lonely road and found that you had left your jack at home. How could you raise your car to remove the tire?

7. Why does a large steering wheel make steering easy?

8. Look about your garden, home, farm, or camp to see if you can save labor by using a lever or other simple machine in some piece of work that should be done.

9. Study a sewing machine, a lathe, or some other piece of machinery and decide of what simple machines it is made.

10. You have a heavy rowboat lying high on the beach. Think out some simple machines from the material lying around that would enable you to move the boat into the water.

11. If your wheelbarrow, lawn mower, or bicycle works hard, what trouble should you suspect first, and how should you correct it?

12. Think of at least two ways in which friction is increased as you turn a corner in an automobile. Why should you want to increase friction?

13. If you brush an ant from your shoulder, it lands on the ground unhurt. If you fell that distance and did not land on your feet, you might be badly hurt. Why?

14. Why do the brakes of an automobile sometimes catch fire going down a mountain?

15. Compare the pictures of automobiles of today with those of cars of fifteen years ago. What advantage is there in the shape of a modern automobile?

16. When brakes are jammed tight on a speeding automobile, a tire sometimes blows out. Why?

17. When a trolley car stops suddenly, why do the straphangers lurch forward?

18. Explain why you can tighten the head of a hammer by pounding on the opposite end of the handle.

19. You can shake the dust out of a rug by inertia. Explain.

20. If you step off a moving car with your face to the rear, inertia may seat you on the ground. Why?

21. Why does jarring a tree bring down the ripe apple?

22. Mention several ways inertia is used in the automobile to make smoother riding.

23. Why are modern automobiles closer to the ground than earlier models?

24. How does inertia help you shovel coal into the furnace?

25. Why do many railroads through the mountains use electric power?

26. Why will the gasoline engine not start if it is flooded with gasoline?

UNIT FIVE

HEAT ENERGY

When you get hungry and weak on a winter hike, you get cold. The Eskimo keeps warm as long as he has enough to eat. The polar explorer keeps going as long as food lasts. When his food fails, his pace slackens, "the cold creeps in," and his journey ends.

The energy that keeps things alive is largely heat. You learned in an earlier unit that heat energy of life comes largely from oxidation. Materials to support the oxidation must come from the environment. Animals eat and breathe these materials. The lower the temperature about them, the more they must eat to keep alive and active. The lumberman in the northern winter eats far more than the office worker. We are all usually hungrier in cold weather.

Heat energy, too, is man's chief source of power for his work in the world. Heat runs most machinery and machinery has changed the wilderness to a populated country. Control of heat has given man a control of his environment. Controlled heat has enabled him to plant and raise vast crops, to make buildings comfortable in the coldest weather, to build giant machines and great cities.

What is heat? Where does it come from? How does it travel? What effect does it have on things? How can its effects be controlled? We shall answer these scientific questions in this unit. Then we shall apply this science to such little homely problems as how to keep dinner warm, how to keep our houses warm, and how to have a warm bath.

CHAPTER XIX

WHAT HEAT IS

What is heat? When Count Rumford (1753–1814), an American physicist in the service of the Elector of Bavaria, was boring out cannon, he noticed that the cannon became very hot. He had a cannon weighed when cool, then he had it weighed when hot. It weighed the same in both instances. You can repeat the experiment by weighing a piece of iron, then heating the iron in a gas flame and weighing it again. Rumford concluded that heat was not a substance—not matter.

If heat is not matter, what is it? We experience the sensation of heat when we approach a radiator or a stove. Evidently something is coming to us through the air. We experience the same sensation when we step out into sunshine coming to us through 93,000,000 miles of airless space. Evidently something that makes us feel warm comes to us through space. Scientists say that which comes to us from the sun is energy. To explain the effects of energy from the sun, scientists suppose that it travels in waves.

As we look at waves rolling toward the shore, we see that they differ from one another in two respects, first in height and second in the distance from the top (crest) of one wave to the top of the next wave. This distance from the top of one wave to the top of the next we name the *wave length*. Wave length may be less than a thousandth of an inch or it may be thousands of feet.

A stone dropped into a quiet pool of water will start a series of water waves. As the waves spread out, the height of the waves grows less, but the wave length remains the same. For any particular wave, the wave length remains constant. A convenient way to represent waves is shown in Figure 161 and in Figure 162.

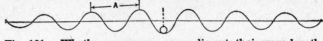

**Fig. 161.   Whether waves run on or die out, their wave length
remains constant.**

Radiant energy.   Energy that is passing out or radiating
from the sun is radiant energy.   The waves of radiant energy
are not all alike.   The different waves have different effects.
Light waves enable us to see.   Other waves do not affect our
eyes but they do affect a photographic plate or film.   Still
others make us feel warm.

The different waves of radiant energy have different wave
lengths.   Light waves have wave lengths varying from
0.000025 of an inch in red light, to 0.000017 of an inch in
violet light.   Still shorter waves are the X rays used in
medicine.   The waves that cause
heat are slightly longer than light
waves, while much longer waves
are used in radio.

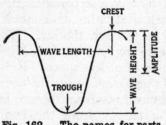

**Fig. 162.   The names for parts
of a wave.**

Remember that when energy
exists as waves, it is not heat.
Although rays from the sun are
passing through the air, the air gets
colder and colder as we go up
from the surface of the earth.
Outside the earth's atmosphere space is cold, but the waves
come through.   It is only after the waves strike some
object, as our bodies, that their energy is changed into heat.

If you put your hand on a windowpane through which
the sunlight is pouring, the glass will probably feel cool.   The
energy waves go through without heating it.   We say the
glass *transmits* (sends through) the waves.   A mirror *reflects*,
that is, throws back, most of the energy.   It, too, will remain
comparatively cool in bright sunlight.   Soil, on the other hand,
transmits and reflects little of the radiant energy.   It *absorbs*
most of it.   As a result, the energy wave is changed into heat
energy and the soil becomes warm.   A piece of black and a
piece of white cloth laid on snow cause two different results.

The white cloth *reflects* much more energy than the black, and the black cloth *absorbs* much more energy than the white. As a result, the snow melts much faster under the black cloth than under the white cloth. Thus, when radiant energy strikes a body, one of three things may happen. The energy may be transmitted, reflected, or absorbed.

When radiant energy strikes a greenhouse used for growing plants, it passes freely through the glass. When it strikes the soil in the greenhouse, the energy waves are absorbed and change into noticeable heat. This heats the air of the greenhouse and the whole place becomes warm. The heat cannot easily escape, for heat does not pass through the glass as readily as do the energy waves which produce it. Perhaps you have noticed this trapped heat in a closed automobile standing in the summer sun.

What heat is. When the black fender of an automobile becomes hot under the summer sun, what have the waves of radiant energy done to it? In other words, what is heat? We have learned that heat is produced by waves of radiant energy, which in themselves have no "heat." We know that the fender, like all matter, is made up of tiny parts called *molecules*. Scientists know from experiments that heat is produced when moving bodies strike other bodies, even the invisible air particles. They conclude that the radiant energy sets up a kind of motion among the molecules of the heated body, and this molecular motion is what we call *heat*. We recognize such motions by a certain sensation, and say a thing "feels hot." A statement based upon such reasoning is called a *theory*. The *theory of heat* is: Heat is a form of molecular motion.

Fig. 163. A radiometer puts light to work.

Putting the sun to work. Figure 163 shows a Crooke's radiometer. It is named after the English scientist who first used it. It is a glass globe in which four vanes are so mounted that they rotate easily. Most of the air is removed from the globe. One side of the vanes is blackened and the other side is silvered. When placed in the sun, the blackened side absorbs radiant energy and warms, in turn warming the air molecules lying against it, and causing them to move rapidly. The heated molecules of the air driving against the black side of the vanes makes them rotate with the silver side ahead. Thus a small bit of the sun's energy does a little work.

In the sunny Southwest great solar (sun) engines have been erected for experimental purposes. These engines have developed enough heat not only to cook food but to melt iron. Perhaps some day in the future solar engines will run factories and power houses.

Other heat sources. Chemical energy produces heat, as when coal is burned. However, as coal is the remains of vegetation that grew because of the energy it received from the sun, the sun rather than the coal is really the source of this energy. When you pour hydrochloric acid on zinc in a test tube, the test tube becomes hot. This also is heat from chemical energy. Mechanical energy, as the compression of air, may also generate heat. Feel the tube of the tire pump after you have pumped up the tire. Friction also gives heat. Protect your finger tip with a piece of paper and rub it on a board. You will soon feel the heat that is produced. The passage of an electric current through a lamp heats the bulb. But by whatever means heat is produced, it is always caused by the setting up of a certain kind of molecular motion.

Fuels. For use in industry and in our homes the source of heat is almost always oxidation. Electricity, often used for heating flatirons, toasters, and similar devices in the home, is usually generated by dynamos driven by burning coal, although the use of water power is rapidly increasing. Many people in the United States use wood for fuel. In cities the fuel is chiefly coal or gas. Natural gas is largely used where there are gas wells. Manufactured gas is derived by heating coal and thus driving off the gas. The coke that remains is also valuable fuel for certain purposes. Oil from petroleum is popular in heating homes because it requires little attention and leaves no ashes.

EXPERIMENT 58

Question: How can I show that dark, rough surfaces are better absorbers of heat than light, polished surfaces?

Materials: Two pieces of paraffin; two square pieces of polished copper sheeting designated as *A* and *B;* desk apparatus.

Directions: Using a luminous, yellow flame, hold copper square *A* in this flame to coat one side of it evenly with a layer of soot.

Gently warm two pieces of paraffin of equal size and weight and press one against the unblackened surface of square *A*, and one against either surface of *B*, so that the paraffin sticks.

Hang the copper squares each about 4 inches from a lighted Bunsen burner, so that the sides on which the pieces of paraffin are placed are turned away from the flame, and a dark side and a polished side face the flame.

Watch the paraffin.

Diagram: Show the apparatus.

Observations: From which sheet of copper did the paraffin drop first? Which surface absorbed more heat?

Conclusion: What kind of surface is a good absorber of heat? a poor absorber of heat?

EXPERIMENT 59 (OPTIONAL)

How illuminating gas is made.

Arrange the apparatus as in Figure 164. Put powdered coal in the upper test tube. Heat gently with the Bunsen burner. After the apparatus is working, light the gas coming from the pointed tube below. This is a mixture of gases, chiefly compounds of hydrogen and carbon. Coke remains in the heated test tube. Coal tar and other products collect in the cooled test tube below. A large number of valuable products are obtained by distilling coal, among them ammonia, naphthalene, or tar camphor (common moth

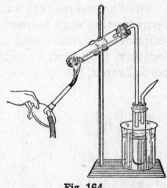

Fig. 164.

balls and moth flakes), carbolic acid, and pitch. The experiment represents on a small scale the dry distillation of coal, the process by which gas is manufactured for cities.

Chapter XX

SOME EFFECTS OF HEAT

Expansion. If you live in the country, you have perhaps watched the blacksmith heat the iron tire of a wagon wheel, then slip it in place on the wheel and rapidly cool it. The tire slips over the wheel easily while it is hot, but after it cools, it holds tight and does not come off. The blacksmith calls this process "shrinking the tire on."

The same principle is shown in the laboratory by a brass ball that is just large enough to pass through a brass ring. When the ball is heated, it will no longer pass through the ring. Heat has expanded the brass ball (Fig. 165).

You will notice between the ends of rails in a railroad track and between concrete blocks on a highway, a narrow space to allow for expansion in summer. Without these expansion joints, the roads would buckle. One end of a long steel bridge similarly allows for expansion.

The thermometers with dials. The expansion of metals upon heating may be used to measure temperature. If two strips of metal, one of iron and one of brass, are firmly fastened together, they form a *compound bar* (Fig. 166). When such a bar is heated, the brass expands more than the iron, and the

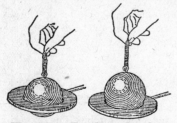

Fig. 165. To show that heat expands the metal ball. Which ball is supposed to be hot?

Fig. 166. The compound bar curves because one metal expands more than the other.

bar curves. If one end of the bar is fastened rigidly, and the other end bears a hand moving over a scale, the amount of deflection of the free end can be read. The higher the temperature, the greater the deflection, so that such an instrument can be used to determine the temperature. In the dial thermometers commonly used, the compound bar is coiled like a spring so that a long bar may be used, the amount of deflection increased and the reading made more accurate. Such metallic thermometers are common, cheap, and accurate enough for household use (Fig. 168).

Fig. 167. The balance wheel on a watch is made of compound bars. If the wheel grew larger in summer, the watch would be off time. How is it kept constant?

How a thermostat controls temperature. Perhaps the temperature in your schoolroom is controlled by a thermostat. Part of this is similar to the metallic thermometer that you have just studied. A short compound bar is mounted so that the loose end of the bar is against the opening of a pipe containing compressed air (Fig. 169). As the temperature of the room rises, the compound bar bends, thus opening the pipe. The compressed air escapes, relieving the pressure on a diaphragm placed in the pipe, and this in turn closes the valve of the radiator. As the temperature falls, the compound bar bends back and covers the opening in the pipe, so that pressure within is restored, and the diaphragm moves to open the

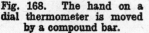

Fig. 168. The hand on a dial thermometer is moved by a compound bar.

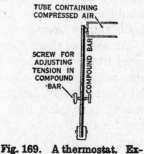

TUBE CONTAINING COMPRESSED AIR

SCREW FOR ADJUSTING TENSION IN COMPOUND BAR

COMPOUND BAR

Fig. 169. A thermostat. Explain why it works.

radiator valve again. Various methods are used to control the steam valve, but the principle is the same in all. The thermostat in your home may be a compound bar that makes and breaks an electric circuit, which in turn operates the draft in the furnace or the motor in the oil heater (Fig. 170).

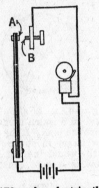

Liquid thermometers. The mercury in the thermometer tube shows you that liquids expand and contract with the heat they absorb or give out. When you place your hand on the bulb, the mercury absorbs heat from your hand, expands, and rises. When you place the thermometer in the refrigerator, the air of the refrigerator absorbs heat from the mercury. The mercury contracts and falls.

Fig. 170. An electric thermostat. What closes the circuit?

You can easily construct a simple thermometer, using water instead of mercury. Fill a 100 c.c. flask with colored water. Close the flask with a rubber stopper carrying a 12-inch piece of small-bore glass tubing (Fig. 171). Insert the stopper in such a way that no air remains in the flask and the colored water shows an inch or so above the stopper. Slip a narrow rubber ring, cut from a piece of tubing, over the glass tube and move it so that it indicates the height of the water inside the tube. Warm the flask. You will be surprised to notice that at first the water in the tube sinks instead of rising as you would expect. The first effect of heating is to expand the flask, thus allowing water in the tube to sink into the flask. As soon as the water itself starts to warm, you will see the liquid inside the tube start to rise.

Water would not be a suitable substance to use in a commercial thermometer, because its boiling point is too low and its freezing point too high. Most house thermometers use mercury for the liquid. In cold climates where temperatures fall lower than 40° F. below zero, alcohol is used, for mercury freezes at about − 39.1° F., and alcohol freezes at − 202° F.

The thermometers you often see with red or blue liquid contain alcohol colored with a dye. The method of graduating a thermometer you will learn from Experiment 60.

Thermometer scales. Expansion and contraction will measure temperatures if we can find a way to indicate the amount. We need a scale for measurement with a high point and a low point and degrees between. There are two thermometer scales in common use. The Fahrenheit scale is used mainly in England and the United States, and the centigrade is used on the continent of Europe and for all scientific work.

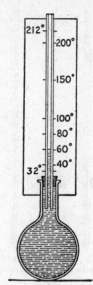

Fig. 171. A water thermometer.

In 1714 Fahrenheit, a German scientist, constructed the scale that bears his name. The lowest temperature he could obtain in his laboratory was that of a mixture of ice or snow and ammonium chloride. This temperature he called 0°. The boiling point of water on his scale is 212°; and the freezing point is 32°.

In 1742 Celsius in Sweden made another thermometer scale. He chose the freezing point of water for his 0° and the boiling point for his high point which he called 100°. This scale is called the *centigrade scale*.

The range of temperature between freezing and boiling point on the two thermometers is divided into 180° degrees (212 − 32 = 180) on the Fahrenheit scale and 100 degrees on the centigrade. One Fahrenheit degree is, therefore, $\frac{5}{9}$ of a centigrade degree (100 ÷ 180 = $\frac{5}{9}$). One centigrade degree is $\frac{9}{5}$ of a Fahrenheit degree (180 ÷ 100 = $\frac{9}{5}$).

To convert one scale reading into the other is simple. If the temperature of your classroom is 68° F., this temperature is 36 Fahrenheit degrees above the freezing point of water.

(68° − 32° = 36°).   But as a Fahrenheit degree is only $\frac{5}{9}$ of a centigrade degree, 36° F. = 20° centigrade (36 × $\frac{5}{9}$ = 20).

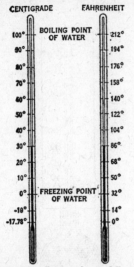

Centigrade zero is at freezing.   While you would call the temperature of this room 68° F., a French student would call the temperature of the room 20° C.   (Fig. 172.)

A French student in a classroom with a temperature of 28° C. might complain of the heat.   To convert this to Fahrenheit we multiply by $\frac{9}{5}$ and obtain $50\frac{2}{5}$° above the freezing point.   Add 32° and we obtain $82\frac{2}{5}$° F., the temperature of the room on our scale.

When is there no heat?   You have already learned two thermometer zeros.   Centigrade zero is the freezing point of water and the Fahrenheit zero is 32 Fahrenheit degrees below the freezing point of water. A third zero is the *absolute zero*, which is minus 273° centigrade, or minus 459.4° F.

The absolute zero is reached when there is no heat.   Heat is the energy of molecular motion.   As heat leaves the body, the molecules move slower and slower and a time must come when molecular motion ceases.   This point is absolute zero.

Scientists have obtained a temperature 0.15 of 1 degree centigrade above this absolute zero.   At this

Fig. 172. Comparison of Centigrade and Fahrenheit.

Fig. 173. A clinical (doctor's) thermometer.

temperature the world would become a very singular place.   Chemical action would almost cease.   Wood would not burn in oxygen.   Oxygen and hydrogen would not unite.   The electrical resistance of metals would almost disappear, and, in short, life as we know it would become impossible.

The doctor's thermometer. One of the things that your doctor relies upon in determining whether you are sick or well is the temperature of your body. Usually the temperature is 98.6° F. Sometimes processes in the body go wrong, and the temperature of our body rises. Then we have a fever or "run a temperature."

To determine the body temperature, the doctor uses a thermometer having a constriction (narrow place) in the bore (Fig. 173). He puts the end of the thermometer under your tongue and the mercury in it rises. When, however, he removes the thermometer and the mercury starts to contract, the thin thread of mercury in the constriction breaks because the molecules of the mercury do not hold together strongly enough to pull the thread of mercury past the constriction and back into the bulb. The mercury in the tube remains in the same position it was when it was taken from your mouth. After the doctor has read the thermometer, a violent shake or two will send this mercury thread back into the bulb.

Expansion of gases. When you studied about air, you learned that a fire balloon would float in the air because heat expanded the air inside it.

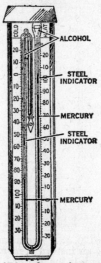

Fig. 174. A maximum and minimum thermometer to register highest and lowest temperatures. Can you think out how it works?

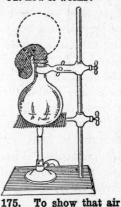

Fig. 175. To show that air expands on heating.

This is one illustration of the fact that heat expands gases. A simple experiment will illustrate this. Stretch a

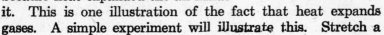

rubber balloon over the neck of a flask (Fig. 175). Warm
the air in the flask, and you will see the balloon stand erect
and expand. The expansion of the gas carbon dioxide in
bread and biscuit makes the dough
rise. The expansion of air in an
automobile tire on a hot day may
cause a weak spot to blow out.

Before our modern thermometers
were invented, Galileo made a thermometer that used the expansion of
a gas (air). Figure 176 shows how
you may make one.

Heat is not temperature. Did
you ever wait for the pot to boil on
the stove or the camp fire? It may
have seemed a long time. If you
place a piece of iron and a vessel containing an equal weight of water on
the stove, the iron will be the first
to reach 212° F., the boiling point

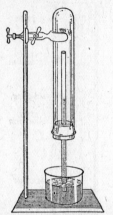

Fig. 176. A thermometer
using air instead of mercury.
Water is in the beaker. How
does it work?

of water. It takes more heat to raise the temperature of
water 1 degree than the same weight of iron. You must be
sure that you understand the distinction between the amount
of heat that a body may have and its temperature. A burning match has only a small amount of heat, but its temperature is high enough to burn your finger if you put it into
the flame. To bring a quart of water to boil requires twice
as much heat as to bring a pint of water to boil, but the
temperature will be the same in both cases, 212° F.

Measuring amount of heat. You cannot measure the
amount of heat with a thermometer. You can measure only
temperature. There are two units in common use for measuring the amount of heat that a body contains. One, the
British Thermal Unit (B. T. U.) is used extensively by
engineers. It is the amount of heat that is required to heat a
pound of water 1° F. The second unit, the calorie, is the
amount of heat required to heat 1 gram of water 1° C. A
large Calorie, written with a capital C, is 1000 small calories.

A pound of ordinary coal in burning will give about 15,000 B. T. U. In our science work we shall use the calorie, as the B. T. U. is rather large for our purposes. One B. T. U. equals 252 calories.

Hidden heat. Suppose you take a gram of water at 0° C. and slowly heat it. When it has absorbed 1 calorie, the temperature is 1° C. When it has absorbed 100 calories, the temperature has reached 100° C. Then the temperature rises no higher with continued heating. The water continues to absorb heat, but the heat, instead of raising the temperature, changes the water to steam. A gram of water at 100° C. absorbs about 539 calories in changing into steam. The heat, amounting to 539 calories, absorbed by a gram of water at 100° C. in changing into steam or vapor at 100° C. is called the *heat of vaporization.*

If you take steam and cool it, it condenses to liquid water at 100° C. In changing from vapor to liquid each gram gives up the 539 calories of heat of vaporization. For that reason a burn from steam is more severe than a burn from water at the same temperature. There is more heat given out from the condensing steam than from the water at the same temperature. The heat of vaporization is hidden, or *latent*, in the steam, but becomes sensible when the steam is condensed.

If you place a thermometer in a vessel of water with lumps of ice and allow the vessel to stand for some time, you find the temperature is 0° C. If you slowly heat the vessel, the temperature remains at 0° C. until all the ice melts. During this time the water and ice have steadily absorbed heat, but the heat does not raise the temperature. While the ice remains, the absorbed heat is used in melting the ice. When a gram of ice at 0° C. melts, it absorbs 80 calories in changing to water at 0° C. The 80 calories are called the *heat of fusion* (melting). Heat of fusion is also latent heat.

When water freezes, it gives up its heat of fusion. Florists and those who store vegetables sometimes use the heat of fusion to prevent the freezing of flowers and vegetables. Tubs of water are placed in the conservatory or the vegetable cellar on a cold night. If the temperature falls below 32°, some of the water may freeze; but in freezing it gives up enough heat to save the flowers or vegetables.

Note that for pure water 100° C. is both the point of vaporization and the point of condensation; a gram of water at 100° C. will vaporize if it absorbs 539 more calories, and steam at 100° C. will condense if it gives up the absorbed heat. Similarly, 0° C. is the fusion (melting) point of ice and also the freezing point of water; a gram of ice at 0° will melt (fuse) if it absorbs 80° calories, and water at 0° will freeze if it gives up the absorbed heat.

How the freezer makes ice cream. In the ice cream freezer we make use of the heat of fusion (melting). When we dissolve salt, sugar, or other substance in water, the solution boils at a higher point and freezes at a lower point than does pure water. A saturated solution of salt in water freezes at 7.6° F. (−22° C.). The less salt in the solution, the higher the freezing point until the freezing point of pure water is reached at 32° F. (0° C.).

When you put salt on ice to pack in the ice-cream freezer, the salt absorbs water from the surface of the ice and forms a solution of salt. If you place pieces of ice in salt solution at 0° C., the ice melts. The ice in melting takes up heat (the heat of fusion) and so lowers the temperature of the solution. When the ice in the ice-cream freezer melts in the salt solution, it takes heat from the cream inside the can and lowers its temperature below the freezing point of the cream.

How the antifreeze protects the car. To prevent water from freezing in automobile radiators, pure water is drawn out and a solution substituted. The solution freezes at a lower temperature. Alcohol and ethylene glycol are common substances dissolved in the radiator water to lower its freezing point. The more concentrated is the solution, the lower the freezing point.

Heat and physical state. Just as water changes its state from solid to liquid and then to vapor on the absorption of heat, so do other substances. Some liquids, like alcohol and gasoline, evaporate readily at room temperatures. Such liquids are said to be *volatile*. Our common gases, such as air, oxygen, hydrogen, change to liquids and then to solids at very low temperatures. Oxygen becomes liquid at −182° C. (which is also its boiling point) and freezes solid at −218° C. Many substances that are ordinarily solids are melted and then vaporized at very high temperatures. Thus the melting point of iron is 1530° C. (2786° F.) and its boiling point 2450° C. (4442° F.).

EXPERIMENT 60

Question: How can I make a thermometer?

Materials: Small vial; stopper with hole; glass tube; mercury; Bunsen burner; beakers; cracked ice.

Directions and Results: (a) Fill a small vial with mercury and cork it with a one-hole rubber stopper that has a narrow tube through it. Adjust the level of the mercury in the tube so that it is 3 inches above the stopper.

(b) Immerse this thermometer into a beaker containing cracked ice. Be sure to cover the vial completely. Mark the level of the mercury in the tube with a rubber band. We call this mark a fixed point of the thermometer, i. e., the point fixed by the temperature of melting ice.

(c) We must now locate another fixed point, i. e., the point fixed by the temperature of boiling water. Fasten your crude thermometer to a ring stand and slowly lower it into a beaker of boiling water. Fix this level with a band. This is our second fixed point.

(d) To make a Fahrenheit thermometer, mark the freezing point 32 and the boiling 212, and divide the space between the two fixed points into 180 equal parts or degrees. This may be done by dividing the distance into 18 equal parts each part representing 10 degrees. To make a centigrade thermometer, label the freezing point 0 and the boiling point 100. Then divide the distance into 100 equal divisions.

(e) Record the room temperature on your homemade thermometer. Compare it with the reading of a standard thermometer.

Diagram: A Homemade Fahrenheit Thermometer.

Observations: What happened to the mercury when the bulb was placed in melting ice? What happened when it was placed in boiling water? The room temperature as measured by the thermometer was _____degrees.

Conclusion: How would you make a thermometer?

EXPERIMENT 61

Question: What happens to solids, liquids, and gases when heated?

Materials: Two flasks fitted with one-hole stoppers and straight glass tubes about 4 inches long; glass vessel of water; ring stand, wire, weight; Bunsen burner.

Directions: (*a*) With the wire hang the weight from the ring stand so that it just grazes, but does not touch, the base. Heat the wire and note result.

(*b*) Fill the flask with water to the very top, and insert the stopper so that water rises in the tube. Heat the flask and note result (Fig. 177).

(*c*) Hold the second flask filled only with air so that the tube is under water. Note height to which the water rises in the tube. Heat the flask very gently and note change in level of water in tube.

Results: Record what happened in each case.

Conclusion: Answer the question.

Application: Why is a space left between the ends of two successive rails of a railroad? Why does a thermometer measure temperature? Could you make a thermometer using the expansion of air instead of mercury?

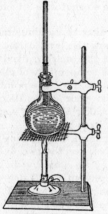

Fig. 177.

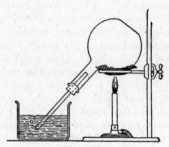

Fig. 178.

Chapter XXI

CONTROLLING THE PASSAGE OF HEAT

Passing heat along. If you pick up a hot pot by its
metal handle, you may drop it quickly, but you can often
pick up just as hot a pot by a wooden handle without dis-
comfort. If you are a camper, you no doubt have learned
to fasten a wooden handle to the frying pan. You would
probably say that wood does not get so hot as metal. The
scientist would say that metal is a better *conductor* of heat
than is wood.

When you touch a piece of iron lying on a table, the iron
feels cooler than the wooden table because the metal conducts
the heat away from your finger more rapidly than the wood
does. Similarly, the metal handle conducts the heat from the
pot to your hand. Heat, as you have learned, is a motion of
molecules. Setting the molecules in motion in this manner
makes the thing hot. You can make iron hot by pounding it
or by friction (rubbing). These operations set the molecules
in motion. *Conduction* of heat is the passing of this molecular
motion from one group of molecules to another group.

It is readily possible to measure the heat conductivity
of different substances. If we represent the conductivity of
silver by 10, the conductivity of iron is 2, wood 0.003, and
flannel 0.0004. These numbers are only approximations, but
they will give you some idea of the very great difference that
exists between the ability of different substances to conduct
heat. Different metals conduct heat at different rates. It
is an interesting home experiment to put a pint of water into
an enamel saucepan. Put the pan on the stove and measure
the time it takes the water to boil. Repeat, using a pint of
water in an aluminum saucepan of the same size as and of
similar shape to the enamel pan. If you will compare the

time taken to heat water in the two pans, you will learn something of the conducting power of enamel that will be of use to you.

Have you wondered why test tubes and beakers in which we heat liquids in the laboratory are made of *thin* glass? It is because thin glass when heated does not break so easily as thick glass. When we heat a thick glass tumbler, the outside starts to expand. Glass is a poor conductor of heat, so that the inside of the tumbler warms slowly and, therefore, is slow to begin to expand. The rapid expansion of the outer surface of the glass breaks the tumbler by pulling the molecules apart. In a thin beaker the inside surface receives its heat sooner and starts to expand sooner. Therefore the thin glass is less likely to break when it is heated.

Fig. 179. How a room heats. What makes the convection currents?

How a room heats. Have you ever noticed that a room is hotter near the ceiling? Sometimes a schoolroom may be quite warm enough for the teacher who is standing, and uncomfortable for small children at low desks. The usual explanation is that heated air rises. A little more accurately, air on heating expands and is lifted by cooler air. To see how air moves in a room, hold a smoking punk stick above the radiator in a room near the window, and at other places where air might be heated or cooled (Fig. 179).

How water heats. Did you ever boil water in a paper cup? Fold a sheet of paper into a paper box. Fill it with water and place on a wire gauze. Heat it with the gas flame until it boils. You can do this because water moves around the vessel as air does around the room, carrying the heat away before the paper reaches the ignition temperature. You can see the currents by dropping a few bits of sawdust into a glass beaker of water over a gas flame.

Both air and water are poor conductors of heat (Fig. 180). They absorb heat, expand, and move freely about their containers until all is heated. The scientist says they heat by *convection*. The heat is carried around (Lat. *veho, vectus,* carry).

You will find many instances of convection as you look about: in the ocean currents, the winds (see page 639), the radiator of an automobile (Fig. 181). Test your grasp of the idea by explaining the movement of the fluids in these instances.

Fig. 180. How does this experiment show that water is a poor conductor of heat?

How heat is transmitted. Your hand is warmed in the sun while the air above it is cool. We say the radiant energy of the sun is absorbed and sets the molecules of the flesh in more rapid motion. In this instance heat is transferred by (1) *radiation*. When you hold one end of a wire in the flame, the other end soon gets hot. The molecules of iron set in motion by the flame pass the motion along. Heat is transferred by (2) *conduction*. When air or water is heated at the bottom of a container, it moves upward carrying the absorbed heat. Heat is thus transferred by (3) *convection*.

Thermos bottles. In refrigerators, thermos bottles, and fireless cookers we try to prevent the transmission of heat. The construction of a thermos bottle is shown in Figure 182. You will see that the bottle is really two bottles; one inside the other. The air has been drawn out from between these two bottles and the bottles

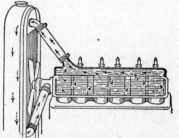

Fig. 181. Convection in the cooling system of an automobile. Water pumps now aid the circulation.

silvered. When the bottle is filled with hot coffee and corked, the coffee can cool by one of the three methods of

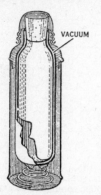

VACUUM

heat transfer—conduction, convection, radiation. It cools very slowly by conduction, for glass and cork are very poor conductors of heat. It cools very slowly by convection for the air over the coffee cannot escape. It cools slowly by radiation because the silvered mirror reflects back into the coffee the radiant energy that it may give off. The object of creating a vacuum between the two bottles is to prevent conduction and convection from occurring.

Fig. 182. Why does a vacuum bottle keep contents either cold or hot?

A thermos bottle will keep water cool as well as keep coffee hot. The process is the same. If heat cannot escape from the bottle, neither can heat enter it. Such thermos bottles constructed of metal are used as tank cars in carrying milk long distances.

How a fireless cooker cooks. The fireless cooker is really a box made of some nonconducting material. A cereal you may wish to cook is first heated to the boiling point on the stove and then the pot is placed in the fireless cooker. Since the walls of the cooker will not transmit heat, the pot of cereal must remain hot and the cereal continues to cook for hours. The cooker simply serves to keep a hot food hot. Just as it keeps hot food hot, it keeps cold food cold, for all that it really does is to prevent the transfer of heat. When you go camping, build yourself a fireless cooker from an old wooden box, crumpled newspapers and sawdust to serve as insulating packing, and an ordinary kettle with a lid. You will find it a great con-

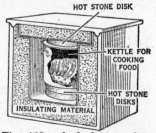

HOT STONE DISK

KETTLE FOR COOKING FOOD

HOT STONE DISKS

INSULATING MATERIAL

Fig. 183. A fireless cooker. Insulated walls retard the passage of heat. Where does the heat come from?

venience to start your beef stew going before you set out on your hike and to come back, tired out, with dinner practically ready to eat.

Stopping the passage of heat. A refrigerator must be so built as to keep out heat. That is, the walls of the refrigerator must be built of a nonconducting material. A refrigerator with

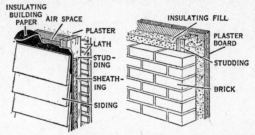

Fig. 184. How house walls retard the passage of heat.

solid metal walls would be useless, as the metal could conduct heat readily into the interior of the refrigerator. In practice, refrigerators are built with thin inner and outer walls, and felt, sawdust, and air spaces between these walls, acting as nonconductors or insulators.

When you are camping where ice is difficult to obtain, you may keep a reserve supply by wrapping the extra ice in newspapers and burying it in sawdust. Ice thus wrapped and well surrounded by sawdust will keep for a long time. The more sawdust, the less heat will reach it, and the longer it will keep. This is the commonest method of preserving natural ice in ice houses. When ice is cut from the ponds, it is placed in large houses having double walls often filled with sawdust. The ice is covered with sawdust and, so protected, will last through the following summer.

Dwelling houses are insulated in a manner similar to that used for refrigerators. Insulating (nonconducting) material in the walls and roof, or air spaces between double walls, retard the passage of heat outward in winter and inward in summer (Fig. 184).

How ice cools the refrigerator. An *ice refrigerator* cools the food in the refrigerator by the melting of the ice. To change from ice into water, the ice must absorb heat. (Heat of fusion, page 199.) You have learned that to change a gram of ice to water at the same temperature, the ice absorbs 80 calories. The heat that melts the ice in the refrigerator comes from the air in the refrigerator and from the food. Taking heat out of the food cools it. Insulated walls prevent or reduce passage of heat from the outside into the refrigerator (Fig. 185). The food is cooled because the ice melts. If you wrap the ice in newspaper before placing it in the refrigerator, the ice will last longer but it will not cool the refrigerator so well.

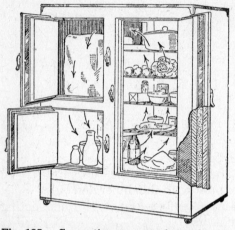

Fig. 185. Convection currents in an ice refrigerator. Note insulated walls.

The electric refrigerator. Mechanical refrigerators, whether electric, gas, or oil, cool by boiling or vaporizing a liquid. They use the heat of evaporation. You must heat water to boil it because water takes up heat in changing to steam. You learned that it takes 539 calories to change a gram of water at 212° F. (100° C.) into steam at the same temperature, the heat of vaporization. Whenever any liquid changes to vapor, it takes up heat. That is why your wet hand feels cool as it dries in the air and why your perspiring face feels cool when you fan it. In changing to a vapor, the water takes heat from your face or hand. In the mechanical refrigerator, whether electric, gas, or oil, a liquid is changed to a vapor or gas, and in so doing takes up heat from the food compartment, thus lowering its temperature.

In mechanical refrigerators a gas is used that easily changes into a liquid and back to a gas. Ammonia, sulphur dioxide, carbon dioxide, and others are employed. When ammonia gas is compressed, it changes to a liquid. When the pressure is released, it changes to a gas and in so doing takes in heat. In the *electric refrigerator* a pump driven by a motor compresses the ammonia gas and changes it to a liquid. The liquid ammonia is released from pressure in pipes around the food compartment. In vaporizing when the pressure is released, it takes heat from the food compartment and cools it. The ammonia is then led away through pipes and again compressed by the electrically driven pump.

Gas or oil refrigeration. The cooling effect of the evaporation of a liquefied gas also cools the gas and oil refrigerators. The gas, however, is compressed in a different manner from that in the electric refrigerator. Ammonia gas readily dissolves in water, but is easily driven out of the

Fig. 186. An electric refrigerator.

Fig. 187. The motor of an electric refrigerator.

solution by heat. In the refrigerator, the water containing the dissolved ammonia gas is sealed in a system of pipes so that it cannot escape. At one place in the system it is heated by the gas or oil flame and the ammonia gas is so driven out of the solution. As it leaves the water, the

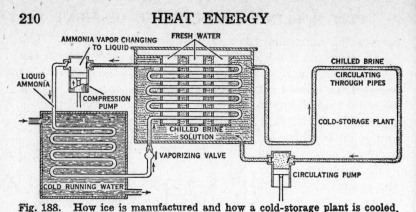

Fig. 188. How ice is manufactured and how a cold-storage plant is cooled.

ammonia gas expands. Because the gas cannot escape, the expansion increases the pressure. The increased pressure liquefies the ammonia gas. Then the liquefied ammonia gas is allowed to evaporate. The evaporation cools the refrigerator. Finally, the ammonia gas is again dissolved in water and carried back to the flame. There are thus several scientific principles involved in the operation, but the cooling effect is due, as in the electric refrigerator, to the evaporation of a gas that has been liquefied.

A process similar to that employed in electric refrigerators is used in the manufacture of ice. Pipe coils in which the ammonia or other liquid vaporizes are immersed in tanks of brine (solution of salt). This brine will be cooled below the freezing point of water without itself freezing. Cans of pure water are lowered into the cooled brine and their contents freeze, making the ice which we buy from the iceman. Cold storage rooms are cooled by brine circulating in pipes (Fig. 188). Air-conditioned buildings are cooled by currents of air that have passed over similar coils of cold pipe.

EXPERIMENT 62

Question: How is heat transferred?

Materials: A metal rod 8 inches to a foot or more long; a little wax or candle grease; a beaker of water; a little sawdust; a tripod; a reading glass.

Method: 1. Support the metal rod on a tripod; attach a bit of wax or candle grease to one end. Heat the other end. 2. Drop a little sawdust into the beaker of water. Set on tripod. Slowly heat one edge of the bottom. Note behavior of the grains of sawdust. 3. When the sun is shining through a window, place your hand on the window sill and then on the windowpane. Note temperature of each. 4. Focus the sun's rays on the head of a match with the reading glass. When the match ignites, feel the temperature of the reading glass with your hand.

Results: Record.

Conclusion: Was the heat transferred by the same process in each case? Describe and name each method.

EXPERIMENT 63 (OPTIONAL)

Why do pots have wooden handles? Arrange rods of iron, copper, aluminum, and glass on a wooden holder as in Figure 189. Attach drop of candle grease to outer ends. Heat inner ends. Note order in which drops of candle grease melt. Does the wooden handle become too hot to hold? Which substances are good conductors and which poor conductors of heat?

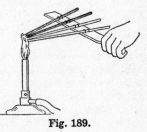

Fig. 189.

EXPERIMENT 64 (OPTIONAL)

Another method of showing the convection in liquids. See Figure 190. Fill one of the small bottles with ice water colored with black ink. Fill the other with hot water colored with red ink. Tie a string around each and lower into the battery jar filled with clear water. Note movement of colored water. Explain.

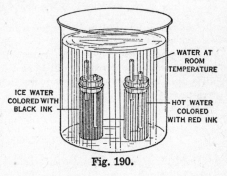

WATER AT ROOM TEMPERATURE

ICE WATER COLORED WITH BLACK INK

HOT WATER COLORED WITH RED INK

Fig. 190.

EXPERIMENT 65

Question: Does heated air weigh the same as cold air?

Material: A flask; a balance; set of weights; Bunsen burner.

Directions: Place the flask on the balance pan and balance with weights. Warm the flask gently with the Bunsen burner.

Results: Report what happened.

Conclusion: Answer question.

EXPERIMENT 66

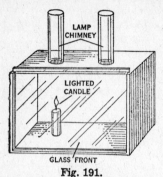

LAMP CHIMNEY

LIGHTED CANDLE

GLASS FRONT

Fig. 191.

Question: What happens to air when it is heated?

Materials: Box with glass front as in Figure 191; candle; 2 lamp chimneys; Chinese punk.

Directions: Light the candle. Hold the punk first over one chimney, then over the other.

Results: Which way was the air moving over the cold chimney? Over the heated chimney?

Conclusion: Answer the question.

Practical application: Why is the air warmer near the ceiling of a room? By what process does the warm-air heater heat the house? How can this principle be used in ventilating a room? With the Chinese punk examine the air currents in your room near the ceiling; near the floor; near the windows; above and below the radiator. Open the windows a little, first at the top and then at the bottom. Examine the currents at the top and bottom of the opened windows and at the space between the upper and lower sashes.

EXPERIMENT 67 (OPTIONAL)

Heat insulation. Why are the walls of fireless cookers and refrigerators packed with cork, felt, or asbestos? Fit two wide bottles with stoppers through which thermometers are thrust. Wrap one with felt, wool, or cotton. Fill both bottles with the same amount of hot water at the same temperature, about 180° F. Take the temperature of each bottle every 5 minutes for 20 minutes. Then empty the bottles and fill with ice water. Read temperature as before.

EXPERIMENT 68

Question: How can I show that the evaporation of a liquid cools the surroundings?

Materials: 100-c.c. beaker; block of wood; ether; bicycle pump.

CAUTION.—Do not have gas or other flame in the room. Ether vapor is very inflammable and explosive. Do not breathe the ether fumes. They are dangerous.

Directions: On one of the square sides of a wood block 2″ × 2″ × 1″ place 3 drops of water. Set on top of this a beaker which has been filled to a depth of ½ inch with ether.

Holding the beaker firmly on the block, have your assistant direct a stream of air from the pump over the surface of the ether in the beaker. Why?

When all of the ether has just evaporated, try to lift the beaker from the block.

Observations: Why did the beaker stick to the block?

What happened to the film of water?

Where did the heat that was used to evaporate the ether come from?

Conclusion: What effect does evaporation produce?

Practical application: When a runner has finished a race, why does he put on a sweat shirt? Why is it unwise to sit in a draft when perspiring?

EXPERIMENT 69 (OPTIONAL)

Question: How can I see the cooling effect caused by the evaporation of a liquid?

Materials: 8-oz. bottle; cork; cotton wicking; carbon bisulphide.

CAUTION.—Carbon bisulphide is very inflammable. It must be kept away from fire.

Directions: Cut a hole about $\frac{3}{4}''$ in diameter in the cork. Through this pull cotton wicking. Make the wicking long enough to reach the bottom of the bottle and project about 1″ beyond the cork. Fill the bottle about $\frac{3}{4}$ full of carbon bisulphide and fit the cork tightly into the mouth of the bottle. Put the bottle in the open air outside the window. Let it stay there for at least 15 minutes. The time necessary will depend upon the amount of moisture in the air and the temperature at the time the experiment is performed.

Bring the bottle into the room and touch the deposit on the wick. 1. What has formed on the wick? 2. How can you explain this formation? 3. What has happened to the liquid in the bottle?

Diagram: Show bottle, wick, and snow formation.

Conclusion: Answer the question.

Practical application: Think of two or three cases in which you have made use of this fact.

Chapter XXII

HEATING OUR HOMES

Early methods. We know of no men who did not use fire. Cave men of the Old Stone Age have left their fireplaces. The Indians built a fire in the center of their wigwams and

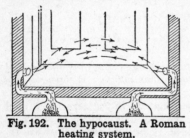

Fig. 192. The hypocaust. A Roman heating system.

allowed the smoke to pass out through an opening in the top. As man became more settled and learned to build houses, the difficulty of keeping warm in these houses in winter was great. The Romans overcame this difficulty with what they called a *hypocaust* (Fig. 192). This consisted of small compartments built under the house. Here fires were placed and the hot air passed by convection through openings into the room above. It finally occurred to some bright man that it would be possible to replace this by a chimney and an open fireplace. In the pioneer days of America the open fireplace was used (Fig. 193).

Fig. 193. A Colonial fireplace.

In 1742 Benjamin Franklin invented what was called a *Pennsylvania Fireplace* (Fig. 194). This early form of stove made it possible for the first time in history to warm a dwelling place in the winter time. We still use open fireplaces, but they are very inefficient as heating devices and are used mainly for the pleas-

(214)

ure of sitting by an open fire. A stove is much more efficient. Today, we use hot-air heating, steam heating, and
hot-water heating as means of keeping ourselves comfortable
in the winter time. In the latest systems thermostats keep the rooms at the desired temperature. Experience and experiment have shown
that the best temperature is 68° F.

Warm-air heating. The simplest method
of heating a house is warm-air heating. An air
compartment is placed over the fire
box of a furnace and fresh cold air is
brought in to the air compartment
from the outside of the building
through a pipe or conduit. The cold
air, when heated by the furnace, becomes lighter, and rises through
pipes that lead to the rooms above.
The warm air passes directly into the
rooms through openings in the wall
or floor and thus the cooler air of
the room is replaced by warm air.
Hence, convection is the method of

Fig. 194. A Pennsylvania
fireplace. Really a simple
stove set in the fireplace.

getting heat from the furnace to the rooms (Fig. 196). Ventilation of the rooms is secured by the constant admission of
fresh air to the air compart-
ment in the furnace.

The disadvantages of this
method are the difficulty of
obtaining a uniform heating
of the house, and the space
that the pipes require. A
strong wind blowing against
one side of the house changes
the direction of the rising currents of warm air, so that
certain rooms become difficult to heat when the weather
is windy.

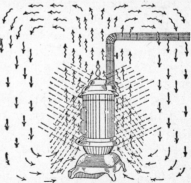

Fig. 195. A stove heats a room by
radiation and convection. Why does
the air circulate?

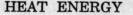

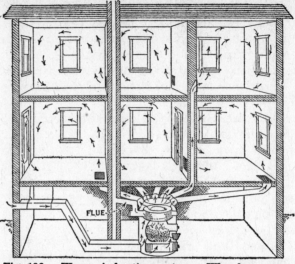

FLUE

Fig. 196. Warm-air heating system. Why does warm air go to the rooms? Where does more air enter the system? Do burned gases enter the rooms? (Note the flue.) How does this system aid ventilation?

Steam heating. Steam is generally used for heating apartments in large cities. The heating plant consists of a water boiler with a fire underneath it. The water is boiled, converted into steam, and this steam is forced by its pressure through pipes to the radiators placed in the various rooms. In the radiators, steam is condensed to water, and the water then flows down a pipe back to the boiler (Fig. 197). Convection thus carries the heat to the radiator. The radiator heats the air about it. The heated air rises and so the room is heated by convection.

The heat that warms the room in a steam system is chiefly the heat of vaporization. You have learned that when a gram of water at 100° C. changes to steam at 100° C., it absorbs 539 calories. When the steam is condensed, all this heat of vaporization is given out.

Steam heat is a cheap, quick way of heating. It has the disadvantage that it is difficult to have only a little heat. On a chilly day the rooms are likely to become too hot.

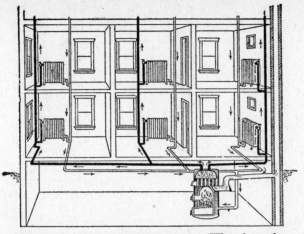

Fig. 197. Steam-heating system. Why does the steam go to the radiators? In many systems there is only one connection with each radiator. How does the condensed steam return to heater?

If a partial vacuum is maintained in the steam pipe, water may be made to boil at a lower temperature. By using this principle in a steam-heating plant, it is possible to get a small amount of heat for a chilly spring day. This is the *vapor system of heating.*

Hot-water heating. The hot-water plant in the basement consists of a larger boiler than would be used for a steam plant and hot-water pipes leading from the boiler to the radiators in the various rooms. The entire system is filled with water. The fire heats the water in the boiler, it expands, becomes less dense, and rises to the radiators. Here it warms the radiators and these in turn warm the room. As the water in the radiator cools, it becomes heavier and returns through a second pipe to the bottom of the water boiler. Thus a constant circulation of water takes place (Fig. 198).

As the water is heated, it expands and some provision must be made to take care of this expansion, as otherwise a pipe would crack. An expansion tank is often placed in the attic. When the water expands, it rises into the expansion tank, and when the water in the system contracts, it flows back

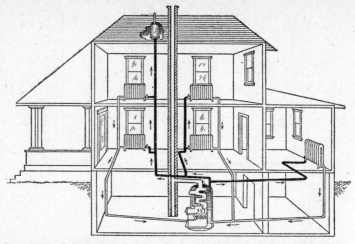

Fig. 198. A hot-water heating system. What is indicated by the black pipes and the white pipes? Why does the water circulate? What is the purpose of the tank in the attic?

again. Sometimes instead of an expansion tank small valves are placed in the water pipe connecting the boiler with the house water system. These valves are so arranged that when expansion occurs, a small quantity of water is forced out of the hot-water system through the valve. If the fire is extinguished, a small amount of water is admitted to the system from the water pipe. Hot-water heat has the disadvantages that usually larger radiators are required than with steam and that its first cost is greater. It has the advantage that it is possible to obtain a small amount of heat by using a small fire.

Heating by electricity. Where electricity is cheap, a very simple and convenient way of heating homes is by the use of electric heaters. When an electric current passes through a wire that offers a considerable resistance to its passage, the wire becomes hot. An electric light bulb is warm when the current is on. Thus electrical energy is changed into heat energy. Electric heaters are often provided with polished reflectors so as to direct heat where it is needed. They are very convenient, but the cost of operation is usually so high that they are used only as a means of obtaining a small amount of heat, as when we wish to raise the temperature of the bathroom a few degrees.

Gas and oil. Gas is a convenient fuel. Like electricity, however, it costs more than coal, so that, while it has the advantage of leaving no

Fig. 199. The burner of a gas stove. Compare with a Bunsen burner, Figure 203.

ashes to be carried out, most of us cannot afford to use it as a fuel for heating our homes.

Of late years *fuel oil*, one of the products obtained in refining crude petroleum, has been used extensively as a fuel. A heating plant which uses oil as fuel combines the maximum of convenience with the minimum of attention required and costs only a little more than a plant which uses coal. Either a steam or hot-water system can be used. The boiler in the cellar is heated by a flame of burning oil. Thermostats are provided in the various rooms so that when the temperature becomes too high, an electric device in the cellar cuts off the supply of oil. In a well-designed plant, after the first lighting of the oil burner in the fall, the plant needs little attention until spring makes it possible to extinguish the fire for the remainder of the warm season (Fig. 200).

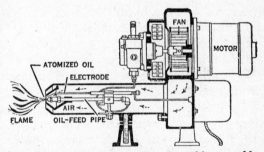

Fig. 200. An oil burner. How does this resemble a Bunsen burner? Why is a fan necessary? Why is the oil atomized?

Ventilation. Heating must always be considered in connection with ventilation. A room may be heated to the proper temperature of 68° F; but if it is not ventilated, it soon becomes uncomfortable and dangerous to health. Odors from the body contaminate the air. Moisture from the body

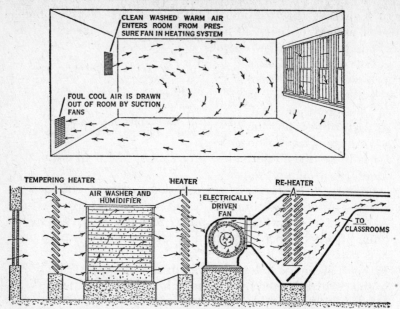

Fig. 201. A system of forced ventilation for schools and other public buildings.

may make it too humid for comfort. Stagnant air does not carry away the heated moist air next our bodies, and so interferes with evaporation of perspiration and cooling. Ventilation to be fully satisfactory must perform three functions: (1) It must supply fresh air and remove the air tainted with bodily odors. (2) It must correct too great humidity that interferes with evaporation of perspiration, and it must correct too great dryness that irritates the mucous membranes. (3) It must create gentle currents of air that are not strong enough to be dangerous drafts.

The open fireplace creates its own ventilation. A stove equipped with fresh-air drafts heats the air that is turned into the room. The warm-air furnace is similarly equipped. Steam and hot-water systems do not provide their own ventilation. In schools, theaters, and other places of assemblage, fresh air is admitted and foul air removed through air passages. The air passages are often heated by steam radiators.

Fans are sometimes installed in the air passages to blow the fresh, heated air into the rooms, or draw out the foul air (Fig. 201). In our homes we rely largely upon window ventilation, and schoolrooms are generally improved by the additional ventilation at the windows. As long as the temperature of the air outside is lower than that inside, convectional currents will ventilate. Windows should be open at the top and bottom. A window board at the bottom should be used to prevent drafts upon persons near the windows

Fig. 202. How to ventilate a room. Note the window board. Account for the path of the current.

(Fig. 202). The cooler air will enter the bottom of the window and lift the warmer, lighter air, which will pass out the top (Experiment No. 73).

EXPERIMENT 70

Question: To illustrate the construction and use of a Bunsen burner.

Materials: Desk apparatus; Bunsen burner; limewater; charcoal; glass rod.

Directions: (a) Unscrew the barrel from the base of a Bunsen burner. Slip the collar (regulator) from the tube. Connect the base of the burner to the gas outlet. Light the gas at the base and note the color of the flame. Extinguish, and assemble the parts of the burner. Turn the collar so as to close the holes, and light the burner. Note the color of the flame. Turn the collar so as to open the holes, and again note the color of the flame. 1. Compare the color of the flame when the holes are open with the color when the holes are closed.

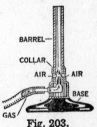

BARREL—
COLLAR
AIR — — AIR
BASE
GAS
Fig. 203.

(b) Tap a piece of charcoal (carbon) against the open holes. Note the change in the color of the flame. Close the holes and hold a glass rod in the flame for a second or two. 2. Why did the charcoal make the flame luminous? 3. What is the deposit on the rod? Hold the blackened glass rod in blue flame. What happens to flame and deposit?

(c) Hold an empty 4-oz. wide-mouth bottle inverted over the blue flame for a few seconds. Make the test for the presence of carbon dioxide by shaking a teaspoonful of limewater in the bottle. 4. Account for the milky precipitate in the bottle.

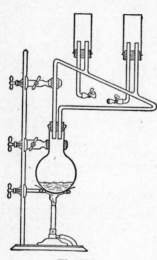

Fig. 204.

(d) Hold a cold, dry, 4-oz. wide-mouth bottle inverted over a Bunsen burner flame for two or three seconds. 5. What collects on the inner surface of the bottle? Since the air furnishes the oxygen necessary to make this compound, what element must be furnished by the gas?

Conclusion: 6. How does the burner of a gas stove resemble a Bunsen burner? 7. How should you remedy a smoky flame? 8. What should you do to prevent a flame from striking back, i. e., burning inside the tube at the base? 9. Explain why the flame of a Bunsen burner loses color when the regulator holes are opened. 10. What is the advantage of the Bunsen burner?

EXPERIMENT 71 (OPTIONAL)

To make a model of a steam-heating plant. Arrange apparatus as in Figure 204. Draw a diagram of your arrangement and label the parts to correspond with those of a steam-heating plant as in diagram.

EXPERIMENT 72

Question: How does a hot-water boiler or a hot-water heating system work?

Materials: Apparatus arranged as in Figure 205. Fill with water, using the funnel tube to fill the tubes.

Method: Heat the water in the flask. Feel the tubes at various parts every few minutes.

Results: Record the observations in the change of temperature and movement of water.

Conclusion: What mode of heat transference is involved in this heating system?

Application: Compare with page 62, and on your diagram of the apparatus label the parts corresponding to the water jacket around the heater or the heating coil, the water storage tank, the radiator. Compare this apparatus with the radiator system in an automobile. Compare with Figure 198 and identify corresponding parts.

EXPERIMENT 73

Question: How should a room be ventilated?

Materials: A box prepared as shown in Fig. 206; Chinese punk or other source of smoke.

Method: Light the candles and close the glass front of the box. 1. Remove a cork at the top of one side. Insert a lighted, smoking stick of punk in the top hole and note the direction of the smoke current. 2. Remove the corks at the bottom of one side and note the currents. 3. Remove corks from top and bottom of the same side and note currents by holding the punk just outside and then just inside the holes at the top and bottom. 4. Now try removing the corks at top of one side and bottom of the other side and study the currents.

Results: Draw a series of diagrams showing how the air circulates in each case.

Conclusion: How should windows be opened to secure continuous ventilation of a room?

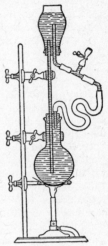

Fig. 205.

QUESTIONS TO THINK OUT

1. When the screw top of a jar sticks, it can sometimes be loosened by plunging the top for just a moment into hot water. Why should it not be longer than a few seconds?

2. How would nightfall affect the altitude of a balloon?

3. When alcohol is used in an automobile radiator, why is the radiator not filled to the top?

4. If you have a coffee percolator at home, examine it to learn why the water circulates.

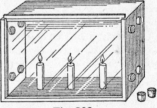

Fig. 206.

5. Is water hotter when boiling vigorously than when boiling slowly?

6. How cold could a thing be? How hot could it be? Give reasons for your answers.

7. What is in the bubbles that rise in boiling water? Why do they rise?

8. A South African water bag is made of material that allows water to ooze through very slowly. When hung in a tree, the water inside cools to a pleasant drinking temperature. Why?

9. In horse-and-buggy days people sometimes put a hot stone or flatiron in the carriage to warm their feet on cold winter drives. Would

a hot-water bag at the same temperature and of approximately the same weight be better or poorer?

10. Explain several ways in which you could keep food cool in camp.

11. Why do pokers often have coiled wire handles?

12. Growers of winter wheat (wheat planted in the fall) like to see snow lie on the ground all winter. Why?

13. Is it a good or poor plan to paint a radiator in your home?

14. Why are building tiles hollow?

15. Would a tank of ice water cool a refrigerator as much as an equal volume of ice at the same temperature? Explain.

16. Why is ice placed at the top of a refrigerator?

17. Is it good or poor economy to wrap ice in a newspaper before putting it into the refrigerator?

18. When a fire is being lighted in a fireplace, smoking may often be prevented by holding burning paper at the top of the fireplace. Why does this prevent smoking?

19. Explain why a high chimney makes a better draft.

20. Why is iron better material than stone to build stoves? What would be better than iron?

21. Why are furnaces sometimes covered with asbestos?

22. Study the possibilities of heat leakage in your home, and the correction. Study at the same time the ventilation.

23. Water may leave a radiator at the same temperature as that at which the steam entered. What then gives heat to the room?

24. Why does a hot-water system need larger radiators than a steam system?

25. A man found that his furnace fire would not burn brightly when there was an east wind. His neighbor's house on the east was higher than his. How could he get a better draft without the expense of building a higher chimney? Before reading further, stop and think about it. After you have thought about it, read in the next sentence what he actually did. He substituted coke for coal in his furnace and had no further trouble. Can you explain why?

26. In sunny climates, such as California and Florida, water for the house is sometimes heated in a set of pipes on the roof, as in the figure below. Explain how it works.

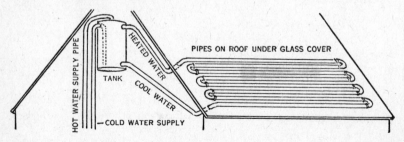

UNIT SIX

SOUND

Close your eyes and sit very still for three or four minutes. You know that an automobile went down the street and stopped to let a trolley car pass. You know that a person walked down the hall and entered the next room. You know whether it was man or woman, boy or girl. How do you know? Sound reached you.

No other element of our environment except light is of more help in avoiding danger and in enjoying life than is sound. By it we learn, we communicate with others, we are warned of danger, we enjoy one another's company, and we enjoy the art of music. We find it so, too, among many wild and domestic animals—the warning cry, the call to food and shelter, the love song, and the song for the fun of it. There may be animals that live in a soundless world; but it would be hard to make sure of it, for sound or something like sound penetrates the rocks and the soil and the depths of the ocean.

You have probably never asked what sound is, how it reaches you, how you hear it, what makes one sound differ from another. They are the sort of questions that the scientist asks. Then he seeks by experiment and observation for answers.

Learning the laws of sound and other laws of science has made it possible to let a large medical audience listen to the beating of a patient's heart. Sound is energy and may be converted to other forms of energy. It is so converted by nature in our ears. It is so converted by man in the radio that it enables an officer on the ground to talk with the distant airman and Admiral Byrd to talk from the Antarctic to the folks at home. These latter conversions of sound we shall study in our unit on electricity, for it is through electric

(225)

energy that the voice and other sounds are sent to distant parts of earth.

In this unit we shall study the answers to the questions raised, and shall learn a little about how the use of sound adds to the harmony and melody of our environment. The art of music arose in the dim past of the human race. Savages in the tropical forest are musical. Today the great musicians are familiar with the findings of science, and in their hands sound has become, so some say, a vehicle of the highest form of art.

Chapter XXIII

WHAT SOUND IS

What starts sound? Perhaps you have seen a toy consisting of a big cardboard bumblebee fitted with a rubber band that hums as one swings it around on the end of a string. Let us see why the bee hums. Stretch a rubber band and pluck it to make it vibrate. You hear it hum. The vibration starts the sound. Touch the middle of a vibrating rubber band to a light suspended body, as a ping-pong ball, or a pith ball. The ball is thrown to one side, showing that the band strikes it with considerable force. The vibrating rubber band makes the cardboard bumblebee's hum. Strike a tuning fork and touch it to the pith ball or touch it very lightly to the surface of water in a glass (Fig. 207). Do the same with a sounding bell. These sounds are evidently started by vibration.

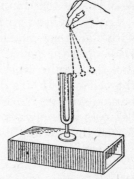

Fig. 207. Showing that a sounding tuning fork vibrates.

Let us examine a few more sounds. Place the pith ball or a few tiny shot on the head of a drum or the bottom of a dishpan. Beat the drum or the dishpan. Here is more vibration. Suspend a light pith ball in a test tube and blow across the end of the test tube. More vibration. Lay the pith ball on the end of a table and strike the other end with a hammer. More vibrations. You can easily devise other simple experiments to investigate the cause of other sounds.

What carries sound? An air pump, a bell jar, and an alarm clock will help us to get an answer to this question.

(227)

Set the alarm clock on the platform of the air pump, cover it with the bell jar, and let the alarm go off. You can hear the bell. Then pump out the air and let the alarm go off again. You cannot hear it, or you can hear it only very faintly. The vibrating bell sets the air to vibrating. The air vibrations, or *sound waves*, as they are generally called, carry the bell's vibrations to your ear.

When you were in swimming, did you ever hold your head under water while someone knocked two stones together? If so, you heard the knocking better than through the air. A hundred years ago it was determined in Lake Geneva that sound travels about five times as fast under water as through air. Fog signals sent out under water from a lighthouse or other station can be picked up by ships. In modern sea warfare listeners are constantly on the alert for under-water sounds that tell that an enemy submarine is near.

Lay your head with one ear on a table, close the other ear with your finger,and have someone tap the far end of the table. How does the sound travel to you? Have you noticed the racket upstairs when somebody pounds the steam pipes in the cellar? It was difficult in the war for soldiers to cut the barbed wire in No Man's Land without being detected, for listeners were always "on the wire." Did you ever put your ear on the rail and listen for a distant train, or have you put your ear on a trolley pole? Have you read how the Indians or the Africans put their ears to the ground to listen for the sound of distant marching men? The dentist's grinding is louder to you than to the dentist because the sound reaches you through the bones of your head. Deaf persons can sometimes hear by means of an instrument that carries sound vibrations through the skull instead of through the ear channel.

Air, water, wood, metal, bone, and many other substances carry sound vibrations. Some liquids carry certain vibrations better than does air. Solids in general are still better for the transmission of sound. On the moon, where there is no atmosphere and no liquid, there can be no transmission of sound except through solid material.

Fig. 208. Waves of air carry sound. The waves travel away as expanding spheres, but are shown here as circles.

Velocity of sound waves. In a thunderstorm the flash of lightning and the thunder are produced at the same instant, yet we often hear the thunder a considerable time after we see the lightning. This is because the velocity (speed) of light waves is very great, 186,000 miles a second, while the velocity of sound waves is very much less, being only about 1100 feet a second. Knowing this figure, you can often tell how far away a storm is. Suppose you see a flash of lightning and 10 seconds later you hear thunder. The time taken by the light waves (lightning) to reach your eye is such a small fraction of a second that we can neglect it. Since sound travels 1100 feet a second, in 10 seconds it will have gone 11,000 feet, or the storm is more than 2 miles away. Try the game during the next thunderstorm. You will count seconds if you say the following at ordinary conversational rate: "A bushel of thunder, 2 bushels of thunder, 3 bushels of thunder, etc." Divide the number of seconds by 5, for 1100 feet equals about $\frac{1}{5}$ of a mile. The result will tell you about how many miles away the lightning flashed.

Echoes. Have you shouted at a cliff and heard the echo?
Or have you heard an echo in an empty auditorium? You
can imitate with water waves the process that causes the
echo. Fill a vessel with water and then strike the water
gently in the center. You will see that a wave is produced
that gradually spreads out until it reaches the wall of the
vessel. After breaking against the restraining wall, the wave

REFLECTING SURFACE

SOUND
WAVE

REFLECTED SOUND
WAVE OR ECHO

Fig. 209. Water waves reflected from sides of pan.

Fig. 210. Echo is due to
sound waves reflected.

doubles back toward the center of the water. This doubling
back is called *reflection* (Fig. 209). Sound waves may be
reflected in a similar way. If we face a cliff and shout, in a
short time the sound returns to us because the sound is reflected from the cliff and comes back to us as an echo (Fig. 210).
If we hear the echo two seconds after we shout, we know that
the cliff must be 1100 feet away. It takes the sound one
second to travel to the cliff and another second to travel
back. In narrow valleys between two mountains the sound
waves may be reflected many times. In this way multiple
echoes that last for some time are produced. A well-known
example of multiple echoes occurs during the delightful trip
down the Saguenay River in Canada. At a bend in the river
the shore line rises in high cliffs (Fig. 211). When the ship
reaches this part of the river, the captain has the whistle
blown. The cliffs reflect the sound and the echoes are repeated many times.

Fig. 211. Cape Trinity on the Saguenay River, Canada, reflects the sound waves from the steamboat's whistle, making an echo.

The reflection of sound waves in water is used in deep-sea sounding instruments (Fig. 212). These instruments are used to determine the depth of the ocean. A sound is produced in the ship. This sound travels downward from the ship and is reflected from the ocean floor. The interval between the start of the sound and the instant the reflected sound is heard is recorded. The velocity of sound in sea water is 4800 feet a second (Fig. 213). Knowing the time the sound took to reach the ocean floor and return, the depth of the ocean at that point can be easily calculated. In determining depth by this method on a ship, a clock measures the

Fig. 212. This instrument tells the depth from the time it takes sound waves to travel.

Fig. 213. Measuring depth with sound. The time for sound waves to travel from the oscillator to the bottom of the ocean and back to the hydrophone tells the depth.

Fig. 214. The Tabernacle in Salt Lake City reflects sound so perfectly
that a whisper can be heard by the audience.

lapse of seconds from the sending of the sound until the return of its echo and a hand points to the number of feet in depth.

Sound in the auditorium. With a small audience present in a large hall the echoes often make it almost impossible to understand the speaker. Generally such echoes are much less noticeable when an audience fills the hall because sound is not reflected so well from the clothing of the audience as from the more resonant material of the empty seats. Curtains and draperies are sometimes hung in the rear of an auditorium to absorb these sound waves which produce echoes when reflected.

In the Tabernacle in Salt Lake City the ceiling is curved in such a way that it reflects sound waves almost perfectly (Fig. 214). As a result, a whisper by the speaker is distinctly heard by everyone in the large audience. It is necessary, though, that everyone be quiet, for a slight rustle in the audience is magnified by reflection of the sound waves

Fig. 215. The outdoor music shell concentrates the sound waves.

until it becomes a roar. The music shell in which the orchestra plays out of doors serves to concentrate and **direct** the sound waves in a similar manner (Fig. 215).

EXPERIMENT 74

Question: Can vibrations cause sound?

Materials: Tuning fork; pith ball; a bell; a small hammer; stretched wire; paper stirrup; violin bow; test tube.

Directions: (*a*) Strike tuning fork. Look at the prongs. 1. Are they vibrating? 2. What must this vibration do to the air in contact with the prongs? Touch the sounding tuning fork to a suspended pith ball. 3. Explain what happens to the ball. When the fork has almost ceased to sound, again touch it to the pith ball. 4. Explain the change in the behavior of the pith ball.

(*b*) Strike the bell with the hammer. Touch the sounding bell to the pith ball. 5. What happens to the pith ball?

(*c*) Stretch a violin or piano string on a board (sonometer). Bow the wire, and notice the sound produced. Look at the sounding wire. 6. What does the wire seem to be doing? Put your finger on the wire to stop the sound. Place a small paper stirrup on the middle of the wire. Bow the wire again. 7. What happens to the paper stirrup and why?

(*d*) Blow across the end of a test tube. 8. Note the sensation in the finger held lightly near the top of the test tube. Why is a sound produced?

(*e*) Strike a tuning fork and hold it near another tuning fork of the same pitch. Place your ear near the second tuning fork. 9. Is the second tuning fork vibrating? 10. How did the vibrations travel from the first to the second tuning fork?

Diagram: Show the tuning fork and pith ball in action.

Conclusion: Answer the question.

Practical application: 1. Why is a violin made hollow, of thin wood, and with openings to the air? 2. Why does a large drum give more sound than a small drum?

EXPERIMENT 75 (OPTIONAL)

Question: How can I find the velocity (speed) of sound in air?

Materials: A stop watch; some means of making a loud noise; a measuring tape.

Directions: (*a*) Look around your city until you find a steam whistle that blows at a time when you are free. Measure the distance in a straight line to a point several thousand feet from the whistle. You can step it off after measuring your step. The longer the distance you use, the better your results will be.

(*b*) Stand at the point, the distance of which from the whistle you know. Watch the whistle, and the instant you *see* the steam, showing that the whistle has been blown, start the stop watch. (A stop watch is a watch so arranged that pressing a knob starts the second hand. A second pressure on the knob stops the hand. The hand usually measures fifths of seconds.) When you *hear* the whistle, stop the watch.

(*c*) You have measured the distance from the whistle to your ear. The watch gives you the time it took the sound to travel this distance. From these figures you can find the velocity of sound.

Conclusion: 1. State the velocity of sound as you found it. 2. State the velocity of sound given in your textbook. 3. Give a reason why the two may not exactly agree.

Practical application: 1. Why is the weather man interested in the velocity of sound? 2. How can you use the velocity of sound in determining the distance a thunderstorm is from you?

NOTE: If you have no stop watch, a pendulum will answer. Hang an iron ball by a short string. Adjust the length of the string so that the pendulum beats 300 times a minute—that is, marks fifths of a second. Have a comrade keep the pendulum vibrating in such a position that you can see both the whistle and the pendulum. Count the beats of the pendulum between the time you see the steam and hear the sound. Then proceed as in (*c*). A rough estimate may be made by counting the seconds. Practice with a watch having a second hand. It is easier to count two to the second than to count one to the second.

Chapter XXIV

WHAT MAKES SOUNDS DIFFER?

Sounds not all the same. You would never mistake the human voice for the big bass drum. When you hear the same note sounded on a violin and by a human voice, you have no doubt as to the source of each sound. A cornet note could never be mistaken for a piano note of the same pitch and loudness. This difference between sounds we call the *quality* or *timbre* of the note. Let us see what makes the difference between the bass drum and the canary, a loud sound and a soft one, a high whistle and a low-pitched whistle.

What is loudness? Strike an unmounted tuning fork gently and then forcibly. Listen to the loudness of the sound. Again strike the fork and this time put the end of the fork on a wooden table top. Notice that the sound is much louder. When the fork is placed on the wood, not only the fork but the wood vibrates. The size of the vibrating body is increased. More air is set into wave motion, and, therefore, the sound is louder. Note, however, that you give a certain definite amount of energy to the fork when you strike it. If the sound from the fork is made louder by forcing the wood to vibrate, you use up this energy faster, and the sound quickly fades.

For the same reason a drum, to give a loud sound, should have a large head. It will require more effort, however, to beat the drum because you must give the drum more energy to make the sound last.

What makes pitch? One way of distinguishing sounds is by their *pitch*—that is, whether they are high or low. A bass has a low-pitched voice while a soprano has a voice of a high pitch. Stretch a piano wire on a hollow wooden box.

(236)

in such a way that you can change the tension (pull) on the string (Fig. 216). The wire should be at least 30 inches long. A commercial sonometer is convenient. Measure the length of the string between the supports. Draw a violin bow over the wire at a point about one fifth of the distance from the end. Listen to the sound. Change the tension of the wire

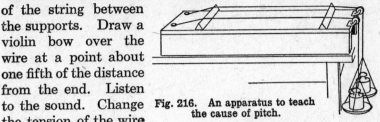

Fig. 216. An apparatus to teach the cause of pitch.

and bow it again. You will see that the pitch of the note produced has altered. *Increasing the tension raises the pitch.*

Put a second string on the sonometer. This second string should have the same diameter as the first wire but be made of different material. If the first was a piano string, use a violin string for the second. Bow both wires after you have made the tension the same on each. The sounds produced will vary in pitch. *The pitch of the wire varies with the material.*

Replace the second string with a wire made of the same material as the first but having a different diameter. Make the tension on both wires the same and bow them. Again the sounds will vary in pitch. *The pitch of a wire varies with its diameter.*

Using a piano wire, adjust the tension until the wire gives about middle "c" on the piano. Measure the length of the vibrating part of the wire. Put a bridge under the wire so as to cut it to half its original length. Again bow the wire. Notice that the wire now gives the octave above the original sound. *Pitch varies with the length of the wire.* Slide the bridge under the wire and bow, using different lengths of wire, until you see how the violinist changes the pitch of the note on his violin by using his fingers to change the length of the vibrating part of the string. Can you devise a very simple experiment with a rubber band that would tell you about pitch?

Sound quality. Why do we not mistake a police whistle for a baby's rattle? By sound quality we mean the some-

17

thing about a sound that tells us its source. Its cause is the
fact that a vibrating body can vibrate not only as a whole,
but in parts as well. Tie the end of a long rubber tube to the
wall. Holding the other end in your hand, pull the tube
taut and then shake the end to and fro. You will find that you can make the tube vibrate in halves. By changing the tension and rate of shaking you can make the tube vibrate in thirds, and if you are skilful, even in quarters. The vibrations can easily be seen by the eye (Fig. 217).

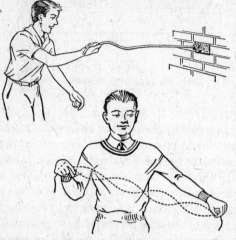

Fig. 217. Study sound waves by means of waves in a string.

The pitch of a note depends, as we have found, on the vibration rate. If we have a string vibrating not only as a whole, but at the same times in halves, we will get a *compound note*. We call the main note the *fundamental*, and the other notes present the *overtones*. The character of a sound depends on the number of overtones present (Fig. 218). It is difficult to believe that a string can vibrate as a whole, and at the same time in halves, but this is a fact. If a note gives a disagreeable sound, it is because some of these overtones do not harmonize with the fundamental.

Noise and music. Does your neighbor's radio make noise or music? The distinction between noise and music

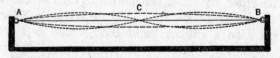

Fig. 218. Production of overtones. The string vibrates both as a whole and in halves. The halves give a note an octave higher in pitch.

depends first on the ear.   If the sensation caused by the sound is pleasing, we call it music.   If the sound is disagreeable, we call it noise.

If you sound four tuning forks that vibrate 256, 320, 384, and 512 times a second, you get a pleasant mingling of sounds. You have produced simple music, and a musician would say that you have sounded a *major chord.*   If you examine the four numbers, you will see that they have the ratio of $4:5:6:8$. If you chose four tuning forks that have vibration ratio of $10:12:15:20$, you again have music.   The musician would say that you have sounded a *minor chord.*   The vibration rates in music form ratios of simple whole numbers.

In a noise no such regular intervals between the notes exist.   Striking a metal sheet gives a noise; striking a piano string gives music.   Yet if we strike a number of piano strings at random, we also get a noise, for we have produced a medley of vibrations with no regularity.

EXPERIMENT 76

Question: How can pitch be changed?

Materials: Commercial sonometer or a homemade one as in Fig. 219; rubber band; 3 test tubes.

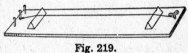

Directions: (*a*) Stretch a wire string on a sonometer.   Pluck the

Fig. 219.

string.   Listen to the sound.   Turn the screw so as to stretch the wire (increase the tension).   Again pluck the string.   1. Is the sound produced higher or lower?   2. How does the pitch vary with the tension?

(*b*) Below the middle of the stretched string place a bridge so as to cut the length of the string to half its original length.   Pluck the string. Move the bridge so as to divide one of the halves again into halves, so that the two sections of the string are one fourth and three fourths of the original length.   Pluck the string again.   3. How do the sounds produced vary?   4. How does the pitch vary with the length?

(*c*) Stretch a thicker string on the sonometer.   Pluck the thick string and then the thin string.   5. Is the pitch the same for both wires?   6. How does the pitch vary with the thickness (mass)?

(*d*) Stretch a rubber band, having the same diameter as the wire, on the sonometer.   Make the tension on both the same.   Pluck the wire and then the rubber band.   7. Is the pitch the same for the wire and the rubber band?   8. Does the material of the vibrating string affect the pitch?

(e) Place 3 test tubes in rack.   Pour 2 inches of water in first, 1 inch in second, and none in third.   Blow across each.   9. The water merely reduces the height of the air column.   How does the height of the vibrating air column affect the pitch?

Diagram: Show the sonometer you used, and the test tubes in the rack.

Conclusion: Answer the question.

Practical application: These facts are made use of in stringed and wind instruments.

Chapter XXV

HOW WE HEAR AND SPEAK

Receiving sound waves. Put a megaphone to your ear or cup your hand beside your ear and notice how much louder sounds are. *The external ear* collects the sound waves in the same manner and directs them into a small curved tube that leads inward. At the end of this tube is a membrane called the *tympanic membrane* or, popularly but less correctly, the *eardrum*. This membrane separates the external ear from a small pocket or cavity called the *middle ear*. In the middle ear are three curiously shaped and very tiny bones. They are fastened to the membrane and also to one another in a kind of chain. The inmost bone of the chain fits into a little window or opening covered with another membrane that leads to the inner ear. The *inner ear* is shaped like the coils of a snail shell. It is filled with a liquid. In one part of the coil are three thousand or more tiny filaments (threads) which unite to form the *auditory nerve*. This nerve leads to the brain.

What happens to all of this complicated machine when we hear? The air vibrates, the sound waves travel in through the curved canal and set the tympanic membrane vibrating. It in turn sets in motion the three little bones. Their motion sets up a motion in the thin membrane between the middle and the inner ear. The motion of the membrane causes the liquid in the inner ear to vibrate. That motion affects the little nerve fibers. Their activity sends an impulse or message to the brain, and finally we hear. *Sound* is the sensation that arises when the impulses reach the brain.

When you went down in an elevator to the bottom of the shaft, did you ever feel pressure on the eardrums? Perhaps you noticed the effect in driving downhill. You swallowed and the ears felt comfortable again. Your ear was uncomfortable because the pressures inside and outside the eardrum were unequal. The swallowing allowed the air pressure inside the middle ear and outside to equalize. The *Eustachain tube* connects the middle ear with the throat. It is ordinarily closed, shutting off the middle ear. When you swallow, it opens for a moment and the external air pressure balances the pressure in the middle ear.

Taking care of the ears. The tympanic membrane is thin and easily broken. A blow on the side of the head may cause enough air pressure on the membrane to break it. Even a loud shout directly into the ear may do the same. The gunners of the coast artillery and on battleships are often deaf for hours or permanently deaf after firing practice. To avoid this trouble, an increased air pressure is now maintained in the ship's turrets, thus preventing the trouble. Stuffing the ears with cotton and standing on the tiptoe helps to reduce the blow of the sound wave.

For most persons the best way to take care of the ears is to let them alone. An old saying is that nothing smaller than your elbow should ever be put into your ear. The tympanic membrane is located so near the surface of the head that poking hard objects into the ear is likely to rupture it. Washing, or the use of a soft cloth to remove the waxlike substance (earwax) that accumulates at the outer end of the tube, is all that is permissible.

Should an insect fly into the ear, a very little lukewarm olive oil dropped into the ear will float the insect to the top of the tube, when it can be removed with absorbent cotton without injury to the ear. The cotton also serves to remove the oil, or a medicine dropper may be used to remove it. In the case of an earache the application of mild, dry, heat (a hot cloth or a hot-water bag) will sometimes afford relief. Colds, catarrh, and scarlet fever often cause an inflammation (infection) of the Eustachain tube, causing it to close. If this condition lasts, it may cause deafness. If you have any trouble with your ear, go to a physician at once. Delay may cost you your hearing.

The voice. At the upper end of the windpipe or trachea is the organ of voice, called the *larynx,* or *voice box.* Its walls are made of cartilage and muscle. Across the top of the larynx are stretched two thin strips of membrane called *vocal cords,* with a small space between them (Fig. 220). It is possible, with the aid of the throat muscles, to stretch vocal

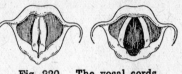

Fig. 220.   The vocal cords.

cords. Air from the lungs passing over the cords sets their edges into vibration, and sound is produced. Vocal cords are usually shorter and lighter in women than in men; hence, women's voices are usually higher and shriller than those of men.

We vary the pitch of the sounds we produce by varying the tension (pull) on the cords. When we have a cold, the cords become thickened and mucous is deposited on them. The air passing over these roughened cords produces the odd sounds characteristic of a cold.

At the time when a boy's voice changes, his larynx grows much larger and the vocal cords lengthen and thicken. Look at your piano and you will see that the bass notes are made by the long, heavy wires. Lengthening and thickening the vocal cords lowers the pitch of the voice. The bass voice is produced by longer and thicker cords than the soprano.

Care of the voice. A cheap violin gives a harsh, crude sound, while a valuable instrument gives a smooth, mellow tone. The differences are due to very small variations in the shape of the sound box and elasticity of the wood used, and other things hard to recognize. Just as the tone of the violin is modified by the sound box, so the voice is modified by the mouth, nasal cavity, teeth, and tongue; and just as a very small difference between the two violins causes a tremendous variation in their tones, so small differences in our bodies cause great differences in our voice quality. Violinists tell us that playing a violin improves it and that part of the superb quality of sound given by old violins depends on the fact that they have been played for years by great

Fig. 221.   A Stradivarius violin.

masters. So, intelligent practice with our voices can improve them. We cannot all become Carusos, but we can all learn to avoid the harsh, strident voice that is a handicap throughout life.

When your voice is changing, or when you have a severe cold, you should not sing or strain your voice. Prolonged and intense cheering at the football game may help you to express your joy at the success of your team, but it may also injure your voice. Cheer with some restraint. You will be able to cheer longer and will not run the risk of voice injury.

Why the phonograph talks. Mount a short needle on a thin sheet of mica in such a way that you can speak against the mica and set it into vibration (Fig. 222). While the disk is vibrating, place under the needle point a wax plate so mounted that it can be driven along under the needle point and in contact with it. When you speak close to the disk, causing it to vibrate, and at the same time drive the wax plate under the needle point, the needle point will be set into motion and will cut a groove in the wax. Examine the groove under

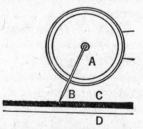

Fig. 222.   Making a simple phonograph record. A, diaphragm; B, needle; C, wax; D, glass.

the magnifying glass and you will see that the groove is not uniform, but is made up of hills and valleys caused by the to-and-fro motion of the needle point (Fig. 223).

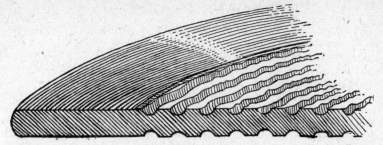

Fig. 223.   Grooves in a phonograph record cause the needle to vibrate,
thus moving the diaphragm.

Now place the wax plate under the needle point again,
keeping the needle point in the groove.   The hills and valleys
of the groove will move the needle up and down and thus
set the mica disk in vibration.   These vibrations will reproduce the original vibrations of the disk caused when you
spoke against it.   The vibrations then must reproduce the
original sound.   You will have made a crude phonograph
record.

Wax plates may be bought on which you can make a record
of your own voice that can be reproduced on your phonograph.   Such reproducing machines are often used by business men for dictating letters.   Later a stenographer plays
the record and writes the letter thus dictated on her type-
writer.

Commercial phonograph records are not made of wax because wax is so soft that the record quickly wears out.   Instead, a composition that is hard and tough is used.   A
master record is made first.   From this a metal mold is prepared, and this metal mold is used to press out the phonograph records we buy.   In this way thousands of records
can be made from one master record.

EXPERIMENT 77 (OPTIONAL)

Question: How can one imitate the vocal cords?   Stretch two pieces
of rubber dam across the bowl of a thistle tube, leaving a slit between
the two pieces.   Blow through the tube.   Watch what the rubber
pieces do.   Place the finger on the larynx or Adam's apple while you
talk.   Note the similarity.

EXPERIMENT 78 (OPTIONAL)

Question: How would you make a tin-can telephone? Punch a hole in the bottom of each of two tin cans. Thread each end of a long, stout string through a hole and knot the string so that it will not pull out. Stretch the string taut. Use as a telephone. What carries the vibrations of the voice?

Rub a part of the string with rosin. While one tin can is held to the ear, have someone rub the rosined part of the string. Account for the noises. Compare the noise when the can is held against the bones' about the ear and when it is held off a little distance. Account for the difference.

QUESTIONS TO THINK OUT AND TO INVESTIGATE

1. If we could make a loud enough sound, could we send a sound signal to the moon? Explain.

2. Devise an experiment to show that water will carry sound.

3. Is shouting more easily heard in the woods or in the open? Why?

4. Is a speaker on the platform more easily heard indoors or outdoors? Why?

5. Is sound more easily heard in fog or clear weather? Try to find out by experiment.

6. Explain the sound of the sea when you hold a sea shell to your ear.

7. Is the hum of a bee higher or lower than the hum of a bird's wings? Why?

8. What travels through the string in the tin-can telephone? Experiment 78, page 246. What travels through the wire in a real telephone?

9. If you listened at one end of a long hose while a person spoke in the other end, would you hear more or less distinctly than through the open air? Reason it out, then try it.

10. In a long column of marching men, the men in the rear are sometimes out of step with men in the front but in step with the band at the front. Explain.

11. Why is the sound deadened when you touch a bell?

12. Grasp your "Adam's apple" lightly and sing, "Ah, ah, ah, ah," up the scale. Tell what you discover and explain. Try whistling up the scale. What produces change in pitch?

13. Pronounce the vowels a-e-i-o-u without change in pitch. What produces the change in sound?

14. When a circular saw cuts through a heavy timber, does its pitch rise or fall? Why?

15. How does the hum of a streetcar or a vacuum sweeper change in pitch as it slows down?

16. In Figure 213, page 232, if it took one half second for the sound to travel from the oscillator to the hydrophone as indicated, how deep is the water? See page 231.

Chapter XXVI

THE ORCHESTRA

Musical instruments. You can scarcely believe when listening to a jazz orchestra that the players are using only three methods of producing the many sounds. Yet music is produced only by the use of mechanisms of three simple types. These types are represented by *vibrating strings* set in motion by bowing or plucking; *vibrating air columns* set in motion by air currents; and *vibrating solids* set in motion by blows.

In instruments of the first type, tightly drawn strings are set in vibration by being struck as in the piano, plucked as in the banjo, or rubbed as in the violin. Stretch a rubber band between your thumb and first finger. Pluck it with the thumb nail of your other hand. The rubber will vibrate and give out a tone. By stretching the rubber tighter, you can produce a tone of higher pitch. A thin band will give a higher tone than a thick one at the same tension.

In instruments of the second type a column of air is set to vibrating in various ways. In the organ, a current of air is blown upon a thin edge, the lip, at one end of the column of air, and the column is thus made to vibrate. In the reed instruments, as the clarinet, an air current is blown upon a thin piece of wood or metal, the reed, in the mouthpiece; the reed vibrates and communicates its vibration to the air column. In the cornet the method is similar, except that the lips of the player vibrate in place of the reed, and set the column to vibrating.

Blow across the end of a test tube. The air inside the tube is set in vibration and produces a tone. A long tube produces a deeper tone than a short one; hence to produce notes of different pitch, organ pipes of different lengths are

used. Pull the outside off a mouth organ (harmonica). **Put
your finger lightly on one of the metal reeds and then blow
through the instrument.** You will feel the reed tremble, or

vibrate. An examination of the different reeds will show you how they
are altered to produce different tones.

In instruments of the third type,
either a solid or hollow body is set
in vibration by being struck, as in
the drum or cymbal. Strike two
tin pie plates together, and you will
have crude cymbals (Fig. 224).

Vibration instruments are called
*stringed instruments, wind instru-
ments,* or *percussion instruments,* depending on the method used to produce the sound. In the following

Fig. 224. Homemade cym-
bals.

paragraphs we will consider some of these that are used in
modern orchestras.

Stringed instruments. These are the violin, the viola,
the violoncello (or cello), the double bass (or contrabass), the
piano, and the harp. You are of course familiar with
the violin. It is a hollow sounding box with four strings,
the tension of which can be adjusted by turning pegs. It
would of course be impossible to use a separate string for
every note, so their length is changed by sliding the fingers
up and down, thus varying the pitch. The strings of the
violin are set in vibration by the hair of the bow passing over
them. The bow is rosined so as to make it catch the violin
string and draw it slightly to one side. The string then slips
back, causing it to vibrate (Fig. 221).

The viola is the violin's big sister. It is shaped like the
violin and has a similar arrangement of strings. The string
of highest pitch on the violin is taken off, and a lower one
added. Because it is larger, it gives a lower pitched tone.
Its quality of tone is melancholy and somber. Of the two
the viola is the older instrument, going back in its present
form to the fifteenth century.

The cello is much larger than the viola, but has the same construction and method of playing. It is just an octave lower in pitch than the viola. The double bass is the grandfather of the family (Fig. 225). It can be easily recognized by its huge size and deep bass notes. It is taller than its player, who is obliged to stand when he plays it.

The harp differs from all the above in that there is a string for every note that is to be sounded. The strings are plucked by the fingers of the player, and the tones produced are sweet and mellow.

The piano has at least one string for every note. These strings are struck by felt-covered hammers, moved by striking upon the piano keys. The piano is tuned by varying the tension on the strings. Open your piano and you will see the pegs, which can be turned to change the pull on the strings and hence the pitch.

Wind instruments. These are divided into two sections: wood winds and brasses. In the wood winds the flute and

Fig. 225. Representative musical instruments of a modern orchestra: 1-4, stringed instruments played with a bow (1, violin; 2, viola; 3, violoncello; 4, contrabass); 5, harp; 6-12, wood-wind instruments (6, flute; 7, piccolo; 8, English horn; 9, bassoon; 10, oboe; 11, clarinet; 12, bass clarinet); 13-17, brass-wind instruments (13, cornet; 14, trumpet; 15, trombone; 16, French horn; 17, bass tuba); 18, saxophone; 19-22, percussion instruments (19, kettledrum; 20, bass drum; 21, cymbals; 22, snare drum).

piccolo are tubes having a row of openings. By covering and uncovering these openings with the fingers, the length of the vibrating air column can be changed, thus changing the pitch of the tone produced (Fig. 225). The air column inside the tube is set into vibration by blowing across a hole near one end of the tube.

The flute is one of the oldest of musical instruments, going back in its original form to about 3000 B.C. In its middle register the tones are mellow, but its low notes are dull and its high notes shrill. The piccolo resembles a small flute. Because it is smaller, its tones are an octave higher than those of the flute. It is used mainly for special effects in its upper register, as its low notes have no character.

The other wood winds, the oboe, English horn, clarinet, and bassoon, contain thin pieces (reeds) mounted in the mouthpiece. These reeds are set into vibration when the player blows air against them and communicate their vibration to the air column in the main tube of the instrument. The length of the vibrating air column is changed by opening and closing the stops.

The English horn, which is neither English nor a horn, is a large, or alto, oboe. Because of its larger size, it gives a deeper tone. The tone of both the oboe and the English horn resembles that of the old shepherd's pipe. They are both difficult to play.

The clarinet differs from the other wood winds in that it has only one reed, while the others have two. It gives a better graduation of tone than the other wood winds; has the widest range of all wood winds; and is, therefore, the most expressive and useful. In the middle register its tones resemble those of the human voice. The bassoon and contrabassoon are the bass instruments in this section.

The brasses, as the trumpet, French horn, and trombone, contain no reeds. The air column is set into vibration by the vibrating lips of the player held against a cup-shaped mouthpiece. Note the sliding tube in the trombone (Fig. 225). Moving this back and forth changes the length of the vibrating air column, and so alters the pitch of the tone produced.

In the trumpet, French horn, and tuba, keys are used to open holes in the pipe, thus changing the length of the vibrating air column.

The cornet and the trombone are perhaps the best known of the brasses. The trumpet is an enlarged cornet with a brilliant and clear tone. The French horn has been developed from the old huntsman horn. Its tone is smooth and velvety. The tuba is the brass bass. Its tone is harsh and gruff. The saxophone you are all familiar with. It is ranked with the brasses, but its mouthpiece contains a reed. The tone of the saxophone is, therefore, a combination of the wood and the brass tones of the horn and the clarinet. It is popular in jazz orchestras, yet Mendelssohn thought its tone "too mournful" to use in his sacred music.

Percussion instruments. The drum, xylophone, and tambourine, and the cymbals and castanets are percussion instruments. Some percussion instruments, like the kettledrums or tympani, have a definite pitch. Drums are tuned by changing the tension of the head. The less the tension and the larger the head the lower the pitch.

The following chart contains a summary of some musical instruments:

STRINGED	WIND	PERCUSSION	REED
Violin	Organ	Kettledrum	Saxophone
Viola	Trombone	Bass drum	Harmonica
Cello	Piccolo	Castanets	Oboe
Ukulele	Flute	Bells	Clarinet
Piano	Bugle	Xylophone	Bass clarinet
Mandolin	Cornet	Triangle	Bassoon
Harp	Trumpet	Tambourine	Contrabassoon
Guitar	Tuba	Cymbals	English horn

EXPERIMENT 79 (HOME)

Question: How can I make some musical instruments?
Materials: A board and 9 straight pins; drinking glasses; water.
Directions: (a) Drive 8 pins into the board, giving them graduated lengths. With the other pin, pick at each pin and produce a tone. Play

a simple tune. 1. What is vibrating? 2. Which pin produces the lowest tone? 3. Which pin produces the highest tone?

(b) Set up a row of drinking glasses and pour different quantities of water into different glasses. Tap each with a pencil. Note the difference in tone. Try to graduate the quantity of water and arrange the glasses to produce the musical scale. Try to play a simple tune. 4. What is vibrating? 5. Which glass produces the highest and which the lowest note?

Diagram: Show pin piano.

Conclusion: 1. The longer the pin or the column of air, the .... the note. The shorter the pin or the column of air, the .... the note. 2. How does this apply to stringed instruments?

Practical application: 1. How many strings are there on a piano? 2. How many strings are there on a violin? 3. How can the violin be made to produce so many different notes?

QUESTIONS TO THINK OUT

1. Which gives more trouble with echoes, a large hall or a small room? Why?

2. Why are echoes often louder at evening than at noon?

3. Does an automobile horn sound the same when it approaches you as when it has passed you and is receding? Why?

4. (a) Does a church bell sound equally loud at 100 feet and at a mile? Does it have the same pitch? (b) Do sounds of different pitch travel at different rates? Mention an observation in support of your answer.

5. Tell everything that happens in a conversation between the speaking of the word and the understanding by the listener. For what happens in the ear, see page 241.

6. Why does your voice sometimes have a lower pitch when you have a cold?

7. If you speak in the same pitch, why does your voice change when you hold your nose?

8. Look at Figure 225, page 249. Which instrument has a mechanism most resembling the vocal cords? the piano? Which strings of the piano vibrate most rapidly? How does the piano tuner raise the pitch of a string? Does the trombone give a higher or lower note when the slide is drawn out? When the drum head is tightened, does the drum give a higher or lower note? Why? Why is the French horn made so long that it is wound in a circle?

UNIT SEVEN

LIGHT

Can you picture in your mind the earth without light? If no light came to us, probably there would be no heat, at least not enough to sustain life. Bare rocks would cover the earth. Nothing could live in the utter darkness. There must be light to support life. Without light this would be a cold, dead world. How life depends upon light is the story in another unit. In this unit we shall study what light is and how it is put to service.

Perhaps when you were camping, you have been awakened on a cold night as a storm ripped away your tent. If you have stumbled around in the dark trying to find shelter and some of your clothing and food, you may have some slight idea of the plight of the men of the Old Stone Age at night. Science has provided light so as to make night as comfortable and in a measure almost as convenient as day. We shall see in the following chapters how science provides light when nature denies it.

We shall study the instruments which control beams of light to show us what the eye alone never can see. The microscope enables us to see objects so small that their existence was unknown before the development of this branch of science. The marvelous increase in the length of human life is due largely to the discoveries made with the microscope. Industry and agriculture also have advanced through microscopic studies.

The telescope has brought us information of worlds at distances too vast for our minds to grasp, worlds beyond the reach of exploration except by means of the rays of light that come to us from them. By means of it, scientists are able to gain valuable information about the stars and planets.

The human eye is an optical instrument developed by nature. We shall see how its structure agrees with that of man-made instruments.

The camera has become commonplace, but to the scientist it continues to reveal marvels of nature. The astronomer searches photographic plates for news of heavenly happenings that the human eye is not delicate enough to see directly. Medicine, industry, and many kinds of scientific study and investigations make constant use of photography. We shall study the principles of the camera and of photography.

The "movies" and the lanterns that bring to us distant scenes and reconstruct processes of nature are instruments of science and education as well as of entertainment. We shall see how lanterns project large pictures and how the movies move.

Finally we shall study color, one of the very striking properties of light. Nature uses color to maintain life; science uses it to maintain and restore health; and art uses it for beauty. We shall see what color really is and how it is produced.

CHAPTER XXVII

HOW LIGHT BEHAVES

How light travels. Light travels fast, 186,000 miles a second. It travels from the sun, 93,000,000 miles away, in 8 minutes. Light travels in straight lines, therefore, you cannot see around a corner, since you can see an object only when light rays come from it to your eye. Because light travels straight, you can tell where to put your hands to catch a ball or to lift the baby. Experiment 80 shows definitely that light travels in straight lines.

Light cannot travel through a board or a stone, and therefore you cannot see through them. Such objects are said to be *opaque*. Light does travel through glass or pure water, and therefore you can see through them. Such objects are *transparent*. If you look at the glass edgewise, or look into deep water, you cannot see through. They are not perfectly transparent. Ground glass and wax paper let light through, but you cannot see through them. Such objects are *translucent*. If you cut slices of wood thin enough, a yellowish light comes through. If you beat sheets of gold out thin enough, a greenish light comes through. They are then translucent.

Shadows. Any opaque object in the path of rays of light will stop them, and the space behind the opaque body will be in shadow. If the rays of light come from a point, an opaque object will cause a shadow with sharp edges (Fig. 226). If, however, the source of light is a broad flame, or the broad disk of the sun, the darkest part of the shadow, called the *umbra*, will be edged by a lighter band, which shades off gradually to the full illumination where there is no shadow at all. This band or edge is called the *penumbra;* it arises because points near the edge of the shadow get light from a part of the source of light, but not from all (Fig. 226). The farther the shadow from the object, the wider the penumbra, and the more gradual the shading off from the umbra to full

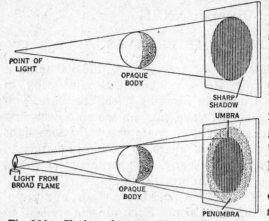

illumination. You have all seen the shadow of a flag-pole on the ground, with edges sharply defined near the base and more and more indistinct the greater the distance from the pole.

When the moon comes between the sun and the part of the earth on which we happen to be,

Fig. 226. Shadows from a point of light and from a broad flame.

we say there is an eclipse of the sun. A part, or sometimes all, of the sun's disk is concealed from us. People on the moon would say that their shadow was falling on the earth. (See page 662.)

The light we see by. The traffic policeman's white cape at night shines out at the crossing, but you do not see the man in the dark suit walking across the street. The white markings at dangerous curves show plainly, but you do not easily see the trees. In a dark room you see nothing. When you turn a flashlight about, certain objects shine out by reflected light and others are dull because they reflect little light. You see an object by the light that reaches your eyes from the object. Some objects give out their own light (*luminous bodies*), but we see the majority of objects only by reflected light.

Such an object is the moon, which we see as we see most objects on earth during the day—by the light which falls upon it from the sun and is reflected back to us. But if the earth comes between the sun and the moon, its shadow falls

Fig. 227. The snowy heron reflects light different from its surroundings.

Fig. 228. The woodcock is protectively colored. It reflects light similar to its surroundings.

upon the moon—that is, part or all of the light from the sun is cut off—and there is an eclipse of the moon. This does not mean that something opaque hides the moon from us, as is the case with an eclipse of the sun, but that the rays of the sun do not fall upon the moon, and hence are not reflected back to us. It is just as hard to see the moon when it is in the dark as it is to see a book or a chair in the dark.

In general, objects are conspicuous to the sight when they stand out from their surroundings—that is, when they reflect a different kind of light. A white bird in the reeds reflects light strikingly different from that reflected by its background; and hence it is easy to see (Fig. 227). If, however, objects reflect light much like their surroundings, they are inconspicuous, like the woodcock in the brown leaves (Fig. 228), or the polar bear on the ice. In times of war, ships and big guns are camouflaged so that they blend with their surroundings and are hard for the enemy to see.

The law of reflection. When a ray of light strikes a plane mirror perpendicularly, it is reflected straight back to its source. But if it strikes the mirror obliquely, it is reflected obliquely. The angle between the perpendicular and the direction of the ray of light as it comes to the mirror is called the *angle of incidence;* the angle between the perpendicular and the direction of the ray as it leaves the mirror is called the *angle of reflection.* The law of reflection states that *the angle of incidence is equal to the angle of reflection.* If we can measure the angle at which light strikes a mirror, we can use this law to calculate where it will go after reflection (Fig. 229).

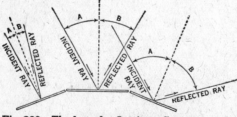

Fig. 229. The law of reflection. Compare angle A with angle B.

How you see yourself in a mirror. When you look into the mirror, you see your image apparently standing behind the mirror. If you will examine Figure 230 and perform

Experiment 83, you will know why you see yourself in a mirror as you do. You can readily make out the fundamental laws of the mirror. (1) *The image is as far behind the mirror as the object is in front of it.* (2) *It is of the same size as the object.* (3) *It is erect (right side up).* (4) *It is reversed; that is,* when you raise your left hand, the image raises what appears to be its right hand.

[There is, in reality, no image behind the mirror. No ray of light goes through the mirror to form an image where you seem

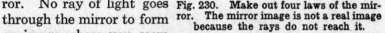

Fig. 230. **Make out four laws of the mirror. The mirror image is not a real image because the rays do not reach it.**

to see it. Light is reflected by the mirror, as you can see by reflecting sunlight to the wall from a small mirror. But you cannot reflect your own image to the wall. If it were a *real image,* you could catch it on a wall or on a screen and see it as you see a picture from a lantern. The rays of light that make the image in the mirror *seem* to come from a point behind the mirror. Such an image formed by rays of light that seem to come from a point other than their true source is called a *virtual image.* We shall learn more about real and virtual images when we study lenses.]

Curved mirrors. Did you ever look at yourself in the "funny mirrors" at the amusement park or in a sideshow at the circus? One mirror makes you look "skinny"; another makes you look fat and "squatty" (Fig. 231). These mirrors are not plane mirrors, but are curved, usually somewhat like a part of the side of a great cylinder in an upright position (for the "skinny" mirror) or horizontal (for the "squatty" mirror). You can make such mirrors with a sheet of polished tin. Look into the sheet of tin as a mirror and make it bulge toward you, watching your image as the tin bends. You will find that it continues to act as a mirror, but that your image is distorted. The curved mirror is still obeying the universal law of reflection; but rays do not travel the same direction when reflected from a cylindrical surface as when reflected from a plane surface.

However, a mirror does not need to have a plane surface to be useful. A *concave* mirror (curved somewhat like the inside of a hollow ball) is used in the headlight of an automobile. The mirror is so curved that all the rays of light falling on it from the lamp (if the lamp is in the correct position) will be reflected forward in almost parallel but slightly divergent (spreading) lines. The concentration of the rays wastes so little light that a small lamp can light the road far ahead (Fig. 232).

Fig. 231. The "funny" mirrors are curved. What are the two curves? What does each do to the image?

In the reflecting telescopes used by the astronomer the parallel rays from a far-distant source are reflected by a concave mirror to produce a small sharp image which is then magnified by lenses. In the dentist's mirror rays from the tooth close to the mirror are so reflected that they produce an enlarged image. *Convex* mirrors (curved like the outside of a ball) are sometimes used in automobiles to give the driver a view of a large area in a small mirror.

Why a wall is no mirror. A light streaming through the window of a room striking the opposite wall obeys the universal law of reflection. The surface of the wall, however, is rough so that if two light rays are parallel when they strike the wall, they will, after reflection, leave the wall in very different directions (Fig. 233). These two rays will, after traveling through the room, strike the wall or the ceiling and will be reflected once more. We speak of this reflection from roughened surfaces as *diffuse reflection*, and it is by means of this diffuse reflection that we ordinarily see objects.

The behavior of light rays makes care necessary in the selection of wall paper or paint for a room. Imagine a room with walls, floor, and ceiling painted a dull black. A window opening into the room might send a stream of sunlight into it. The room, however, would be dark and gloomy, for the dull black would reflect only a small amount of light. Of course, no one would attempt to live in a room of this character, but we do sometimes go too far in that direction. A dark brown, dull paper combined with a dark rug and walnut furniture will give a room such a gloomy air that we are glad to escape from it. On the other hand, a light cream paint in the kitchen or white tile in the bathroom gives the rooms a bright, cheery appearance.

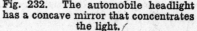

Fig. 232.   The automobile headlight has a concave mirror that concentrates the light.

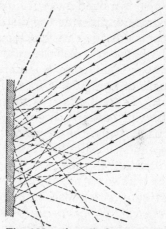

Fig. 233.   A wall shows irregular reflection.

In selecting and furnishing a home, it is well to bear such things as this in mind. Remember, too, that direct sunlight is valuable. It may fade the carpet or the draperies, but it will also kill tuberculosis and other germs, and provide us with energy. Nevertheless, it is possible to go too far in making rooms bright and cheerful. A white enamel paint covering the walls and ceiling of a room, furniture painted white, and a very light rug would produce an impression of cheerfulness. You would find such a room difficult to work in, however, because the glare of the reflected light would be injurious to your eyes.

Candle power. We measure light by its candle power (c.p.). By candle power, we mean the light given out by a *standard candle*. A standard candle is one made of sperm whale oil, seven eighths of an inch thick, burning 120 grains an hour. Today, we compare lights with the brightness of electric lights of known candle power instead of directly with a candle. An ordinary candle gives approximately 1 c.p.; a 20-watt electric lamp will give about 16 c.p.

Fading with distance. Light spreads out as it travels away from a lamp. When pictures are thrown on a screen from a projection lantern, the picture becomes larger as the lantern is moved away from the screen. Likewise the picture becomes dimmer as the distance increases, just as your book becomes dimmer as you move it away from the lamp. The light fades at a definite rate which may be calculated. If a beam of light from a lantern 1 yard from a screen forms a square of light just 1 foot on a side, it illuminates 1 square foot. If the lantern is moved 2 yards from the screen, the light will cover a square 2 feet on a side or 4 square feet. Thus at twice the distance the light covers 4 times as much area and the illumination will be one fourth as intense. If the lantern is moved 3 yards from the screen, the beam of light will cover a square 3 feet on a side or 9 square feet, and the illumination will be one ninth as intense. *The intensity of the light varies inversely as the square of the distance.* This statement is known as the *law of inverse squares* (Fig. 234).

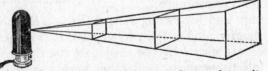

Fig. 234. As light travels away from a lamp, it spreads out and loses intensity at a regular rate. The Law of Inverse Squares.

What candle power do we need? We call the amount of light received on a plane surface placed 1 foot from a lighted standard candle a *foot-candle*. For reading, your book should be illuminated by 6 or 7 foot-candles. The general illumination of a room should be from 2 to 3 foot-candles. The closer the work that you are doing, the more foot-candles you require.

Direct and indirect lighting. If you have ever attempted to read a book in direct sunlight, you know that the intense light hurts your eyes. Do not injure your eyes that way. Also, you will injure your eyes by reading with a bright light shining into your eyes as well as on your book. Direct lighting, with the light falling straight

Fig. 235. Are these positions good?

on your work, is often the best way of lighting your work, but you must be careful that neither the direct rays from the lamp nor glaring reflected rays strike your eyes (Fig. 235).

If you place the light inside a bowl of ground or opal glass, this bowl becomes the source of the light rays. The light rays no longer come from a point but from a large area, giving a much softer light and one that is easier on our eyes. This is, of course, more expensive than direct lighting, for not only must we pay for the glass bowl but we must pay for the light that is absorbed by the bowl. This method of lighting a room we call *diffuse lighting* (Fig. 236). We can secure some of its advantages by using a frosted bulb instead of one of clear glass.

The third method of lighting is to use a light contained in a bowl so arranged that much of the light strikes the ceiling and is reflected downward. This method gives the most diffused lighting and, therefore, is the pleasantest to work by, but it is expensive. It is known as *indirect lighting*.

Fig. 236. Diffuse lighting.

Some lamps are now arranged with a reflector below the lamp (Fig. 239). This throws the light on the ceiling where it is reflected downward. With a 200-watt bulb, such lamps will light an ordinary room well.

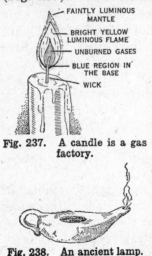

FAINTLY LUMINOUS MANTLE

BRIGHT YELLOW LUMINOUS FLAME

UNBURNED GASES

BLUE REGION IN THE BASE

WICK

Fig. 237. A candle is a gas factory.

Fig. 238. An ancient lamp.

What is a flame? Light a candle and let it burn for five minutes or so. Quickly press out the flame. You will see a smoke rising from the wick. Hold a lighted match in this smoke and you will see that it catches fire and the flame runs down to the wick. The smoke contains a gas. The candle is really a miniature gas factory. Flame is burning gas. The heat of the flame changes the wax of the candle to a gas. The heat of this burning gas decomposes the wax,

Fig. 239. Indirect lighting. Why is this better than direct lighting?

setting free tiny particles of carbon, and it is these glowing carbon particles that give the candlelight (Fig. 237).

Artificial light. The ancient Romans placed grease in a shallow cup, put in a rag to serve as a wick, and lighted the lamp (Fig. 238). The smoky flame gave little light. Candles today give an artistic touch to a dining table or a soft light for a conversation, but if you have tried in camp to write letters home by candlelight, you know how feeble it is.

With the discovery of crude oil (petroleum) came the kerosene lamp (Fig. 240). This was a great improvement on any of the previous methods of lighting a house, but it, too, had its disadvantages. The lamps had to be filled daily and the wicks trimmed. If any kerosene was spilled on the outside of the lamp, the heat of the lamp vaporized it and caused an unpleasant odor.

GLASS CHIMNEY

BRIGHT YELLOW LUMINOUS FLAME

KEROSENE CHANGING INTO GAS (DARK BLUE SECTION OF FLAME)

AIR

AIR

WICK ADJUSTER

WICK

KEROSENE

Fig. 240. The kerosene lamp.

Illuminating gas, made by heating soft coal out of contact with the air, was also used a few years ago for city and town lighting. The gas was convenient but gave a yellow flame of a rather low candle power. Then Auer von Welsbach, an Austrian chemist, discovered that when oxides of certain rare elements, such as thorium, were heated in a colorless Bunsen burner flame they glowed with an intense bright light. This was the start of the mantle (Welsbach) light used very extensively about 1895 (Fig. 241). At the present time all these methods of lighting have been superseded by the incandescent electric light, invented by Thomas A. Edison (Fig. 242). A fine wire is heated to incandescence (glowing) by its resistance to electric current. The modern electric bulbs use a wire of the metal tungsten, and are filled with either nitrogen or argon gas to prevent the vaporization of the metal and "burning out." (See pages 43 and 44.) The incandescent lamp is the most convenient and most economical form of lighting where electricity is available.

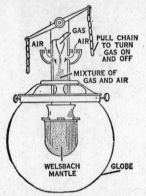

Fig. 241. A Welsbach light. This is a Bunsen burner that heats a mantle to incandescence (glowing). Compare with Bunsen burner Experiment 70.

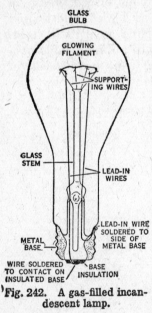

Fig. 242. A gas-filled incandescent lamp.

Another very satisfactory light is that obtained by converting gasoline into gas, burning this gas, and using the heat developed to heat a Welsbach mantle. These portable gasoline lamps, though attended by some little fire risk, are used quite extensively in the country. They give a very bright light.

Fluorescent lamps are glass tubes coated on the inside with certain chemicals. The tubes contain a little mercury. Heated by an electric current, the mercury gives out rays which strike the coating substances and fluoresce, or give out light rays.

Bending light. You have probably noticed that a stick thrust into the water or the oar of a boat in the water looks bent. If you have not noticed the effect, put a pencil into a tumbler of water. Look at the pencil from various angles. We know that the pencil is straight, yet it looks bent. This is because in going from water to air, the light waves are going from one substance to another substance of different density. This causes the light waves to bend at the point of contact between the air and the water. In the water and in the air the waves travel in straight lines, but at the point where they leave the water, they change their direction. This bending is called *refraction* (Fig. 243).

Fig. 243. Why does the pencil in the water seem bent? See Experiment 84.

You will probably see refraction if you will look at the wall back of your kitchen stove when the stove is lighted. The air over the hot stove is heated and this alters its density. This in turn changes the direction in which the waves of light travel and, in consequence, straight lines become very much distorted. You may have noticed the same thing at the beach on a hot summer's day. Look at a pole so placed that the currents of hot air from the sands are between you and the pole. Not only does the pole seem distorted, but this distortion changes from moment to moment as the currents of hot air change. Diamonds and other precious stones owe much of their beauty to the refraction of light that takes place at their polished faces.

Lenses. Lenses make things seen through them appear larger or smaller. A magnifying glass or reading glass is a lens. By the word *lens*, we ordinarily mean a piece of glass having one or two curved sides. A lens need not be of glass, it may be of any transparent material. Your eye contains a lens made of an animal substance. For certain optical work lenses are made from crystals of quartz (rock crystal).

You can make a burning glass (or lens) of ice. Select from your ice box a small piece of ice, choosing a piece as transparent and free from flaws as possible. With a knife, chip the ice until it is roughly the shape of the double convex lens shown in Figure 244. Wet a towel in hot water and use this to smooth the rough surfaces of the lens. Remember that you are trying to produce two curved surfaces that are portions of a sphere. With a large ice lens you can scorch a piece of paper held at the focus of the lens (where the rays passing through the lens come to a point).

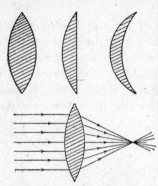

Fig. 244. Convergent lenses. How do they bend the rays? Double convex, plano-convex, and concavo-convex lenses.

There are many different forms of lens (Fig. 244). Those that are thin at the edge and thicker in the middle are called *convergent lenses;* that is, they bring rays of light passing through them to a point called a *focus.* Those that are thick at the edge and thin in the middle are called *divergent lenses;* that is, they scatter the rays of light passing through them (Fig. 245).

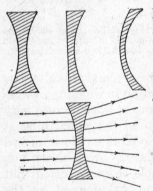

Fig. 245. Divergent lenses. These are concave lenses.

[**Real and virtual images.** Hold a convex (converging) lens close to a white wall opposite a window. Move the lens to and fro. You will find that when it is at one certain distance from the wall, you will obtain on the wall a small inverted picture of the window. We call this picture a *real image,* because it is really formed by the rays of light that actually do reach the wall on which we see it. Repeat your experiment, using again a convex lens, but one having a different curvature. You will find that you again obtain a real image on the wall. You will also find that this real image is sharp and distinct only when the lens is held at a different distance from the wall than was necessary in the first case. If you will try a dozen lenses, all of varying curvature, you will see that the position of the lens necessary to cast a sharp image changes with the curve. The greater the curve of the lens the nearer the lens must be placed to the wall to obtain the sharp image. You will also find that the size of the image depends upon the degree of curvature. The greater the curvature, the smaller the image produced. In every case, however, a real image will be obtained.

The test as to whether an image is real or virtual, as in a plane mirror is whether we can catch it on a wall or screen. If we can it is real, otherwise it is *virtual* (not real). If you substitute a concave (diverging) lens for the convex lens, you will find that no matter where you place it, it is impossible to get a real image upon the wall. If, however, you look through the lens, moving to and fro, in front of your eye, you can easily obtain a virtual image of the window.]

EXPERIMENT 80

Question: How can I show that light rays travel in straight lines?

Materials: Three pieces of cardboard, *A*, *B*, and *C*, each mounted on a wooden support. Each card has a small hole punched through it and all the holes are exactly the same height from the table. A bright light—candle or an electric light.

Directions: (*a*) Support the lamp so that the flame is opposite the hole in the card *A*. Place the card *B* 1 foot from *A*. Look through the hole in *B*. Move *B* to and fro until you can see the light through the hole in *A*. Put card *C* about 6 inches from *B* and adjust its position until, on looking through the hole in *C*, you can see the light shining through the holes in *A* and *B*. Take a stiff straight wire or glass rod and push it through the holes in *A*, *B*, and *C*. The wire represents the path of the light rays. 1. Is the path of the rays of light curved or straight?

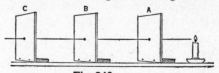

Fig. 246.

(*b*) Place a straight stiff wire through the holes in the cards *A*, *B*, and *C*. Put the candle flame opposite the end of the wire. See that the cards are about 10 inches apart. Remove the wire and look through the holes. You will see the candle flame. Move card *B* slightly to one side so that the holes are no longer in line. 2. Why do you no longer see the candle flame?

Diagram: Show apparatus in use.

Conclusion: Answer the problem.

Practical application: Sighting a gun, catching a thrown ball.

EXPERIMENT 81 (OPTIONAL)

Question: Which objects do you see? Get some dead black cloth such as velveteen; two small balls, one of which is white; a shining object, such as an apple; a dull object, such as a potato; a candle. Set some books on a table to form a background; cover the background and the table in front with the velveteen. Wrap one ball in a small piece of velveteen. Set the objects, including the wrapped ball, in a row on the black cloth. Darken the room. Which can you see? Light the candle. Which now can you see most easily?

EXPERIMENT 82

Question: In what direction does a mirror throw a beam of light?

Materials: A large cardboard to cover a windowpane; a rule; a small mirror; a little chalk dust or talcum powder; a white card.

Directions: Cover a sunlit windowpane with a piece of cardboard in which a small hole has been punched. If there is no sunlit window, a lantern may be substituted. Darken the room. Reflect the ray of light to the ceiling with the mirror. Have someone blow the powder across the beams of light. Hold the rule at right angles to the mirror, with its end at the spot where the light is reflected. Note the angle between the rule and the beam of light on each side of the rule. How does the angle on the side from which the light strikes the mirror (the angle of incidence) compare with the angle on the side toward which it leaves the mirror (the angle of reflection)? Replace the mirror with the white card. Blow some dust as before. Does the card reflect a ray of light to the ceiling? How does the reflected light seem to leave the card? This is diffused light.

Results: State what you observed.

Conclusion: How does the angle of incidence compare with the angle of reflection? How does reflection from a polished surface differ from reflection from an unpolished surface?

EXPERIMENT 83

Question: Where is the face in the mirror? Is it your face? What is the law of reflection?

Materials: Mirror; lighted candle; book; rule; 2 pieces of white paper; 2 pins; protractor.

Directions: Support the mirror perpendicularly to the surface of the table. Place the rule at right angles to the mirror, with the 1-inch end touching the mirror. 1. Place the candle at the 4-inch mark and the book at 8-inch mark. How far does each seem to be behind the mirror? 2. Look in a mirror and wink your right eye. Does the image wink its right eye? Write your name on a piece of paper and hold the name up to the mirror. How is the image name changed? 3. Lay a sheet of paper on the table with its edge against the mirror. Stick a pin upright in the table about 4 inches from the mirror. Place your eye on the level of the table farther to the right. Stick a second pin in the table on a line with the mirror image of the first pin and the same distance from the mirror. Stick a third pin at the edge of the paper, next to the mirror, in line with the second pin and the mirror image of the first pin (Fig. 248). Now draw a line with the rule from the first to the third pin. This line marks the direction of a ray of light from the first pin to the mirror, the *incident ray*. Draw another line from the second pin to the third pin. This line marks the path of the ray of light after it is reflected by the mirror, the *reflected ray*. Draw a line perpendicular to the mirror at the third pin. This line is called a *normal*. The angle between the incident ray and the normal is the *angle of incidence*. The angle between the reflected ray and the normal is the *angle of reflection*. Measure the two angles with a protractor.

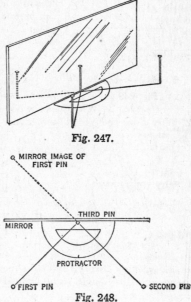

Fig. 247.

Fig. 248.

Results: Record your observations and draw diagrams to illustrate the experiment.

Conclusion: How far behind the mirror does an image seem to be? There is not really any image behind the mirror. It is a *virtual*, not a real image.) Are the right and left sides in their real position or reversed? (The image is "perverted," or a "mirror image.") How does the angle of incidence compare with the angle of reflection? In what way does the face in the mirror differ from your face? What is meant by a mirror image?

Experiment 84

Question: How can I illustrate refraction of light?

Materials: A lead pencil; water; 2 cups; 2 pennies.

Directions: (a) Place the cups side by side. Put a penny in the center of the bottom of each. Move back from the cups until the pennies are just hidden by the rims of the cups. Then have a classmate pour water slowly into the second cup.

(b) Hold a lead pencil, in a slanting position, partly under water in a tumbler as in 249b.

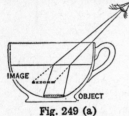

Fig. 249 (a)

Result: 1. What happened when the water was poured into the second cup? If the penny did not come into view, repeat the experiment changing your position a little. 2. What was the appearance of the pencil?

Diagram: Show the rays of light coming from the penny in the second cup and the path of the rays of light coming from the portion of the pencil in the water.

Conclusion: 1. Why does the penny come into view in the second cup? 2. Why does the pencil seem bent? 3. What name do we give to this bending of light rays? 4. Why does an oar partly immersed in water seem to be bent at the point where it enters the water? 5. Why does a pond seem to be shallower than it really is? 6. If you were spearing a salmon, where would you aim, directly at the fish, above it, or below it?

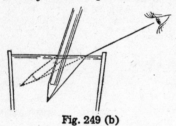

Fig. 249 (b)

Practical application: It is by refraction that lenses have their effect of magnifying, bring rays to a focus, etc.; it is refraction that makes it possible for images to be formed in our eye.

Experiment 85 (Optional)

Question: What is the relative intensity of light from lamps using gas jet, gas mantle, and tungsten filament? At one end of a table set a lighted gas jet. A foot away lay a sheet of white paper. Set a spool in the middle of the paper. On the edge of the paper opposite the gas jet set a lighted gas-mantle burner. Darken the room. Move the mantle burner away until the shadows on each side of the spool seem to be of the same density. Replace the mantle burner with a 50-watt tungsten lamp. Again adjust the distance until the shadows are equal. A gas mantle at .... inches is equivalent to a plain gas jet at .... inches. A 50-watt tungsten lamp at .... is equivalent to a gas jet at .... inches.

Chapter XXVIII

THE CAMERA AND THE EYE

Chemical changes from the sun. Many a girl has had the experience of buying a delicate pink or blue dress in the spring to find by fall that the color has changed to an unattractive shade. Such chemical changes produced by sunlight make photography possible. There are many substances that are changed by the sun's rays, but the best for photography are silver salts.

An "ordinary" photographic plate is a piece of glass coated with a mixture of silver bromide and gelatin. The roll film has the same mixture on a transparent, flexible (capable of being bent) film. The finished photograph is made on paper coated with a similar mixture.

How photographs are made. The camera consists essentially of a box with a convex lens on one side and a photographic plate on the opposite side (Fig. 250). When the camera is pointed at a tree and light is allowed to pass through the lens for a very brief time, the image of the tree that falls

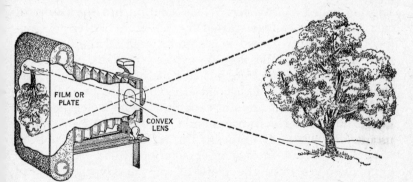

Fig. 250. How the object appears on the film of a camera.

(273)

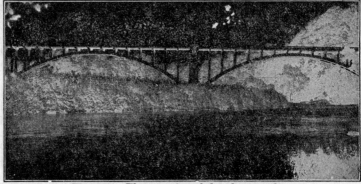

Fig. 251.   The negative of the photograph.

on the photographic plate starts a chemical action.   This chemical action is proportional to the amount of energy that affects the silver salt in the different parts of the image. The image of the blue sky is very bright.   It contains much "photographic" energy.   The part of the photographic plate on which this image falls, therefore, will undergo a considerable chemical change.   As the trunk of a tree is dark, its image will be dull, and the part of the plate on which the image of the tree trunk falls will undergo only a small chemical change.

If you examine the plate after exposure, you will see no evidence of a chemical change.   But the plate is put into a solution called a *developer*.   This solution has the power of carrying on the change started by the light.   After development, the plate is rinsed in water to wash all the developer from it.   If it should now be exposed to light, you would have a picture of the tree, but this picture would slowly disappear.   The parts of the plate that have not been affected by the development are still capable of being acted upon by light and, as a result, we should eventually have a plate completely black.   To prevent this, after the plate has been washed, it is put into another solution called *hypo*.   The hypo dissolves from the plate all of the silver compound that was not affected by the exposure, but leaves unaltered the black image produced by the developer.   This treat-

Fig. 252. The positive of the photograph.

ment is called *fixing* the plate. Finally the plate is washed and dried and we have a negative (Fig. 251).

In the *negative*, the lights and shades of the scene are reversed. The sky in nature is bright. The image of the bright sky produced a considerable chemical change on the plate so that on development the sky turned black. A tree trunk that in nature was dark, caused little chemical change so that on development it remained light. Black becomes white in the negative and white becomes black. For this reason we speak of our result as a negative.

If now we place another photographic plate in contact with the first, expose it for a short time in such a way that light gets to it only through the first plate, and again develop, fix, wash, and dry, we shall obtain a *positive* (Fig. 252). In the negative the sky was opaque. Little light passes through it to the plate underneath so that on developing, the sky portion of the plate remains comparatively clear. The tree trunk in the negative is almost transparent. Light readily passes through it and affects that portion of the plate directly under it. On developing, this portion of the plate turns black. The positive thus reverses the lights and shades of the negative, and restores them to their condition in nature. It is in this way that lantern slides are made. If, instead of using a glass plate, we use paper coated with the same light-sensitive emulsion, we obtain an ordinary photograph on paper.

Knowing that light affects the sensitive plate or film, you may wonder how it is possible to work in a photographer's dark room. It is true that the plate is somewhat sensitive to all light. The ordinary plate or film, however, is almost insensitive to a dark red light. Dark rooms are, therefore, lighted dimly with red lights.

If you had on a yellow or red dress when photographed with ordinary plates or films, you would find in the finished photograph that your dress would appear to be black. If you had on a white dress with blue, red, and black figures, you would hardly recognize the dress in the finished photograph. The blue figures would hardly show, and the red and black would be equally dark. In ordinary plates and films blue and white affect the silver about equally, while red, yellow, and black hardly affect it at all. By adding certain dyes to the silver and gelatin mixture, the silver compounds can be made sensitive to yellow and red lights. Films sensitive to yellow are now sold by most dealers. *Panchromatic* plates and films, sensitive to all colors, are widely used by both professional photographers and amateurs.

What a camera does. Open an ordinary small camera and examine it. If it is not fitted with a ground glass at the back, remove the back and use instead of it a piece of ground glass or wax paper fastened with rubber bands. Notice that the lens in the front of the camera is convex, and that a shutter admits or shuts out the light. A diaphragm or stop allows all of the lens or only a small central portion to be used. It is also possible in the better cameras to change the distance of the lens from the back of the camera in order to obtain sharp images.

Point the camera toward a large near-by sign or any object with sharply marked outlines, using the largest stop or diaphragm. Move the lens back and forth until the image on the ground glass is sharp. As the image on the ground glass is very faint, it is a help to throw an opaque cloth (focusing cloth) over your head and the camera so as to shut out as much of the outside light as possible. You will notice that the image is inverted (upside down). Now point the camera at some bright distant object. To make its image sharp, you must move the lens closer to the ground glass. Replace the large stop by a small one. You will see that the image is

fainter, because not so much light can get through the small stop as passed through the larger stop. You will also notice that the image is sharper.

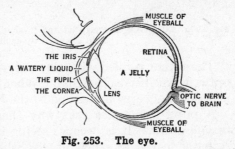

Fig. 253. The eye.

The human eye. The human eye is an almost spherical ball about one inch in diameter. The front of the eye contains a slightly bulging, transparent covering called the *cornea* (Fig. 253). Behind this is a colored curtain called the *iris*. The adjustable opening in the iris is the *pupil*. Just behind the pupil is a small, very convex *lens*. In the back of the eye is a sensitive coating, the *retina*, which contains the nerves of sight. The spaces of the eyes are filled with a transparent fluid and jellylike substances which keep the eye in shape.

In a word, the eye is a *camera*. It has a lens, an adjustable stop or diaphragm, and a sensitive film. When you look at this page, your eye is acting like a camera. The lens of the eye is forming a small, inverted, sharp image on the *retina*. Under proper conditions this image in the eye can be actually seen. By examining it, physicians learn of defects that may exist.

The pupil of the eye operates as does the diaphragm of the camera. If the light is dim, the pupil opens, permitting more light to fall on the retina. If the light is bright, the pupil contracts, cutting down the light that would otherwise dazzle the eye. The eye of the cat has a diaphragm which permits very wide opening. This enables the animal to see better than others in a dim light. Observe a cat's eyes in the bright sunlight and again in a dim light. You will readily see why its vision is superior to yours when the light is dim.

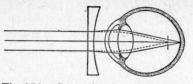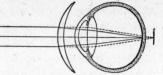

Fig. 254. Correcting nearsighted and farsighted eyes. How are the rays of light changed by each lens?

The retina is filled with tiny nerve filaments leading to the optic nerve (nerve of sight). When the image falls on these nerves, they carry a message to the brain, and one sees.

A pupil sometimes asks why then we do not see things upside down. It is because seeing is a matter of education. A baby learns to reach up for what he wants when light from the object strikes the lower part of his retina, though he does not know, of course, what becomes of the light inside his eye. He learns to reach down when light strikes the upper part of his retina. He learns to reach in the direction from which the light comes without knowing that up and down are reversed on his retina. The important thing is where the light comes from.

When we are taken away from our usual surroundings, our eyes often play us false. For example, we are accustomed to judge distance largely by the distinctness with which we see objects. Perhaps we have learned by experience in our home town that when a tree is a mile away, it has certain indistinct appearances. If we go to Arizona, where the air is much clearer, to produce the same appearance of indistinctness, a tree must be three miles away. We shall misjudge distance badly until we have become accustomed to our new environment.

To obtain a sharp image in the camera, we vary the distance of the lens from the plate. In the eye, the distance between the lens and the retina is not changed. Instead, the shape of the lens is changed by a band of muscle that surrounds it, which can make the lens more or less convex. Through this process the eye has the power of focusing for both near and distant objects. This is called *the power of accommodation.*

Eye defects. If the distance through the eyeball from lens to retina is a little too great, it is impossible for the eye muscle to relax enough to give the lens the proper shape to bring near objects into clear focus. They focus at a point in front of the retina. Distinct, sharp vision is impossible. People with such eyes are said to be *nearsighted* (Fig. 254). This condition may be remedied by the use of glasses with concave lenses, which slightly diverge the light rays, causing them to focus in the proper position on the retina.

If the eyeball is too short from front to back, the reverse defects exist. The lens is not sufficiently convex to bring the image of near objects to a focus on the retina, but instead the point of focusing is back of the retina. Such an eye cannot see near objects clearly. Persons with such eyes are said to be *farsighted* (Fig. 254). To remedy this condition convex glasses are used so as to increase the curvature effect of the lens and so focus the rays nearer the lens.

As we grow older, the eye lens hardens, and it becomes impossible for us to change its shape sufficiently to bring near objects into focus on the retina. The power of accommodation is lessened. Convex lenses aid in correcting this condition. Accommodation to different distances is provided by bifocal lenses, the lower segment being used for reading and the upper for seeing objects at greater distances.

One of the common defects in eyesight is *astigmatism*. This is a condition in which the eye lens does not have a truly spherical curvature. It is often possible to wear glasses so ground as to correct this defect.

The common test for astigmatism is to use a chart, such as is shown in Figure 255, and note whether all the sets of parallel lines are seen with the same degree of distinctness. If any of them look blurred and gray, a more complete test should be made by an oculist.

Care of the eyes. Nature has done her best to protect our eyes. They are set within a deep, bony socket so as to avoid injury from blows. This socket is lined with fat and with a smooth tissue so that the eye turns readily in its socket. Muscles that are attached to the eye are provided so that the eye may be moved in various directions. The pupil contracts, protecting the retina from too intense light. An eyelid closes over the eye in case of danger and to keep out light while we sleep. Eyebrow and lashes drain off perspiration so that it does not fall into the eyes. The tear glands secrete a liquid to wash the surface of the eye, keeping it clean and moist. Tears also kill bacteria; they are antiseptic. Nature has done her part well for us.

For your part, never read in a dim light nor in a light that is too bright and glaring. The light should fall on the book, not on the eyes. An eye shade sometimes helps; but in general you should not face the light while reading. Try out the positions of light and book until you secure good, even light without a glare. In writing, the light should usually come from over the left shoulder so that the shadow of the hand and pencil may not be inconvenient as you work. About thirteen inches is the normal distance from book to eye. If you find that you naturally use a much longer or shorter distance, you should see the oculist, the doctor who specializes on eyes.

Avoid too close use of your eyes under unfavorable conditions. Use glasses when necessary. Never overtire the eyes. Stop reading every little while and rest the eyes by shutting them or looking off at a distance. If you read lying down, prop up the head and hold up the book squarely in front of the eyes so that they are not under continued strain of looking down. It is much better to sit up when you read.

There are certain practices that you should avoid. At a motion-picture show, the closer one sits to the screen, the greater the strain upon the eyes. Sit far enough back to avoid straining your eyes. Test yourself carefully to find out what distance is easiest for you. Do not make a practice of reading on trains and trolleys. The constant jar of the train shakes the book slightly and makes a strain upon the eye muscles that is very tiring. Do not read in a flickering light. Do not rub your eyes with your fingers. Fingers are rarely clean, and may cause an infection. If your eyes are

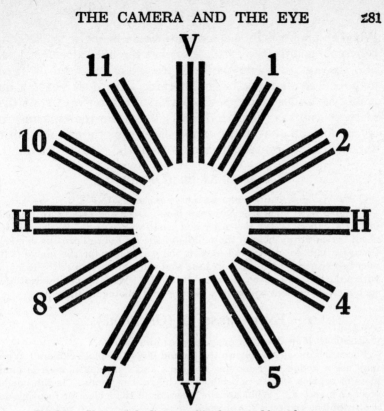

Fig. 255. If any of the lines on this chart are blurred, your eyes need attention.

irritated, a solution of boracic acid, or ordinary salt water, applied with the aid of a medicine dropper will wash dust from the eyes and refresh them, and is mildly antiseptic. Usually, however, the tears provided by nature are sufficiently soothing. The irritated eye is generally relieved by closing it for a while. Swimming pools may convey disease to eyes and skin as well as to air passages and digestive tract. It is well to learn how the water in a pool is disinfected before using the pool.

If your eyes are uncomfortable in bright sunlight, shade them with a hat. A baby's eyes are very sensitive to light and may be permanently injured by too bright sunlight.

When the baby is in the sunlight, shade his eyes; if he is in his carriage, turn the carriage so that the baby does not look into the sun, or shade his face with the carriage top. Turn your bed so that the bright morning light does not fall on your eyes either before you are awake or afterward. At the seashore you may find that dark glasses are the only means of comfort on the bright sand. Many motorists also wear dark glasses to protect their eyes from the glare of the road.

EXPERIMENT 86 (OPTIONAL)

Question: How can I make a pinhole camera?

Remove both ends from a cereal box. Over one end paste tin foil or black paper. Over the other end paste wax paper. With a sharp needle prick a tiny hole in the middle of the tin foil. Turn the camera toward a lighted object and look at the wax paper for the image. It may be necessary to cover your head and the rear portion of the camera with a dark cloth to see the image distinctly. With proper precautions such a crude camera will take a picture on a photographic plate.

EXPERIMENT 87 (OPTIONAL)

Question: How does the image appear in a camera?

Focus the image sharply on the ground glass of a plate camera. You may use a kodak by removing the back and replacing it with ground glass or a piece of wax paper held on by rubber bands. Is the image erect or inverted? What are the positions of the lenses for focusing on a near object and on a far object?

EXPERIMENT 88

Question: How does light print a picture?

Materials: A little silver nitrate ($\frac{1}{4}$ ounce); small flat dish; beaker of water; an ounce of common salt; several pieces of paper about 2 inches square.

Directions: Put the silver nitrate in the dish and add about 2 tablespoonfuls of water. (This solution will stain fingers and clothes.) Put the salt in the beaker of water. Soak the paper in the salt solution. Drain the paper and lay in the silver nitrate solution until covered with a thick white film. Lay the paper in the sunlight and immediately cover with an object such as a button. Watch.

Results: State what happens in the sunlight.

Conclusion: Compounds of what metal are easily affected by sunlight? What kind of energy brought about the change in the solution?

EXPERIMENT 89 (OPTIONAL)

Question: How are blue prints made?

Light changes certain compounds of iron so that they may be used in photography. Blue prints used extensively in shop drawings and elsewhere are produced by such action. Secure blue-print paper, lay on it a leaf or a photographic negative, weight it down with a piece of glass. Expose to the sunlight for a few seconds. Then wash in water. The parts on which the sunlight acted changed to a deep blue, while the unexposed parts wash out to a pure white.

QUESTIONS TO THINK OUT AND TO INVESTIGATE

1. If a ball were perfectly transparent, what would it look like?

2. You can look at the image of the sun in water at noon, but in the late afternoon it is too dazzling. Why should it be more dazzling when there is less light?

3. Why does the sun give less light in the later afternoon than at noon?

4. It is said that we can see the sun after it is really below the horizon. Why?

5. Bifocal lenses are made with two lenses for each eye, a wider lens and a smaller additional lens. What is the purpose of each lens? Which one is "stronger"?

6. Paint a wide strip of white paint across the middle of a mirror or paste a strip of dead-white paper. Go into a darkened room and with the mirror reflect a beam of sunlight on a white wall. Describe and explain the effect on the wall.

7. Arrange two mirrors so that you can see over a wall. This is a crude periscope. Explain it to the class. Try to improve it by means of a cardboard tube.

8. Consult a textbook on physics to learn the principle of the range finder used with a camera to enable one to measure the distance to an object.

9. Why are two eyes better than one? Close one eye. Have a classmate hold up a finger within your reach. With a slow side swing try to touch the tip of your classmate's finger with the tip of yours.

CHAPTER XXIX

SEEING THINGS THROUGH LENSES

Seeing tiny things. If you want a good look at a tiny bug, you use a *magnifier*. This is a simple convex or converging lens. Figure 256 will show you the principle upon which this depends. Reading glasses are examples of such simple magnifiers.

To see a very tiny bug we use a "thicker" magnifier. By increasing the curvature of the simple lens used in the magnifying glass, we increase its magnifying powers. There is a practical limit to this, however, for the greater the curvature, the smaller the lens. The smaller the lens, the smaller the area we can see through it, and the more difficult it is to handle.

To see a bacterium, we use a *compound microscope*. Here a small lens called the *object lens* (Fig. 257) produces a magnified [real] image. A second lens called the *eyepiece* forms an enlarged [virtual] image of the first image. The two magnifications make it possible to see very small objects. The mirror is placed under the microscope to throw

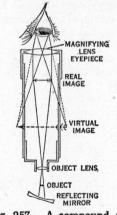

Fig. 257. A compound microscope.

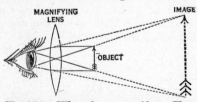

Fig. 256. Why a lens magnifies. How does this convex lens change the rays? Why do we see the object larger than it is?

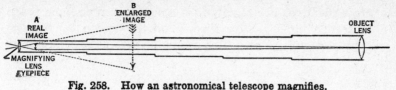

Fig. 258. How an astronomical telescope magnifies.

a beam of light through the object and the system of lenses.

Seeing distant things. To see a distant star, a large number of light rays are collected by a large object lens or objective (Fig. 258). The objective forms an image of the distant body at A and the eyepiece magnifies this image and forms an enlarged second image at B. The great telescope at the Yerkes Observatory in Wisconsin has an objective 40 inches in diameter mounted in a tube 63 feet long. The 100-inch telescope at the Mount Wilson Observatory, California, uses a concave mirror instead of an objective lens to collect the rays of light from the distant heavenly bodies.

The image seen in the telescope used by the astronomers is inverted. For terrestrial use (for seeing objects on the earth), as in the spyglass, another lens is added to invert again the inverted image and thus give us an erect image (Fig. 259).

In all these optical instruments, it is necessary to make some provision for focusing, that is, making the image sharp and clear. This is usually done by providing the eyepiece with device by which it can be moved to and fro, so that the distance between eyepiece and objective can vary, depending upon the distance of the object (Figs. 260 and 261).

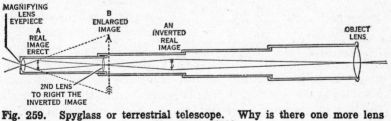

Fig. 259. Spyglass or terrestrial telescope. Why is there one more lens than Figure 258?

How pictures are thrown on a screen. You have probably seen a large picture thrown on the screen by the use of a projection lantern. The source of the light used may be a carbon arc lamp or a powerful incandescent lamp. The light is sent through two lenses which direct the light through the slides in parallel rays (Fig. 262). The slide is always put in inverted to reverse the inversion caused by the objective. To focus the image on the screen, the extension bellows carrying the objective is moved back and forth.

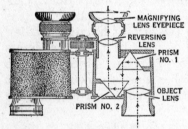

Fig. 260.   How lenses change the rays in an opera glass.

Seeing things that are gone. A flash of lightning lasts about five millionths of a second, as measured by an electrical device. To the eye it seems that the flash lasts much longer. That is because the effect of the flash lasts in the retina of the eye or the brain long after the lightning bolt has disappeared. This *duration of vision* persists from about $\frac{1}{20}$ to $\frac{1}{10}$ of a second after the light stimulation has stopped.

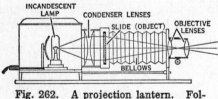

Fig. 261.   The construction of a prism binocular.

The next time you gaze at a red neon advertising sign you will see an excellent example of this *persistence of vision*. The red light given off by the lamp

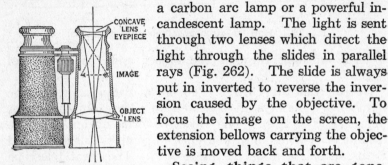

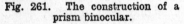

Fig. 262.   A projection lantern. Follow the rays of light through the lenses.

really goes on and off several thousand times a second. Your eyes do not detect this because during the very small fraction of a second that the lamp is dark, the eye still sees the red flash that occured less than a thousandth of a second before. The bright red flashes persist and blend with one another, giving us the impression of a steady light.

When you look at a carriage wheel that is turning slowly, you see each spoke of the wheel plainly. If you spin the wheel faster, you cannot see the number of spokes, but you see the wheel as a more or less solid mass. Each spoke lingers in your eye for a fraction of a second after it has passed along to another position. This *after image* blends in with the image of the next spoke.

Motion pictures. The amateur motion-picture camera is like an ordinary camera except that the pictures are automatically taken at the rate of 16 a second. A picture of a baseball player sliding to first base is taken by the camera as a series of rapid pictures, each exposed for $\frac{1}{32}$ of a second, and each shows him a little nearer to first base.

When this film is put into a motion-picture projector in action, we see "motion pictures." The pictures do not really move. The motion-picture projector is a type of projection lantern, in which the pictures are flashed on the screen very rapidly, at the rate of 16 a second. After one picture of the film has been flashed for $\frac{1}{32}$ of a second a revolving shutter darkens the screen while the next picture of the film is moved into place. The eye does not see the dark inter-

Fig. 263. A motion-picture film of a child speaking. The shaded bands at the left edge of the film are the sound track that makes the talking. See page 358.

vals because of the persistence of vision (Fig. 263). The picture that is flashed on the screen lingers in the eye until the next one is flashed. Thus the pictures of the baseball player, showing him getting nearer to first base, fade into each other. To the eye, this appears like continuous motion.

EXPERIMENT 90

Question: How do convex lenses affect rays of light?

Materials: A convex lens, preferably one having a focal length of about 6 inches; a bright light; a rule; talcum powder or chalk dust.

Directions: (a) Hold the lens in a beam of sunlight. With the lens focus the beam of light (move the lens back and forth) on a sheet of white paper, until the light seems to form a point. The point is called the *principal focus* of the lens. Then have someone scatter the talcum powder or chalk dust on the beam of light before it enters the lens and after it leaves the lens. 1. How does the lens change the rays of light? Draw a diagram. 2. Measure the distance from the lens to the principal focus. This distance is called the *focal length* of the lens. Mark it on the diagram.

(b) Use a wall opposite a brightly-lighted window as a screen to receive the image. Hold the lens in your hand and focus by moving it toward or away from the wall until you see on the wall an image of the window. You will notice that only when the lens is in one particular spot is this image clear and distinct. 1. What must the lens have done to the light rays coming from the window? 2. Is the image on the wall erect or inverted? Is it larger or smaller than the object (the window)? Draw a diagram.

(c) Darken the room. Place a bright light about 6 feet from the wall you are using as a screen. Place the lens between the light and the wall and move it back and forth until you get a sharp image. Move the light nearer the wall, and farther from the wall, and focus the image on the wall. Note in each case the distance from lens to image. Put your results in the table.

	FIRST POSITION	SECOND POSITION	THIRD POSITION
Distance of light from lens (in inches)			
Distance of image from lens (in inches)			

(d) Look at the page of a book through the lens. Move the lens closer to and farther away from the book until you see a clear, enlarged image of the printed words.

Conclusion: As the light approached the lens, what happened to the image? The image (approached, went farther from) the lens. The image became (larger, smaller). Why are the lenses on the best cameras mounted so that the distance between the lens and the film sensitive to light can be altered? Answer the question of the experiment.

Practical application: Lenses are used in cameras, in microscopes and telescopes, in eyeglasses, and in many optical instruments. If the lens used is a convex one, in every case it is used because it draws together (converges) the rays of light. There must always be a certain relationship between the distance of object and image from the lens if we are to get a clear image. In cameras in which the lens does not move, it is fixed at such a distance from the film that all objects (except those that are within a few feet of the camera) are in focus or very nearly in focus. The blurring of the image is so slight that we do not notice it. If such cameras, however, are used to take pictures of very near objects, this blurring becomes so great that the picture is useless.

EXPERIMENT 91

Question: How do concave lenses affect rays of light?

Materials: A concave lens having a focal length of about 6 inches; a bright light.

Directions: (a) Use a wall opposite a brightly lighted window as a screen. Hold the lens in your hand and learn whether you can focus an image on the wall. Look at the window through the lens. What kind of image do you see?

(b) Place the light 6 feet from the wall and try to get an image on the wall by moving the lens toward and away from the wall. 1. Can you get a real image on the wall? 2. What is the lens doing to the light rays?

(c) Hold the lens over the page of a book. Move the lens up and down, at the same time looking through it at the printed matter on the page. What do you see?

Diagram: Show the lens scattering rays of light.

Conclusion: Answer the question. Will a concave lens throw an image on the screen?

Practical application: Concave lenses scatter or diverge light. They are used in eyeglasses, in reducing lens by artists to make an object seem smaller, in opera glasses, and other optical instruments.

EXPERIMENT 92 (OPTIONAL)

Question: How would you make a microscope and a telescope?

Get a lens having a focal length of about 3 cm. for the objective (lens nearest the object), and one having a focal length of 15 cm. or less for the ocular (eyepiece). Support the lenses about 15 to 20 cm. apart.

The object to be magnified should be about 4 cm. beyond the objective. Focus with the ocular until the image is sharp.

To make an astronomical telescope use similar lenses and turn your instrument upon a distant object. Focus with the eyepiece. You will notice that the image is inverted.

To make a telescope for objects on the earth, get three lenses having focal lengths of 15, 4, and 4 cm. Set up the first of these, and about 23 cm. from it set up one of the other lenses. This is the inverting or correcting lens. About 11 cm. beyond this lens set the third lens or eyepiece. Turn the telescope upon a distant object and focus with the eyepiece. You will notice that the image is right side up.

QUESTIONS TO THINK OUT

If you cannot think out these questions, read Chapter XXX, and then try again.

1. If you look at oil floating on water, the colors change as you change your position. Why?

2. Why is snow white, but a block of ice transparent? Why is fog white?

3. Account for the colors of the sunset.

4. Why does the laundress use bluing? Devise an experiment to learn if its use is justified.

5. Why does a blue suit often look black by artificial light?

6. When a whistling locomotive passes you, the whistle changes to a lower pitch. Light shows a similar effect, called a Doppler effect. How does it change light? Try to figure it out from the facts on page 291. If after an honest effort you cannot figure it out, turn to page 690, and do some more thinking.

7. Here is another hard one. Why is the sky blue? Think it out this way: If you see blue, what wave lengths are reaching your eyes? If you do not know, see pages 291–293. If you see white, what wave lengths are reaching your eyes? As you look up toward the "sky," is there anything "up there" to send the blue wave lengths to your eyes but not the wave lengths that make white light? If you cannot think it out, consult a textbook in physics.

8. The stratosphere fliers found that the sky darkened as they rose to great heights. This is in agreement with theory. At very great heights the sky would seem black overhead, if you did not look at the sun. Why?

9. Why is the sun red through smoke or fog? Here are the steps in reaching an answer: What wave lengths reach your eyes when you see red light? What wave lengths make up the visible sunlight? What must happen to sunlight to make it appear red? Is there anything in smoke or fog to change the sunlight in this manner?

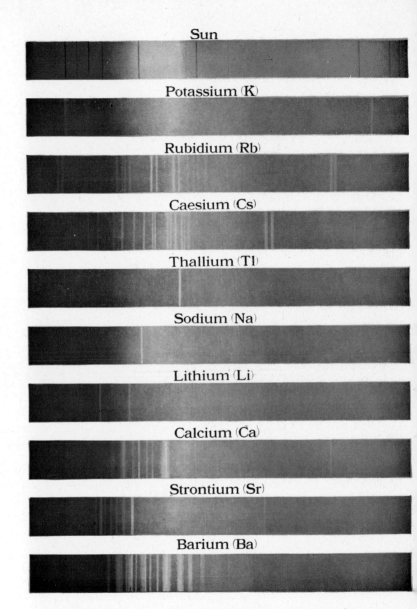

Fig. 264. The spectrum of the sun and of various elements shown against the sun's spectrum. These elements show only the bright lines, thus Sodium has only yellow light.

CHAPTER XXX

COLOR

What colored light is. White light is really a mixture of all the colors of the rainbow. Sir Isaac Newton was the first to show this. He passed a narrow beam of light through a prism (Fig. 265) and found that the prism not only bends (refracts) the light, but that it separates (disperses) it, so

that the narrow beam of light appears on a screen as a band. This band is composed of the colors of the rainbow; it is called a *spectrum*. If instead of throwing the dispersed rays of the spectrum upon a

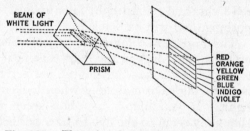

Fig. 265. The prism bends the rays and produces the spectrum. These colors form the spectrum of sunlight.

screen, you pass them through a second prism so as to bring the band of colored light back to its original size, you will obtain the original white light.

You have probably seen spectra outside the laboratory. Pieces of glass shaped like a prism are sometimes hung in windows where the sunlight will fall on them, and the colored bands of light appear on the wall. Borrow a prism and look through it at a window frame and the sky beyond. You will notice that the edge of the window frame appears to have a narrow fringe of color about it.

We believe that each color of the spectrum is caused by a distinct wave length. That is, a wave length of 700 millionths of a millimeter produces red light, a wave length of 600 millionths of a millimeter will produce orange light

(291)

and a wave length of 400 millionths of a millimeter will produce violet light. We usually drop the phrase "millionths of a millimeter" and speak of a wave length of 700.

Why the rose is red. A red rose in one sense is all colors of the rainbow except red. The rose is red because when white light, which is a mixture of all wave lengths between the limits of visible light (400 to 700), falls on it, the rose absorbs all of the various wave lengths except the particular wave length that corresponds to red light. This it reflects to your eye. Since this red light is the only light that enters your eye, you see the rose as red. If the red rose is put in a green light, which contains no red wave lengths, the rose will be unable to reflect any light, since it can only reflect red light, and no red light falls upon it. Then it will reflect nothing, and will be black.

The apparent color of an object, then, depends not only on the object, but on the light that falls on the object. This explains why colors that match perfectly in the daylight may be very far from matching when looked at under an electric light. If you match two blue-green ribbons by daylight, they may seem to the eye to be a perfect match and yet may really be made up from quite different color combinations. If these two ribbons are viewed under an electric light, which is very rich in red and yellow and is deficient in blue, the two ribbons may no longer reflect the same kind of light. One may appear blue and the other green. Colors must always be matched in the light in which they will be used.

Most colors as we see them in nature are not pure. That is, they really are made up of several colors mixed together. An orange marigold seems to the eye to reflect nothing but orange, but in addition it reflects some red, yellow, and green.

It is a very interesting experiment to throw a bright spectrum on the wall and then hold colored ribbons in the various colors. From the results you can tell a good deal about what colors the ribbons are really reflecting.

One-color light. A few bodies when heated shine with a light of one color only (monochromatic light). Soak an asbestos string in a solution of washing soda (sodium car-

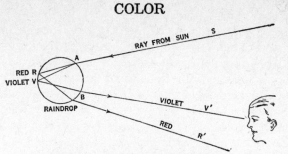

Fig. 266.   The cause of the rainbow.

bonate) and hang it in a colorless Bunsen burner flame.   An intense yellow light will be given out.   Darken the room and hold a colored picture in this light.   If you will recall the paragraph on the red rose, you can explain what you see.

The rainbow.   In Figure 266 *S* represents a ray of white light coming from the sun, low on the horizon.   To the east rain is falling.   One of the raindrops, enlarged, is shown by the circle.

As the white light enters the drop at *A*, it is refracted and dispersed (scattered).   When it reaches the back of the drop, it is reflected, and it is again refracted as it leaves the drop at *B*.   The white light is dispersed and forms the spectrum V'-R'.   If your eye is at V' and you look along the ray, you will see at *B* a violet light from this raindrop.   Drops above this one will send other colors to your eye and you will see the rainbow.

Color blindness.   Certain persons cannot be trusted to pick strawberries because they cannot tell red berries from green.   It is said that the poet Whittier once put a red patch on a green wall paper, for both looked alike to him.   We say that such persons are color-blind.   Color blindness may be a serious handicap.   Railroad and steamship employees are tested for color blindness.   Traffic engineers are now discussing the substitution of other signals for colored lights on the highways, for one man in every twenty is color-blind to some extent and one woman in two hundred.

Colored book pictures.   Have you wondered how the colored plates in this book were made?   Look at Figure 267.

First the paper was run through a press that printed with yellow ink. Then it went through a press that used red ink and finally through one that printed with blue ink. These three colors in various combinations make pictures of all colors.

Sunshine and health. You are sunburned chiefly by rays which you cannot see. Beyond the wave lengths that cause visible violet light, there are wave lengths which do not affect the retina in the ordinary way, and hence are invisible, but which have an intense chemical activity. These we call *ultra-violet rays*. A moderate exposure of the body to their action is healthful. We must be careful, however, not to carry the exposure too far. The continued chemical action of these ultra-violet rays on our skins may cause such a deep burn as to be painful or even dangerous. In the same way, exposure to sunlight may bring about a sunstroke. Clothing serves to protect our bodies from these rays. In India and other tropical countries, white persons find it necessary to protect themselves from the intense action of the sun's rays. No white man in those countries would think of going out without a hat to protect him.

One of the reasons why we like to live in the country is that sunlight reaches us without having to pass through the smoke and dirt of the city air. People who live in the open air receive more of these healthful rays than do the city office workers. Glass, which is transparent to light waves, shuts out ultra-violet rays or most of them. If, therefore, you are recovering from a cold and the doctor tells you to sit in the sunlight, sit in front of an open, not in front of a closed, window. Hospitals sometimes have a room fitted with windowpanes of quartz (rock crystal) or certain other substitutes for glass that allow the ultra-violet rays to pass through. Even chicken houses are sometimes fitted with glass substitutes to keep the hens in health and vigor.

To help city dwellers get the sunlight that is so healthful, several of the electric companies are manufacturing lamps that generate large quantities of ultra-violet rays. These lamps may serve a very useful purpose, but their use should be attended with some care. They should be used only

The Four-color Process of Printing

Fig. 267. This page was sent four times through the printing press. It was printed successively with yellow, red, blue, and black inks. Examine the picture with a lens.

under the doctor's directions. Remember that if you fall
asleep while the lamp is acting on your skin, and wake up an
hour later, you will have developed a painful case of sunburn.

You certainly would not be foolish enough to look directly
at the sun. If you did, your eyes would receive so much
energy that they might easily be permanently injured. Remember this in using ultra-violet ray lamps. You do not see
these radiations but they exist, and if you gaze at the lamp
for some time, your eyes will be injured.

Another value of sunlight is that it kills most disease germs.
Such germs as those that cause tuberculosis prefer to live in
dark, damp places. If you expose them to clear, dry sunlight,
they die. If you are planning to build a new home, remember
that there are certain rooms that need much sunlight. Your living room, your kitchen, and the children's rooms are all rooms
that will be much used in the daytime, and these are the rooms
that should be on the healthful or sunny side of the house.

EXPERIMENT 93

Question: What colors are in sunlight?

Materials: A glass prism; a white screen.

Directions: Hold the prism in a beam of sunlight so that the rays
are thrown on a white screen or on the opposite wall.

Results: Draw a diagram of the spectrum as it appears on the screen.
Name the colors in order or color them with crayon.

Conclusion: Answer the question.

EXPERIMENT 94

Question: What determines the color that we see?

Materials: Pieces of glass, blue, green, yellow, red, and such other
colors as may be obtained; pieces of cloth of similar colors; a projection
lantern; a white screen; a glass prism.

Directions: (a) Project the spectrum of sunlight as in Experiment
93. Hold each piece of colored glass in turn between the prism and
the screen. Notice what happens to each color of the spectrum.

(b) Darken the room. Use the pieces of colored glass as lantern
slides or hold them in front of the lens. Examine each piece of colored
cloth in turn in each colored light.

Results: Arrange two tables recording: 1. What happened to each
color of the spectrum as each glass was placed in front of the prism;
2. The appearance of each colored cloth in each light.

Conclusion: Name two factors which determine colors that you see.

UNIT EIGHT

ELECTRICITY AND MAGNETISM

Lightning no doubt startled primitive man and sent him slinking into his cave. Long ages later Benjamin Franklin drew electricity from the cloud on his kite string and showed that lightning is due to electricity. Before Franklin's day, and for years afterwards, people looked upon electricity as a plaything of the scientist. But scientists were not playing. They were searching in deadly earnest for an explanation of electrical action, so that they might find a means of control.

In 1819 Oersted, the Dane, discovered that if one sends an electric current through a coil of wire, the wire becomes a magnet. In 1831 Faraday, the Englishman, and before him, Henry, the American, discovered that turning a coil of wire between the poles of a magnet sets up a current of electricity in the wire. To the average person of the time such experiments seemed useless, but from these two simple discoveries have come the current that lights our cities and homes, and runs our vacuum sweepers, trolley cars, and electric locomotives. Who shall say what scientific experiment is useless? Try to think of our lives today without electricity—no electric lights on the streets, no electric cars, no modern automobiles, no airplanes, none of the modern conveniences from toasters to washing machines, no radio. Try to imagine modern business and industry without the telegraph or telephone.

We are not yet in sight of the end. Scientists are studying electric currents in nerves and muscles. Do our brain cells work by electricity? Do we think by electric currents? Physiologists hardly say that, but they have measured the current in a working nerve. Radio electricity is a new field. Electric waves are constantly whirling through the air and straight through our bodies. Similar waves are coming to us from outside the earth, from the sun and stars and from the depths of space. We can detect them with scientific instruments. Shall we learn how to catch them and put them to work? We have already done so in part.

In this unit we shall study that mysterious force of magnetism which together with the stars guides the mariner in his exploration of the globe. We shall see something of how it acts, and its connection with electricity.

We shall see how current is generated and how it is used in lamps, toasters, and flatirons. We shall study its connection with magnetism that rings our doorbells, clicks our telegraphs, and enables us to hear voices beyond the mountains and the seas. We shall study the principle of the electric motor that drives vacuum sweepers, trolley cars, and electric locomotives. Finally, we shall see a little of those electric waves that sweep about the earth and come in to us from the heavens beyond the earth. We have learned to start some of these waves in our radio and to pick them up again. They are the latest development in man's age-long efforts to communicate with his fellows. Let us hope that they will be the means of bringing us to such an understanding of one another that nation shall not rise up against nation and that steel shall not be used for building battleships and monstrous guns, but for constructing ocean liners and machines of industry.

Chapter XXXI

MAGNETISM

The magnetic compass. Were you ever lost in a deep forest, unable to find your way out? Have you ever been sailing out of sight of land, not knowing what direction your boat was going? A wise camper in the big woods marks his trail, and, like the sailor, carries a compass. The compass was invented centuries ago, we do not know by whom, since the Chinese, Arabs, Italians, Greeks, and others all claim the invention; it consists of a magnetic needle or bar magnet balanced or suspended so that it turns freely on its support, above a circular card on which the points of the compass are shown.

Natural magnets are found at certain places on the earth. They are magnetic iron ore. Pieces of such magnetic ore are called *lodestones* or *leadstones*. They were probably the first compasses.

If you will stroke a steel needle with a lodestone or some other magnet, you will find that the needle will itself become a magnet. You can prove that the needle is an artificial magnet by placing it near small bits of iron or steel and noting how it will attract them to itself.

You can make a simple homemade compass by pushing a magnetized needle through a cork and floating it in water.

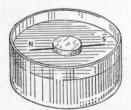

The cork holds the needle flat (horizontal) (Fig. 268). You will find that one end of the needle will point to the north; this end is called the *north pole* of the compass, while the other end is called the *south pole*. This is a simple form of the magnetic compass that is used by aviators

Fig. 268. A floating magnetized needle is a compass. and sailors.

Magnetic attraction. If a bar magnet (Fig. 269) is dipped into a cluster of small nails, there will be no attraction at the center of the magnet, and the greatest number of nails will cling to the ends of the magnet. These are called the *poles* of the magnet. If we suspend this bar magnet freely by hanging it from a thread, it points north and south.

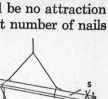

A north pole of a bar magnet held close to the north pole of your compass needle will cause the compass needle to swing away. But a north pole held near a south pole will show

Fig. 269. **A magnet attracts iron at its poles.**

attraction. Let us call these facts the law of magnets. *Like magnetic poles repel, unlike poles attract.*

The magnetic field. When we move a compass needle about near a strong magnet, we find that, although the magnet is a foot away, it still will attract the needle. This seems to show that the attractive force of the magnet spreads out in all directions and to some distance from the magnet.

We can detect this *field of force* by covering a horseshoe magnet with a sheet of glass or cardboard and sprinkling on the glass a thin coating of iron filings. A gentle tapping on the glass with a pencil will cause the little filings to arrange themselves in curves running from the north pole to the south pole. Each little bit of iron behaves like a little magnet and is pulled along in its line of attraction, which is called its *line of force* (Fig. 270).

We conceive of the earth as being a huge magnet. Compasses on it behave as did these little bits of iron. They are pulled parallel to the direction of the magnetic lines of force of the earth.

Where the compass points. In most places on the earth the compass does not point due north, that is, it does not point to the

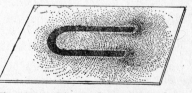

Fig. 270. **Lines of magnetic force shown by iron filings.**

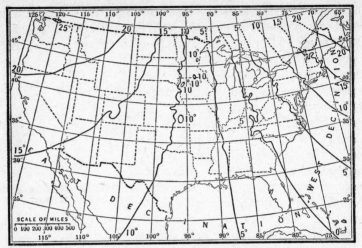

Fig. 271. Magnetic declination. Only on the 0° line does the compass point due north. Eastward of the 0° line the compass points west of north by the number of degrees indicated. Westward of the 0° line the compass points east of the true north. How does the compass point in your town?

geographic North Pole, the most northerly point on the earth. It points to the magnetic north pole. The magnetic poles are not on the geographic poles. The north magnetic pole is about 1200 miles south of the geographic North Pole, a little west of Hudson Bay near the Arctic shore. When a ship is east of the geographic pole, its compass points west. If it is north of the magnetic pole, its compass points south. If a compass is directly on the magnetic north pole, the needle, if it is free to dip, points straight down. Magnetic maps show the difference between the true north and the compass direction. (The angle between the true north and the direction of the needle at any point is called the *magnetic declination*.) (Fig. 271.)

EXPERIMENT 95

Question: How may I determine the laws of magnetic attraction and repulsion?

Materials: Thread; steel darning needle; bar magnet; cork; dish of water.

Directions: (*a*) Stroke the darning needle with the north pole of the magnet, beginning at the eye and stroking toward the point. Ten strokes are sufficient.

(*b*) Push the needle through the cork so that it floats in a horizontal position in a dish of water, and find out which end is the north pole. Remember this for the next step in the experiment.

(*c*) Tie a string midway along the needle and hang it about a foot below a support. Bring the north pole of the bar magnet near the point of the needle; near the eye of the needle. What happens?

(*d*) Repeat this procedure, bringing the south pole of the bar magnet near the two ends of the suspended needle. Result?

Diagram: Show the suspended needle.

Conclusion: State the law of magnetic attraction and repulsion.

Practical application: How does the magnetic compass work? What is its use?

EXPERIMENT 96

Question: How may I see a magnetic field?

Materials: Horseshoe magnet; pane of glass or cardboard; shaker with iron filings.

Directions: Cover the magnet with the pane of glass or with the cardboard and sift the filings lightly and evenly on it. You can do this well by holding the shaker two feet above the table. Tap the glass lightly. What happens? Why did the filings move? What happens to iron or steel when placed near a magnet?

Diagram: Draw the position of the filings.

Conclusion: What is every magnet surrounded by? How can you see this field of attraction?

Practical application: The earth's magnetic field causes the compass needle to point north and south. Why?

EXPERIMENT 97

Question: How does a free-floating magnet behave in the field of a larger magnet?

Materials: Flat glass tray; bar magnet; broad darning needle; cork.

Directions: (*a*) Stroke the darning needle from eye to point with the north pole of the magnet. Repeat this action several times until the needle is a magnet. How will you show that the eye end of the needle is a north pole?

(*b*) Push the needle through the cork from side to side so that when placed in the glass tray the needle will float with the eye end (the north pole) in the water and the point of the needle will stand up out of the water. You have thus made a floating magnet (Fig. 268).

21

(c) Place the bar magnet in the tray filled to a depth of one inch with water. Place your floating magnet over the north pole. Result? Repeat this several times so that your floating magnet makes four trips on each side of the bar magnet. Draw a map of the paths that the magnet made.

Diagram: Show a diagram for *b* and *c*.

Conclusion: Answer the problem.

NOTE: The path that the floating magnet took about your magnet is called a *line of force*. The entire region, containing hundreds of these lines of force, is called a *magnetic field*.

QUESTIONS TO THINK OUT

1. Think up an experiment to show that not only does a magnet attract a piece of iron, but a piece of iron attracts a magnet. Demonstrate to the class.

2. Is magnetism stopped by glass as electricity is? Try it.

3. An iron fence is sometimes found to be magnetized. Why? Would you expect it to be a fence running north and south or one running east and west? Why?

4. If you cut a magnet in two in the middle, would each piece have a north pole? Try it with a magnetized knitting needle or a piece of steel wire.

5. Take two bar magnets. (a) Place the north poles side by side and the south poles side by side. Try attracting iron filings with the pair held together. (b) Reverse one magnet so that the north pole of each lies against the south pole of the other. Then try attracting iron filings with the pair held together. Explain any difference you find.

6. If a knife blade held near a magnetic needle attracts the north pole, does it show that the knife is a magnet? Explain.

7. Would an aviator fly to the North Pole by following the north pole of a compass? Explain.

8. How would the compass point at San Diego, California? See Fig. 271.

9. Suppose when you were on a hike your compass turned from its usual north position and pointed more toward a hill you were walking along. What would you conclude?

Chapter XXXII

WHAT IS ELECTRICITY?

Electricity produced by rubbing. Did you ever hear your hair crackle and see it stand on end as you combed it on a frosty morning? If you blow up a large rubber balloon and hang it from the ceiling so that it is about at the level of the eye and bring your hand near it, nothing happens.

However, if you rub the balloon gently with some fur, and then bring your hand near it, you will notice that it is attracted to your hand (Fig. 272). Evidently this force of attraction must be other than magnetic attraction, because no iron or steel is present. It is called *electrical* attraction.

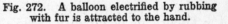

Fig. 272. A balloon electrified by rubbing with fur is attracted to the hand.

Two kinds of electricity. If a hard-rubber rod or a stick of sealing wax is rubbed with fur and suspended so that it swings freely, and if a second rod also rubbed with fur is brought near it, the rods repel each other (Fig. 273). If the same

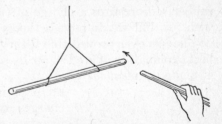

Fig. 273. Two electrified rubber rods repel each other.

thing is tried with two rods of glass that have been rubbed with silk, the glass rods also repel each other. But if a glass rod that has been rubbed with silk is brought near a rubber rod that has been rubbed with fur, then they attract

each other.   From this experiment it is obvious that there
are two kinds of electrification.   Benjamin Franklin called
the kind produced on glass *positive* or plus electricity, and the
kind produced on rubber, *negative* or minus electricity.   We
still use these names, although we do not explain electricity
as Franklin did.   This experiment also shows that *like electrical charges repel and unlike electrical charges attract.*

Conductors and insulators.   If you try to charge a
copper rod by holding it in your hand and rubbing it with
fur or silk, you will find that no charge of electricity collects
on the copper.   You may show that it will not attract bits
of paper, or ping-pong balls.   Rubber or glass similarly rubbed
will attract these objects.   Metals do not hold electric charges
because charges run off the metal to the hand as quickly as
they are formed.   Metals are carriers, or *conductors of
electricity*.

If the rubbing action produces charges that attract bits
of paper, as in rubber, sealing wax, glass, and bakelite, then
these charges of electricity do not run off because these substances do not conduct electric charges.   The electric charge
stays on these substances.   Such materials are called *nonconductors of electricity* or *insulators*.

Theory of electricity.   No one knows certainly why a
rubber rod acquires a charge of electricity when it is rubbed
with fur, but we do have a theory which explains it.   While
no one has ever proved this theory, we use it because it is the
best explanation offered so far by scientists.   Every substance
is made up of *atoms* (Fig. 274).   An atom in turn is made
up of smaller units, thought of as
charges of electricity.   There are
negative electric charges called *electrons*, and positive electric charges
called *protons*.   The atom has the
heavier positive charges, the protrons,
concentrated (gathered) at the center
and the lighter negative electrons
around this center.   When the atom
has an equal number of positive and

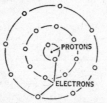

Fig. 274.   According to
theory atoms are made up of
charges of electricity, protons,
+ charges and electrons, —
charges.

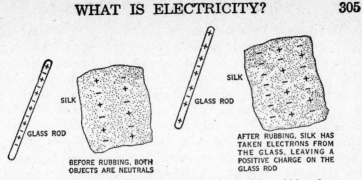

SILK

GLASS ROD

BEFORE RUBBING, BOTH
OBJECTS ARE NEUTRALS

SILK

GLASS ROD

AFTER RUBBING, SILK HAS
TAKEN ELECTRONS FROM
THE GLASS, LEAVING A
POSITIVE CHARGE ON THE
GLASS ROD

Fig. 275. How are the silk and the glass changed by rubbing them together?

negative charges, the substance is said to be *neutral;* it shows no charge. That is the case with most substances around us.

When two unlike bodies are rubbed together, however, it is possible for some of the electrons (negative charges) from the atoms of one body to leave that substance and join the atoms of the other body. According to our electron theory, when glass is rubbed with silk, some of the electrons of the glass leave it and go on to the silk. That means that there are too few electrons on the glass. Glass is deficient in electrons, or it has too many protons or positive charges left. That causes the glass to be charged positively, or plus. The silk, however, gains electrons. This means that it has more than the required number for a neutral body and it becomes charged negatively (Fig. 275).

When rubber is rubbed with fur, the rubber gains electrons from the fur. The rubber has more than the required number of electrons for a neutral body, and is therefore charged negatively. The fur, having lost electrons, has too many protons and thus is charged positively. Protons (positive charges) and electrons (negative charges) attract each other. A substance that has a negative charge will attract a substance that has a positive charge, because electrons attract protons. Two objects that have the same kind of charge repel each other, because electrons repel electrons and protons repel protons.

Electric current. Rub your feet briskly on the carpet some dry winter night. Shuffle over to the metal radiator, and hold your knuckle near it. You may notice a bright spark jump from your knuckle to the radiator. That spark is the effect produced by the passage of millions of electrons from your body to the neutral radiator. These electrons jumping across the air are a current of electricity in the air. Air is a very poor conductor of electrons and will allow electrons to jump across only when the electrical pressure is high. Electrons may be made to move much more easily by offering them a conducting material, such as a copper wire, to flow through. When a copper wire is attached to an electric battery or to a generator, completing the circuit, electrons flow out through the wire. The passage of electrons through the wire is an electric current.

Lightning. In a lightning flash electrons leap through the air between two clouds or between a cloud and the ground. When Benjamin Franklin flew his kite in a thunderstorm, billions of electrons took the easy path along his wet kite string and gave him an electric shock. This was a very dangerous experiment. A few years later a scientist in Russia was killed in a similar experiment. Benjamin Franklin also developed the principle of the lightning rod, in which a metal point or several points on the top of the building are connected by wire to the moist earth.

Scientists do not know just how electricity is generated in a thunderstorm. It may be due to friction of air and water drops, or to the condensation of water vapor to drops of water, or to other causes. Nor do they know why a lightning rod, properly erected, protects buildings. It probably prevents the accumulation of large charges of electricity of one kind that might leap through the air as lightning.

EXPERIMENT 98

Question: How can I get electricity by rubbing?

Materials: Hard-rubber rod; glass rod; silk; fur; string; two rubber balloons.

Directions: (a) Inflate the balloons so that they are fairly firm, and hang them one foot apart and at the level of your eyes. Rub both balloons with the fur. We say that rubbing leaves some electrons (negative particles) on both balloons and therefore the balloons are negatively charged. What happens? How do like charges behave?

(b) Remove one balloon. Rub the remaining balloon again with fur. Rub a glass rod with silk and bring it near the charged balloon. When glass is rubbed with silk, we say it loses electrons (negative particles) and becomes positively charged. What happens to the balloon as the glass rod is brought near? Why?

(c) Bring your hand near a balloon that was rubbed with fur. What happens? Why?

Diagram: Show figures illustrating what you did.

Conclusion: State the law that explains the behavior of positively and negatively charged bodies. What theory explains a positively charged body?

Practical application: A flash of lightning is produced by a surge of electrons between clouds or between cloud and earth.

NOTE: Before we had the present theory of electricity, it was customary to say that electricity flows from positive to negative. We still use this method of marking diagrams of cells and electrical devices. For such diagrams, it makes no difference which way the current really flows, as long as we all agree on a uniform method of marking it.

Chapter XXXIII

ELECTRONS FROM CHEMICALS

Electrical energy from chemical energy. We do not use electricity from cat's fur or from silk to ring the doorbell. The electrical energy from fur or silk has been created by mechanical energy in rubbing one substance to give it a negative charge, and the other a positive charge. For the doorbell we use the energy that is found in chemicals or in a current from a dynamo.

What is a wet cell? You can easily make a battery that gives an electric current from chemical energy. Mix in a fruit jar one part sal ammoniac (ammonium chloride) and four parts water. Then place in the jar a carbon rod, obtained from an old dry cell, and a strip of zinc so placed that they do not touch (Fig. 276). If you fasten a copper wire to the carbon and another to the zinc and connect these two wires to an electric doorbell, the bell will ring. Experiments show that the chemicals in the jar or cell produce a positive charge on the carbon rod and a negative charge on the strip of zinc. When these are connected by a wire running through the bell, a flow of electrons in the wire (an electric current) rings the bell. The electrical energy comes from the chemical energy of the zinc. If this cell is operated for several hours, the zinc is gradually used up by being dissolved in the solution. Electricity is produced, but at the expense of the zinc. The minus (or negatively) charged zinc and the plus (or positively) charged carbon are called *electrodes*, and the sal ammoniac solution is called the *electrolyte*.

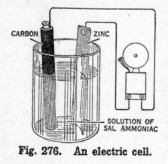

Fig. 276. An electric cell.

(308)

What is in a dry cell? The wet cell is not very convenient. The sal ammoniac solution spills or evaporates. In addition, bubbles of hydrogen gas formed in the chemical action clog the carbon electrode. These difficulties are overcome to some extent in the *dry cell* such as is used in a flashlight or doorbell circuit. A dry cell is not dry inside but contains a thick paste of sal ammoniac, powdered carbon, zinc chloride, and manganese dioxide (Fig. 277). In the center is a carbon electrode as in the wet cell. The other electrode is the zinc cup on the outside. The paste is prevented from drying by sealing it in waxed paper with a layer of pitch at the top.

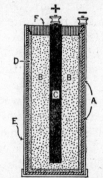

Fig. 277. A dry cell. A, zinc can. B, powdered carbon mixed with ammonium chloride, zinc chloride, and manganese dioxide. C, carbon rod.

The action of the dry cell is the same as that of the wet cell. The zinc accumulates a great many electrons that will move to the carbon when connected with a wire. But this electrical energy is gained at the expense of the zinc which is dissolved in the process. Finally the current weakens and the cell must be thrown away.

The battery in your car. For a steady and cheaper source of current, as in automobiles, *storage* cells are used. These cells do not store electricity, as their name implies. Instead, they store chemicals whose action corresponds to the action of the wet cell (Fig. 278). In the storage cell the plates consist of lead and the electrolyte is one part

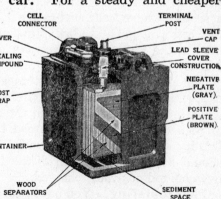

Fig. 278. A storage battery for an automobile.

sulphuric acid by volume and four parts water. If these are connected to a bell, nothing happens because the lead plates are alike and neither plate accumulates more electrons than the other from the acid. The cell has to be *charged;* to do this, the plates are connected to a source of direct current or a few dry cells.

When *charging the cell,* the current causes a chemical change, so that the lead plate, which is connected to the positive end of the current supply, attracts charged atoms of oxygen from the water. This changes the positive lead plate to red lead peroxide on the surface. The lead plate which is connected to the negative end of the current supply remains gray lead. In this charging process the acid becomes thicker, or denser, and the electrical energy has produced chemical changes in the storage battery. Chemical energy has been stored.

Now the cell is ready for the *discharging* process, in which it may light a lamp, ring a bell or turn the motor to start it. When such a cell is connected by wires to an electrical device, the red lead peroxide plate behaves like the carbon in the wet cell. In its chemical action with the acid it loses electrons or is charged positively. The gray lead plate in its chemical action gains electrons or is charged negatively. If the two are connected through a lamp, the electrons flow through a wire. Thus in your car when the storage battery, which is a series of such cells, lights the lamps, it behaves like the wet cell you have studied previously. In this discharging process the plates become similar and the acid becomes less dense.

You may see whether a storage battery is in a charged or discharged condition by testing the cells with a *hydrometer,* which measures the density of the acid (Fig. 279). An acid of high density shows a charged battery. An acid of low density shows a discharged condition. This type of battery should be kept filled with distilled water and must not be overcharged or overdischarged.

Electroplating. You have seen how electrical energy may be obtained from chemical energy. You have also seen how electricity may produce chemical changes in decomposing water into its elements, oxygen and hydrogen. Again, in depositing the thin film of silver on your breakfast spoon and the chromium plate on the bumper of an automobile, electrical energy is used.

Place a rod of carbon, such as the "lead" of a lead pencil, which is not lead at all but graphite (carbon), and a strip of copper in a solution of blue vitriol, or copper sulphate. Connect the carbon with a wire to the zinc or the negative end of a dry cell, and the copper to the positive or carbon end of the cell (Fig. 280). After the current has passed for three minutes, examine the carbon and you will see that a thin film of copper has formed on the carbon. The carbon is said to be *plated* with copper.

In electroplating, the negative electrode (called the *cathode*) receives the metal that came from the positive end (called the *anode*). The electrolyte should be a salt of the metal to be deposited. In this way, one metal may be coated with another. For example, articles of brass or iron which corrode in the air may be coated with nickel or chromium, which do not corrode. Similarly much cheap jewelry is plated with gold or silver. Many knives, forks, and spoons are silver-plated. Steel is often plated with copper. Iron is plated with brass by using salts of copper and zinc.

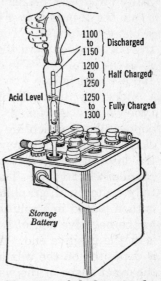

Fig. 279. A hydrometer for testing an automobile battery. The hydrometer is the small glass inside the outer glass syringe. The denser the liquid the higher the hydrometer floats.

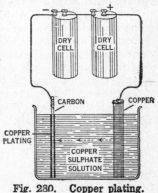

Fig. 280. Copper plating.

Refining of metals by electricity. Metals are sometimes refined by electroplating. Copper as it comes from the smelting works, where it is extracted from the ore, contains many impurities. This impure copper is made the anode and a thin bar of pure copper is made the cathode. The electrolyte is copper sulphate. The passage of the current takes away the pure copper from the mixture of impurities and deposits it on the cathode. The copper obtained in this way is almost 100 per cent pure.

Electrotyping. Books are not always printed from the type which was originally set up. Most books are made from copper plates which are obtained from the original type by electroplating. The type is pressed on a slab of wax so that the imprint of every letter is on the wax. Wax does not conduct electricity. Therefore this wax impression is carefully coated with graphite, a form of carbon. The wax mold is then placed in a solution of copper sulphate and connected to the negative end of a source of current. A bar of copper is at the positive end. When the current passes, the copper is deposited on the wax and forms a thin copper shell having the exact shape of the wax mold of the type. This thin shell is reinforced with lead to make it strong enough for printing.

EXPERIMENT 99

Question: How can I make a wet cell?

Materials: Sal ammoniac; large glass jar; carbon rod (obtained from old dry cell); strip of zinc; bell; and wires.

Directions: Fill the jar with a solution consisting of one part sal ammoniac dissolved in four parts of water. Fasten a wire securely to the carbon rod and another to the strip of zinc. (See Fig. 276.) Place carbon and zinc rods in the solution so that they do not touch. Connect both wires to your doorbell. What happens? Where does the energy required to ring the bell come from?

Conclusion: Tell how to make such a wet cell.

Practical application: These same substances are used in a flashlight dry cell.

NOTE: The cell that you have made will not long continue to furnish electric current. It should be used for short intervals only because gas bubbles clog the carbon rod. When this happens, remove the carbon, dip it (carefully) into dilute nitric acid solution and then hold it in a flame for a few minutes. It will then work again.

EXPERIMENT 100

Question: How can I make and charge a storage battery?

Materials: Two pieces of sheet lead (1 in. x 5 in.); three dry cells; sulphuric acid; a large glass jar; an electric doorbell.

Directions: (a) Prepare a solution of sulphuric acid by slowly pouring one part of acid into four parts of water. DANGER!—*Do not pour the water into the acid. It may spatter your hands, face, or clothing.* Insert the strips of lead so that they do not touch, and connect them with copper wires to a bell. Does the bell ring? Do not worry if *nothing* happens, because the cell is not charged.

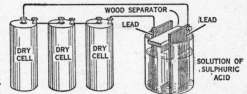

Fig. 281. Charging a homemade storage battery.

(b) Connect the dry cells in series (see Figure 281) and connect them to the lead plates. What happens to the lead plates? Which turns red? Why? This is the charging process. Keep this up for 5 minutes.

(c) Disconnect the dry cells and connect the lead plates to a bell. How long does it ring? What happens to the plates?

Diagram: Show the storage battery "on charge."

Conclusion: Tell how to make a storage cell.

Practical application: What is the use of the storage battery in the automobile? Storage batteries are used to supply electric lights in home lighting plants. The storage batteries are charged by a dynamo driven by a gasoline engine or sometimes by water power.

EXPERIMENT 101

Question: How can I make a copper plating of my initials?

Materials: Dry cell; dilute solution of copper sulphate; No. 20 bare copper wire; tumbler; cardboard; soft lead pencil; bell wire.

Directions: (a) Print your initial on a card in broad letters with a soft lead pencil. Be sure to make a heavy, wide pencil line. Attach the bare copper wire firmly to the initial in several places, not merely to the card. Attach a piece of bell wire to this bare copper wire and to the zinc terminal or minus end of the cell. Next make a little coil of another piece of bare copper wire and attach to the bell wire that runs to the carbon (plus) terminal of the dry cell. Lower gently both the card and the copper coil into the tumbler of copper sulphate solution and keep them there for half an hour. What happens? Why is copper deposited on your carbon initials? What happens to the copper coil? If you leave this for a few hours, your plating of copper may be thick enough to be carefully removed.

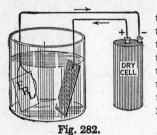

Fig. 282.

(b) We say that the current flows from the carbon of the battery through the wire to the copper coil; through the copper solution to the carbon initials on the card; through the wire to the zinc of the cell; through the cell to the carbon again. Repeat this experiment reversing the terminals of the dry cell; that is, change the plus and minus connections. Does anything happen?

Diagram: (Fig. 282) Draw the apparatus in use.

Conclusion: How is copper plating done?

Practical application: Explain electrotyping. Silver plating is similarly carried on by the use of a silver solution instead of a copper solution, and a silver bar instead of the coil of copper wire.

EXPERIMENT 102 (OPTIONAL)

An easy way to clean silver. Dissolve some salt and washing soda in hot water. Lay a piece of aluminum or zinc in the vessel and a piece of tarnished silver touching it, or the tarnished silver may be boiled in an aluminum vessel with salt and soda.

QUESTIONS TO THINK OUT

1. Take apart an electric flashlight. Trace the circuit and show the class.

2. Why is the life of an automobile battery so short? What has happened to a "dead" cell?

3. How could you nickel-plate a piece of iron?

4. Why can you not use ordinary house-lighting current in electro-plating?

5. Why are plants for production of aluminum located near water power?

6. Why should you insist on dated dry cells when purchasing?

7. Examine Fig. 281, noting the connecting wires from central to side posts of the cells. What would happen if you connected the center post of a cell directly to the side post of the same cell?

8. Why should you disconnect a dry cell or open the circuit when it is not in use?

CHAPTER XXXIV

MEASURING ELECTRICITY

How does the electric company find out how much electricity you use during a month? As the water company measures the flow of water through the pipes, the electric company measures the current that flows through the wires. You can easily measure it yourself. To understand how electricity is measured, you should learn something about the units or yardsticks used.

Electrical pressure or voltage. When you open the water faucet over your sink, the water probably flows out of it with a great deal of force. The pressure behind the water is great if your supply tank is several stories above the sink. However, if you live on the top floor and the supply tank is just above you, then the force or pressure of the water will be less. Electricity also has a pressure. When a dry cell is connected to a bell, you may imagine the cell as pumping electrons through the bell. To drive electrons or the electric current through the bell, the pump or cell must exert a certain pressure. The electrical pressure is measured in *volts*. This electrical pressure unit is named in honor of Alessandro Volta (1745–1827), an Italian scientist. The instrument that measures the number of volts is called a *voltmeter*. This pressure is sometimes spoken of as an *electromotive force* (e.m.f.). The ordinary dry cell when new furnishes 1.5 volts. The ordinary house circuit supplies us with 110 volts. A three-cell storage battery of a car has a pressure of 6 volts.

Electric current or amperage. When you open the water faucet in your kitchen slightly, the amount of water that flows out in a minute is much smaller than when you open the faucet fully. It is possible to measure the rate of flow of the water. It may be 2, 4, or 6 gallons a minute.

In an electric circuit you may also measure the rate of flow of the current. When you turn on several lamps in your house, you are evidently using more electricity than when you turn on one lamp. You may therefore say that the current or the number of *amperes* that you are using for four lamps of the same kind is four times the number that you are using for one lamp.

The ampere, named after André Ampère (1775–1836), a French scientist, is the unit for measuring the *rate of flow* of the current. The instrument that measures the number of amperes is called the *ammeter*. A 60-watt house lamp uses about one half an ampere. An electric iron uses from 4 to 6 amperes.

Resistance to electricity. A stream of water flowing through long narrow pipes meets a greater resistance than a stream traveling through short, wide pipes. This resistance is due to the rubbing action or *friction* of the water inside the pipe. A stream of electrons will likewise meet a resistance to its flow in the wire.

A long, narrow wire has a greater resistance than a short, thick wire. A copper wire has one seventh the resistance that iron wire has. The amount of resistance is measured in *ohms*. An *ohm* is named after Georg Simon Ohm (1787–1854), a German scientist who studied electrical circuits. The filament of the ordinary 60-watt electric lamp in your house has a resistance of about 250 ohms.

[**Ohm's law.** If the resistance (ohms) of an electric circuit is increased, the rate of flow of the current (amperes) is cut down. If the voltage or pressure in a circuit is increased, then the flow of current is also increased. This principle or law is known as Ohm's law: *The number of amperes is equal to the number of volts divided by the number of ohms.*]

Joining cells in series to increase pressure. Suppose you had a doorbell that needed a pressure of 4.5 volts to operate it, and you had 3 dry cells that furnished 1.5 volts each. How would you connect them to operate your bell?

If you had three tanks of water, and you wanted to increase the pressure of the water three times, you would connect the

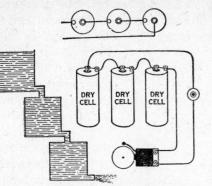

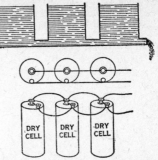

Fig. 284. Cells connected in parallel compared to tanks of water. The pressure or voltage is the same as of one cell, but the current flows for a longer time.

Fig. 283. Cells connected in series compared to tanks of water. The pressure or voltage is increased.

tanks one above another (Fig. 283). In electricity we increase the pressure of a group of cells by joining them *in series*, so that the electrons, after being pushed by one pump (cell), are pushed by the next pump (cell), and the next. If the zinc of the first cell is connected to the carbon of the next, and so on down the line, we have a connection in series.

Joining cells in parallel for longer life. If you want to make dry cells last longer, it is always a good plan to join the positive (carbon) terminals to one wire and the negative (zinc) terminals to the other wire. Then join these wires to the device. Cells so arranged are joined *in parallel*. If you join three cells in this manner, the combined voltage of all three cells will be no more than for one cell, but the cells will last longer (Fig. 284).

Buying electricity. How much does a radio set cost to operate if it is played three hours a night for a month? Is it true that an electric iron costs only four cents an hour? These questions have probably occurred to you and you can answer them if you learn how to read your electric meter and how to calculate the *watts* consumed in an electrical device.

The amount of work that electricity does depends upon two things: first, the number of volts, which is the *pressure* in the line, and, second, the number of amperes, which is the *rate of flow* of the current. The number of volts (pressure) multiplied by the number of amperes (flow of current) gives the number of *watts*. For example, if your lamp operates on a

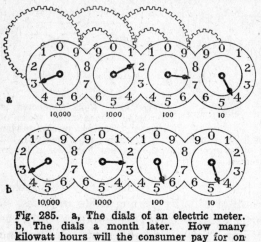

120-volt circuit and a current of ½ ampere passes through the lamp, the number of watts used an hour is found by the calculation 120 × ½ = 60; the lamp is a 60-watt lamp.

A *kilowatt* is 1000 watts. One kilowatt used for an hour is called one *kilowatt hour*. Electric power companies charge by the kilowatt hour.

Fig. 285. a, The dials of an electric meter. b, The dials a month later. How many kilowatt hours will the consumer pay for on this month's bill?

Your electric meter has usually four dials which indicate the number of kilowatt hours that have been consumed since the meter was installed. These dials are read just as you would read the hour hands of a clock, except that two of the "clocks" seem to run backwards or counterclockwise. The dial on the left indicates thousands, the next hundreds, the next tens, and the last units. If the first hand is between 3 and 4, it reads 3000; if the second hand is between 1 and 2, it reads 100; if the third hand is between 7 and 8, it reads 70; and if the fourth hand is between 4 and 5, it is read 4. This makes the total number of kilowatt hours 3174 (Fig. 285).

If your meter last month read 3140 and this month 3174, then 34 kilowatt hours of electricity have been consumed during the month. If your power company charges you 10 cents a kilowatt hour, then your bill should be 34 × 10 or $3.40.

The salesman may say, "This device costs almost nothing to operate." You can check the truth of his statement if you know the number of watts required and the charge for a kilowatt hour. Many electrical devices, such as toasters, are marked with the watts they use. Examine your toaster and calculate the cost of operating it for a half hour. If the name plate of your toaster reads 400 watts, that means that your toaster uses 400 watts of electrical energy each hour. If you use your toaster for 15 minutes, you consume $\frac{1}{4}$ of 400 watts or 100 watts. If the cost of a kilowatt (1000 watts) hour is 10 cents, the cost of 100 watts is $\frac{1}{10}$ of 10 cents or 1 cent.

CHAPTER XXXV

HEAT AND LIGHT ENERGY FROM ELECTRICITY

Electric heating. Most houses that have electricity to-day use at least one device that transforms electrical energy into heat. Electric irons, ranges, toasters, grills, water heaters, room heaters, coffee percolators, chafing dishes, and heating pads all use the same principle. Electricity while flowing through wires produces heat. If a thin iron wire about 8 inches long is connected across the terminals of a dry cell, the wire will become very warm. If two cells are used in series, the wire will become hot enough to glow.

If the same thing is tried with copper wire, it will be found that not so much heat is developed as in the iron. When electricity flows through a wire, electrical energy is used up in overcoming the resistance that the wire offers to its flow. The used-up energy appears as heat. This causes the wire to become hot. Iron, which offers greater resistance to the passage of the current than copper does, heats more quickly than copper. The amount of heat is increased also by increased flow of current, as is shown by increasing the number of dry cells. The total heat produced is dependent too on the time during which the current flows.

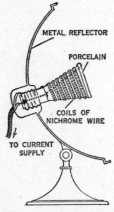

METAL REFLECTOR

PORCELAIN

COILS OF NICHROME WIRE

TO CURRENT SUPPLY

Fig. 286. An electric heater.

The electric toaster. The heating unit in the electric toaster is a coil of nichrome wire (pronounced nĭk′rōm). Nichrome is an alloy (mixture) of iron, nickel, and chromium. It is used for heating coils because it does not melt at heating tempera-

(320)

tures; it has a high resistance; and it does not oxidize in the air when heated. The passage of a current through the coils heats them. They become red-hot, and the bread is toasted.

The electric flatiron. The electric flatiron has in its base a tape of nichrome. Heat is developed when the current passes through this tape. The first irons that were used were inconvenient because of the necessity of switching the current on and off to regulate the heat. These irons also increased the fire hazard. A forgetful housewife who might leave an iron on the board to go to the telephone might return to find the ironing board in flames. Irons with automatic temperature control are now in use. A thermostat switches the electricity on and off, thus keeping the temperature constant.

The electric range. For cooking purposes electric ranges are becoming more popular. While cooking by electricity is more expensive than by gas in most communities, it is cleaner and in some ways more convenient. The electric range, like the toaster, consists of a long coil of nichrome wire that is coiled into a spiral and set in a groove in porcelain. The coil used in the range is much heavier than the toaster coils and consequently consumes about six times as much electricity.

Electric heaters. Spirals of nichrome wire are also used for small portable heaters for rooms. The nichrome coil is wound around a porcelain cylinder. This is placed at the center of a concave reflector made of polished metal. The reflector sends the heat and light rays straight out from the heater.

Household appliances that use electricity to provide heat are in general more expensive of current than those in which electricity provides light. While costing more than other means of heating, electric heaters are quick, clean, and portable (Figs. 286 and 287).

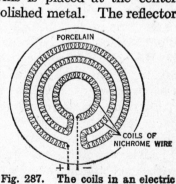

Fig. 287.   The coils in an electric hot plate.

Light from electrical energy. Sir Humphry Davy about 1825 made the first electric light by connecting two thousand cells to two pieces of coal which touched each other.

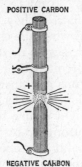

POSITIVE CARBON

+

−

NEGATIVE CARBON

Fig. 288. Electric arc carbons.

Upon separating the two pieces of coal he noticed a bright electric flash. William Wallace, using this experiment about 1875, devised a lamp by connecting the current from a dynamo to two pieces of carbon. The carbons were then touched and separated about a quarter of an inch. The resistance of the air in this gap to the passage of the electric current is so great that a tremendous amount of heat is produced. The heat energy is so great that it vaporizes the carbon; the vapor is incandescent (glowing hot). The carbon vapor then conducts the electricity across the gap in what is called an *arc*, because the path sometimes appears to be curved (Fig. 288). The light produced by this lamp, called a carbon *arc lamp*, is very intense.

Although arc lamps are suitable for street lighting, they need regulation because the carbons burn away about an inch every hour. About 1900 Charles Steinmetz, later known as the "Wizard of Schenectady," was looking for a better material than carbon and for some device to regulate the burning away of the carbons. He found the new substance in an oxide of iron, magnetite, which gave out a brilliant blue illumination. He regulated the space between the carbons by the action of an electromagnet. For several years the arc lamp was used extensively for street lighting. Today the incandescent lamp has supplanted it almost completely.

For public parks and recreation fields flaming arc lights were once employed. These arcs had carbons with a center or core of calcium or magnesium compounds. A golden light which is very efficient resulted. White arc lights have carbons with a core of iron oxide. Motion-picture projection machines still use this type of lamp.

Edison's electric lamp. The arc lamp is unsuitable for home lighting. Thomas Alva Edison had the persistence, patience, and courage to search for the method and materials to make an incandescent lamp. Edison and his staff of a hundred assistants tried 6000 substances before they found a suitable substance. It was known that metal wire could be heated to incandescence (glowing) by the passage of an electric current, but the wire burned up in the air. Edison and his assistants found that a bamboo thread charred until only carbon remained furnished a suitable light. He then perfected a pump that would exhaust the air from the bulb in which the carbon wire was sealed.

The modern incandescent lamp. The incandescent lamp of today is quite different from Edison's carbon-filament lamp. To secure greater brilliance, a metal, tungsten, is used as the filament. The use of tungsten makes the lamp $2\frac{1}{2}$ times as efficient as a carbon lamp. To prevent the filament from burning up, Edison exhausted the air from the bulb. It has been found that by filling this bulb with nitrogen or argon, two very inactive gases, the life of the filament as well as its brilliance is increased.

Tungsten is a highly resistant metal which when heated to 2100° gives off a brilliant white light. The hotter the filament becomes, the greater the percentage of the electrical energy that is changed to light energy. A good lamp is made to last 1000 hours. After that time the constant heat of the filament causes it to change into a gas or to evaporate. When the filament, because of the evaporation of the tungsten, becomes so thin that it breaks, the lamp is no longer useful. Nitrogen- or argon-filled lamps last longer because the pressure of these gases on the filament retards the evaporation of the tungsten (Fig. 242).

Notice the number of watts marked on bulbs. Incandescent lamps are graded by the rate at which they consume electricity. A store window-display lamp uses from 100 to 250 watts. Lamps in the home use from 15 to 75 watts. A lantern-slide machine uses about a 400-watt lamp. Theater spotlights use from 1600- to 2000-watt lamps.

Switches. To get light from your lamp there must be a flow of electrons or current from the dynamo in the power house through the wire filaments inside your bulb and back

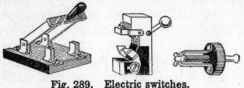

Fig. 289.   Electric switches.

to the dynamo. An electric current must have a complete circuit. First the main switch, usually located in your basement, must be closed. After this you must close another switch which establishes a circuit through your lamp bulb. You close this second switch when you press a light button in the wall. Trace out the course of the current in Figure 290.

Fuses. In the basement of your house is a fuse box with little sentinels on guard against danger. Electricity, like fire, is a useful servant when kept under control, but when it gets out of control, it is dangerous. We have seen how electricity produces heat and that the greater the flow of current the greater the heating effect. Every electrical device offers a resistance to the flow of current. If you examine circuit 2, Figure 291, you will see that the wires coming from the fuse box encounter either a resistance through the lamp or a resistance through the toaster.

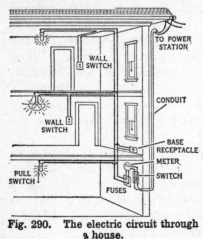

Fig. 290.   The electric circuit through a house.

Suppose that wires C and D should accidentally touch. This may happen when the insulation in a lamp cord is rubbed away, causing the two bare wires to touch. This would provide an easy path for the current to surge through. Electricity, instead of flowing through the higher resistance of the lamp or toaster, would take the easier path. We say a *short circuit* is produced. Since there is no resistance to restrain the flow of current through the short circuit, a large current will flow and produce a terrific heating effect in the circuit. If there were no protective device to cut off the current automatically, the wires would melt or the electrical device would be ruined or a fire would break out.

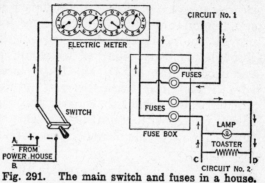

Fig. 291. The main switch and fuses in a house.

Down in the fuse box the fuse is on the job. A fuse such as A (Fig. 292) is simply a cartridge with a strip of fuse wire embedded in it. This wire melts when the heat developed by the short circuit becomes too great for safety. The fuse wire is a lead alloy with a low melting point. A fuse that is rated at 10 amperes will melt when the current in the line exceeds a flow of 10 amperes, which will be caused by a short circuit. When a fuse melts or "blows," it breaks the circuit. Breaking the circuit has the same effect as opening the switch. The screw-base type of fuse (type B) is a more convenient form.

Danger from electricity. A harmless-looking wire may be very dangerous to handle. One should be careful never to touch a bare wire, unless it is known to be "dead." Electricity passing through the body causes the muscles of the body to contract. If the current should pass through the heart, death may result because the heart muscle is paralyzed.

A wet hand is a good conductor of electricity. Electrical fixtures should never be handled with wet hands because the current may pass through

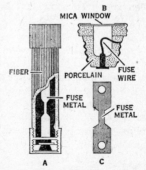

Fig. 292. Electric fuses. A, Cartridge fuse. B, Plug fuse. C, Fuse metal for cartridge.

the body. The higher the voltage the greater the danger. There have been cases of fatal shock when a person in a bathtub of water reached up with wet hands and touched an electric socket that carried the ordinary 110 volts. A person standing on the ground and touching a live trolley wire would provide an opportunity for the current to pass to the ground through his body (that is, he would *ground* the current) and would probably be killed. A bird can alight on the wire without harm, because it does not touch anything else to which it can transmit the current through its body. A good rule to remember in electrical work is to stand on an insulated support, and to handle only one wire at a time to avoid grounding.

EXPERIMENT 103

Question: How does electricity produce heat?

Material: A foot of bare No. 36 copper wire (bell wire); a few inches of iron picture wire; iron support; three dry cells; 3 or 4 feet of bell wire.

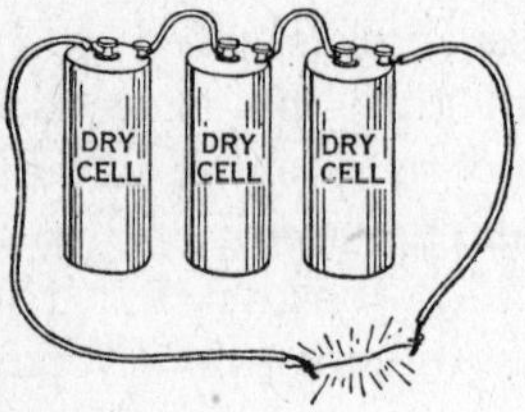

Directions: Connect as shown in Figure 293.

(*a*) Hold the free ends of the bell wire together. 1. Do you feel any heat in the wire?

(*b*) Connect the free ends of the bell wire with the No. 36 wire. 2. Is there heat?

Fig. 293. To show that a current heats iron wire.

(*c*) Connect the ends of the bell wire with the picture wire. 3. How do the results compare with those of *a* and *b*?

Results: Record answers to 1, 2, and 3.

Conclusion: Heat is produced when the current meets resistance. 4. What has the diameter of the wire to do with resistance? 5. Which material used offers greater resistance?

Application: Electric stoves, toasters, flatirons, and other heating devices use the principle you have just demonstrated. Nichrome, an alloy of chromium, nickel, and iron, is generally used to provide resistance.

EXPERIMENT 104

Question: How does a fuse protect the house?

Materials: Dry cell; knife switch; two pieces of fuse wire; several feet of copper wire; compass.

Directions: Connect the circuit as shown in Figure 294. The copper wire is the circuit through the house. Lay it across the compass. Close the switch. Does the compass needle move? What does that show? Now with your knife or a small piece of copper wire short-circuit the long copper wire as shown in the diagram. What happens?

Results: Report what happened when you short-circuited the house circuit.

Conclusion: Answer the question.

Application: Locate the fuses in your circuit at home and in your automobile. How does each furnish protection?

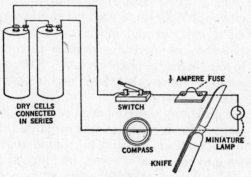

Fig. 294.

QUESTIONS TO THINK OUT

1. In an incandescent bulb, could oxygen be used? Could helium? See pages 39 and 44.

2. Why do the wires leading to an electric bulb not give light as does the wire inside the bulb?

3. If you could not find a copper wire about the house and used a steel wire to string electric lights, what might happen?

4. How can wires be "overloaded"?

5. Why should you not replace a fuse with a copper cent when the fuse blows?

Chapter XXXVI

WHAT MAKES ELECTRICITY DO WORK?

Putting the current to work. Why does a little black instrument on the end of a wire enable you to talk to a person a thousand miles away? How does the little clicking instrument on a telegraph operator's desk carry messages? What makes a trolley car run and a vacuum sweeper do work? All things that move by electricity depend upon the power of electricity to magnetize a piece of iron. The discovery of this partnership between electricity and magnetism made possible the age of electricity.

In 1831 Joseph Henry, an American scientist, learned that an electric current flowing through a wire caused that wire to become a feeble magnet. When he wound several feet of insulated wire into the form of a coil, he found that he could concentrate the magnetism. By using an iron core in the center of the coil of wire, he found that his magnet became still more powerful. Such magnets are called *electromagnets*. Near his electromagnet Henry placed a piece of steel; and when he passed electricity through the electromagnet, the piece of steel was pulled toward the magnet, and an extension of it struck against a gong. Thus he discovered the principle of the electric bell and telegraph, but he left their development to other scientists. Large electromagnets are now used for handling masses of iron weighing several tons (Fig. 296).

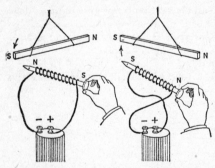

Fig. 295. A homemade electromagnet.

Fig. 296. This electromagnet lifts the ball of iron weighing
8400 pounds and drops it to break up the scrap iron.

You can easily make an electromagnet by wrapping some insulated wire around a nail and connecting with a cell (Fig. 295).

The right-hand rule. If you bring one end of your electromagnet near a freely swinging bar magnet, you will notice that one end of your electromagnet will attract the north pole and repel the south pole. This shows that this end is a south pole and the other end is a north pole. If you disconnect the wires on the dry cell and reverse the wires (Fig. 295) so that the current flows through the coil in the opposite direction, you will notice that the former north pole of your coil is now a south pole and the former south pole becomes a north pole. In other words, there is a definite relation between the direction of the current in the coil and the polarity of the electromagnet. A rule for finding the north pole of any electromagnet is this: *Grasp the coil with your right hand, having the fingers pointing in the direction of the current in the wire; then the thumb will point to the north* *pole of the magnet.* This is known as the right-hand rule. The current in a wire is said to flow from the plus terminal (carbon, in the center) of a dry cell to a minus terminal (zinc, on the outside).

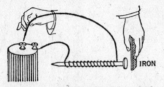

Fig. 297. The principle of the telegraph. When the wire is touched to the binding post, the electromagnet formed by the coil and nail attracts the iron.

Strength of electromagnets. If you connect your nail electromagnet to two dry cells instead of one, you can tell that its magnetic force is doubled from the fact that it picks up twice the number of nails. Thus, an increase of current increases the power of attraction.

If you had only one cell and wanted to increase the strength of the magnet, you could do so by winding more turns of wire around the nail. Twice the number of turns will double the force of attraction.

Soft-iron cores make stronger electromagnets than cores of any other material. To concentrate the magnetic force, electromagnets are wound around cores which are bent into the shape of horseshoes.

How the telegraph works. The telegraph system we now use was devised in 1832 by Samuel F. B. Morse. But

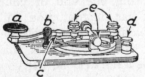

Fig. 298. When the operator pushes down the key (a) to the contact (c) the circuit is closed and the lever bar in the sounder at the receiving station is drawn down. The switch (b) is kept closed when no message is being sent. d, binding posts for wires. e, adjustment screws.

it was not until May 24, 1844, that the famous message "What hath God wrought?" was successfully sent by Morse from Washington to Baltimore. Today the telephone and the radio have supplanted the telegraph to a great extent; yet there is hardly a town in this country that has not a telegraph for news or for business messages.

If you hold a piece of iron near the end of an electromagnet, and connect the ends of the coil to a dry cell, the iron will be drawn to the magnet with a click. If you break the circuit, the force of your hand will pull the iron back (Fig. 297).

Every time you complete the circuit the movable iron, called the *armature*, is pulled down. When you break the circuit, the electromagnet loses its hold on the armature and your hand pulls the armature back to its original position.

In the telegraph the part that acts as a switch to open and close the circuit is called the *key;* it is located at the sending station (Fig. 298). The key is connected with wires to a source of current, then to the receiving station where the *sounder*, consisting of an electromagnet and an armature, is located (Fig. 299). When the key is pressed in one station, the current flows and causes the electromagnet in the other stations to attract the armature of the sounder. The armature will click against the metal frame. When the key is released at the sending station, the current stops flowing through the electromagnet of the sounder at the receiving station, and a spring pulls the armature back. As it springs back, it hits the upper part of the metal frame. This causes another click (Fig. 300). Originally two wires were used to complete the circuit. With the modern telegraph one wire is used. The circuit is completed by connecting both ends of the line with the ground, the earth serving as the return wire.

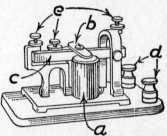

Fig. 299. A telegraph sounder. The current enters and leaves by the binding posts (*d*). The armature (*b*) is fastened directly to the lever bar (*c*), and both move together as the armature is drawn to and then moves backward from the poles of the horseshoe electromagnet (*a*) below. A spring acts on the short arm of the lever bar in opposition to the magnetic pull. Adjustment screws are indicted by (*e*).

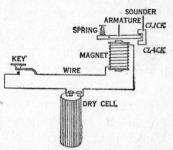

Fig. 300. A telegraphic circuit. The key is at the sending station and the sounder at the receiving station.

The language of the telegraph. Both sending and receiving stations have keys and sounders. They are connected

American Morse and Continental Morse Signal Codes

Letter	Continental Morse	American Morse	Letter	Continental Morse	American Morse
A	·—	·—	T	—	—
B	—···	—···	U	··—	··—
C	—·—·	·· ·	V	···—	···—
D	—··	—··	W	·——	·——
E	·	·	X	—··—	·—··
F	··—·	·—·	Y	—·——	·· ··
G	——·	——·	Z	——··	··· ·
H	····	····			
I	··	··	1	·————	·——·
J	·———	—·—·	2	··———	··—··
K	—·—	—·—	3	···——	···—·
L	·—··	—	4	····—	····—
M	——	——	5	·····	———
N	—·	—·	6	—····	······
O	———	· ·	7	——···	—·—··
P	·——·	·····	8	———··	—····
Q	——·—	··—·	9	————·	—·—·
R	·—·	· ··	0	—————	—
S	···	···			

as is shown in Figure 301. If St. Louis wishes to send a message to Chicago, the Chicago operator must close his key, because if both keys were open there would be two breaks in the circuit. When the St. Louis operator presses his key down and then quickly releases it, he causes two clicks in rapid succession in Chicago. This sound is called a dot. When the time between the clicks is longer, it is a dash. Dots and dashes are combined to make letters and words.

With a teletype machine as each key is pressed, an electromagnet on the receiving machine, miles away, pulls down the corresponding key and types the letter on a strip of paper.

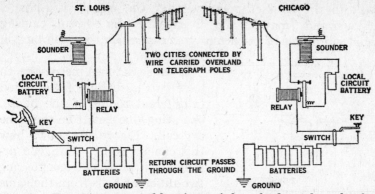

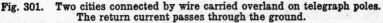

Fig. 301. Two cities connected by wire carried overland on telegraph poles. The return current passes through the ground.

The electric doorbell. The movable part of the electric bell, carrying the hammer which strikes the bell, is called the *armature* (Fig. 302). Attached to the armature is a brass spring that causes the armature to rest against the *contact point*. The lower end of the armature is connected by a wire to a horseshoe electromagnet. The other end of the electromagnet is joined to a *push button*, or *switch*. The switch is connected to a dry cell, and the cell to the contact point. Trace all these connections in the figure.

When the spring is resting against the contact point and the push button is pressed, current will flow through the electromagnet. The magnetic force of the magnet will pull the armature away from the contact point toward the magnet. This action causes the hammer to strike the gong. At this instant, however, the circuit is broken because the armature has been moved away from the contact point. The electromagnet, therefore, loses its magnetism. The spring then causes the armature to be pulled

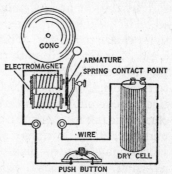

Fig. 302. Showing how an electromagnet rings the bell. What happens to the armature when the button is pushed?

23

back to the contact point so that the circuit is remade. These rapid "makes" and "breaks" in the current, causing rapid vibrations of the armature, cease when the push button is released.

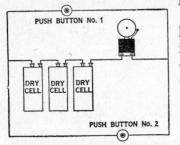

Fig. 303.   Explain how either of two buttons may ring one bell.

It is sometimes necessary to have two push buttons, situated in different rooms of the house, operating one bell from the same dry cell. Figure 303 shows how this can be done. Can you arrange two push buttons to ring two different bells from the same dry cell?

How the telephone works. The telephone was invented in 1875 by Dr. Alexander Graham Bell. To understand the operation of a simple telephone, we must first examine the parts.

The part of the telephone that we talk into is called the *transmitter*. Its secret is a box that is filled with grains of carbon. One wire is connected to the front of this box and another wire to the rear of the box. A metal diaphragm, which catches the sound waves in the air that are spoken into the mouthpiece, is attached to the front of the carbon box (Fig. 304). Air waves or vibrations are set up when we speak so that the air at any point varies in density several times a second. Each compression of the air pushes the carbon particles closer together. This reduces the resistance and makes it easy for the current to flow through the transmitter. As the air becomes less dense, the carbon particles spring back to their original position. This makes it more difficult for an electric current to pass through the carbon box and thus the current is decreased for an instant. Thus when you sing the middle *c*, 256 pulsations a second are set up in the air. These vibrations cause the disk to vibrate back and forth 256 times a second. This means that the carbon particles are compressed and separated 256 times a second. This causes a current to pulsate 256 times a second to the receiver at the other end of the line.

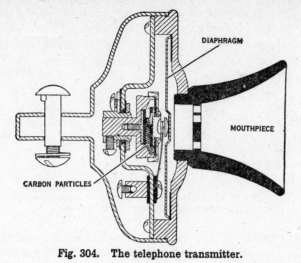

DIAPHRAGM

MOUTHPIECE

CARBON PARTICLES

Fig. 304.   The telephone transmitter.

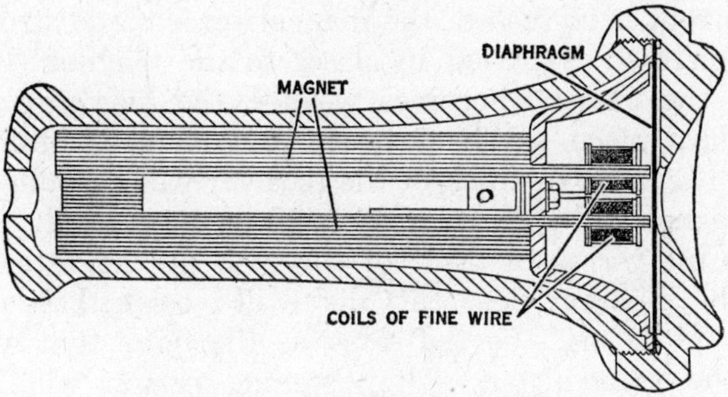

DIAPHRAGM

MAGNET

COILS OF FINE WIRE

Fig. 305.   The telephone receiver.

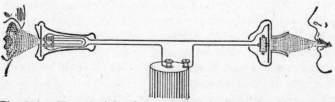

Fig. 306.   The principle of the telephone.   Tell what happens at
each step from speaker to listener.

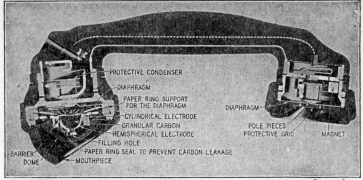

PROTECTIVE CONDENSER
DIAPHRAGM
PAPER RING SUPPORT
FOR THE DIAPHRAGM
CYLINDRICAL ELECTRODE
GRANULAR CARBON
HEMISPHERICAL ELECTRODE
FILLING HOLE
PAPER RING SEAL TO PREVENT CARBON LEAKAGE
BARRIER
DOME
MOUTHPIECE

DIAPHRAGM
POLE PIECES
PROTECTIVE GRID
MAGNET

Fig. 307. The hand-type set telephone. The transmitter and receiver are combined in one instrument.

The *receiver* of a telephone consists of an electromagnet, usually horseshoe-shaped. Supported near the magnet is an iron disk, or *diaphragm*. The pulsating current from the transmitter is sent to the coils of the receiver. Every time the current is increased, the magnetism is made stronger and the iron disk is pulled in closer to the magnet (Fig. 305). When the current becomes weaker, the diaphragm springs back into place. When the current changes intensity 256 times a second, the disk of the receiver will be pulled toward the magnet and then released 256 times a second. This will set up air waves in front of the disk at the rate of 256 a second. The ear near this disk will receive these air waves whose pitch will be the same as the note that was sung into the transmitter. The listening person will hear the note *c*.

Electrical energy changed into mechanical energy. One of the most useful of all electrical devices, depending for its operation on the electromagnet, is the *electric motor*. The electric fan, the vacuum cleaner, the street car, the electric refrigerator, the electric shovel and dredge, the tunnel and building ventilating systems, the elevators of buildings, the escalators (moving stairways), and hundreds of other devices depend upon electric motors. In all these cases the energy of electricity is made to move things about (Fig. 308). To do this, the energy of electricity is transformed into moving or mechanical energy by the electric motor.

How the electric motor works. If you magnetize two pieces of iron, their like poles will repel each other and their unlike poles will attract each other. Magnetic attraction and repulsion turns the electric motor. In the electric motor the iron is magnetized by electric currents, that is, electro-magnets are used.

Now look at Figure 309. A stationary magnet is called the *field magnet*. In the motor this is an electromagnet but is shown here without the coil of wire. Another electro-magnet, called the *armature*, rotates between the poles of the field magnet. In the diagram the armature is shown wrapped with a coil of wire. When the current goes through the armature, it becomes a magnet. Its

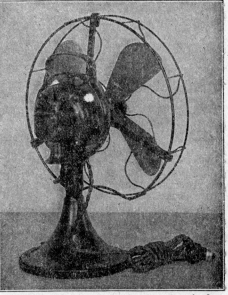

Fig. 308. A motor drives the electric fan.

north pole is then repelled by the north pole of the field magnet and its south pole is attracted to the north pole of the field magnet. The armature rotates. When the north pole of the armature reaches the south pole of the field magnet, the rotation should stop. But the current is then sent through the coil in the opposite direction, and the pole of the armature that was north

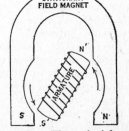

Fig. 309. The principle of the electric motor: like poles repel, unlike poles attract.

becomes a south pole and the pole that was south becomes a north pole. The new like poles repel, the new unlike poles attract, and the armature turns farther. If the direc-

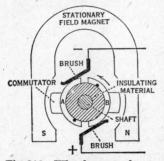

Fig. 310. Why the motor keeps turning. The poles of the armature are reversed every half turn. How?

tion of the current in the coil is reversed every half turn, the armature will keep on turning.

How do we reverse the current in the armature? Look at Figure 310. The wires of the armature are attached to two half rings *A* and *B*. These half rings are called the *commutator*. They turn with the armature. Touching the commutator are two metal strips or two carbon blocks called *brushes*. The brushes lead the current into and out of the motor. When one half of the commutator *A* is in contact with the upper brush and the other half *B* is in contact with the lower brush, the current flows through the armature in one direction. When the commutator is turned halfway round, *B* is in contact with the upper brush and *A* with the lower brush. Then the current flows through the armature in the opposite direction. Every time the direction of the current is changed in the armature the north and south poles of the armature change ends.

EXPERIMENT 105

Question: How can I make an electromagnet?

Materials: A large nail; some small nails or iron filings; some insulated wire; a dry cell.

Directions: (a) Wrap several turns of insulated wire around the large nail. Connect each end of the wire to the dry cell. Bring the nail to the small nails or iron filings. 1. Is there any evidence of magnetism? 2. Bring large nail to a compass. Which is the north and which the south pole of the electromagnet?

(b) Disconnect the wires at the dry cell and connect to opposite poles of the cell. 3. Test as before. Unwind the wire and wind it in the reverse direction. 4. Again test it. 5. Determine the north pole of the electromagnet by the right-hand rule (see p. 329).

Results: What happened in the experiment?

Conclusion: How is an electromagnet made? What effect has the direction of the current?

EXPERIMENT 106 (OPTIONAL)

How to make a telegraph instrument. Arrange the apparatus as shown in the diagram. The sounder is a hinge. If it is not free enough to fall easily, tack a rubber band to the bottom board and carry it over the free end of the hinge. To make a dot, push down the key and release it immediately. To make a dash, hold down the key for a moment (Fig. 311).

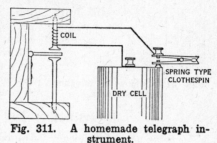

Fig. 311.   A homemade telegraph instrument.

EXPERIMENT 107

Question: How is an electric-bell circuit connected?

Materials: Dry cell; insulated bell rire; electric bell; push button.

Directions: (*a*) With two pieces of wire connect the bell and dry cell so that the bell rings. Try it until you work it out.

(*b*) Take the push button apart and see why it works. Connect the push button in the circuit.

(*c*) Work out a system for ringing one bell from either of two push buttons. Try it until you make it work.

Results: Draw diagrams, fully labeled, of *a*, *b*, and *c*. Show clearly to which binding posts each wire is connected in *a* and *b*.

Conclusions: Answer the question.

Application: If your electric bell does not work, in what places would you look for the trouble? Work out a method of ringing the same bell from buttons at both the front and rear doors.

EXPERIMENT 108 (OPTIONAL)

How a telephone transmitter works. Attach wires to two light carbons like the "leads" from pencils or small carbons for arc lights. Lay them on a cigar box and lay a third across them. Lead one wire from a carbon to a telephone receiver. Attach the second wire to a dry cell. Connect the receiver to the dry cell with a third wire somewhat as in Figure 312. Hold the telephone receiver to your ear while you tap the box gently. Then lay a watch on the box. The slight vibration of the carbons makes and breaks the current. This action is similar to that of the carbon button in the transmitter of the telephone (Fig. 304).

How a telephone receiver works. Attach one end of a piece of insulated wire to a telephone receiver and the other to a dry cell. Attach one end of a second piece of wire to the receiver and the other end to the iron

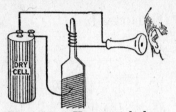

handle of a file. Attach a third piece of wire to the remaining pole of the dry cell and leave the other end free. Put the receiver to your ear. Scrape the free end of wire along the file. Electrical contact is made only when the wire touches the ridges. What do you hear? Unscrew the cap of the receiver and examine the electromagnet inside (Fig. 312).

Fig. 312.   How a telephone receiver works.

EXPERIMENT 109 (OPTIONAL)

To make an electric motor. Around a cork about two inches long wrap about 20 turns of No. 22 insulated wire to form a coil. Cut two pieces of bare copper wire about No. 18. Push them into the ends of the cork. Fasten the ends of the coil to the short wires. Thrust a

knitting needle clear through the cork, so that it projects from both ends. This is our "armature." Support the armature that you just made on the ends of the knitting needle as in Figure 313. Stand a horseshoe magnet over the armature. Connect wires to the dry cells as shown. Touch the bared ends of the cell wires to the short wires to which the coil is attached. If the armature does not turn, try adding more dry cells and magnets.

Fig. 313.   To show how a motor moves.

QUESTIONS TO THINK OUT

1. In telephoning from New York to Los Angeles, how far do the sound waves travel? In telephoning from New York to London by radio?

2. In installing a one-wire telephone in a station in the woods, a ranger was careful to place the incoming wire where it would be dry and insulated, but ran the ground wire into a brook bed. Why?

3. Would a steel rod do as well as an iron core in an electromagnet?

4. How many appliances around your home and school use electric motors?

CHAPTER XXXVII

HOW WE GET ELECTRIC POWER

The dynamo or generator. The electric energy that supplies our houses and cities could not be obtained from chemical energy in batteries such as we have studied. Our large supplies of electrical energy come from either the energy of burning coal or the energy of falling water. The *dynamo* or *generator* converts such energy into electrical energy.

We owe the dynamo to the English scientist, Michael Faraday (1791–1867). Faraday made many investigations in physics and chemistry, but we remember him best for his discovery of an efficient way of getting electricity in large quantities.

It was known that an electric current in a coil of wire makes a magnet or produces a magnetic field. Faraday wondered, "Could I reverse the process and get an electric current from a magnet and a coil of wire?" He connected a coil of wire to an instrument which is used to detect feeble electric currents, called a *galvanometer* (Fig. 314). When the coil was turned between the poles of the magnet, a current was induced in the coil. This little experiment was the basis for the dynamo. Dynamos consist essentially of the same pieces of apparatus that Faraday used, except that they are built on a larger scale. Instead of a horseshoe magnet, powerful electromagnets are used. Turning between these magnets are many coils of wire (Fig. 316). These coils end either in a *commutator* (p. 343), or two metal rings called *slip rings* (Fig. 315). *Brushes*

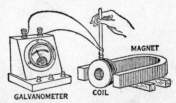
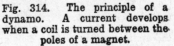

Fig. 314. The principle of a dynamo. A current develops when a coil is turned between the poles of a magnet.

touching the commutator or slip rings carry away the electricity that is produced in the armature coils. The brushes have wires connected to them which conduct the electricity

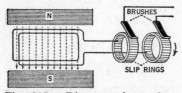

Fig. 315. Diagram of an alternating current dynamo.

through electric cables, mains, and thereby to our homes and factories.

The parts of a dynamo are exactly the same as the parts of a motor. There is only one difference. Electrical energy is fed to the motor, which transforms it into the mechanical energy of the turning armature. In the dynamo exactly the reverse occurs. We feed mechanical energy into it by turning the armature; the dynamo transforms this mechanical energy into electrical energy. The armatures of dynamos are turned by steam or water power.

Alternating current. As the coil of an armature of the dynamo turns around halfway, a current is produced in a certain direction. When the coil completes the second half

Fig. 316. A dynamo disassembled. Above: the stationary field coils. Below: the armature that rotates between the field coils.

of its turn, it is found that the current flows in the opposite direction. For each complete turn that the armature makes a current is produced in the coils which changes its direction twice. Each end of the coil is attached to a *slip ring* (Fig. 315). The brushes which lean against these slip rings pick up a current which flows first one way and then the opposite way. Such a current is called an *alternating current* (A. C.). A 60-cycle A. C. current means that the current changes its direction 60 times a second.

Direct current. When the end of the armature coil of a dynamo is attached to a ring split in two, called a *commutator*, we obtain a current at the brushes which flows in one direction only (Fig. 318). This flow is called a *direct current* (D. C.).

Fig. 317. A dynamo assembled.

Although the direction of the current in the armature coil still changes at each half turn, the commutator also turns round each half turn. As a result, when the current does change its direction, that current is fed to the opposite brush, and continues to go through the circuit in the same direction (Fig. 318). The brush from which the current leaves the dynamo is called the *positive* or *plus brush*. The brush to which the current returns to the generator is called the *negative* or *minus* brush.

Heating devices or electric lamps may use either A. C. or D. C. However, a D. C. motor should usually be supplied with a direct current and an A. C. motor should be fed by an alternating current. Universal motors may be operated by either type of current.

The sun turns the dynamo. Whether the power that turns the dynamo comes from burning coal or from falling water, the power comes from the sun. Today our electricity is largely obtained from

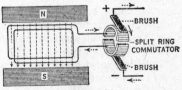

Fig. 318. Diagram of a direct current dynamo.

generators whose armatures are turned by steam engines. Coal comes from trees that decayed thousands of years ago. The trees got their energy to grow from the sun. The solar energy that has been stored up in coal turns the electric generator that runs our machinery and lights our cities.

The snows melting on the tops of high mountains have been called *white coal*. Melting snow forms rivers which flow down the mountain sides. This falling water or water power is used to turn machinery or dynamos. Falling water, like coal, is transformed sun power. The heat of the sun evaporated the water that later fell as rain or snow on the mountain top. The sun is the great source of power for the earth.

EXPERIMENT 110

Question: How does a magnet and a coil of wire generate electricity?

Materials: A coil of several hundred turns of copper wire; a galvanometer; a bar magnet.

Directions: Connect the ends of the wire coil to the galvanometer (Fig. 314).

(a) Thrust the bar magnet through the coil while you watch the needle of the galvanometer.

(b) Hold the bar magnet still in the coil and note the galvanometer.

(c) Watch the galvanometer as you withdraw the bar magnet from the coil.

Results: What happened in *a*, *b*, and *c* above?

Conclusion: Does the magnet produce a current in the coil when it is held still? when in motion? What effect on the current is produced by reversing the direction of motion? Recall the lines of magnetic force in Experiment 96. The current is produced when the lines of force move across the coil of wire.

QUESTIONS TO THINK OUT

1. Trackless trolley cars, which are really rubber-tired busses driven by electricity, have two trolley poles and two wires overhead. Why?

2. Why is a short circuit likely to set your house afire?

3. Tell several ways by which you can determine if a current is passing through a wire.

4. Why can you not charge your automobile battery directly from your house-lighting circuit?

5. Could you use your house current for electroplating?

CHAPTER XXXVIII

RADIO AND ELECTRIC WAVES

Radio is not all concerts and jazz, plays and bedtime stories. A speech by our President or a European chancellor keeps statesmen and bankers at the radio, too anxious to wait for cablegrams. A frost warning from the Weather Bureau starts a thousand fires in the orchards of California. A crop forecast sends prices up or down. A call of distress from a ship at sea sends other ships hurrying to the scene.

The discovery of electric waves. A Scottish scientist, Clerk-Maxwell, reasoning from mathematics, said in 1868 that light was electric waves. Twenty years later a German, Heinrich Hertz, discovered the waves. At one end of his laboratory Hertz set an induction coil, a device that produces electric sparks. At the other end he held a loop of wire with a gap in it about a quarter of an inch wide. Hertz noticed that when the induction coil sparked at one end of the room, a spark jumped across the gap in the wire loop at the other end of the room, although the loop was not connected with the induction coil. That was the first radio message. Electric waves crossed the laboratory from the induction coil to the loop and reproduced the spark. Radio waves are sometimes called *Hertzian* waves in honor of their discoverer.

Sending messages by electric waves. A young Italian scientist, Guglielmo Marconi, searched for a way to send messages by the Hertzian waves. A French scientist had succeeded in ringing a bell in a distant part of his house. Marconi succeeded in sending a wireless message across the English Channel, and in 1901 from England to Newfoundland. Now powerful stations bind the civilized world, and ships are required by law to carry wireless operators. Only the screw propeller has done so much for safety at sea.

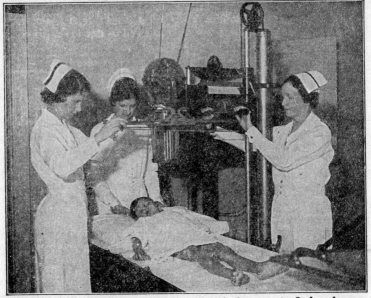

Fig. 319. The X-ray machine uses electrical waves to find and cure disorders of the human body.

In Marconi's system a key opening and closing a circuit in an induction coil discharges sparks. A spark is a surge of electrons. At each spark electric waves surge out through the air and space as light waves do, for light is electric waves. To send waves clear across the ocean, powerful waves are needed. One end of the spark gap is connected to a string of wires high above the ground, the *aërial*. The other end of the gap is connected with the ground. Every time the key is pressed electric waves leave the wires of the aërial and pass around the earth just as light waves pass from the wire in an electric bulb. The spark system is now rarely used.

The nature of electric waves. Electrical waves differ in wave length. The longest waves are those used for *radio* and *wireless*. Shorter waves are the *infra-red* or *heat waves*. We can detect these waves with our skin. The eye is sensitive to still shorter waves, the *light waves*. Shorter yet are the *ultra-violet waves* that affect photographic plates and tan our skins. They are too short for the eye to detect. Shorter still are the *X rays*. They have a wave length so short that they penetrate the flesh. They do not penetrate the bones, however, and the shadows cast by the bones make X-ray photographs (Fig. 320). The smallest rays that we know are called *cosmic rays*, discovered by Dr. Robert Millikan. Cosmic rays are believed to come to the earth from outer space.

All seven groups of waves are alike except in wave length. The length of some light waves is less than a billionth of an inch, while wireless or radio waves vary from a few feet to several miles in length. Some radio waves commonly used are 1500 feet in length, while extremely short radio waves are less than an inch.

Electric waves, whether of light, heat, or radio, have the same velocity or speed. When the waves are long, as in radio, the number of waves sent out in a second is less than when they are short. The number of waves a second is called the *frequency*. Frequency is the number of times the electrons in the wave swing back and forth in a second. The term *cycles per second* is often used to express the frequency. The frequency of radio waves varies from 10,000 to 400,000,000 cycles a second. These numbers are so large that the term *kilocycle* is used, *kilo* meaning *thousand;* 10 kilocycles is 10,000 cycles.

Receiving electrical waves. At the receiving end of a wire-

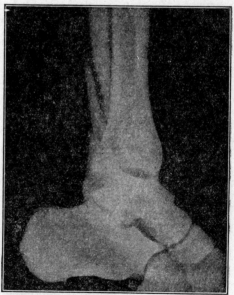

Fig. 320. The X ray reveals what happened to a famous ball player when stealing second

less station is another aërial which absorbs the energy of the waves sent out by the sending station. The receiving aërial sends this energy down the wire as rapidly varying electric currents caused by electrons surging down the wire. These rapidly changing currents are alternating currents. An alternating current, as previously explained, is a current in which the electrons reverse their directions several times a second. The alternating current in your home is usually a 60-cycle current. Its direction is reversed 60 times a second, or we may say that its frequency is 60. The frequency of the current that is led down from the aërial is very high. A naval radio station that sends waves of 2500 meters has a frequency of 120,000 cycles or 120 kilocycles.

The average human ear hears sounds when it receives vibrations whose frequency is between 20 and 10,000 cycles or vibrations a second. Frequencies within this range are said to be *audio-frequencies* because they can be heard. Frequencies above 10,000 are said to be *radio-frequencies*.

The current from the aërial of the wireless set is led to telephone receivers. In the receivers for wireless telegraphy the message is heard as long and short buzzes, produced as the sending key is pressed at the distant station. The buzzes spell out the dots and dashes of the telegraphic code. A short buzz is a dot and a long buzz is a dash.

The current brought down from the aërial has such a high frequency that the disk of the telephone cannot move back and forth fast enough to keep pace with it. Furthermore, the human ear cannot hear it. These high-frequency currents are therefore *rectified* or changed to low frequency by vacuum tubes. The rapid vibrations are replaced by vibrations of audible frequency.

Radio broadcasting. In broadcasting, electrical waves that encircle the globe are substituted for air waves from the human voice that will not travel a quarter mile. The broadcaster speaks into a *microphone*, which resembles a very delicate telephone transmitter. Sound waves there set up electric waves as in the telephone. The electrical waves run through radio tubes. In the tubes these waves carrying the message regulate a powerful current called the *carrier current*. The carrier waves modified by the waves bearing the message then run up through wires to the antennae. From the antennae, waves flow out around the earth somewhat as light waves flow out from an electric lamp.

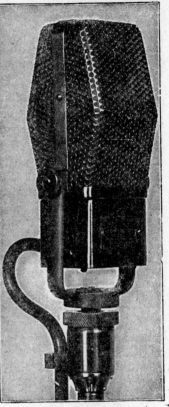

The waves sent out from the antenna of any station are of one wave length only assigned to that station by the Federal Radio Commission. If more than one station used the same wave length, the programs would be hopelessly mixed. The waves of any wave length carry the message or program from only one station.

Receiving the radio program. At the receiving station the speeding electrical waves produce vibrations that we can hear. Instruments are adjusted to receive only waves of a definite length, so that only one broadcaster is heard at a time. Adjusting the instrument to receive waves of a given length is "tuning in." The selected waves are led into the vacuum tube. There they set up waves similar to those

Fig. 321. A microphone.

that left the microphone at the broadcasting station. These waves are used to move the diaphragm in a loud speaker which in effect is a telephone receiver. The vibrating diaphragm causes air vibrations which we hear. The intricate operation of the various parts of the radio system is explained briefly in the next section. Radio is being intensively studied by scientists, not only because of its practical use, but because of what it teaches about the nature of matter and energy.

The Radio (Optional)

The vacuum tube. The secret of the modern radio is in the vacuum tube. To grasp the idea of radio operation, you must have at least a general idea of what the tube is and how it works.

Edison discovered that a separate plate sealed inside a lamp bulb but not touching the filament will under certain conditions pick up a current from the filament. When a wire from the plate is led outside the bulb and connected with the positive wire, a current flows through it, forming a circuit called the *plate circuit*. When the wire from the plate is attached to the negative wire, no current flows through the plate circuit.

When the filament is hot enough, some of the electrons flowing through it fly off through the vacuum to the plate that is positively charged. If the plate is negatively charged, its electrons (negative charges) repel the electrons from the filament and no current flows through the plate circuit. Here is the primary secret of the radio tube.

DeForest discovered another secret. If a wire screen, called *the grid*, is placed between the filament and the plate and connected to another battery or other source of current, the flow of electrons from the filament to the plate can be increased or decreased by the current sent into the grid (Fig. 322). If the grid is charged positively, it attracts an increased flow of electrons from the filament to the plate, and the current through the plate circuit is greatly increased. If the grid is charged negatively, the electrons on the grid

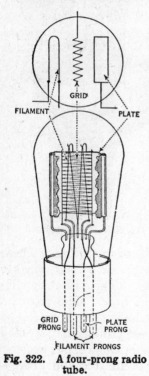

Fig. 322. A four-prong radio tube.

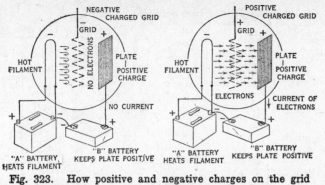

Fig. 323. How positive and negative charges on the grid affect the passage of electrons to the plate.

repel the electrons from the filament and the current in the plate circuit is diminished (Fig. 323). Thus changes in weak currents passing through the grid circuit produce much stronger currents in the plate circuits. Such a tube is used to *amplify* or strengthen weak currents. Several tubes used one after another can amplify the current many times. Such is the general plan of amplifying tubes used in radios, in amplifiers for auditoriums and outdoor speakers, and in repeating or re-laying long-distance telephone messages.

Figure 324 shows a tube of this kind. Two of the prongs are connected to the filament. A third prong is connected to the plate and a fourth to the grid. The filament, the grid, and the plate are parts of three circuits that are connected with different sources of current. When batteries are used, the filament circuit is

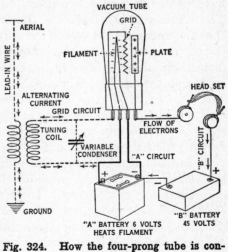

Fig. 324. How the four-prong tube is connected.

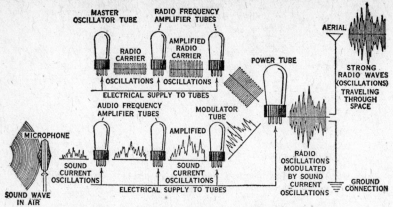

Fig. 325.   The plan of radio broadcasting apparatus.

connected to the A battery, the plate to the B battery, and the grid to the C battery.   Today batteries are seldom used where there are other sources of current.   The current coming into our homes from the power house can be suitably altered by tubes so that we can "plug in" at an ordinary lamp socket.

Screen grid tubes.   If you are interested in radio, you have probably seen a five-prong tube, the screen-grid tube. The screen grid is attached to the fifth prong.   We have seen that the vacuum tube passes the current in one direction from the hot filament to the plate.   Actually there is a small leakage from the plate or grid back to the filament.   Ordinarily this causes no trouble, but when high amplification is wanted, the leakage backward may cause squeaks and howls.   In the screen-grid tube a wire screen catches this backward flow of electrons.   This tube makes possible a smaller number of tubes because of the greater amplification possible with each tube.

Broadcasting.   Figure 325 shows the general plan for broadcasting.   In the microphone the air waves set up waves or oscillations of electrons.   In referring to the behavior of electrons in the apparatus, we generally use the term *oscillation*.   A series of tubes represented in the lower part of the diagram amplifies these oscillations.   These waves of low frequency are the sound, or *audio*, waves.

Another series of tubes represented in the upper part of the diagram creates and amplifies a series of high-frequency oscillations or waves. Waves of such high frequency cannot be heard by the human ear. They are the radio *carrier waves*.

The two types of waves are combined in a tube to produce the series of *modulated waves* that surge through the aerials and out into space.

The sending station from which the waves are broadcast may be miles from the studio where the artists or actors send sound waves into the microphone. In national broadcasts wires carry the waves of electrons from the studio to the broadcasting stations located in different parts of the country. The broadcasting stations receive waves through the wires and send waves out through space to be picked up by the radio receivers in our home.

The receiving apparatus. High-frequency radio waves coming through the air must be replaced by low-frequency sound waves in order to be heard.

In our radio sets the radio waves delivered to a series of tubes set up waves that can affect the human ear (Fig. 327). Radio waves arriving through space are weak. They therefore are sent through a series of amplifying tubes. In a

Photo by U S. Army Signal Corps

Fig. 326. The "walkie-talkie" portable two-way radio is an important instrument in military communications.

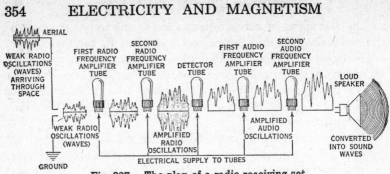

Fig. 327. The plan of a radio receiving set.

detector tube the high-frequency waves set up low-frequency or audio waves. The audio waves are then amplified and delivered to a loud speaker that operates much as does a telephone receiver.

(NOTE: **Direction of flow.** On page 314 you learned that the current flows from the positive pole of a battery through the wire to the negative pole. The electrician who strings the bell wire speaks in this way, as we do also ordinarily in the laboratory. The early students of electricity so viewed the "flow of the current." However, when radio waves were discovered and controlled by the vacuum tubes, it was found the former idea of the direction of the "flow of the current" would not explain the results. The scientist now explains the results as produced by electrons or negative charges attracted to the positive pole. To avoid confusion we speak in this book of the "flow of electrons" and understand that electrons are attracted by the positive pole.)

Television and Talking Pictures (Optional)

The electric eye. Have you heard of the "electric eye" that turns on the lights in an office building when clouds cover the sun or counts automobiles as they pass? You have seen how the ordinary incandescent lamp changes electrical energy into light energy. The electric eye or *photo-electric cell* does just the reverse. It changes light energy into electrical energy and the electric energy turns on the light or operates the counting machine. When

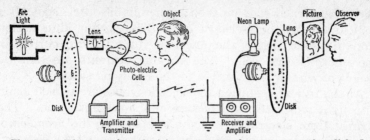

Fig. 328. Diagram of a television apparatus that uses scanning disks.]

this cell is in the dark, no electrical effect occurs, but when it is exposed to a source of light, the light energy produces an electric current within the cell.

The cell consists of a vacuum tube with two connections. One terminal, connected to the plus end of a battery, consists of a nickel wire ring in the center of the vacuum tube. The other terminal, connected to the minus end of a battery, leads into the inside surface of the tube, which is covered with a light-sensitive material such as potassium. In the dark no action takes place, but when light falls on this "electric eye," electrons are knocked off the coating of potassium upon the glass and are attracted to the loop of nickel in the center of the tube. This flow of electrons or feeble electric current may be made to switch on a more powerful current.

The photo-electric cell produces a very weak current when a dim light falls on it and a stronger current when a bright light falls on it. This action is the first step in television.

Television. Would you like to see a friend across the ocean while you talk to him this evening? You may talk to him over your telephone, and perhaps at no very distant date you may see him with a television apparatus. This apparatus reproduces instantly distant objects, pictures, or moving scenes while they are taking place. The results at present are far from perfect, but perhaps science has learned the secret.

The television transmitter is an electric eye or photo-electric cell that inspects or *scans* the object to be sent.

Light from each spot on the object falls in order, spot after spot, upon the photo-electric cell. The varying illumination from different parts of the object sets up a varying current in the photo-electric cell. The varying currents are sent by means of wire or radio waves to the receiving station.

At the receiving station the electric waves are turned again into light which forms a picture of the distant scene. The change from electricity to light is made by the *neon lamp*. An ordinary lamp will not do because it does not flash on and off instantaneously. The fraction of a second that the filament glows after the current is cut off makes it useless to transform electrical energy into light energy in a television receiver.

In the neon tube thousands of miniature lightning flashes may occur every second if the proper kind of electric current is fed into it. The tube consists of two metal plates in a bulb from which most of the air has been exhausted and neon gas added. A proper current flowing through the tube causes a pink glow between the plates. The glow will cease instantly when the current is removed. The red glow in some advertising signs is due to another form of the neon lamp.

In television the flashes of the neon lamp at the receiving station are caused by the varying electric waves arriving from the transmitting station. At the transmitter the electric eye is causing the varying currents by responding to the bright and dull spots of the scene. The flashes of the neon lamp must be arranged in the same order and position as the bright and dull spots that fell on the electric eye.

In one form of television apparatus to secure lighting in the required order the inspection of the object by the electric eye and the projection of the image by the receiver are governed by rotating disks called *scanning disks*. A scanning disk is perforated with a series of holes arranged in a spiral (Fig. 328). Light shining through the holes of the scanning disk in the sending station illuminates the object. Each hole illuminates a spot on the object. The spiral of holes on the rotating disk illuminates the entire object. The disk rotates

18 times a second. To your eyes spots of light following one another so rapidly blend into a continuous light, just as separate pictures blend into a motion picture. This effect is due, we learned, to the persistence of vision in the human eye. The electric eye or photo-electric cell, however, does not have this persistence of vision; it detects the separate spots of light. Each spot of light reflected from the object to the electric eye causes a current, a strong current if the light is strong, a weak current if the light is weak, no current if no light is reflected. These varying currents are amplified and delivered by wire or radio to the receiving station where they cause the neon lamp to glow and fade.

In front of the neon lamp in the receiving station is another scanning disk, an exact duplicate of the scanning disk at the sending station and rotating at the same speed. A special electric circuit keeps the two disks in step, or *synchronized.* A person at the receiving station looks through the scanning disk at the neon lamp. The separate flashes thus viewed blend into a complete picture.

Television with cathode rays. A newer method of television does away with the scanning disks. A camera lens focuses the scene upon a screen made up of hundreds of minute electric eyes. This screen is inside a large vacuum tube (Fig. 329). The electric eyes change the light rays into electric charges. Over the screen moves a beam of electrons. This beam is a *cathode ray,* a beam or ray of electrons streaming out from the minus pole (called the cathode) of an electric circuit inside a vacuum tube. It is the same sort of beam used to excite X rays. The beam of electrons, or cathode ray, moves across the electric-eye screen line after line somewhat as your eye does in reading a book. The cathode ray, however, moves very fast, covering the whole screen in one twenty-fourth of a second. During that one twenty-fourth of a second, the varying light of the scene changes to a varying electric current. The varying current modifies radio waves sent out to the receiving station.

At the receiving station the radio waves cause another vacuum tube to send a beam of electrons or cathode ray over

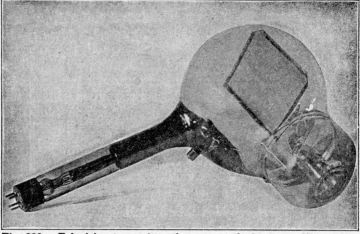

Fig. 329. Television transmitter that uses cathode rays. The rectangular screen is made of hundreds of electric eyes.

another screen (Fig. 330). The receiving screen is fluorescent; that is, it shines out with light when the cathode ray strikes it. The fluorescence is due to a coating of a certain compound of zinc which glows as electrons strike it. The receiving screen thus changes electric current into light while the electric-eye screen changes light into electric current. The cathode ray in the receiving station is governed by waves coming in from the sending station. The cathode ray moving over the fluorescent screen in the receiving station, therefore, keeps time with the cathode ray moving over the electric-eye screen in the sending station. Due to the persistence of vision, the glowing spots of the fluorescent screen blend into a picture.

Talking pictures. In recording sound for a talking picture a record of the sound called the *sound track* is made on picture film. A microphone, a sensitive telephone transmitter, is placed near the actor. The microphone is connected to a lamp which throws a tiny beam of light on the photographic film. As the actor speaks, the sound waves enter the transmitter. The sound waves, just as in the telephone, cause the current to vary. The varying current flashes the lamp. The light strikes the photographic film leaving its

Fig. 330. Television receiver that uses cathode rays.

record as the sound track. The record is a series of bands, some dark, some medium, some light (Fig. 263, p. 287). The density or darkness of the band depends upon the loudness of the sound.

Another method of recording the light that reaches the film is regulated by a slit that is opened and closed by the current from the microphone. In still another method an oscillating mirror throws the varying amounts of light on the film. The sound track may be recorded as a band of varying width instead of varying density.

The sound track may be made along the side of the picture film in the camera or it may be recorded on a film in a separate apparatus at the same time the picture is taken. Recording on separate film permits different treatment of the film in developing and finishing the negative, and therefore has certain advantages. When the positive print (the film that runs through the picture machine in the theater) is made, the sound track is printed at the side of the picture.

When the film is run through the motion-picture projector, the picture is thrown on the screen. At the same time a bright light shines through the sound record at the side of the film to a photo-electric cell. As the record runs between the light and the photo-electric cell, the light and dark bands vary the illumination. The photo-electric cell is connected to a speaker behind the picture screen in the theater. The varying current from the photo-electric cell operates the speaker just as the varying current in the telephone operates the telephone receiver.

The Electron Microscope. (Optional.) Through the recent centuries the scientist has tried to see smaller and ever smaller things. The invention of the compound microscope revealed germs of disease too small to be seen with the naked eye, for example the germ that causes typhoid fever. But there are disease germs too small to be seen with the compound microscope, for example the germ, called a virus, that causes influenza. Using light to see by, the diameter of the smallest object that can be seen with a microscope is about one-half the wave-length of light, about 0.0002 mm. The particles of the virus of influenza are still smaller, and so are invisible with light.

In the new electron microscope the scientist uses, not waves of light, but waves of electrons, the cathode rays (see page 357). They may be focused by an electric field or by a magnetic field as waves of light are focused by a glass lens. The waves of electrons cannot be seen, but they are focused on a fluorescent screen or on a photographic plate as are X rays. The electron microscope may magnify an object 100,000 times or more, while a compound microscope generally is limited to about 1500 times. The smallest object revealed by the electron microscope is about 0.000005 mm. in diameter. A virus, too small to be seen with the microscope, has been photographed with the electron microscope.

UNIT NINE

LIVING THINGS

Can you imagine an earth without a living thing, just rocks, soil, lakes, rivers, and great gray oceans? The earth as we know it is clothed with life, with green forests or grass covering the hills, the valleys, and the vast level plains. Narrow stretches of sea beach may be beaten bare of living things by the ceaseless waves, but the narrow strip skirts the life-covered continent. Stretches of desert have comparatively few living things, yet most of what we call desert is the home of many plants and animals. Even on the face of rocky cliffs and in dark caves are living things, breathing, feeding, growing, reproducing their kind. The lakes, the streams, and the oceans teem with life, from gigantic whales and seaweeds hundreds of feet long to tiny creatures too small to see without a microscope. And we are sure that there are other living things too small for us to see even with our most powerful microscopes.

Living things are a part of our world, part of our environment. We use them for food, for work, for pleasure, and to change the character of our environment, as in our lawns and parks.

Living things are built of the stuff of earth—carbon, hydrogen, oxygen, nitrogen, and other elements. These same elements and others make up the rocks, the water, and the air. There is nothing else on earth for living things to be made of. All their substance must be drawn from their environment.

The energy of life is the same kind of energy that we have been studying so far—science knows no other. Chemical changes turn food from one substance into another of more use to the body. Chemical changes turn the food into living substance. Chemical energy becomes heat energy in the body.

(361)

The energy of heat maintains life. The energy of light produces our food. The energy of sound and of light are means of warning us of danger, of enabling us to exchange ideas with one another, and of yielding us pleasure. Electrical changes which we can measure are constantly occurring in the living body. Though we cannot say just what life is, we know many of the chemical and physical changes that go on in the living body and to some extent how the body benefits by them.

The science of life, *biology*, is saving human lives. A new-born baby in ancient Greece could be expected to live, on the average, 29 years; in modern United States, about 60 years. The great white plague, tuberculosis, has decreased 50 per cent in the past 30 years. Typhoid fever, smallpox, and plague have been conquered. Diphtheria, hookworm, and malaria may be diseases of the past in our country as soon as the people understand and follow the teaching of biological science. Knowledge of proper food has helped to correct bowlegs and crooked spines due to faulty diet.

These improvements in human life have come because we have studied and learned how things live. We have learned much of the chemistry and physics of the human body, of plants and animals, of those minute living things that cause disease. We have learned how animals and plants develop. We have learned some of the laws by which good plants and animals, as well as poor plants and animals, are produced. We are applying this knowledge in the development of better breeds of animals and better varieties of plants. Our teeming farms and ranches fill the food bins of the world until the farmers complain that they can find no buyers for their crops.

In this and succeeding units we shall try to answer the question as to what living things are and how they manage to live. We shall study the processes of living. We shall see how the minerals of earth and the elements of water and air become our food. We shall see how they give rise to living matter and supply the energy of life. We shall see how new living things arise and spread over the earth. We shall see how they live together—sometimes helping one another, sometimes destroying one another—yet apparently always helping life to cover every nook and cranny of the earth. We shall see how man by understanding these processes is controlling his environment and becoming "lord of the fowl and brute" as well as of the plant life of earth.

Chapter XXXIX

WHAT LIVING THINGS ARE

Earth's living things. When you see a dog bounding down the street or a mouse scurrying over the barn floor, or when you watch a sea gull gracefully circling about the harbor, or a turkey buzzard drifting away through the sky, they seem very different from the trees and the grass and the weeds that stand still in the dust by the roadside. These animals have eyes to find food and shelter and to warn them of enemies. They have mouths for eating, and stomachs and intestines for digesting food. They have muscles to move them, and nerves to make the muscles work. Yet plants, with none of these organs, must have food and moisture, and must avoid the attacks of enemies. The plant world has solved the problems of life quite as well as has the animal world. Many of the problems of life are the same for both, and both classes of living things are built of the same living substance, not very different, so far as we can make out, in a squash plant and the brain of a man.

Life must have oxygen and water. All living things need these two important substances. If you try to hold your breath for even so short a time as one minute, you will find that it is very difficult to do, if not impossible. Even the pearl divers remain under water only forty-five seconds to a minute. Fish, too, must have air. The air they breathe is dissolved in the water. If you place a fish in an air-tight aquarium, it will soon die. Plants, too, breathe oxygen. They will not live where the air is robbed of oxygen. Experiment 111 shows that plants breathe.

Water is the second principal need of living things. Wild animals drink often at forest pools. We leave basins of water on the floor for our dogs and cats, and build bird baths

for the birds. Stabled horses must be led to water regularly.
The roots of plants search for moisture in the soil and die if
they are unable to absorb enough of it. It is lack of water
that makes the great deserts where few things or none can
live. All the intricate bodily changes that constitute living
can go on only in the presence of water.

Living things must feed. Both plants and animals
require food to keep them alive. Animals eat plants and
change them into muscles, bones, skin, nerves, blood; in
fact, into all the parts which go to make up the animal.
Animals that do not eat plants eat other animals that do, in
turn, eat plants. Plants, therefore, are the basis of the food
supply of the world.

Green plants make their own food. They make it out of
a gas, minerals, and water. They take the gas from the air,
and the minerals and water from the soil. Only the green
plants can make their own food, and they do it with the
energy of the sunlight. The magic green stuff of plants
enables them to use this energy from the sun. With it they
break apart carbon dioxide absorbed from the air and water
absorbed from the soil, and from the broken parts build up a
new substance—sugar. This is the first food. Other foods
are built by additions of other elements obtained from the
minerals of the soil.

What living substance is. The bodies of living things
are made up of a jellylike substance called *protoplasm*, which
is the essential part of every living organism. The manufacture of protoplasm can be accomplished only by living
things; that is, only protoplasm can produce more protoplasm.
Although chemists can determine the chemical elements of
which it is composed, it dies while being analyzed. Man has
never been able to put together the chemical elements which
are found in protoplasm in such a manner as to produce a
living substance.

Cells. We see a huge dray horse moving an enormous
load. The horse is a living thing, therefore he is made of
protoplasm. His protoplasm is organized into magnificent
muscles, into wonderful organs by which he sees and hears,

25

organs that digest and secrete, heart and vessels, delicate and sensitive nerves, and brain. The power, strength, and ability of muscles and organs to perform their work depend upon how protoplasm is arranged and how it acts.

With the aid of a microscope we can see that the protoplasm is arranged in little masses which are called *cells* (Fig. 331). Cells from different parts of the animal body differ in shape and size according to the work they have to do. Plant cells also differ in shape from different parts of the plant. Each cell, however, is made up of protoplasm. Usually the tiny drop of protoplasm is surrounded by a thin *cell membrane* or a *cell wall*.

A small body inside the cell is called the *nucleus* (Fig. 331). The nucleus seems to be the governing center of the cell that regulates its life processes, such as growth and reproduction. The nucleus is composed of a denser kind of protoplasm than the surrounding parts. Often a cell contains little masses of food or other material. Little "bubbles" of gas or liquid are often seen. These are called *vacuoles*.

Cells may exist alone; that is, one cell may exist as a complete plant or animal, too small to be seen without the aid of a powerful microscope; or they may live in colonies or groups where each group of cells has a definite kind of work to do. It is in groups that most cells live in the horse, in a man, in a tree, or in any living thing that is big enough to be seen with the unaided eye. *Groups of cells, living attached to one another, form tissues.* Thus the horse is made up of groups of muscle cells, bone cells, skin cells, fat cells, nerve cells, digestive cells, etc. There is a division of labor among the cells of a body, each tissue having its own work to do (Fig. 331).

An animal of one cell. Fortunately it is a simple matter to see some of these tiny units of life, the cells. If you collect a jar of water containing some dead leaves from the edge of a lake or pond, or if you place a handful of hay in a jar of water and let it stand at room temperature for a few days, you may find great numbers of living things composed of only one cell each. If you put a drop of such water under the microscope, you may see a multitude of objects darting about. At first they go so fast that you can make out very little of how they are built. They are magnified 50 to 250 times and their motion is magnified in the same proportion. When they

settle down, as they will when the water evaporates a little, you can see them better.

They are animals belonging to the group called *Protozoa*. Animals of this group are made of only one cell each. There are thousands of different kinds of protozoa.

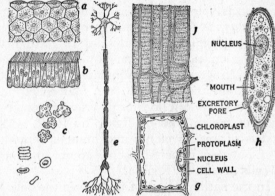

Fig. 331.   Various forms of cells.   (*a*) Tissue, lining abdomen. (*b*) Tissue, lining air passage. (*c*) White blood cells. (*d*) Red blood cells. (*e*) Nerve cell. (*f*) Muscle cells. (*g*) A cell from a leaf. (*h*) Paramecium.

One of the common kinds we find in stagnant water is called *Paramecium*. It has no common name. Figure 331 shows how it is built. It darts around by the motion of extremely fine little projections called *cilia*. You will not be able to see one of these cilia as it darts about, but you can make out that there is something moving about the edge of the body. You can make out a groove slanting into a mouth opening. Inside its body you will see little objects, some of which are bits of food. If you are very patient, you will see also the little star-shaped organs by which liquid wastes are cast out of the body. You will see these excretory (casting out) organs only for a moment as the star changes into a bubble and then bursts. Sometimes you can make out the nucleus, but this is more easily seen when the cell is stained with certain dyes.

How new cells arise.   Sometimes you may see a paramecium that seems misshapen, constricted in the middle as if a string were tied around it. Such a cell is dividing to form two cells. If you keep your eye on it patiently, perhaps for nearly an hour, you may see the division completed and the two new animals swim away (Fig. 332).

At other times you may see a heart-shaped object somewhat like that in Figure 333. Each such object is made of two paramecia joined together. The animals are said to be in *conjugation*. After a time the two separate and swim away. After conjugation each divides to form new animals. In conjugation each gives a small piece of its nucleus to its mate. The exchange seems to stimulate each to more rapid division.

Tissues and growth. A one-celled individual which reproduces by division forms two new one-celled individuals each of which goes on living by itself. Most cells in the bodies of higher plants and animals reproduce by division also, but they remain attached to one another to form groups of cells or *tissues* (Fig. 331).

In the earliest stage of their lives the cells of higher plants and animals divide rapidly to form new cells. This is one part of the process of growth. These cells give rise to different groups of cells. Groups of cells later become differentiated; that is, one group becomes different in structure and arrangement from others. Each such group has a different work to do in the body. One group forms skin; another, muscles, and another, digestive organs. Each cell also must increase in size. Growth is thus a complicated process in living things composed of many cells. It includes the division of cells to make new cells, the differentiation of cells to form tissue and organs of different kinds, and the increase in size of the cells.

Each cell alive. Each cell in a body must do its own living. It must take food, oxygen, water; it must get rid of wastes that would poison it. All living protoplasm must do these things. If the protoplasm makes up a one-celled animal like a paramecium, it takes its food and oxygen from the water in which it lives and gives off its waste to the water. If the protoplasm makes up a cell buried deep

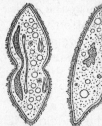

Fig. 332. A paramecium dividing. Fig. 333. Two paramecia conjugating.

in one of our muscles, it must take its food from the surroundings and give off waste to them. The bodies of higher animals and plants have methods of bringing foods and oxygen to these deep living cells and of taking away wastes.

Plants of one cell. In the water where we find the one-celled animals we may find also one-celled plants. Sometimes they form dense green coatings on the top of stagnant pools and on submerged objects. Some of them are bright green, taking the place in the microscopic world of grass and other larger green plants. Some are colorless like our toadstools and mushrooms. Figure 334 shows some of these one-celled plants that you may find. You may see them in stages of division, forming new one-celled plants; for they divide much as one-celled animals do. Some of these microscopic plants move about like the one-celled animals. Others live attached to stones, mud, sticks, or other things under water.

The great microscopic world. Many thousands of microscopic animals and plants are known. Many have been named and studied. We can scarcely find a place where they do not live. They are in fresh water and in the sea. They are on the rocks and on the soil and under the ground. They are on the outside of plants and animals, and inside them, too. Our mouths and intestines swarm with them.

Many of this great population seem to do us neither good nor harm directly, but some are beneficial and others harmful. Without the bacteria of the soil we should get no crops. On the other hand, some bacteria feed inside our body and produce poisons or toxins which make us ill. Probably every kind of plant or animal that lives is subject to disease caused by such germs.

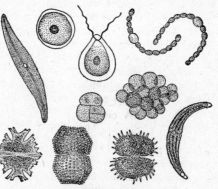

Fig. 334.   Plants of one cell.

EXPERIMENT 111

Question: What gas do plants and animals give off in respiration?

Materials: Two wide-mouthed bottles; two 2-hole stoppers; two glass tubes that will reach to the bottoms of the bottles; one shorter

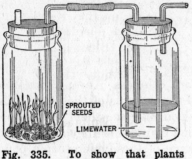

glass tube bent at right angles; a piece of rubber a few inches long to slip over glass tubes; limewater; sprouted seeds.

Directions: (*a*) Arrange as shown in Figure 335. Allow to stand 24 hours. Put fresh lime-water into bottle at right. Draw out the air from this bottle.

SPROUTED SEEDS

LIMEWATER

Fig. 335. To show that plants breathe.

(*b*) Exhale through a glass tube into a test tube of lime-water.

Results: What happens to the limewater?

Conclusion: Answer question.

Practical applications: Is your respiration like or unlike that of the plant? What effect will a plant have in the aquarium at night?

DEMONSTRATION

Question: What is the appearance of living cells?

Materials: A compound microscope; slides; a knife; a medicine dropper, a tumbler; a plate of glass to cover the tumbler; a small handful of hay; a small piece of bark from a tree trunk bearing the green mosslike material.

Directions: (*a*) Ten days before you study cells, put a handful of hay into a glass of water and allow it to stand in the room, covered with a plate of glass to reduce evaporation.

(*b*) Mount on a microscope slide a little of the green from the tree trunk and examine it under the microscope. With a medicine dropper place on the slide a drop of water from the glass in which hay has been soaking, and examine it under the microscope.

Observations: (*a*) You see microscopic plants composed of one cell each. How do you account for the little bunches of cells? Do you see a clear cell wall around the cells? Draw sketches showing single cells and little bunches of cells as you see them under the microscope.

(*b*) You will see many one-celled animals moving swiftly about. How do they move? Can you see a mouth? Can you make out anything inside the animal's body? Try to find the structures described on page 367. Do you see any as in Figure 332? Do you see any conjugating as in Figure 333?

DEMONSTRATION

Question: What is the appearance of tissues?

Materials: An onion; a small knife; slides; a compound microscope.

Directions: With the knife strip off a little of the skin of one of the inner leaves or scales of the onion. Mount it on the slide with a drop of water. Examine under the microscope.

Observations: Note the shape of the cells, how they are fitted together, whether there are any openings between the cells. Look for a little round body inside the cell. It may not be seen in all the cells. It is the nucleus. Does there seem to be any material in the cells outside of the nucleus? Both the material of the nucleus and the sandy material outside of the nucleus are living substance, protoplasm. Draw a sketch showing what you have made out.

CHAPTER XL

HOW A PLANT GETS WATER AND MINERALS

The living plant. When you look at the living plant in your garden or in the laboratory, you see stems and leaves, perhaps also flower or fruit. Down in the ground, away from the sunlight, are the roots. Each part has its own particular

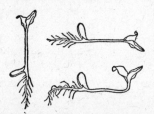

Fig. 336. The seedling was turned upon its side. How did stem and root change their directions?

work to do. The root holds the plant in place and gathers minerals and water from the soil. The stem holds the leaves up where they can get the energy of the sunlight, and carries the water and soil minerals to them. The leaves make the food, and the stem carries some of it down again to the parts of the plant below. Flowers are organs in which new plants are made.

How roots hunt water. If you turned a young plant upside down, would its root become a stem and grow leaves and its stem grow into the ground and produce roots? Figure 336 shows an experiment to determine that. A seedling was turned on its side after it was well started. You notice that the root turns down again as if it knew it belonged in the ground. We have not discovered why roots grow down, but down they go. Water is generally in the ground below and they grow toward the water. Roots from a Carolina poplar have been known to grow fifty yards directly toward a drain pipe, and then enter the pipe through the joints. In many communities planting of poplar trees is prohibited because their roots search out drain pipes and fill them. Figure 344 shows an experiment that demonstrates how roots go out of their way to reach water.

How a plant drinks. Try a simple experiment in which you use laboratory apparatus to show how plants absorb water.

You will need a glass tube and an egg with the shell chipped off at the large end, leaving only the membrane lining. Insert the tube well down into the small end of the egg, making a hole through the shell and the membrane, and seal them together with sealing wax. Set the end of the egg with the membrane exposed in a tumbler of water with the tube upright (Fig. 337). Here you have the thick substance of the egg separated by a membrane from a thinner (less dense) substance, water. The upper part of the egg is open to the air by way of the glass tube. Set the experiment up one day and put it aside. By next morning the egg

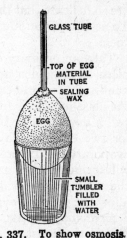

Fig. 337. To show osmosis.

has entered the glass tube and stands above the shell. Leave it another day. The rising process continues until the egg runs out of the top of the tube.

A similar experiment could be tried with a parchment (membrane) bag containing molasses or sugar solution, tied over the end of a tube and placed in the water (Fig. 338). The molasses will be pushed up the tube. Later, if you test the water outside the bag, you will find that some of the molasses has come out of the bag. The escape of the molasses will continue until the liquids inside and outside are equally dense. The greater flow at first is toward the thicker or denser liquid. The process whereby liquids pass through membranes in this manner is called *osmosis*.

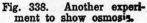

Fig. 338. Another experiment to show osmosis.

Root cells that absorb. We shall first see how root cells are so adapted that they absorb water and dissolved material from the soil. If you pull a root from the ground, you seldom see the structures that do the actual work of absorbing. They are so delicate that they are destroyed as you pull up the plant. To see them you must grow plants in such way as to preserve them.

Take an ordinary drinking glass and stretch over the top a piece of mosquito netting. Fasten it tightly with a rubber band. Pour water carefully through the mosquito netting into the glass until it is full enough just to touch the cloth. Place half a dozen oat or barley seeds on top of the net. Set aside for two or three days, adding water to replace any lost by evaporation. Before long the seeds will sprout. Little shoots will spring upward and little roots will grow downward through the net into the water. As the roots grow into the water, allow the water to evaporate somewhat or remove some with a a medicine dropper, as the root's absorbing organs develop best in the moist air above the water. Using great care, hold the glass up to the light from time to time. You will discover, growing out from the sides of the roots above the water, something that looks like delicate fur. By using a hand magnifier you can see that the "fur" is made up of delicate transparent projections from the root. The projections are called *root hairs*.

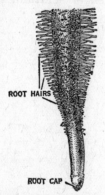

ROOT HAIRS

ROOT CAP

Fig. 339. The tip of a root highly magnified.

Each root hair is a projection of an epidermal (skin) cell (Fig. 339). Inside the cell is protoplasm and a liquid known as cell sap (Fig. 340). The protoplasm and the cell sap are denser solutions than the water in the soil. As the soil water is a weaker (less dense) solution, the water passes from the soil into the root hair by osmosis, and finally into the epidermal cell of which it is a part.

How water is passed along. When the soil water enters an epidermal cell, it dilutes or thins its contents, making this cell less dense than the cell that has not yet received the soil water. Water and dissolved substances pass into the next cell. This process repeats itself. Each cell passes water on to its neighbor.

How plants get minerals. Water in the soil is never chemically pure. It dissolves some of the minerals that it meets in the soil. Just as some of the sugar in our experiment passes through the membrane by osmosis, so some of the minerals dissolved in the soil water pass into the cells. These minerals are necessary in the plant to build some of its foods. Carbon, hydrogen, nitrogen, potassium, calcium, magnesium, phosphorus, sulphur, iron, and other elements in smaller quantities are found in plants. All these enter the plant dissolved in water from the soil. Carbon and oxygen also enter the plant through the leaves from the air.

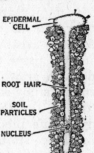

Fig. 340. A single root hair.

How a root is built. Certain cells in the root are especially adapted to absorb water from the soils, others to pass solutions along rapidly, and still others to store materials. When you split a carrot lengthwise, you can easily make out three distinct regions—the *epidermis* (outer skin), the *central cylinder* (a more woody part in the center), and the *cortex* (the fleshy part between the epidermis and the cylinder) (Fig. 341).

When you look at these regions of a root under the microscope, you find that each is composed of its own special kind of cells. On this close examination you find that the *outer layer* (the epidermis) is composed of oblong cells. The function of these cells is to protect the parts inside. On a small part of each fine root are

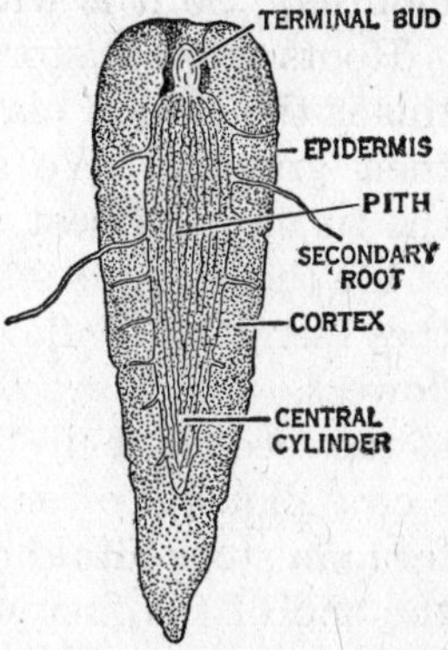

Fig. 341. The root of a carrot plant.

the root hairs extending from epidermal cells. In the *central cylinder* we find cells which give toughness and strength, and transfer liquids and air to and from the other parts of the plant. These cells toughen as they grow and often are woody in appearance. The *cortex* holds soil water and transfers liquids to and from the central cylinder and the epidermis. It serves also as a storehouse for food (Fig. 342).

Another tissue that is found in roots is *cambium*. It has to do with growth. You will learn more about this tissue when you study stems.

Storing for the future. As you proceed through the study of life processes of living things, you will find that living things store food against a time when it may not be

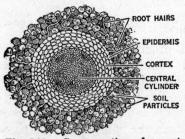

ROOT HAIRS
EPIDERMIS
CORTEX
CENTRAL CYLINDER
SOIL PARTICLES

Fig. 342.   Cross section of a root in the soil.

plentiful. Wild animals store fat in their bodies and become sleek when foraging is good. After a hard winter, when the snow has covered the plants which they eat, they are thin, but they have been able to subsist on the fat that they had stored up.   Bees and some other animals spend the whole summer storing up food for the winter months.   So it is with plants.

Roots serve as storehouses of food in some plants. Usually this is the case in plants that require two seasons to complete their growth.   We are all familiar with the *fleshy roots* of the turnip, the beet, and the carrot. During their first year of life these plants store food in their roots. The second spring they send up a flower stalk and produce a large head of flowers. Seeds are formed in the flowers; but the formation of the seeds uses up the food supply. If the plant is grown as a crop plant, it often does not get a chance to make its seeds; for man steps into the plant's life to rob it of the stored food at the end of the first summer before it produces its flowers. If beets, carrots, and turnips are allowed to grow the second season, there is no food left in the root for man to eat.

EXPERIMENT 112

Question: In which direction do roots and stems grow?

Materials: Two pieces of glass 4 or 5 inches square; a piece of heavy cloth or several pieces of blotting paper the same size as the glass; radish or other small seeds for sprouting.

Directions: (a) Lay one of the pieces of glass on your desk. Place on it the heavy cloth or blotting paper. Place several seeds of about the same thickness about $1\frac{1}{2}$ inches apart on the cloth or blotter. Lay the second piece of glass over the seeds. With a piece of string, or rubber bands, fasten the pieces of glass tightly enough to hold the seeds in place. You have made a "pocket garden."

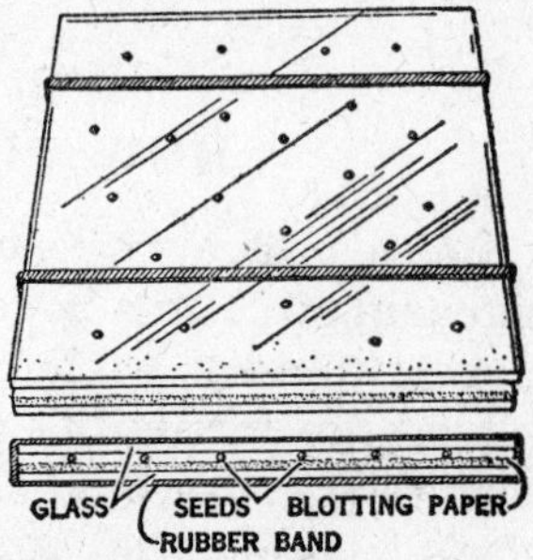

GLASS SEEDS BLOTTING PAPER
RUBBER BAND

Fig. 343. A pocket garden.

(b) Stand the pocket garden edgewise in a pan containing about an inch of water. The water will wet the cloth, which will in turn moisten the seeds.

(c) After a few days you will be able to see the sprouting seeds develop their roots and stems. 1. In which direction do the roots grow? 2. In which direction do the stems grow?

(d) When you are sure of the direction of growth of the roots and stems, turn the pocket garden so that one of the side edges is in the water. Watch it for several days. 3. Do the roots and stems continue to keep growing in a straight line toward the edges of the glass they originally started for? 4. What seems to determine the direction of growth?

Diagrams: 1. Pocket garden as first built. 2. Pocket garden, after seedlings show direction of growth. 3. Pocket garden showing direction of growth after turning.

Conclusion: Answer the question.

EXPERIMENT 113 (OPTIONAL)

To show that roots grow toward water. Replace the bottom of a box with wire screen. Put in an inch of wet moss or sawdust. Support it so that you can see the bottom from below. Plant beans or peas at one edge. Do the roots grow down or do they follow the wet moss?

Fig. 344. To show that roots seek water.

Chapter XLI

HOW PLANTS MAKE FOOD

Leaves face the sun. When we seek the shade of a spreading tree on a hot summer day, we take advantage of the tree's necessity. The tree must spread itself in the sun to get energy for its life work. It must hold its leaves up so that they can get all the sunlight possible. Leaves are the tree's food factories, and these factories run by sun power.

If you examine the arrangement of leaves on a twig, you

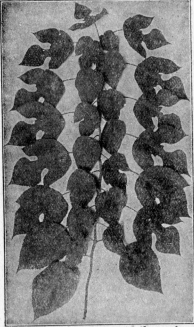

Fig. 345. Leaves arrange themselves to catch the sunlight. A branch of mulberry.

will find that the leaves are fitted together to display the greatest possible surface to the sun (Fig. 345). Probably you have noticed house plants on a window sill growing toward the light until their leaves are flattened against the windowpane.

Sun power makes food. Let us show by experiment that green leaves manufacture food, and that they do it in the sunlight but not in the dark. Set a plant in a dark closet and another in the sun. After several hours remove a leaf from each plant. Kill the leaves by plunging them into hot water. Then soak them in alcohol until all the green substance is dissolved. The green substance is called *chlorophyll*. When the leaves are bleached white, put them into a solution of iodine. A dark color, black or blue, develops in the leaf that was in sunlight but not in the leaf that was in the dark. Iodine turns starch blue. This shows that starch forms in the leaves on which the sun shines. The process is therefore called *photosynthesis* (putting together by means of light).

Where the plant gets raw materials. Starch is composed of the three elements carbon, hydrogen, and oxygen. These three must pass into the plant to be used in making starch. Carbon and hydrogen are not found free about the plant. A gas of the air, however, carbon dioxide, is composed of carbon and oxygen (CO_2). Hydrogen is one of the elements of water (H_2O). We have learned that water enters the roots from the soil. Carbon dioxide from the air enters the leaves through microscopic openings.

How leaves are fitted for their work. Most leaves are broad and flat and lie with the flat side to the sun. Those that are narrow like the grass leaves are long as well. Leaf stalks (petioles) often show twistings that turn the blades (broad part) flat to the sun. Leaves thus seem especially designed by shape and growth to fit them for the work that goes on in the sunlight. You will notice if you hold a leaf to the light that it has a system of veins arranged to bring the supplies of water to every part of the leaf surface.

The cells of a leaf also are arranged to help the great work of photosynthesis. The outside layer on the upper and lower sides of the leaf (the epidermis) is colorless so that the sunlight passes straight through. Inside a leaf are layers of cells that contain round green bodies, the *chlorophyll bodies*. Chlorophyll is the most important part of a leaf, for it alone, of all the substances we know in nature, has the power of using the sunlight to make starch from carbon dioxide

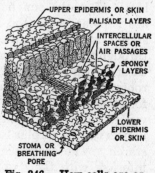

UPPER EPIDERMIS OR SKIN
PALISADE LAYERS
INTERCELLULAR SPACES OR AIR PASSAGES
SPONGY LAYERS
LOWER EPIDERMIS OR SKIN
STOMA OR BREATHING PORE

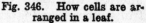

Fig. 346.   How cells are arranged in a leaf.

and water. The layer of internal cells (mesophyll cells) lying next the upper epidermis or skin is packed close (the palisade layer). This gives a good exposure of chlorophyll to the sun.

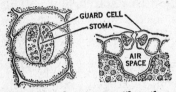

Fig. 347. A stoma or "breathing" pore of a leaf.

The cells below are loosely fitted together (spongy layers), permitting gas and water vapor to circulate freely. Veins bringing water branch among the loose-fitting cells. Microscopic mouths (stomata) open through the epidermis, especially on the lower side of the leaf. Each microscopic mouth is surrounded by two guard cells that open and close the mouth (Fig. 347). Gases pass through the stomata entering or leaving the leaf. The spaces between the loose-fitting cells (intercellular spaces) are in communication with the stomata so that gases from the air may reach the working cells. Excess gases from the interior cells and excess water vapor pass out the same channels.

Digesting and forwarding foods. The chemist can show that the first food made by the leaves in the sunlight is not starch but sugar. Sugar is very similar to starch chemically, being composed of the same three elements—carbon, hydrogen, and oxygen. The sugar when formed in photosynthesis is immediately changed to starch. But the starch is in the leaf for only a short time. If we pluck a leaf from a plant a few hours after the sun has left it, we find no starch. There are substances in the leaf called *enzymes* that change the starch to sugar again. Sugar in solution readily passes through the cell membranes by osmosis and so is passed down through the veins and stem even as far as the root. In roots and stems enzymes again change the sugar into starch for storage in the cells, for starch does not pass through cell walls by osmosis. Cells in roots and stems may act as storehouses for the surplus food. Few leaves act as storehouses for starch. The accumulation of starch in the leaf cells might interfere with their work of making more food. Seeds and fruits receive and store a large part of the food.

Elements to make fats and proteins. In addition to starch and sugar, all living things need other foods. Proteins and fats must be supplied. The plant must make them also. Fats, like starch, are composed of the three elements—carbon, hydrogen, and oxygen. Proteins need, in addition, the elements, nitrogen, sulphur, and phosphorus. These additional elements come into the plant dissolved in the soil water and are carried by the veins.

Fig. 348.   Tendrils of the pea.

Getting rid of wastes. The plant takes up from the soil a great deal more water than it needs in starch making. A current of water passes steadily up from the roots to the leaves. Water has many things to do in the plant. One of these is to carry substances up the stem, for all solid substances must be dissolved to travel from cell to cell. When the water has done its work, the surplus must be gotten rid of. It passes off as water vapor through the stomata. This passing off of water vapor from the leaf is called *transpiration*. Figure 352 illustrates an experiment to show transpiration.

Still other matters pass from the leaves as waste. The cells of the leaf get more oxygen from the water and carbon dioxide than they use for starch making. The surplus oxygen is given off through the stomata. Carbon dioxide, too, sometimes passes out of the stomata. Plants, like animals, breathe. They take in oxygen and give out carbon dioxide as waste. While photosynthesis is going on, there is no surplus carbon dioxide, but at night the carbon dioxide is in excess and must be passed out from the leaf as animals pass it out through the lungs.

Special jobs of leaves. Some leaves do special work. These leaves are especially modified or adapted to carry on such work. Some plants use their leaves as climbing organs or tendrils (Fig. 348). Others, like the sedums, use them as storehouses. Others again, like the barberry, have

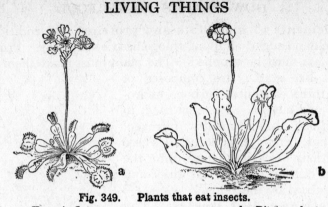

Fig. 349.   Plants that eat insects.

a, Venus's flytrap.   b, Pitcher plant.

them changed to thorns which serve for defense against
browsing animals. The insect-eating plants, as sundews,
pitcher plants, and Venus's-flytraps, use their leaves to catch
insects (Figs. 349 and 350).

When their work is done. After leaves have performed
their life work, their cells die and they fall to the ground.
Some plants, however, such as pines, spruces, and hemlocks,
retain their leaves for two years or more. These trees are
always green. When we walk in an evergreen grove, we find
that the floor of the forest is covered with the tiny leaves
(needles). The leaves are falling a few at a time. As the
old leaves die, new ones take their
places.

Fig. 350.   The sundew
catches small insects on its
glistening leaves.

Many trees, such as the maple,
elm, and most oaks, shed all their
leaves at the same time—in the fall
of the year. First, the leaves begin
to change in color. Cold weather
comes on or food conditions become
unfavorable, and the activity of the
cells of the leaves stops. The tree
is going into the winter sleep. The
red, russet, orange, and brown of the
fall foliage is due to the waste substances that have accumulated as

the chlorophyll stops work and is destroyed. In a wooded, mountainous country the colors may be so beautifully blended as to remind one of the richest oriental tapestry. It is a sign of death, of completion of the work of these leaves. When the leaves fall away from the trees, a waterproof layer appears on the scar left where each leaf has broken off. This prevents loss of sap while the tree is in the quiet state.

EXPERIMENT 114

Question: Under what conditions is starch made by green leaves?

Materials: Desk apparatus; a vigorously growing plant such as a geranium; tin foil or black paper; paper clips; alcohol; solution of iodine.

Directions: With the paper clips fasten two small squares of black paper opposite each other on upper and lower sides of a leaf. Place in the sun for several hours. Then pluck the leaf with the paper squares and immediately kill in hot water. Place in alcohol until next day or bleach white in hot alcohol. The safest way to heat alcohol is to place a beaker of alcohol in a larger beaker of boiling hot water with no flame under it and no flame on the table. Alcohol vapor is very inflammable. When leaves are bleached, soak in iodine solution.

Results: What happened to the leaves in the iodine?

Conclusion: Answer question.

EXPERIMENT 115

Question: What waste substance is given off when plants make starch?

Materials: Some Elodea or other plant that grows submerged; a six-inch battery jar; a glass funnel that fits inside the jar; a test tube that fits over the tube of the funnel.

Directions: Nearly fill the jar with water. Put in the Elodea. Cover the plant with the funnel tube pointing upward. The water in the jar must cover the upper end of the funnel tube. Fill test tube with water, cover with thumb and invert over end of funnel tube so that it remains filled with water (Fig. 351). Stand it in the sun. Examine at hourly intervals. Repeat the experiment away from the sunlight.

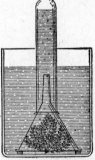

Fig. 351. To show that green plants give off oxygen in sunlight.

Results: What happens to the water in the test tube? When full, try with the spark test.

19

NOTE.—As this gas is not pure oxygen but is mixed with air, the spark test we used in the study of oxygen sometimes does not work.

Conclusion: Answer the question.

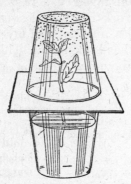

Practical application: What effect would such plants have upon the water in an aquarium? Would they benefit or harm the fish and other animals?

EXPERIMENT 116

Question: Does moisture pass off from leaves?

Materials: Two tumblers; a card to fit across top of tumblers; a freshly plucked leaf.

Directions: Arrange as shown in Figure 352. Place in the sun and examine shortly.

Conclusion: Answer the question.

Fig. 352. To show that leaves give off water vapor.

CHAPTER XLII

HOW STEMS SERVE THE PLANT

A stem's work. Green leaves make the food supply for the world and stems make the wood supply. Primarily wood serves the plant. It is evident that it holds the stem erect so that the leaves are up in the sunlight. It has another function (use to the plant) that you may see by standing some twigs overnight in red ink. By cutting slices across the stem next day, you can see that the red ink has passed up the stem through the wood. Wood carries up sap. If you examine the cut end of an oak branch, you will see small holes like pinholes in the wood. These are the cut ends of fine tubes called *ducts* or *vessels*. The vessels are the chief upward channel through which the sap flows. The downward flow is through tubes (sieve tubes) in a part of the inner bark (the *phloëm* or *bast*) (Fig. 353).

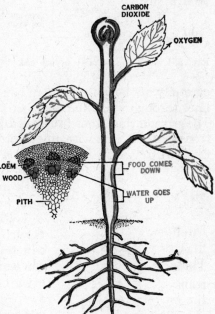

Fig. 353. This picture illustrates the passageways of water upward and sap downward through the plant.

Woody stems. When you cut a maple or an apple stem crosswise, you may see that there are three regions similar to those found in roots (Fig. 354).   They are the *bark*, the *wood*, and the *pith*.   When you peel the bark from the stem, you will find also a slippery layer between the bark and the

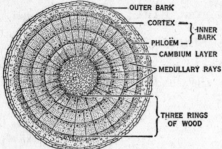

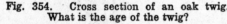

wood, which is known as the *cambium*.   The cambium has a most remarkable function.   It builds the outer layer of the wood and the inner layer of the bark.   The work of the cambium is thus to provide for the growth of the plant.   The pith acts as a storage place for food.   If you look

Fig. 354.   Cross section of an oak twig. What is the age of the twig?

carefully at the cut end of an oak twig, you will see radiating lines through wood and inner part of inner bark (the phloem). These radiating lines are called *pith rays*.   Their use is to transfer food crosswise in the stem.   A closer inspection of the bark reveals a corky outer layer which serves to protect the delicate tissues from drying out.   Heavy layers of outer bark in old trees protect the trees from animals and passing wagons.

Telling a tree's age and history.   From a stump foresters can tell the age of a tree.   They can learn in what year there was a severe drought and when a fire swept through the forest.   On the cut end of a tree trunk you will see rings that grow around the center of the tree (Fig. 354).   By these rings you can tell the age of a tree. Let us understand how.   The cambium lying at the outer edge of the wood grows more rapidly in spring than later in summer.   The cells of the cambium make new cells by

Fig. 355. Cross section of a piece of spruce wood showing the cells in spring and summer wood.

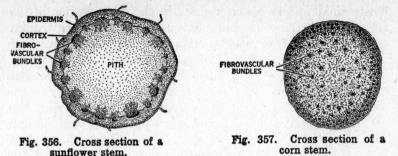

Fig. 356. Cross section of a   Fig. 357. Cross section of a
sunflower stem.   corn stem.

division somewhat as the one-celled paramecium divides. In
the spring these cells are well supplied with nourishment
and they grow large. The growth of cells formed later in
the season is slower, and they are smaller in size. Every
year, therefore, the wood is made up of large cells formed in
spring and smaller cells formed later in the summer. It is
easy to pick out the spring wood and the summer wood
(Fig. 355). In this way rings of wood arise. Each ring
represents a year's growth. By counting the annual (yearly)
rings you can tell how long the tree has been growing. A
wide ring indicates a good growing year; a narrow ring shows
a season of poor growth, probably due to drought. By
examining the rings of the big trees of California, scientists
have obtained a record of the weather for hundreds of years
back into the past.

After living several years, the cells of the wood die. These
dead cells become darker. They form the *heartwood* of the
tree. They then serve the tree only by giving support.
The sap is carried only by the outer few rings of wood, which
is called the *sapwood*. In old trees most of the wood is
heartwood. In some trees the dead center wood readily
rots away, but as long as the sapwood is alive, the tree may
live on.

A cornstalk. Let us examine a cross section of a cornstalk. The first thing we observe is the outside layer, which
is called the *rind*. The rind acts as a protection to the
inner parts of the stem and gives strength. Inside the rind
we find pith with little specks scattered through it (Fig. 357).

These small specks which you see in the cross section of the cornstalk are the wood bundles. Like wood in tree trunks, they contain ducts or vessels and are, therefore, called *vascular bundles* (bundles of vessels). Every little bundle has its own vessels and cambium. When the cornstalk reaches a certain size, the cambium stops work and growth ceases. The energies of the plant are then put forth to hold the leaves up to the light and to mature the seeds and fruit.

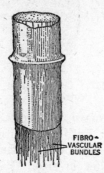

Fig. 358. The rind and the bundles of a corn stem.

The vessels of the plant make a continuous channel for the sap from the roots to the leaves and flowers. The wood in the central cylinder of the root continues into the stem which in turn sends branches off to the leaves where we see them as veins. Branches also go into the flowers and fruits.

A winter twig. Let us examine a horse-chestnut twig in the winter or in the early spring before the buds have opened (Fig. 359). Look carefully for the markings. First you will find little triangular scars opposite each other on the stem. These are the scars where leaves of the preceding summer have broken off. They are *leaf scars*. If you look carefully at these scars, you will find little dots on each one. These little dots are the ends of the vascular bundles which carried liquid while the leaf was attached, but the ends of which were sealed when the leaf fell. Just above the leaf scar in each case you will find

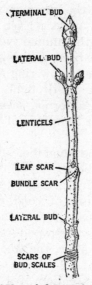

Fig. 359. A horse-chestnut twig in winter.

a tiny projection. This is a little bud which will produce a branch when the tree resumes growth. If you find one pair of leaf scars on the east and the west sides of a stem, the pair immediately next above or below will be on the north and the south sides.

On the end of the stem you will find some larger buds with heavy, overlapping scales. These *bud scales* are often covered with a sticky substance which prevents loss of water and discourages any bugs that might try to enter the bud. Most twigs have buds on the end (terminal buds) and on the sides (lateral buds). The end (terminal) bud on the horse-chestnut twig grows out in the spring to become a bunch of flowers. The side (lateral) buds below the terminal flower bud produce branches. Between two twigs you will find a scar marking where a flower bud grew at some previous time.

When the terminal bud opens in the spring, the heavy scales drop off, thus forming a *ring scar* about the stem which shows where the bud scales were previously fastened. The distance which the stem grows in one year is the distance between the bud-scale scars. Scattered on the bark are little brown spots. They are really little openings (*lenticels*) which admit air and also permit the escape of water vapor.

The grain of wood. Examine the cut end of an oak twig, branch, or stump. Compare with Figure 354, Page 386. You can readily see the lines radiating out like spokes of a wheel. They are the medullary or pith rays. You can see the rings of tiny holes that are the vessels or ducts in the spring wood. You can see the denser wood of late summer. If you next cut a slice from the side of the twig, or better from a branch as thick as your wrist, you can see the grain. [This cut face is called the *tangential section*.] Trace a medullary ray over the edge from the cross section, and you will see it as a thin, short line. A medullary ray is a sheet of tissue. On the sliced face you will see the vessels again as holes arranged in a pattern, and the denser summer wood between the lines of vessels. Cut a twig or branch lengthwise through the center. You may see the medullary rays as patches, for they are not exactly straight as wheel spokes and so can not easily be cut along their entire length. On this face (the radial section) you will see the vessels as fine grooves or as oval holes where they have been sliced. You can easily see the lines of the grain due to spring wood and the denser summer wood.

Now that you have identified the structures that make up the grain, study the grain in a board or the top of your desk. Select the spring wood, summer wood, and medullary rays.

Pine, spruce, and the wood of other cone-bearing trees, has no vessels and the rays are so fine as to require a microscope or lens to be visible. The grain that you see in these woods is due to the alternating spring and summer wood.

EXPERIMENT 117

Question: Through what part of the stem does sap rise?

Materials: Willow twigs; stalks of celery or young corn or any clear weed stem; red ink; a quart jar.

Directions: Put an inch of water colored with red ink into the jar. Stand the stems in it. Examine in a half hour and again next day. Cut slices across the twigs.

Results: Where has the red ink risen?

Conclusion: Answer the question.

EXPERIMENT 118 (OPTIONAL)

Question: Through what part of the stem does sap descend?

Materials: A willow twig; a quart jar with an inch of water; a knife.

Directions: Cut two rings around the twig about half an inch apart; remove the bark but not the wood between the rings, stand twig with the lower end in the jar of water, keeping the portion with the bark removed just above the water.

Results: In a few days you will notice the bark at the edge of the bare ring beginning to swell and then roots beginning to jut out. At which edge of the bare ring do the roots develop?

Conclusion: Through what part of the twig does the sap come to supply the growth of the new roots?

Practical applications: When a ring of bark is removed from around a tree, even if the wood is left uninjured, the tree eventually dies. Why?

A wire wrapped tightly around a tree eventually kills it, but a bolt driven straight through does not. Why?

Chapter XLIII

HOW THE RACES OF PLANTS GO ON

What good are flowers? When we walk in a flower garden, we are impressed by the fragrance, the color, and the shape of the flowers. We are likely to regard them only as growing for our enjoyment, and the bees buzzing among them as interlopers that have discovered by chance that flower nectar will afford a store of fine honey for the winter.

The flowers, however, perform a service for the plant, and the bees have their part in helping them perform it. If we watch a flower from the time it bursts from the bud until it withers and dies, we shall find that its main business is to develop and ripen into a fruit which contains seeds. These seeds, under favorable conditions, will produce new plants that are like the parent plant.

Parts of a flower. Upon examining a blossom of one of our common flowering plants, we usually find a set of small leaflike parts at its base on the stem (*peduncle*). These were folded around the complete flower when it was in the bud. They are the *sepals* (Fig. 360). Just above the sepals are the larger, beautifully colored flower leaves which expand as the flower opens. They are the *petals*. The profusion of color in our gardens is chiefly due to brightly colored petals. Inside the petals is a circle of slender, stemlike organs, the *stamens*, which usually surround a single organ, the *pistil*. The organs of the flower which are necessary for its work are the stamens and the pistil. For this reason they are often referred to as the *essential organs* of the flower. The flowers of a few kinds of plants consist only of essential organs.

A stamen is composed of two parts (Fig. 361). Its stem is the *filament*. On the end of the filament is a pouchlike or purselike form, the *anther*. When it is ripe or fully developed,

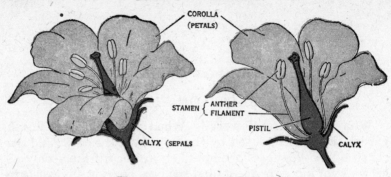

Fig. 360. The parts of a flower.

the anther bursts open and releases myriads of tiny grains of a dustlike substance called *pollen*.

The pistil usually has three parts, called *stigma*, *style*, and *ovary* (Fig. 361). The *stigma* is the outer end of the pistil; it is often feather-like or sticky, so as to be adapted for catching and holding the dusty pollen grains. The *style* is the slender stalk which supports the stigma. The *ovary* is the enlarged lower part or base (Fig. 361); it contains minute, egglike objects, called *ovules* (little eggs).

Fertilization. By ways we shall study presently, pollen reaches the stigma, and the flower is then said to be *pollinated*. When the pollen grains fall upon the stigma, they are held fast by the moist surface. Then from each little pollen grain a long projection grows downward through the style. This projection is called the *pollen tube*. It continues to grow until it reaches and enters an ovule. Inside the ovule is an *egg cell*. When the pollen tube enters the ovule a special cell, called the *sperm cell*, leaves the pollen tube and unites with the egg cell, their protoplasms intermingling and fusing. This union of sperm and egg cells is called *fertilization* (Fig. 362).

Growth after fertilization. The fertilized egg cell promptly divides to

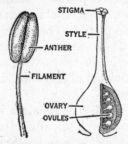

Fig. 361. The stamen (left) and the pistil (right).

form two daughter cells. Each daughter cell grows and divides again. This process is repeated until a young plant or embryo is formed. At the same time food is stored inside the embryo or packed around it. The coats of the ovule enlarge and become tough and often very hard. Such a developed ovule, containing a young plant and food for its future growth inclosed in a protective coat, is a *seed*.

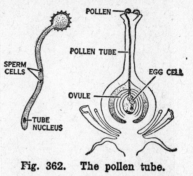

Fig. 362. The pollen tube.

Fertilization also stimulates the ovary to renewed growth. It may increase greatly in size. The pea pod and the watermelon are two such enlarged ovaries. The enlarged and fully developed ovaries are called *fruits*.

Self-fertilization and cross-fertilization. In many plants a sperm cell from the pollen grain of a flower unites with an egg cell in an ovule of the same flower. For some reason, nature often provides against this *self-fertilization* and arranges a plan whereby the pollen grains of one plant find lodgment on the stigma of another plant of its own kind. This process, called *cross-pollination*, results in *cross-fertilization*. Cross-pollination is assured in several different

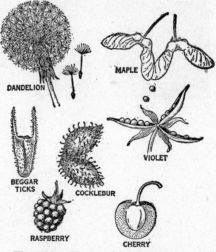

Fig. 363. Fruits of several plants.

ways. For instance, sometimes the stigma has not matured enough to receive the pollen dust when the anthers on the

Fig. 364.   Staminate flowers of the
willow.

Fig. 365.   Pistillate flowers of the
willow.

same flower ripen to give it off, or the stigma of a flower may ripen before the pollen is shed.   Often we find that the stamens and pistils are of different lengths so that the anthers cannot rub against the stigma (Fig. 366). Frequently we find that one plant produces flowers which have stamens only (*staminate* flowers), while another plant of the same kind produces flowers having pistils only (*pistillate* flowers).

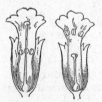

Fig. 366.   Flowers of the primrose.   How is the chance of self-pollination reduced?

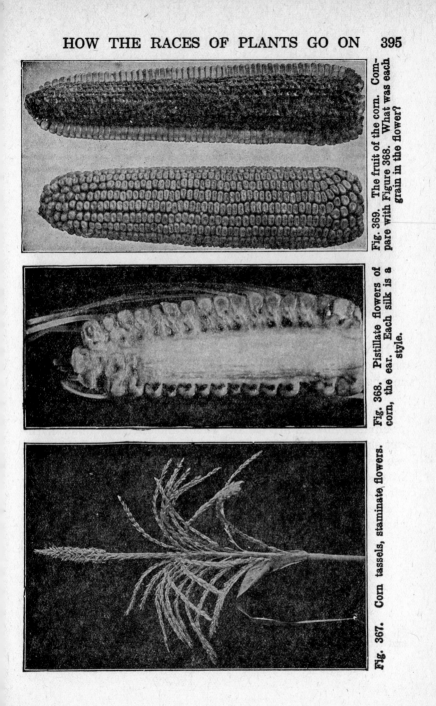

Fig. 369. The fruit of the corn. Compare with Figure 368. What was each grain in the flower?

Fig. 368. Pistillate flowers of corn, the ear. Each silk is a style.

Fig. 367. Corn tassels, staminate flowers.

Fig. 370. Staminate flowers of corn.

How pollen travels. Certainly, since nature has set up this complicated means of reproduction, there must be some means of transportation of pollen. One means is the wind which picks up the pollen grains from the ripe anthers and bears them along to a ripened stigma (Fig. 370). Wind-pollinated flowers are usually small and inconspicuous, without showy petals. If you look at them closely, you will often see anthers dangling where the pollen will be shaken out and carried away by the wind. The stigmas, too, are often dangling out like tiny feathers (Fig. 368).

Bees busily visiting flower after flower are the best known carriers of pollen. The bright color, the odor, the nectar for the manufacture of honey, and the pollen itself for "bee bread," are the attractions that keep the bees at work in the flowers. The bee, entering a flower, brushes against the anthers and is daubed with pollen. It rubs some of this pollen unintentionally on the stigma of the next flower it

Fig. 371. A pistillate (left) and a staminate (right) flower of the pussy willow.

visits.   Moths, butterflies, flies, and humming birds also carry pollen.

The pea seed.   The fruit of the pea plant is a pod which contains several seeds.   Each seed is fastened to the pod by a special stem (Fig. 372).   The scar on the seed where it was attached is called the *hilum*.   Just outside the hilum is a tiny hole about the size of a fine needle point.   Through this opening the pollen tube usually enters the ovule.   This little hole is the *micropyle* (Fig. 372).

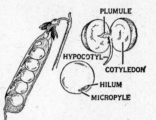

Fig. 372.   The fruit and seed of the pea.

Inside the seed coat (*testa*) is the young plant, or *embryo*.   Most of the seed consists of the two sections of the embryo.   These two thick, oval objects are the first leaves of the young plant.   They are called *seed leaves* (*cotyledons*).   The seed leaves contain food stored up for the embryo to use when it begins to grow.   They are attached to a tiny sproutlike stalk (called the *hypocotyl*).   The root grows down from the lower end of this stalk.   Inclosed between the two cotyledons is a little leaflike object which is attached to the stem and to the seed leaves.   This is the stem bud (*plumule*).   When the embryo begins to grow, the seed leaves give up their nourishment and wither away, and the plumule grows up to become the stem and leaves of the plant (Fig. 373).

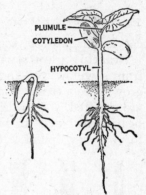

Fig. 373.   Seedling of the bean.

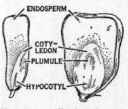

Fig. 374.   Grain of corn.

The grain of corn.   The food for the young plant is not always part of the embryo.   For example, the corn embryo lies at one side of the food.   The food for the corn embryo is in the starchy white or hard, yellow substance. A drop of iodine will stain the starchy part black. Food stored outside the embryo of a seed is called *endosperm*. The corn has only one seed leaf (cotyledon). It lies like a white shield against the endosperm. The hypocotyl is a little point jutting down toward the scar where the grain was attached. The plumule is a point jutting in the opposite direction (Fig. 374). [Plants such as corn, having one cotyledon, belong to the group called *monocotyledons;* those with two, such as the bean, are *dicotyledons;* while the pines, with many cotyledons, are *polycotyledons.*]

Fig. 375. Seedling of corn.

Starting plants without seeds. If you break a switch from a willow tree and stick it into the ground, it will often grow to be a tree. In growing sugar cane sections of the stem are planted. In raising potatoes a portion of the potato bearing an "eye" or bud is planted. The bud grows out to form a new plant. Grapevines, roses, and many of our

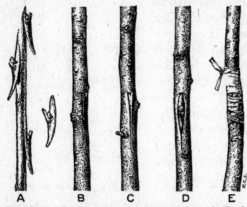

A   B   C   D   E

Fig. 376. Bud grafting of fruit trees. A, Bud scion. B, T-shaped cut through the bark of the stock. C, Bark raised to admit the bud. D, Bud in place. E, Bud wrapped with raffia.

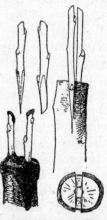

Fig. 377. Cleft grafting.

flowering plants similarly grow from cuttings or slips. Fine fruit trees are carried on by cutting twigs or buds from the desired variety and grafting them into twigs or branches of another tree (Figs. 377 and 378). Fruit trees grown from seeds may produce worthless fruit. Reproduction by parts of the plant other than seed is called *vegetative* or *asexual* (without sex) *reproduction*.

EXPERIMENT 119
(DEMONSTRATION)

Pollen tubes may be grown by placing pollen in a solution of sugar (3 to 10 per cent). Try several kinds of pollen and several dilutions of sugar. Put the sugar solution in a concave microscope slide or in a watch glass. Touch a camel's-hair brush or the tip of a pencil to an anther that is shedding pollen and then to the sugar solution. Examine under the microscope in one hour, two hours, and next day.

Fig. 378. Whip grafting. A, Scion and stock prepared. B, Fitted together. C, Wrapped with waxed twine.

EXPERIMENT 120

Question: How do seedlings (young plants) develop from the embryo?

Materials: Sawdust; a flat pan; peas; beans.

Directions: (a) Place about two inches of sawdust in a pan. Place 25 or 30 peas and beans just below the surface of the sawdust and about equal distances apart. Add enough water to moisten the whole mass. Set it in a warm, sunny place and keep the sawdust moist.

(b) After a few days you will notice that the seeds are beginning to sprout. What happens to the covering of the seeds? Make a diagram of one of the seeds when the sprouts are about a quarter of an inch long.

(c) As the sprouting goes on, take out one or two of the sprouted seeds (seedlings) each day. You will soon find that a part of the sprout grows downward and another part grows upward. Make other diagrams when this begins to happen.

(*d*) As the seedlings continue to grow, you will find that it is harder to pull them out of the sawdust and that more sawdust clings to them. What is forming at the lower end of the sprout?

(*e*) A sprout appears above the surface and turns green. Which part of the plant is this?

(*f*) As the upper part of the seedling comes out of the sawdust, we notice that the thick parts of the bean seed are lifted out into the air. Watch these parts a few days and explain which part of the seed becomes the first leaves. Hunt for similar parts of pea.

Diagrams: Show by a series of diagrams all stages of germination from the time you plant the seeds until the roots, stems, and leaves are developed.

Conclusion: Answer the question.

Practical application: The seed has everything in it needed for producing a young plant. There is no plant food in sawdust; therefore, everything which made the plant must have been in the seed.

Man has learned to appropriate to his own uses the food that nature has stored up in seeds for the use of the young plants. By long selection he has developed plants which produce more seeds, and which store more food in each seed, than the plants which his ancestors knew. By always selecting the best of the crop for seed, man has increased both the quantity and the quality of the food contained in the bean seed.

EXPERIMENT 121 (HOME)

Question: What are the moisture and temperature requirements necessary for sprouting (germinating) of seeds?

Materials: Twine; 20 beans; 20 peas; 4 pieces of muslin 4 inches wide and 15 inches long.

Directions: (*a*) Prepare 4 small rag-doll testers as follows: Lay off each of the 4 pieces of muslin in rectangles, 2 by 3 inches. In the center of each rectangle place a bean or a pea. There should be 5 beans and 5 peas in each "doll." Roll the doll together, taking care to keep the seeds in position. Wind loosely with a piece of twine and tie to hold it together.

(*b*) Number the doll testers, 1, 2, 3, 4. Place number 1 in the ice box and keep it dry; saturate (fill) number 2 with water and place it in the ice box. Number 3 is to be kept dry in a warm (not hot) place and number 4 is to be kept moist in a warm place.

(*c*) After 4 days carefully unroll your testers and record the conditions in the table. Roll them up again. Examine and record after 6 days and again after 8 days. You must be sure to return each doll to its original place so that the conditions for the seeds will not change through the experiment.

Results:

TABLE

TESTERS	CONDITIONS	NUMBER OF SEEDS SPROUTED		
		AFTER 4 DAYS	AFTER 6 DAYS	AFTER 8 DAYS
No. 1..........	Ice box, dry...........	......	......	......
No. 2..........	Ice box, moist.........	......	......	......
No. 3..........	Warm place, dry.......	......	......	......
No. 4..........	Warm place, moist.....	......	......	......

Diagrams: 1. Show a rag-doll tester with seeds on it at the beginning of the experiment.   2. Show number 4 at the end of the experiment.

Conclusion: Answer the question.

Practical application: Inexperienced people often plant their garden seeds too early in the spring.   If the ground is wet and cold, seeds are apt to rot before they get enough warmth and moisture to sprout them.

EXPERIMENT 122

Question: Of what use are the cotyledons to a seedling?

Materials: Some bean seedlings germinating in damp sawdust that have just lifted their cotyledons above the surface; a pair of small scissors.

Directions: (a) Without harming or disturbing the rest of the seedling, cut off both cotyledons of half of the seedlings with the scissors.

(b) After three days, examine the seedlings.   1. Which seedlings are still thriving?   2. What is the appearance of the seedlings whose cotyledons were removed?

Diagrams: 1. Seedlings before cotyledons were removed.   2. Seedlings after cotyledons of half had been removed: a diagram of a seedling with cotyledons, one of a seedling without cotyledons.

Conclusion: Answer the question.

Chapter XLIV

HOW ANIMAL LIFE CONTINUES THROUGH THE AGES

What is an egg? When you are eating an egg, do you ever stop to think about what is inside the egg? Although eggs are important food for us, primarily they are food and protection for the young chick. The limy shell protects the chick from insects and other small animals. The coloring of wild birds' eggs often protects them from the prying eyes of egg-eating animals. If you carefully chip away the shell, you will find a thin, though rather tough, membrane lining the shell. This membrane protects the contents of the egg from bacteria. Through this thin membrane oxygen passes in to the chick and carbon dioxide passes out, for the young chick must breathe, although it does not breathe with lungs as later in life.

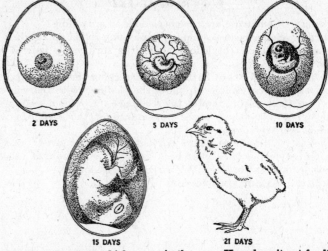

2 DAYS 5 DAYS 10 DAYS

15 DAYS 21 DAYS

Fig. 379. How the young chick grows in the egg. How does it get food? air?

If you carefully open an egg and pour the contents into a flat dish, you will see the almost colorless "white" of the egg and the yellow yolk.   They are the food for the young chick.

On one side of the yolk you will see a small white spot. This is called the *germinal spot* or disk. From it the young chick develops (Fig. 379). Gather some frogs' eggs from a pool in the springtime and watch them develop into tadpoles. Then if you take care of the tadpoles, you can watch them develop into frogs (Fig. 380).

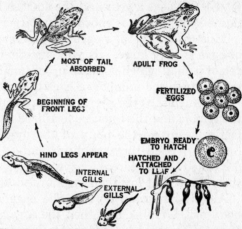

MOST OF TAIL ABSORBED

ADULT FROG

FERTILIZED EGGS

BEGINNING OF FRONT LEGS

EMBRYO READY TO HATCH

HIND LEGS APPEAR

HATCHED AND ATTACHED TO LEAF

INTERNAL GILLS

EXTERNAL GILLS

Fig. 380.   The life history of a frog.   Most of our frogs grow from egg to adult in the first year. The bullfrog becomes adult the second year.

How animals reproduce their kind. In the very simplest animals that we know—animals of only one cell each—the one cell divides into two.   Each new cell is a separate animal.   We cannot say which is parent cell and which is offspring.   Simple plants of only one cell divide in the same manner.

If we trace back the life history of animals, such as frogs and chicks, we find that each animal starts as one cell, the fertilized egg.   The fertilized egg originates by the union of two simple cells.   One of these cells is the sperm cell and one the egg cell (ovum).   You will recall that we found exactly the same condition in flowers, a sperm cell uniting with an egg cell.   This union is called *fertilization* in both plants and animals.

Among many of the lowly animals of the sea, such as starfish and oysters, the females release their eggs in the water and the eggs float away.   Sperm cells are similarly set free by the males to drift away.   Whether a sperm meets an egg and fertilizes it, is largely a matter of chance. If the two cells do not meet, they soon both die. Where so much is left to chance the number of eggs is large. The oyster lays 60,000,000 eggs a year and the starfish lays 200,000,000. The number of sperms is enormously larger.

Most fishes lay their eggs in a similar manner. The number of eggs is very large. If you sometime see on your table the roe of a shad which is made up of unlaid eggs, examine it and try to guess the number of eggs that are in it.

In some fishes the sperm cells are transferred to the body of the female and the eggs are fertilized in her body. The young fish grow inside the body of the mother until they are well formed. Then they are born "alive." Fishes of this type are called "live bearers" (viviparous). They have fewer eggs than those that lay their eggs in the water.

Among birds and reptiles the eggs are fertilized inside the body of the female and then the eggs are laid. In the higher animals (mammals) the eggs are similarly fertilized inside the body, and the young animal lives and grows inside the mother's body until it is born.

Care of the young. The young of most of the lower animals take care of themselves. Those that cannot do so may become food for other creatures. Life or death is often a matter of mere chance. Since the chance of living is small, the number of young is very large. It is not surprising that the sea water is swarming during hatching season with the young of starfishes, lobsters, clams, and other animals. Most of them become food for other creatures.

Some fishes guard their eggs and young, but most fishes leave them to care for themselves. When a little fish hatches from the egg, it has attached to its body a yolk sac filled with food for its immediate use (Fig. 381). The eggs of reptiles and birds contain a great deal of food. Both may be used as food by man and other creatures. Reptiles conceal their eggs and leave them to hatch. The young reptiles generally must shift for themselves. Birds sit upon their eggs (*incubate* them), keeping them warm during development of the embryo to the stage of hatching. If the embryo is chilled, it may die. After hatching her eggs, an old hen's sole object in life for a time is the care of her brood. She defends them from attack, coaxes them to food, cuddles them at night. Have you ever seen the fury of a mother robin as she drives off a marauding squirrel?

Fig. 381. A young fish with yolk sac.

Among higher plants (seed plants) and higher animals (mammals) the young are cared for until they get a good start in life. Food for the young plant is stored inside the seed. This stored food supplies the growing tissues of the young plant until it can send its roots down into the soil and spread its green leaves in the sun. In higher animals (mammals) the young are provided with nourishment before birth by the mother's blood, and after birth they are fed for a time with milk. After the stage of helplessness or infancy is passed, many animals remain with their parents and older members of their group. Bees, antelopes, and cattle remain together for mutual protection in the hive or the herd.

CHAPTER XLV

HOW NEW KINDS ARISE

Darwin's answer. How did the great number of different kinds of plants and animals arise? Many men, scientists and others, have tried to answer this question. After thirty years of study of the problem, Charles Darwin (1809–1882), the English biologist, announced to the world his answer to the problem in his book *The Origin of Species* (1859).

Darwin pointed out that plants and animals produce great numbers of offspring. If all the kittens grew to maturity, in a few years they would eat not only all the mice and rats, but all the rabbits, birds, and other small creatures on earth. A codfish lays 9,000,000 eggs in a year. The descendants of a single pair of codfish in ten years would fill the ocean basins solid with codfish. An oyster produces 60,000,000 eggs a year. The number of its great-grandchildren would be written with 66 followed by 33 ciphers. Write it down and see what it looks like. They would make a pile of oyster shells seven or eight times the size of the earth. If all the descendants of a single pair of human beings lived to maturity, in ten centuries there would not be standing room for them on earth. Some must die. Of all that are born, which live and which die? The young are not all alike. They may vary considerably. Those individuals live who are stronger or quicker or more cunning. They are best fitted to survive. From the great numbers arises a *struggle for existence*, and the struggle results in the *survival of the fittest*. Thus the new kinds of plants and animals in nature, said Darwin, arise by *natural selection*.

Heredity and variation. All the children in a family are not exactly alike, although they are often enough alike to be recognized as belonging to the family. All the kittens in a

litter are much alike, but usually they can be told apart.
When the new generation grows up, it resembles the parents.
Indeed, if you were looking at flies or frogs, you probably
could not tell the parents from offspring unless you had
studied them very closely through life as the biologist studies
them.   The handing down of characters from one generation
to the next is *heredity*.   The tendency to differ is called
variation.

Mendel's discovery.   About the same time that Darwin's
Origin of Species startled the learned world, Gregor Mendel,
a monk who had been growing peas and other plants in a
monastery garden in what was then Austria, announced
a discovery of certain laws of heredity.   Few heard of the
discovery, and it was forgotten until the discovery was again
made in 1900.   Now Mendel's laws of heredity are proving
of greatest value in producing new varieties of plants and
animals.   The new kinds are enabling us to grow more and
better foods.   We are getting new plants and animals for new
lands in the cold regions and in the hot regions, new varieties
to resist diseases, and new fruits and vegetables for our
tables.

Here is a simple statement of what Mendel found.   If a
pea with a yellow seed (called, for convenience, a "yellow"
pea) is crossed with a pea with a green seed, all the offspring,
or second generation, have yellow seeds.   Yellow is *dominant*
(*dominus*-master).   But if yellows of the second generation
are crossed with each other, one fourth of the third generation
are green and three fourths yellow.   If the green are fertilized
with each other, the descendants are all green.   A character,
as greenness, is thus passed down from one generation to
another, although a contrasting character may hide it for a
generation (Fig. 382).   We say that green is *recessive*.

Now let us see the yellows of the third generation.   They
all look alike.   One third, however, are "pure blood."   If
they are crossed with each other, they produce only yellow
offspring, the other two thirds when crossed with each other
produce both yellow offspring and green offspring.   These
two thirds are "mixed strains" or hybrids.

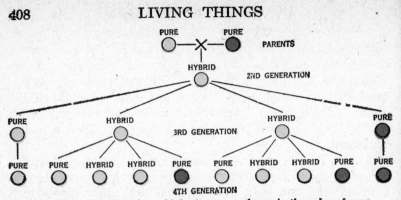

Fig. 382. Mendel's law of inheritance as shown in the color of peas.

[Mendel's findings are sometimes stated as three laws:

1. *Law of Unit Characters.* Certain characters in a plant or an animal, as greenness and tallness, are inherited as "units," each independently of others.

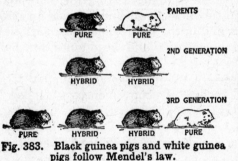

Fig. 383. Black guinea pigs and white guinea pigs follow Mendel's law.

2. *Law of Dominance.* Certain characters are dominant over others. Only the dominant character appears in hybrids. We know that this law does not govern all characters. For example, a red four-o'clock crossed with a white four-o'clock produces pink hybrids. But the law always operates with certain characters as with yellow and green peas.

3. *Law of Segregation.* When hybrids are crossed with hybrid, the dominant character and the recessive character "segregate" in the next generation. They will be pure-blood dominant individuals and pure-blood recessive individuals.]

Sports or mutations. Breeders of plants and animals have long known that suddenly new kinds arise that they have not had in their stock before. Sometimes these new kinds breed true, that is, their descendants are of the new variety. Thus a hornless cow sometimes appears in horned stock. The

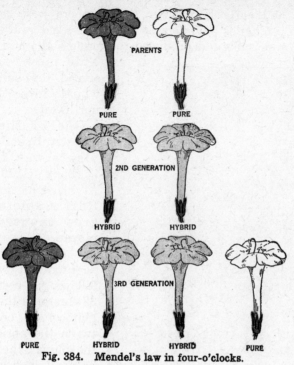

Fig. 384. Mendel's law in four-o'clocks.

seedless orange appeared on trees of a seed variety. A stalk of Cuban tobacco in Connecticut grew 14 feet high and produced 80 leaves. This new variety bred true and added many pounds a year to the crop.

New varieties that appear without warning and breed true are called *sports* or *mutations*. The Dutch botanist De Vries (1848–   ) studied mutations in the evening primrose, and drew the attention of scientists and breeders to their importance in producing new and valuable varieties of plants and animals.

Using the laws of heredity. In our plains states wheat was dying from drought, cold, and disease. Professor Herbert Roberts at the University of Kansas crossed varieties of wheat and produced the famous *Kanred* wheat. In the plains of western Canada wheat was so often killed by frosts in late

August and early September that farmers were poverty-stricken. Charles Saunders at Ottawa crossed wheats from Europe and India and produced the famous *Marquis* wheat.

This new variety spread the culture of wheat into the far northwest.

One of the best known breeders of plants was Luther Burbank (1849–1926). At his home in Santa Rosa, California, he grew thousands of plants. Among the famous varieties that he produced were the following: corn with 32 ears on a stalk; the plumcot, a cross between the apricot and the plum; the Shasta daisy, 6 inches in diameter; a walnut that grew 7 feet in a year;

Fig. 385. Luther Burbank and some of his giant pansies produced in his garden at Santa Rosa, California.

the famous Burbank potato (Fig. 385).

Heredity in man. Intelligence and stupidity have followed Mendel's law of dominance. A large number of families

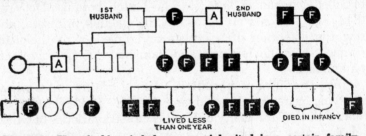

Fig. 386. How feeble-mindedness was inherited in a certain family. F, Feeble-minded. A, Alcoholic. White, normal. Squares, male. Circles, female.

Equipoise, for speed.

Captivator, grand champion Percheron, for strength.

Tam O'Glenburn, a Shorthorn, for beef.

Design's Martina, a Jersey, for butter fat.

Leghorn hen, for egg production.

Plymouth Rock hen, for meat.

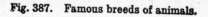

Fig. 387. Famous breeds of animals.

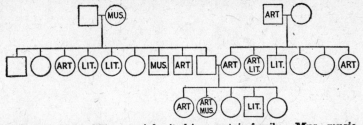

Fig. 388. How ability was inherited in a certain family. Mus., music. Lit., literature.

have been investigated through several generations in America and Europe. In some families run crime, immorality, and feeble-mindedness. In others run intelligence and ability (Figs. 386, 388).

Can we control human inheritance? We can produce families of speedy race horses, of prize cows and hens (Fig. 387). We know that sturdy bodies and able minds in man follow the same laws of heredity. Science has shown how superior cows can be produced. Shall we try to produce superior men in the same way?

EXPERIMENT 123 (OPTIONAL)

Question: How can I show that nature produces vast numbers of offspring? Count or estimate the number of grains of corn on an ear; the number of peas in a pod; the number of pods on a vine; the number of seeds on a weed. If all survived, how many plants would there be the next year? the third year? How much land would be needed to support each year's crop?

EXPERIMENT 124 (OPTIONAL)

Question: Do offspring vary? Measure the length of each bean in a cupful. Record results in a table.

LENGTH IN INCHES	$\frac{4}{16}$, or less	$\frac{5}{16}$	$\frac{6}{16}$	$\frac{7}{16}$	$\frac{8}{16}$	$\frac{9}{16}$
Number of beans.........						

Similarly measure the height of all the members of the class. Record in separate tables height of boys and of girls of each age.

EXPERIMENT 125 (OPTIONAL)

Question: What is the value of protective coloration? Take several potatoes or balls. Paint some white, some black, some mottled to imitate the colors of wild animals and birds. Place in a dark corner or in a darkened box turned on its side. Use various backgrounds. If these objects represented wild animals, which would be more liable to destruction by beasts of prey? Which are protectively colored?

EXPERIMENT 126 (OPTIONAL)

Question: How can I show that certain traits are inherited? Select a certain number of physical characteristics and mental traits. Choose those which are noticeable and remembered, such as stature, complexion, color of eyes, color of hair, excitability, temper, humor, studiousness, skill, etc. Draw a chart of all members of each generation of your family that you can learn about. Show the occurrence of the characters in each generation.

ADDITIONAL QUESTIONS TO THINK OUT

1. How do living things differ from nonliving?
2. How could you show that a sprouted seed was alive?
3. How does a plant differ from an animal?
4. Think of a paramecium living in a pond and of a cell living deep inside your muscle. How can each get food, water, and other necessities of life, and how get rid of wastes that would poison it?
5. Why does a paramecium not need heart and lungs as higher animals do?
6. What is meant by saying that the cell is the unit of the living body?
7. What advantage is it to be made of cells instead of a mass of protoplasm?
8. Of what benefit to a plant is the division of labor among its different parts?
9. Could there be life on earth if there were no soil?
10. Why do land plants need root hairs though seaweeds and freshwater plants get along without them?
11. From what part of the plant does most of our food come?
12. Potatoes stored in the cellar sometimes sprout. Why should the sprouts be removed?
13. Plants grown in deserts usually have deep root systems, and plants in wet places have shallow roots. Why?
14. If you filled a parchment bag with a sugar solution, tied it tight and put it into a bucket of water, what would happen?
15. If you filled the parchment bag with pure water and lowered it into sugar solution, what would happen?

16. Growing fruits, such as tomatoes, sometimes split open in wet weather. Why?

17. Salt will kill weeds and grass. How?

18. Leaves vary more in length and breadth than in thickness. Why?

19. Desert plants may have thick leaves, or, like the cactus, they may have none at all. Why?

20. The pine has needle-like leaves and the oak broad leaves. How does the pine make up for the disadvantage of narrow leaves?

21. Why is the epidermis on the upper side of the leaf usually thicker than on the lower side?

22. Do you see any advantage to the leaf in having most stomata on the lower side?

23. Washing the leaves of house plants often makes them grow better. Why?

24. Do white leaves of plants make starch?

25. Tobacco fields are sometimes covered with cheesecloth. How does that affect the leaves?

26. Celery plants are bleached by piling soil high around the stalks. Why does this practice make them white?

27. Why are celery and lettuce leaves often placed in water before serving?

28. Why does the destruction of leaves of the potato by potato beetles (potato "bugs") reduce the size of the potatoes?

29. Why will the weeds in the lawn die if you continually cut off the leaves above ground?

30. Why do dead leaves, if not raked from the lawn, damage the grass, while dead leaves in the forest do no harm?

31 Why are plants more likely to wither on a clear, windy day than on a hot, humid day?

32. Why does a wilted plant often revive overnight?

33. What is the best time to pick flowers if you want to keep them?

34. Summer is the poorest time to transplant trees. Why?

35. Why are trees pruned (twigs trimmed off) before transplanting?

36. Study sections of wood to see what causes the grain.

37. The grain runs up and down a tree rather than around the trunk. What advantage is that to the tree?

38. Why is it easier to split wood than to cut across the grain?

39. In getting sap to make maple sugar, the tree is tapped only a short way in. Why?

40. Why is it that a tree cut half through will live, but a tree with a ring of bark removed will die?

41. Telephone linemen often brace their poles with guy wires from trees. If the wire encircles the tree, it kills it. If the wire is attached to a bolt running through the trunk, it does not kill the tree. Explain.

42. Why are there few low branches on forest trees?

43. From a twig can you tell the age of the tree on which it grew. Can you tell the age of the twig?

44. Which is the oldest part of a tree trunk?

45. If you drove a nail in a tree four feet from the ground, how high would you expect to find it twenty years later? Would you expect to find it still at the same depth from the surface?

46. What advantage to plants is asexual or vegetative reproduction? Do you know of any cases among animals?

47. Why do the petals usually drop from a flower after pollination?

48. Stormy weather at blossom time often results in a small crop of fruit. Why?

49. Oak trees have very inconspicuous flowers and roses very showy flowers. Why?

50. Flowers that open late in the evening are usually white. Why?

51. How does brightly colored fruit aid the plant?

52. Bees visit only one kind of flower on a trip. How does this benefit the plants?

53. Cucumbers grown in greenhouses in winter, if left to themselves, produce no fruit. Why?

54. How are seedless oranges and bananas reproduced?

55. Is heredity or environment of more importance in a person's life? Argue it out with your classmates.

UNIT TEN

FIELD AND FOREST IN THE SERVICE OF MAN

Farming began when early man or woman dug up a choice root and planted it in a more convenient place, or planted seeds of a wild plant. Agriculture has had a long history. The wild plants that furnished the first crops have, many of them, disappeared from the earth. Corn, for example, is nowhere now a wild plant. Wild

Fig. 389. Little wild potatoes of Chile, three inches long and purple in skin and flesh. Once thought to be the original potato.

potatoes and wild apples are the size of walnuts. Century after century man improved his crops by selecting the best for seed, but progress was infinitely slow until the dis-

Fig. 390. Green Mountain potatoes. One of the many fine, large varieties produced from the little wild potato.

covery of the laws of heredity. Now in a few years the scientist can make more progress in improving plants than the ancient farmers made in centuries.

Farms feed us, with some additional food from the sea. Farms clothe us. Farms furnish a variety of other products—oils, dyes, fibers, explosives. To increase the great variety of the products we can get from the farms of the United States, we import materials from the farms and groves of the tropics—rubber, bananas, fibers, coffee, medicines. The production of all these products is receiving the intensive study of science.

Another product of the soil is the forest. Check over the forest products that you meet in a day. Wood, paper, turpentine, rosin, and a variety of chemical substances derived from forest products are sent to the market in large quantities. Each of them is used in many industries. The Forest Products Laboratory of the United States Department of Agriculture is studying further uses of new forest products. The forest contributes far more than

Fig. 391.   The little wild strawberry.

Fig. 392.   Fine strawberries two inches long, have been developed from wild ancestors less than a half inch long.

its physical products. The control of water supply and of soil are to a very large extent matters of forestry. Growing new forests is a long, slow process, but with the disappearance of our wild forests it is our only hope for replenishing our supply of those products for which we have found no substitute. Good forestry is preserving the forests on government land and growing new forests to replace those destroyed on public and private land.

A farm or a forest is no better than its soil. For four thousand years Chinese farmers have farmed the same soil, and it is now producing heavier yields than do our soils. In America soils are pronounced "exhausted" after twenty-five years, and many are abandoned after five years or less. Chinese methods are not suited to life in America, but soil science is solving the many problems of keeping our soils at their best and restoring those that have been abused. Our government is offering the aid of science to the farmers.

In this unit we study the science of the healthy soil and the means of restoring "worn-out" soils to health, the science of plowing and harrowing, of kinds of farm, of kinds of crop and why they grow, of forest crops that take a hundred years to mature, of the age-old and present-day search for such common things as food, clothes, and string.

Chapter XLVI

MAKING SOIL WORK

Study and care make good soil. Farm soil is not simply dirt. Nor is it merely ground or earth. Soil must contain the building material of the plant's body—not all of the building material, however, for we have seen that a large part comes from the air. Soil must furnish also the means of getting the materials into the plant. Plants cannot eat soil. The vehicle that carries the minerals to plants is water. Too much water, however, drowns the plants and carries away the food minerals. The amount of water in the soil and the loss of food minerals are to a large extent controlled by cultivation of the soil.

Plants and animals change the soil. They take out food minerals, and they put back wastes and eventually their dead bodies. Wastes and dead bodies are of no use to crop plants. If they accumulated, they would merely clutter up the soil. They must be changed to other things. The soil is in a constant state of change. The change may benefit the farmer or it may bring him only loss. His management of the soil determines whether the change shall benefit or harm his crops.

Soils vary. Some produce good crops and some produce only weeds and scrub trees. You have probably seen both kinds as you have driven through the country. Even the best farm soil will not remain good if the farmer does not know how to take care of it, and many a soil poor by nature has been made productive by cultivation. The farmer must know. The scientist is finding out just how each kind of soil should be treated, so that he may pass the knowledge along to the farmer. Soil science is now an important study of government and university scientists in all progressive countries.

Mineral food for the plant. Plants will not thrive unless there are in the soil certain *mineral elements* which can be dissolved by the water in the ground and thus converted into a form that roots can use for making food.

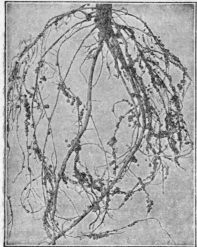

All living matter contains oxygen, hydrogen, carbon, and nitrogen, though in varying proportions. Some of these substances may be found in combination with the minerals which are so necessary to plant life. The farmer needs to supply especially *nitrogen, phosphorus,* and *potassium.* Plants also require *calcium,* which is present in lime, and *sulphur, iron, sodium,* and *chlorine,* as well as other elements in very small amounts. Acids and water in the soil act on soil minerals so that they are dissolved and may be taken in by the root hairs of plants.

Fig. 393. Bacteria that live in these nodules on the roots of clover take nitrogen from the air and change it to compounds the green plants use.

Nitrogen composes about four fifths of the air, but crop plants cannot use it in the state in which it is found in the air. It must be united with other substances in the soil to form compounds of nitrogen. Certain types of bacteria bring about this change. Farmers sometimes plant leguminous crops, such as peas, beans, clover, and alfalfa, in the rows between other crops to aid their growth, or they plant a leguminous crop the year before they plant their other crop. On the roots of these leguminous plants are tiny lumps, or *nodules,* filled with masses of bacteria which absorb nitrogen out of the air and soil and turn it into compounds of nitrogen (Fig. 393). Besides these root-dwelling bacteria, other bacteria living in the soil also take nitrogen from the air and form compounds of nitrogen.

What good are dead things in the soil? The decaying remains of plants and animals, *humus*, give the dark color to the topsoil. Some soils contain very little humus, but rich farm soils generally have an abundant supply. Humus helps to make the soil loose so that air for the young roots may penetrate. It aids also in retaining water in dry weather. Perhaps most important of all, it is the home of bacteria.

Soil science has shown that bacteria are exceedingly important in maintaining fertility. Much of modern scientific farming is designed to improve conditions for the growth of helpful bacteria. One of these conditions is increase of humus. Manure spread upon the fields adds food for the beneficial bacteria. Farmers sometimes also spread waste plants, such as cabbage and other crop plants, and plow them under. Gardeners often use decayed leaves. Sometimes crops, especially oats, are plowed under while green to increase the humus. Clover also is plowed under. This practice is called *green manuring*. It is often employed on sandy soil.

Changing dead material to plant food. Dead things and wastes of living things contain valuable elements, food elements that plants absorbed from the soil. Yet dead things and wastes are not food for crop plants. The food elements in the dead bodies are locked up so that crops cannot get them. These valuable elements are released by living plants and animals that feed upon the dead bodies and return the elements to the soil in such form that crop plants can absorb them.

Bacteria are the most important of the destroyers of the dead bodies. There are several kinds of valuable bacteria in the soil, changing worthless dead material into valuable minerals. Among them are certain nitrogen bacteria that feed upon protein food and change it to nitrates. There are several of these nitrogen bacteria. One set feeds upon proteins and changes them to simpler compounds. Then a second set changes these compounds to still simpler compounds. Eventually the nitrogen lies in the soil as nitrates, one of the valuable mineral foods of crop plants. The farmer pays high prices for nitrates brought all the way from the deserts of Chile or made by electric plants in this country. The nitrogen bacteria that feed on dead things and change them to nitrates may live in the same soils as the nitrogen bacteria of the root nodules that change the nitrogen of the air into nitrates. In the soil that is properly cared for, bacteria are continually building nitrates for the farmer. But these helpful bacteria thrive only when the soils are taken care of.

Controlling soil water. If you scratch away the soil in your garden or field, you will find that the soil just below the surface is damp. It should not be wet or muddy. Few crop plants except rice can live in a water-logged soil. In good farm soils a thin film of water surrounds each soil particle. This film is the water supply of the root hairs as well as their supply of dissolved minerals. As the water is absorbed by the root hairs, more rises from below to take its place.

Water rises through the fine spaces or pores between the soil particles as it rises in a sponge or between the threads of a towel. You have probably seen water rise through a bath towel, the end of which has fallen into the tub. You can see it rise in small glass tubes when you stand them in a tumbler of water. We say that water rises thus through fine, hairlike spaces by *capillary attraction* or *capillarity* (from Latin *capillus, hair*). When the soil is compact, the pores form continuous capillary passageways from the underground supply of water to the surface.

Fig. 394. To show that water rises in small spaces—capillarity.

Water brought to the surface of the soil by capillarity evaporates and more rises to replace it. Water evaporated from the soil is lost. The continued loss of water by capillarity and evaporation may be so serious as to stop the growth of plants. Such loss is controlled by proper cultivation of the soil.

Fig. 395.   A disk harrow turning under a soy bean cover crop, Louisiana.

Cultivation of the soil.   Plowing, harrowing, and otherwise breaking up the soil is called *cultivation*.   The plow turns over large masses and clods of earth.   The harrow and the drag break up the clods and level the surface (Fig. 395).

Cultivating the surface breaks the capillary passages by which soil water rises to the surface.   Frequent harrowing keeps on the surface a loose layer of dirt called a *dust mulch*. Loss of water by evaporation is reduced by such a mulch. Rain compacts the soil, but the farmer, anxious to save the soil water, harrows after a rain as soon as the surface dries a little.   By harrowing the soil of dry regions, farmers sometimes save the little rain for two years before planting a crop.   Truck farmers sometimes cover the ground between the plants with heavy paper to reduce the evaporation as well as to prevent the growth of weeds.

Cultivation of the soil benefits the crops in other ways. It allows tender roots to penetrate the soil more easily.   It allows air to reach roots and soil bacteria, for they must breathe. It allows the escape of carbon dioxide from these and other soil dwellers. It prevents the accumulation of organic matter in clods and distributes the plant food more evenly so that roots can reach it.

Making the most of sand. If you have seen a stretch of barren sand at the seashore or the lakeshore or elsewhere, you would not be tempted to try to farm it. There may be some coarse plants growing in it, but it seems utterly hopeless for farm crops. It has several defects. It lacks important food minerals, especially nitrogen, potassium, and phosphorus. It lacks water. Water runs right through it because it is so coarse. It is dry on the surface almost as soon as the rain stops. It has little or no humus. Its particles are so large that air circulates freely, oxidizing the dead plants that might form humus.

Yet if these defects can be corrected, sandy soil has some advantages. Because it holds little water, it warms up quickly in the spring and is therefore good for early vegetables. Through the South, the sandy Coastal Plain produces train-loads of early vegetables for northern markets.

In the improvement of sandy soils, the missing mineral foods must be added as fertilizer. Humus must be developed. Green manuring is often practiced, especially when the soil is being used for the first time. With abundant manuring and fertilizing, sandy soil may be exceedingly productive for the crops for which it is adapted, especially vegetables and certain small fruits.

The good and bad of clay soil. Pure clay or *kaolin* cannot be used for farming; but if enough humus and sand are present, *clay soil* may be very productive. Clay soil is produced by the weathering of layers of solid clay, slate, granite, basalt, and limestone. It predominates in Great Britain, is distributed widely in the United States, and makes up the adobe soil of the western and southwestern parts of the United States.

Clay soil lacks some of the advantages of sandy soil, but it has many good qualities which sandy soil lacks. The two soils differ in the way in which they react to water. If you

Fig. 396. How a clay soil cracks upon drying.

have used clay in modeling, you know that it is slippery, and that it can be tightly packed together. Its particles are very small. Little water can pass through a mass of it. However, the water that does enter is taken in slowly and held tenaciously. Water cannot circulate so freely in clay soil as it can in sandy soil.

Because of its tendency to hold water, clay soil warms slowly in the spring and is therefore most suitable for crops which grow slowly and ripen late in the season. Corn, wheat, blue grass, oats, barley, and rye are some of the products which grow best in it. Legumes, such as clover and beans, thrive in the looser varieties of clay soil.

Humus accumulates and is readily embodied in clay soil. Such soil often contains abundant supplies of nitrogen and potassium, but it generally lacks phosphorus, which may be supplied by the use of suitable fertilizers.

Improving clay soil. One of the great disadvantages of of clay soil is its tendency to cake and crack when dry. This necessitates careful cultivation at the correct times (Fig. 396).

Clay soil should not be cultivated when it is wet, for when it is wet, it is sticky.   Perhaps you have tried to drive on a "gumbo" road, or you have walked across a sticky mud field with twenty pounds of clay hanging on each foot.   That sort of clay cannot be plowed after a good rain.   It should be plowed directly after it has dried, but before the air has hardened it into lumps and has caused it to crack.

The planting of alfalfa improves the texture of some clay soil because its long roots penetrate and tend to make it more porous.   Another way of improving such soil is to add humus, manure, and lime, which help to keep a crust from forming after rain.   Lime makes the soil drier and warmer so that it can be used earlier for crops.

Soil the farmer loves.   You can easily imagine that the farmer prefers a soil which combines the best features of sandy and clay soils and which lacks their disadvantages. This variety of soil is called *loam*.   It is the typical agricultural soil of the most fertile regions of the world and is found in a large part of the most productive farming area of the United States.

Loam is a mixture of various soils and organic matter. Loam containing a large proportion of sand or gravel, and little clay, is called *sand* or *gravel loam*.   That composed mostly of clay, and containing little sand or gravel, is *clay loam*.   If the greater proportion is silt (fine earth), it is known as *silt loam*.

Most loams contain a large percentage of organic matter and mineral elements.   From its clay content loam derives the ability to hold water, and, because of the sand in it, does not cake and crack when dry.   Loam is porous enough to allow air to enter, but does not allow it to circulate freely and oxidize the organic matter.   When it has a high proportion of organic matter in it, loam is usually of a rich, blackish brown color.

Sour soil.   Plants give off carbon dioxide through their roots.   Bacteria and other living things in the soil also give off carbon dioxide.   Some of this gas escapes into the air, but much of it dissolves in soil water to form carbonic acid.

Other acids are also released in the soil by plants and by the decay of organic matter.

Alkaline substances in the soil combine with the acids to produce neutral salts. Such salts are the mineral foods taken in by roots. When acids are left uncombined either because of shortage of available alkaline substances or for other reasons, they may accumulate and produce an acid or sour soil.

Most crop plants do not grow well in acid soils. If the soil is only slightly acid, however, some crops, such as potatoes, rye, and corn do well. Excessive acid is injurious not only to the crops directly but to the beneficial bacteria which do so much to maintain the fertility of the soil.

Acid soils may be improved by the addition of alkaline substances. These unite with the excess acid and produce salts that can be absorbed by the root hairs of the plants. Lime or finely ground limestone is largely used for this purpose. Scientific farming prevents the production of acid soils by the selection of proper fertilizers and by proper methods of cultivation.

Preventing the loss of soil. It takes nature 400 years to produce an inch of soil. In many parts of the United States that inch of rich soil has been allowed to wash away with the rain in a few years. Forests have been cut down, so that the rain runs freely away, carrying off the soil. The bare soil is sometimes exposed by the burning of grass or the plowing of steep hillsides. Many prairies have had their grass cover destroyed by the pasturing of too many cattle. In some sections strong winds in winter and in the dry season carry away the soil from fields left fallow (bare of vegetation).

Government scientists and others have become alarmed at this swift and steady loss of soil that cannot be replaced in centuries. Extensive experiments to learn the best methods of control are in progress. *Cover crops* are sown to keep the ground covered with vegetation when not used for other crops. Hillsides where there is danger of erosion should be kept in grass for pasture. State and national governments are restoring forest to steep hillsides to reduce the "run-off"

of rain water.   In the public grazing lands government officers limit the number of cattle and sheep so that the grass
cover is not destroyed.

Soil needs fertilizers.   There are several reasons for the
loss of fertility of soil.   Soil sometimes ceases to hold a
sufficient supply of water, bacteria cease growing properly
in it, organic matter escapes through erosion, and compounds
of nitrogen and other necessary elements are washed out
(leached) by rain water.   Substances which plants need for
food may be used up because one kind of crop is grown too
frequently upon the same soil.

When crops grow, they remove substances from the soil
which must be replaced if the soil is to remain fertile.   Nature
returns the dead plants containing the food elements to the
soil.   Man sends away the crops to a distance.   He must
therefore add the elements again to the soil.   This is done
by the addition of commercial fertilizers manufactured
especially for the purpose, or by the addition of organic
matter—manure.

Commercial fertilizers contain varying amounts of nitrogen, phosphorus, potassium, calcium, sodium, and sulphur.
Nitrogen makes leaves grow fast and abundantly, potassium
produces a large supply of seeds, and phosphorus increases
the yield and hastens the ripening process.   Calcium (lime)
neutralizes acids and helps to make other elements available
to plants.   Sulphur produces new tissues in plants.

If a soil lacks sufficient humus, the surface tends to crack
and allow water to escape.   *Manure*, composed of waste
materials from the bodies of living animals, is rich in humus
and is widely used as a fertilizer.   Its rich supply of bacteria
causes organic matter to decay and form more humus.   The
humus loosens the soil, prevents it from cracking, and holds
the water.   It also enables plant roots to penetrate the soil
more easily.

Rotation of crops.   Instead of planting the same crop in
the same field each year, farmers in the intensively cultivated regions plant a succession of different crops.   Thus a
field may be planted in successive years with the following

crops: corn, oats, wheat, grass, and clover. Experiment has shown that rotation may double the yield or do even better. There are probably several reasons for the benefits of rotation. The different crops vary in their demands for the mineral salts in the soil. Allowing the ground a partial rest gives time for more mineral salts to be released from rock particles or to be reformed in the soil. Furthermore certain diseases, weeds, and insects infest particular crops. Growing other crops that do not benefit our enemies reduces their number in the soil. Rotation also permits the growing of a leguminous crop, such as clover, that adds nitrogen to the soil.

EXPERIMENT 127

Question: To find the characteristics of soils.

Materials: Specimens of following and other soils: sand, gravel, clay, silt (fine dirt), humus (leaf mold); magnifier; tumblers; stirring rods.

Directions: Examine each kind of soil as follows: (*a*) Note the appearance to naked eye and under magnifier.

(*b*) Feel between the fingers.

(*c*) Stir a little in a tumbler of water and note what settles easily and what remains afloat for a time.

(*d*) Heat some to kindling temperature.

Results: Fill in the following table in your notebook.

KIND OF SOIL	COLOR	COARSENESS (COARSE, MEDIUM, OR FINE)	BEHAVIOR IN WATER	BEHAVIOR ON HEATING
Gravel...........				
Sand..............				
Silt..............				
Clay..............				
Humus...........				

Conclusion: 1. How is soil made? 2. What types of soil have you distinguished? 3. What types do you find in the best farms or gardens in your vicinity?

EXPERIMENT 128

Question: What are the elements of a fertile soil?

Materials: Four flower pots; clay; sand; garden soil; ¼ teaspoonful ammonium nitrate; ⅛ teaspoonful potassium chloride; 1 tablespoonful rock phosphate, oat seeds.

Directions: Put the clay in pot No. 1; garden soil in No. 2; sand in Nos. 3 and 4. Mix the three chemical fertilizers and add to pot No. 4. Plant a dozen oat seeds in each pot. Record the date of planting. Keep in a warm place. Keep the soil moist, not wet. When the seeds sprout, place the pots in the sun. Watch them for several weeks.

Results: Record the growth at regular intervals, keeping the record of each pot.

Conclusion: Answer the question.

EXPERIMENT 129

Question: How does water rise in soil?

Material: Several glass tubes of different diameters, 4 inches or more long; 4 test tubes with bottoms removed; some sand; some fine soil; some loam of medium fineness; some humus.

Directions: (a) Half fill a tumbler with water, and add a little red ink. Stand the glass tubes in the tumbler. Note the height to which the inky water rises in each tube.

(b) Dry the samples of soil. Pack the 4 samples of soil in the 4 test tubes. Stand the test tubes in water and note the height to which the water rises in each soil.

(c) Take the medium fine soil and compare the height to which the water rises when the soil is packed very loosely and when it is packed tightly.

Results: Record your results in a table.

Conclusions: The water in the glass tubes rises by *capillarity* or capillary attraction. What effect has the size of the capillary space upon the height to which the water rises?

What accounts for the rise of water in soils? How do soils vary in capillary attraction?

How does loosening the soil of a field by cultivation affect the water content?

EXPERIMENT 130

Question: How do soils vary in their retention of water?

Materials: Funnel stand; 4 funnels; a little cotton; clay; sand; garden soil; humus; measuring cylinder.

Directions: Plug the funnels lightly with cotton. Using the same quantity of soil, place each type of soil in a funnel. Pour the same quantity of water through each funnel and measure the quantity that runs through.

Results: Draw a diagram of apparatus.   Record results in a table.

FUNNEL NUMBER	1	2	3	4
Kind of soil.................				
Quantity of soil.............				
Quantity of water poured in...				
Quantity of water recovered...				

Conclusion: Answer the question.

Practical application: Why does a sandy garden require much watering? Why is a forest soil often damp when at the same time meadow soil is dry? Why should soil for starting seeds contain much humus?

EXPERIMENT 131 (OPTIONAL)

Question: How would cultivation help growing plants? If you have a garden, try cultivating the soil frequently on one plot and allowing the same kind of plants to grow without cultivation on a near-by plot. In the cultivated plot keep the soil always finely powdered or mulched. Window boxes filled with ordinary garden soil may be used for the experiment if small, erect plants are grown.

QUESTIONS TO THINK OUT AND TO INVESTIGATE

1. If your garden soil is too sandy, what can you do, in your locality, to correct the condition? if it is stiff clay?

2. If you want soil for potting plants, how would you make it up?

3. Why are seeds and slips often started in sand and later transplanted to heavier soil?

4. Make a survey of soils in your neighborhood and classify them as suggested on pages 424–427. Make a map showing by coloring the different kinds of soils. Your map may cover a large section of your state or a small and varied section of a farm or park.

5. Would you expect to find tender plants or tough and hardy plants growing in sand? Why? On a rocky hill? On a moist meadow? Visit such areas to see.

6. Why is it that farmers generally must add manure or commercial fertilizers to field and orchard, but nature grows luxuriant forests and grass without them?

7. Why must potted plants usually be watered every day, but plants growing in the garden usually need not?

Chapter XLVII

OUR FARMS AND THEIR CROPS

Colonial farms. In the days when there were only a few white people in the narrow strip of scattered settlements along the Atlantic coast, each farmer colonist had to raise the variety of food that his family and domestic animals needed. Vegetables, wheat, corn, hay, and oats were essential. In the rocky acres of New England he had the work of almost a lifetime to clear the trees and stones from a farm of any size (Fig. 397). The miles of stone fences hemming in fields there still testify to the arduous labor he performed with the aid of a few simple tools and a team of horses or a yoke of oxen. The freezing season of six months or more limited the kind of crops he could produce. But farther to the south the colonists could easily till the fertile river-bottom lands and with the warmer sunshine obtain a large yield from their plantations. General Washington was a leader among farmers, and was constantly on the lookout for improved strains and new varieties of foodstuffs and better ways of cultivation.

On the eastern seaboard nearly everything that was needed in a home, from rhubarb for a spring tonic to wool for clothing, was produced on the farm. Luxuries and machinery were imported from France and England.

Towns and cities. For centuries in Europe, use had been made of waterfalls or rapids to grind grain for flour, and our settlers were quick to make use of the many streams to turn wheels in their mills where grain was ground and lumber sawed. The millwright was an important member of a community. Gradually, as the population increased, villages grew up around these milling centers. Shipping always seeks out favorable harbors, and the important ports of Boston,

Fig. 397. The stone fences of the New England farms are built of stone left by the glacier. These two immense boulders were carried by the glacier.

New York, Philadelphia, and Baltimore grew into cities. Stores, printing shops, and manufactories developed in these communities. As a result, there were many people to be fed who did not live on farms, and the farmers were called upon to raise more food than they needed for their own families. The food had to be carried some distance by many farmers and, as the roads were few and rough, carrying was done by water wherever possible. A few canals were dug to aid in transportation where rivers were not available.

Rich land farther west. The pressure of increased population and the promise of free land sent pioneers west. Here, in the region west of the Appalachians and extending across into what is now Nebraska and Kansas, they found that the warm, temperate summers and abundant rainfall would reward them with large crops, especially of wheat and corn. For thousands of years this land had been storing up in the soil elements that had been carried, ground up, and deposited by the glaciers of the Ice Age, and further acted upon by the weathering of wind, water, and sun. Year after year the early farmers were able to raise huge crops for the cultivation only, without the addition of fertilizers. The soil was rich in plant food and it seemed as though the land would never fail.

But as crop after crop of the same kind was taken off, the land became less productive. Then fertilizers were added in the more intensively cultivated regions, but there are still many farms where little or none is used. Rotation of crops was also begun. Even with the best practices many soils are still called *exhausted*. Soil scientists are studying the so-called exhausted soils and finding how each may be restored to the fertility of soils of the Old World that have been farmed for centuries.

Corn. This section of the central states that we have been discussing is so exactly adapted for the growth of corn that it is called the *Corn Belt*. Because its long, thin leaves are susceptible to frost, corn is not planted until that likelihood is past in the spring. If it is to be cut, as in dairy sections, as green fodder for storage in silos for fresh winter food, the seed is planted in hills three or four feet apart to give the plants more space. As soon as the blades appear, cultivation is begun in order to keep the surface of the ground loose and prevent weeds from starting. Nothing contributes more to a good stand of corn than persistent cultivation. Corn relies partly for its quick growth upon a mass of fibrous roots that push to a depth of as much as four feet. Just above the ground short, stalky braces, called *anchor roots*, help to hold the stem erect and resist winds and storms (Fig. 398).

Use of cornstalks and cobs. If the corn is to be used for fodder, the stalks and ears are cut by a power cutter into very short lengths and stored in a silo for use during the winter. If the ears are left to mature, the corn is sometimes gathered into large shocks where it stands to dry and the ears are husked later either by hand or by machine. Sometimes the ears are plucked from the standing corn.

Throughout our history corn has kept its place as food for man and animals. Its greatest use in the United States is for stock feed. It is used also in the form of corn meal and cornstarch in cooking, and in powdered form for starching

Fig. 398. The roots of a corn plant. Note the anchor roots above ground and the wide-spread roots below ground.

clothes. Oil pressed from the grain is used for salad oil and for other purposes. Corn bids fair to become valuable in another way, for chemists have found in its fibrous stalk a source of valuable material—*cellulose*—from which paper, cellophane, lacquers, and other substances can be made. Corncobs may be ground into paper pulp and also made into wood flour, insulation board, and artificial silk. If these products can be manufactured cheaply, the farmer will have an extra source of income from his corn crop.

Alfalfa. No crop is more dependent upon good preparation of the soil than alfalfa. It needs a deep, rich soil with good drainage and plenty of lime. If the soil is deficient in lime, ground lime should be spread on the field. The small leaves and purple blossoms of this legume make a profuse growth so that weeds find it hard to survive in the thick mass. It grows so rapidly that it can be cut for hay from two to four times a year, depending upon the length of the growing season. Because its roots penetrate deep to find moisture, it is valuable to farmers in dry sections; and to farmers everywhere because of its nitrogen-fixing power. Good alfalfa seed is expensive but it gives abundant returns, and the plants persist on well-prepared ground for several years.

Fig. 399.   Harvesting alfalfa.

If his land will produce it, the dairy farmer will find it a valuable crop, as it will supply an abundance of nitrogenous feed for his cattle (Fig. 399).

Dairy farms. The producer of dairy supplies has his peculiar problems. He should, if possible, grow enough hay and grain for his herds. If he has the space and can afford the time to work it, part of his land may be found well adapted to raising fruits or vegetables. Some dairymen plant fields of cabbage. If the cabbage crop does not command a good cash price, they feed it to their cattle. Fertilization on these farms is supplied to a large extent by the stable manure which goes back to the land. If this cannot be drawn daily and spread on the land, it should be kept in pits so that none of its useful compounds will drain away.

Other plants used for hay are clover and timothy grass, which are often planted together. To a greater extent than anywhere else in the United States, hay grows abundantly in the northeastern section and in the states adjoining the Great Lakes. Here, where the land drains in natural slopes

Fig. 400. Dairy barns. The two large cylinders are silos which are filled with chopped green food for winter use.

and the air is moisture-laden from evaporation over these large bodies of water, much general farming is done, and nearly all foods common to a temperate climate can be grown. The rolling land is well supplied with lakes and streams and affords fine pasturage for cattle. The milk produced goes to convenient markets in the numerous large cities of this region.

The demand for milk is so great in Chicago, Philadelphia, and New York that it is shipped daily to these cities from farms 200 or more miles away. After the milk leaves the hands of the dairy farmer, hundreds of men are employed in shipping, pasteurizing, and delivering it to consumers. Part of the milk produced in this dairy region is converted into butter and various kinds of cheese. A large part is canned as evaporated milk.

Meat from the farms. In the old cowboy days cattle roamed the plains and the open lands in the mountains from the Rio Grande to the Canadian border. Cattle were driven with the change of season from Texas to Wyoming. Cowboys still drive cattle on the western ranges, but the great area for the production of meat now centers around Iowa. Farmers of the great corn states found that it paid to feed corn and other crops to cattle and to hogs. In addition to

Fig. 401. Picking cotton. The South also supplies the northern markets with early fruits and vegetables.

cattle born on the farms, trainloads of cattle are shipped to the corn states to be fattened for market. There is a similar movement of cattle and sheep to the sugar-beet areas to fatten on the tops and waste of the beets after the sugar is extracted.

Cotton. Where the eastern mountain ranges level out to the coastal plain of the southeastern states and stretch west to the lower Mississippi, we find rich soil that will raise a variety of crops. Here grow corn, wheat, oats, peanuts, sugar cane, rice, fruit, and garden stuff, but a product grown far in excess of all these is cotton. So much has the economic life of the South centered around it, that it has been called King Cotton.

This is a warm, moist region with soil much like that in the Corn Belt. Cotton does not require so much nitrogen as corn, but it does need more heat. The seeds are planted in four-foot rows to allow for cultivation. Five or six seeds are dropped from a planter in groups not more than a foot apart. Planting takes place from March until May, depending upon location. The white bolls, or fruit, open and are ready to be picked in about four months (Fig. 401). Especial care has to be taken in cultivation to keep the soil around the roots, and to cultivate in such a direction as to prevent leaching, or the washing away of mineral substances in the soil.

For many years the only part of the cotton plant used was the long fiber which clings to the seeds, and which is spun and woven into many grades of cloth. The great mass of cotton seeds which were separated from the fiber by the cotton gin were allowed to accumulate and rot. After a time it was found that the seed could be used as fertilizer. Now oil is pressed from them for the use in cooking and in soaps. The residue forms a meal which is fed to cattle.

During World War I cotton was in such great demand that the fuzz adhering to the seeds was literally shaved off and used as cellulose for explosives. Since then the *linters*, as the fuzz is called, have been manufactured into lacquer, combs, paper, films, rayon, and other articles. The hulls of the seeds from which it is scraped are added to give bulk to cotton-seed meal. They have little food value. Chemists have converted the leaves, burrs, and stalks of the cotton plant into alcohol and wall-board, but these products are not yet commercially profitable.

Peanuts. A valuable southern plant which grows at its best

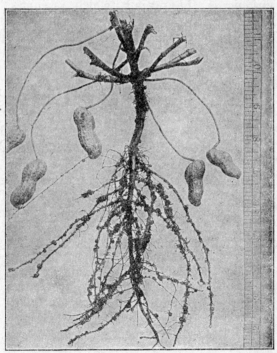

Fig. 402.   The lengthening stems of the young peanuts force them underground where they ripen.

Fig. 403. A field of rice in California.

in the sandy soil of Alabama, Georgia, North Carolina, and Virginia is the peanut, which produces a popular food. In growth it is surprisingly different from other fruits called nuts, for these seed pods grow like garden peas on a leguminous plant a foot or two in height. After the flower has died, the flower stalk lengthens and forces the immature seeds beneath the ground where they develop into tan-colored seeds with their familiar crackly shell (Fig. 402). From this habit they are called *ground nuts*. They have a high food value. A cooking oil is pressed from them, and they are also ground into peanut butter. The leaves make excellent cattle food. In 1930 the value of the crop was $38,226,000.

Gulf state fruits and vegetables. The low borderlands along the Gulf of Mexico and practically all of Florida have a semitropical climate and, like southern California, grow an abundance of citrus fruits (lemons, oranges, grapefruit) and most of the common vegetables which are shipped in great quantities to the northern centers of population.

Rice. Rice, the food which serves one third of the world as its staff of life, is grown under irrigation in California, Arkansas, Louisiana, and Texas (Fig. 403). In appearance it looks like our common grains, having stalks of straw bearing kernels in a head. The hulls of the grain are made into rice flakes and sausage casings. The grains are sometimes ground into rice flour, but are usually cooked whole.

Fig. 404.   Oil pots in an orchard to protect it from frost.

Fruit farms.   In the old days every farmer had his apple orchard.   Surplus apples that the farmer and his family did not eat or turn into vinegar or apple butter were sent to market, if there was a market for them.   Today fruit farmers devote themselves to fruit.   As a result of fruit study by the growers and by the government stations, we have more and finer fruits.   New varieties and new methods of culture are developed for each fruit section.   Certain varieties of apple are suited to New York State, others to Virginia, and still others to Washington and Oregon.   One type of peach grows best in Delaware, another in California, and another in Georgia.   So grapes, oranges, and berries especially suited for each fruit region have been produced by intensive scientific study. We have already studied some of the laws of science that enable us to originate entirely new varieties.

Wheat.   The cereal food upon which Americans rely to the greatest extent is wheat.   Its growth is widely distributed over the United States.   In the southern states it is planted in the fall and gets a start of several inches, then remains dormant during the colder months. In the Dakotas and Minnesota, where the roots would be winter-killed, wheat is not planted until spring. Spring wheat, or hard wheat, contains more gluten than winter wheat and is preferable for a bread flour. The softer types, or winter wheat, make the best pastry flour.

Fig. 405.   Harvesting wheat with a cradle.

In general, wheat needs rather a cold climate and not too much nitrogen, as that produces an overgrowth of straw. The land must be well drained and finely prepared. The seeds are sown in drills four or five inches apart. Commercial fertilizer is often applied by the drill at the same time. Wheat matures in from three to four months.

Oats, rye, and barley also demand a temperate climate for their growth. Naturally, with such closely sown rows these crops cannot be cultivated, but their thick growth tends to crowd out weeds and to conserve moisture.

Machinery has helped to open new land. It is in connection with the harvesting of grains that the greatest development has come in agricultural machinery. Up to one hundred years ago wheat was cut, as in Biblical times, with a curved blade, the sickle, and its later improvements, the scythe and the cradle (Fig. 405). But in 1834 the mower, invented by Cyrus McCormick, was first put to use. It could do the work of at least ten men with scythes. A mower is still used in cutting hay, but a reaper, in which a huge tray for laying the grain in swaths was added to the knives, soon came to be used for cutting grains. In the wake of this

Fig. 406.   Harvesting wheat with a binder.

Fig. 407.   Threshing the harvested wheat.

Fig. 408.   Harvesting wheat with a combine.   This machine harvests
and threshes the wheat.

Fig. 409. Irrigating a field. With shovels the men connect the furrows with the irrigating ditch.

machine men bound armfuls of the grain in sheaves with withes or strands of the grain itself. In 1873 a binder was invented which did this work with twine, and dropped the bundles at intervals to be gathered and stored for threshing, or to be threshed at once in the fields (Fig. 406). On small farms the harvesting and threshing processes do not always follow each other immediately, but on the great prairie farms either long teams of horses or tractors now haul a *combine*. This harvester cuts, threshes, and bags the grain, and as it moves forward, it scatters the chaff upon the ground to be turned under in plowing (Figs. 407 and 408).

Irrigation. When our advancing settlers reached western Kansas and Nebraska, they found that although the soil contained the necessary chemical elements, the rainfall was too slight and uncertain for farming. The high mountains to westward cause the condensation of the moisture brought by the winds. On the western slope there is abundant rainfall. On the east side the descending winds are warmed and retain what moisture they have left. The plains east of the mountains and the plateaus between the Rockies on the east and the Cascades and Sierras on the west are great dry lands.

When the settlers found the land too dry for farming, the farmers abandoned the land to the cattle and sheep raisers and moved on westward. On the Pacific slope they found abundant rain. In Washington, Oregon, and northern California now flourish the fruits and grains of the temperate zone, and farther south, subtropical plants. Winter rains in the south are supplemented by summer irrigation and, where water can be had, irrigation has opened up farm lands in the drier interior plateaus and eastern slopes.

Water is conveyed from its source in the mountains through canals or through wooden troughs to the ranches and orchards. From the main canals smaller ones branch out into ditches that go to each man's holding. From these ditches, by means of movable dams, the farmer may flood his fields at will, or allow the water to run in furrows between the rows of plants or trees (Fig. 409). The Federal government has aided in bringing many acres of desert under cultivation, and by building such structures as the Boulder Dam in the Black Canyon between Arizona and Nevada, and the Roosevelt Dam on the Salt River in Arizona.

Dry farming. Even irrigation is impossible in much of the western prairie land and farmers there have resorted to another method of obtaining moisture. They plow the ground deeply, harrow it well in the fall, and leave it in small furrows running at right angles to the usual direction of the wind (Fig. 410). These furrows catch and keep the fine particles of

Fig. 410.   Furrows at right angles to the wind to reduce soil loss.

soil from blowing away and also hold rain and snow which, upon melting, sinks into the ground. The farmer sows as soon after the rains as he can get upon the land.

Fig. 411. Sugar beets in the field.

Then to conserve the moisture he must be wise and constant as to cultivation and allow no large cracks to develop from which moisture may escape. If the rainfall is too little to allow planting, land is kept fallow, that is, it is plowed but unsown, and is kept in mulch with loose soil on top, to absorb enough water for the second year's crop. Alfalfa, with its deeply penetrating roots, is the main crop grown in dry farming. Sorghums, which are plants resembling sugar cane introduced from dry regions of Africa, are also being raised successfully for grain and fodder.

Swamp reclamation. Other areas of the country have unused land even more fertile than this western section. They are embodied in the large swamps of our southern states and in smaller areas of many other places. Much land has been reclaimed from the Everglades in Florida by drainage. Large ditches are dug to carry off the water, and then the ground is allowed to dry out. The decaying swamp plants form a rich food for the useful plants which are to be cultivated.

Sugar beets. In addition to the crops already mentioned, many sugar beets are raised, especially in Michigan and on irrigated land in Colorado, Utah, and California. The pulp left after extracting the sugar from the beet root, together with the leaves, can be used as food for cattle. Though we produce three times as much beet sugar as cane sugar, the amount of both grown within the United States supplies less than one third of what we consume annually (Fig. 411).

Flax. The Dakotas, Minnesota, and Montana grow practically all the flax produced in this country. It is grown here only for the seed from which is extracted the oil, an essential ingredient in paints. As with cottonseed, the cake which remains after the removal of the oil is used for cattle feed. In the Old World, linen is the chief product of flax and is procured from the long fibers running inside the covering of the flax stem, but with us the labor cost of preparing the fibers for spinning is so great that our manufacturers cannot compete with those of Russia and India.

Railroads and the farms. The rapid settlement on our western farm lands, the development of the large meatpacking centers in Chicago, Kansas City, and other cities near the cattle ranges, and the wide distribution of manufacturing all depend upon the railroads. If widely separated parts of the country were not united by lines of transportation, there would be no market in the north for the perishable southern foods except what could be carried by boat; and similarly the sale of western beef would be much reduced if it could not be delivered quickly in refrigerated cars.

One type of invention leads to another, and most of our factories, aside from those depending upon our mineral resources, depend upon the farmer in this and in other countries for their raw materials.

Government aids. The United States Department of Agriculture and nearly all the states support experimental bureaus where scientists are constantly studying how to keep the soil in a high state of fertility, how to improve and increase crops, and how to rid plants of insect and animal pests and diseases. They introduce new plants from foreign lands and originate others.

Scientific study of heredity has been one of the greatest helps in the increase of production. The discoveries of Mendel and De Vries have led to the production of new varieties and improvement in the old. Chapter XLV on "How New Kinds Arise" shows how new kinds of wheat, produced by crossing, extended wheat growing into the Canadian Northwest. Other experiments have given us drought-resistant and disease-resistant wheat. Corn and other grains have been improved in like measure. New citrous fruits for Florida and California have been produced by crossing and selection. Apples, peaches, berries, and other fruits have been produced for cooler regions. Vegetable crops have been fitted to every soil and climate from the Rio Grande to the edge of the Arctic. Nations with tropical lands have been equally active in producing superior varieties of bananas, sugar, coffee, quinine, rubber, and other tropical products demanded by the world.

Animals, too, have been improved. The Bureau of Animal Industry of the United States Department of Agriculture studies the production of new and better breeds, feeding, care, and protection from disease. Cattle, sheep, hogs, and poultry of finer breeds (Fig. 387) have gradually replaced scrub stock that often is a loss to the farmer.

Among the most important improvements has been the production of varieties of both plants and animals that resist attacks of disease. Now scientists are busy in experiment stations developing varieties that are not attacked by insects.

Agricultural explorers from the Department of Agriculture send home seeds and plants to be tried out in various sections of the country. Durum, a hard wheat, has been introduced from Europe. This wheat is largely used for making macaroni and is now grown in great quantities in the comparatively dry regions of the northwest. It is especially adapted to growing in a dry climate. Seedless oranges were developed from slips brought from Brazil.

One of the most valuable services of government and university scientists has been the study of insect and disease control. It has been necessary to study the life histories of insects and injurious organisms, the plants and animals that aid them and those that destroy them, the conditions of weather and farming that aid them and those that hinder. Sprays that protect the crops have been developed for many fruits and vegetables. Methods have been found for dipping animals in solutions to destroy insects that carry disease (Fig. 412). At the borders of the United States, and at the

Fig. 412. Dipping cattle to kill ticks which carry the deadly cattle fever. Men with poles push the heads of the cattle under the liquid.

ports, officers are stationed to inspect plants and animals brought to the country to see that they are free from disease and harmful insects. At times all importation of certain kinds of plants and animals has been prohibited by embargo.

Information on farm problems is available for the asking in publications of the state institutions and of the United States Department of Agriculture. Timely advice to farmers based on these reports is given over the radio. It is due to such experiments and to study of methods in other parts of the world that land otherwise useless to man has been made to produce good crops.

QUESTIONS TO THINK OUT

1. Why do weeds and some other wild plants harm the farmer? Can you mention some wild plants that aid the farmer?

2. What wild animals are helpful to the farmer and gardener? How?

3. Why are seeds so largely used as food by man and lower animals, including birds and insects?

4. Name some important foods for man and his domestic animals that are obtained from: seeds, roots, stems, buds, leaves, flowers.

5. On a map of the United States show by coloring: the original grass regions, the regions originally forested that have been changed to farms and grass, the remaining forest areas.

Chapter XLVIII

TREES AND FORESTS

Trees for beauty. Most people admire trees. A new house in the suburbs is hardly completed before shade trees are planted (Fig. 413). The popularity of the parks with their trees shows how city people enjoy such trees as are spared them. There are some people, however, to whom the beauty of trees appeals so little that they deface them with signs or ruthlessly break branches.

Trees have a hard time along a street. Pavements shut off rain supply and air for their roots. Gas from leaking pipes poisons them. Careless truck drivers injure their trunks. Caterpillars and other insects feed upon them. Tree trimmers butcher them and leave great wounds for bacteria and fungi to infect. We cannot protect our street trees from all these abuses, but we can relieve them from some of them.

What trees are suitable for the street? Get a book about trees from the

Fig. 413. Trees add to the beauty of the village street and the countryside. Try to imagine this landscape without trees.

(450)

Fig. 414. An elm, a graceful shade tree.

library and learn the names of the trees along your streets. It is not difficult. Then note those that do best and those that suffer from the hardships of city life. Elms were favorites in our older towns and suburbs (Fig. 414). The variety of sycamore known as "Oriental plane" is a favorite in many cities because of its resistance to abuse. Red and scarlet oaks are fine sturdy trees, though of comparatively slow growth. They are rather resistant to many insects. In real-estate developments Lombardy poplars and Carolina poplars (cottonwood) are sometimes used because of their rapid growth. The roots of these poplars, however, so persistently force their way into water pipes that they are prohibited in some communities.

Caring for a tree. It is as important for trees as for children to get a good start in life (Fig. 415). Water, fertilizer, and broken soil for the roots help the young tree along. When a tree is dug up from its place in the earth for transplanting to a place along the street, many of its roots are cut. It is therefore necessary to trim its branches down proportionately, to prevent too great an evaporating surface. After this initial trimming, the less trimming it receives the better for the

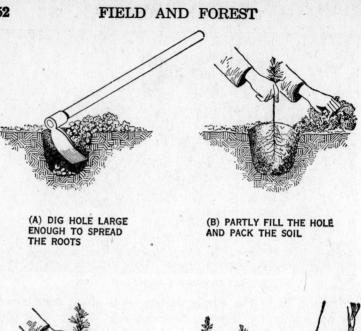

(A) DIG HOLE LARGE ENOUGH TO SPREAD THE ROOTS

(B) PARTLY FILL THE HOLE AND PACK THE SOIL

(C) PACK THE SOIL TWICE BEFORE FILLING THE HOLE

(D) FIRM THE SOIL WITH FOOT, ADD LOOSE SOIL AS MULCH

Fig. 415. How to set out a young tree.

tree. Occasionally a tree may take an undesirable shape and need reshaping. If a branch tries to come into the window or takes the hats off passers-by, it must be trimmed. Unnecessary trimming may result in an unsightly tree throughout the leafless season, the greater part of the year. When a large limb is cut off, the wound should receive a coat of paint to prevent the entrance of wood-rot fungi. Smaller wounds

Fig. 416. Setting out seedling trees in a national forest, Idaho.

should not be painted, for experiments show that wounds heal better and faster without painting. In many cities the owners of properties having trees growing along the street are not at liberty to trim or remove them. Departments of the city government employ tree experts to care for the trees of the city.

The value of the forests. You could easily write a long list of products that the forest yields, from heavy beams to alcohols and "silk" dresses. But the forest is valuable in other ways. Water-power companies spend millions of dollars maintaining forests in their watersheds. When rain falls on unforested lands, much of it immediately runs off. When rain falls in a forest, much of the fallen rain soaks into the spongy forest soil. Measurement has shown that the run-off is twenty-eight times as great in open fields as in the forest. Floods are bad for the water companies. Too much water rushing down the streams means loss. Forests let the water out more slowly through springs and brooks. They tend to stabilize the water supply, reducing both floods and droughts.

30

Fig. 417. Eroded soil. Suitable plant cover prevents such destruction.

Seventeen million acres of farm lands of the United States have been destroyed by fallen rain, according to estimates by the Department of Agriculture. Thousands of acres of fertile topsoil are carried away each year from the fields and hillsides. Once gone, this soil cannot be replaced. No crops can grow on the land (Fig. 417). Keeping forests on the steep hills which are unfit for farming is an important measure in saving the soil (Fig. 416).

Soil and gravel carried away from the hillsides are dropped by the rushing waters in the lower lands, covering up fertile soil and blocking stream channels (Fig. 498). Forests on high hills and on steep sides are our first line of defense against such destruction.

Destroying the forest. We are destroying the forests of America six times as fast as they grow. A large part of the timber cut is utter waste. We use less than 50 per cent of the wood cut, though four fifths of the waste is good timber. The devastation wrought by the American lumberman is hardly equaled by volcanoes. Trees are broken, wasted, and left. Young trees are torn out of the way. Fire often

Fig. 418. Forest destroyed by fire.

follows among the dead trees and branches. Seedling trees are killed. The valuable humus is burned. Rain carries the soil from the hills leaving the bare rocks, then nothing can grow.

Six million acres of timber land are burned each year in the United States. Lightning, careless campers, fires for burning brush in the clearing of land, cigar stumps tossed aside, sparks from locomotives are among the causes of forest fires. The Forestry Service estimated that in one year twenty dollars were spent each minute in the summer months in fighting and preventing fires in the National Forests alone (Fig. 418).

There are many other enemies of our forests. Insects, diseases of trees, and grazing stock destroy forests. The gypsy moth has destroyed large areas in New England. Pine-bark beetles threaten forests in the West. The chestnut-bark disease wiped out the chestnuts east of the Appalachians. The white-pine blister rust threatens to destroy the white pine in the East and the West.

Fig. 419. Timber is taken out but the forest is preserved. Medicine Bow, Wyoming, National Forest.

Saving the forests. New trees must rise to replace those cut. Seed trees left standing in groups will reseed the land around them. Strips cut through the forest are soon closed up again with new trees. To save the forest when lumber is cut, some method should be followed which will supply new seed. Over large areas of waste land in many states, forestry departments and private owners are setting out new trees grown in nurseries. It is much less expensive to let nature reseed the ground by leaving some trees when the forest is cut (Fig. 419). Patrols and lookouts in towers watch our forest in many states and in the National Forests to catch the first glimpse of fire. Trails are kept open through which men and apparatus can be rushed in to stop fires before they get too well started.

Scientists employed by state and National governments and by universities are constantly studying the lives of insects and the diseases of forest trees, and developing methods of control. How trees grow in a forest, what types of trees are

Fig. 420. A dangerous camp fire started among dry pine needles.

Fig. 421. A safer way to prepare a fire. Note the ground has been
cleared of litter and the mineral soil turned up.

Fig. 422. Forest ranger marking timber for cutting, in a National Forest.

adapted to various soils and markets, how to remove the trees and keep new growth coming on, how to reforest devastated land are some of the forestry problems that are engaging the minds of scientists.

Fun in the forest. Thousands of people each year visit the National and state forests for recreation. Fishing, hunting, hiking, and just living out of doors are valuable aids to the health of our people. Educating the people who visit the forests to take care of the forests is one of the problems of forest control. Here are a few things to do when you go out to enjoy the forest:

Cut no living tree. Use dead wood for firewood. Of course, there are regions where a few trees would not be missed, but few city people get into such regions. Make it a rule to cut no living tree.

Fig. 423. Making certain that the fire is "dead out."

In making a camp fire, clean away the dead leaves and branches first. Put out your fire with water before you leave.

Bury or burn all rubbish and wastes. Bury your old tin cans. Keep your camp and the woods sanitary. Keep springs and streams unpolluted.

Do not pull up wild flowers and break shrubs. The forest is less attractive without them.

Help forest rangers and police to keep the forest the way you would like to find it.

Using wood. For many purposes wood is the most useful material available and the most beautiful. The grain and colors of woods have a beauty different from manufactured substances. Weight, flexibility, degree of rigidity, and endurance under proper treatment, are other qualities that make wood valued for its purposes above all other materials. Wood also is converted by the chemist into a variety of substances.

For use as lumber, wood must be seasoned. As a living tree, wood is saturated with sap which may be nine tenths water. As the sap dries out cells and fibers shrink and the wood may bend and crack. The damage may be controlled by proper drying. The lumber may be stacked so that the air may circulate through the pile. More often the lumber is dried rapidly in kilns or drying ovens.

Quartered lumber has a beauty and strength superior to common or slash sawed lumber. Quarter sawing exposes the pith rays as broad patches, adding much to the beauty of the wood. Such wood is less liable to check and warp because it has less sap wood and because the fibers and rays run more nearly straight through the board. Veneering is used for beauty, strength, and lightness. A veneer is a thin slice cut from a log. The slices are dried and flattened under pressure. They are then glued as a beautiful surface to more common wood, or they are glued together in layers for strength and rigidity, forming plywood.

Most houses in the United States are built of wood. It has many advantages over other material. Chief of these advantages are cheapness, availability, and ease of working. Wood houses are drier than houses of stone or brick.

Chapter XLIX

SOME MORE PRODUCTS FROM FIELD AND FOREST

Man's hunt for his clothes. Since a cave man first threw a reindeer skin over his shoulder to shut out the glacial storms, man has busily searched for other and better clothing. In the New Stone Age men—or women—spun wool into thread to weave and sew. Many savage people used fibers from plants to make bark cloth (Fig. 424). If you will break the stems of weeds and bushes, you will find that many have long, coarse fibers. Making clothes was a slow and costly process until the inventions of the nineteenth century—the spinning jenny, then the power loom. The steam engines coupled to these machines and to others first made clothing cheap and plentiful.

Fig. 424. Native Samoans making bark cloth. An exhibit in the National Museum, Smithsonian Institution, Washington.

Since Egyptian days flax has furnished people with threads for making cloth. Linen is made from the fibers of the inner bark. The soft parts are rotted, or *retted*, by soaking the stems in ponds or exposing them to the dew so that bacteria may eat away the nutritious parts. The woody parts are then broken and the fibers combed out by machinery.

Cotton fibers were nature's idea for scattering cotton seeds abroad. You have probably seen similar hairs on milkweed seeds. You could not spin milkweed-seed hairs, however, for the straight hairs would pull apart. Cotton hairs are twisted in a

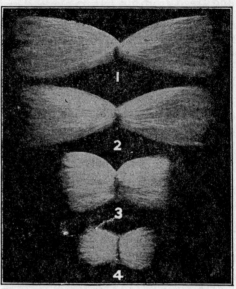

Fig. 425. Cotton fibers attached to seed. 1. Sea island; 2. Egyptian; 3. Texas; 4. Indian.

way that makes them cling together (Fig. 427). Cotton may be treated chemically to give it the appearance of silk or of wool, but the resemblance is in appearance only.

The length of a cotton hair varies from $\frac{3}{4}$ of an inch to 2 inches, depending upon the variety of cotton (Fig. 425). So great is the demand for cotton that the culture is spreading into new lands of America, Asia, and Africa. Science is producing new varieties of cotton to suit the new regions.

Many animal fibers have been used to make yarns. Goat hair makes coarse yarns for blankets and carpets. Alpaca, llama, and camel wools make clothes and blankets. Furs, the soft fibers closer to the skin underneath the hairs, can be beaten and matted together to make felt. Rabbit fur supplies much of the material for felt hats. Certain plant fibers are now also made into felt.

Wool from sheep is by far the most valuable animal fiber today. Its warmth enables sheep to live comfortably amid snow and ice. For use in clothing, the wool is first scoured and freed from its natural grease and dirt. Then it is spun into thread and woven into cloth. In clothing today wool is often mixed with cotton or other fibers, and wool taken from old clothes is often mixed with new, or "virgin," wool.

Silk is formed by many kinds of insects. It is secreted by glands and issues as a liquid that hardens on contact with the air. To the silkworm it is the material of its home, or cocoon, in which it changes from a "worm" into a moth. The cocoon is plunged into hot water just before it would naturally hatch, for the moth in emerging would cut the fibers into short pieces. The silk is then unwound from the cocoon (Fig. 426).

Clothing made by the chemist. Silk is so expensive that many who formerly wanted to be clothed in silk were forced to be content with cotton. Nowadays poor folk may have all the joy they can get out of wearing clothes that look like silk and feel like silk, and for most purposes are just as good as silk. They do not wear long, but they may be replaced cheaply. *Rayon, celanese,* and other names are used for these man-made silks. They are made from cellulose, the substance of the walls of plant cells. Cotton or wood is used as the raw material. Cotton is pure cellulose. Wood is cellulose with hardening materials that support the tree. Most rayon is made from wood cellulose. The hardening material is removed from the wood, and then the cellulose is dissolved. The solution is forced through fine holes and hardened into fine threads.

Clothes for the season. There is science behind the season's clothes. The several scientific principles that we learned in studying heat help us to understand why wool keeps us warm and why cotton and linen are cooler, why it is wise to wear light-colored clothes in summer and dark-colored clothes in winter.

Wool imprisons air, and air is a poor conductor of heat. Wool, therefore, is warm. Several thin layers of wool blankets are warmer than one thick layer of the same weight. Even

Fig. 426. Silk culture. The worker on the right is unwinding the silk from the cocoons and winding it upon the reel.

several layers of newspaper between your blankets or under your sweater keep you warm because of the imprisoned air. Air does not readily conduct away the heat of the body.

If you have ever fallen overboard or have been rain-soaked in wool clothes and again in cotton, you know that wool dries more slowly. You also have noticed that wet wool is much warmer next to your skin than wet cotton. A wet woolen bathing suit is warmer than one of cotton. Wool holds water better than cotton. Wool therefore reduces evaporation. Evaporation takes heat from the body. After exercise an athlete pulls on a wool sweater or wraps himself in a wool blanket to reduce evaporation and prevent chilling of the body. For the same reason the iceman wears a wool shirt even in summer. A cake of ice carried on the shoulder covered with wool is less dangerous to health.

The science of summer clothes involves the same principles of heat and evaporation. Cotton and linen do not retain so much air as wool, and are therefore cooler. They absorb moisture readily from the skin and as readily allow it to evaporate into the air. Evaporation of perspiration is one of nature's methods of keeping down our temperature.

Color also is important. Light-colored clothes are cooler than dark because they absorb less radiant energy. White or tan shoes are cooler than black. White clothes are the white man's dress in the tropics.

How to tell the fibers. Figure 427 shows how various fibers look under the microscope. Experiment 133 shows some tests to distinguish the fibers.

Various substances are used as adulterants in clothing materials. A garment may lose its shape in the first laundering because the starch is washed out. Silk is often artifically weighted with clay and metals because silk that is naturally heavy is expensive. The chemist has tests to detect such adulterants.

Fibers for twine and rope. The world is being systematically searched for fibers for twine, rope, and fiber board. The explorers from the United States Department of Agriculture are in every climate. Hemp is the dependable staple for good rope. It comes, like linen, from the inner bark of a plant. Hemp is grown in Kentucky and Indiana, but most of our supply is imported. Jute is a coarser fiber used in bagging and burlap and carpets; it comes chiefly from India.

Other fibers are the vascular bundles, like the strings in celery and corn. Sisal is such a fiber from a kind of century plant that grows in Mexico. Sisal has gone around the world as "binder twine" with American farm machinery. "Manila hemp" from a species of banana is one of the chief exports of the Philippines. It is used in making rope.

Paper. Paper is one of the foundations of civilization. Try to imagine spreading information and education without it. It has a number of other uses. The United States uses more paper than any other country. The consumption per person is 175 pounds a year. That is equivalent to saying that every one of us uses his weight in paper each year. Paper is one of our chief forest products. Thousands of square miles of our country that once yielded lumber now

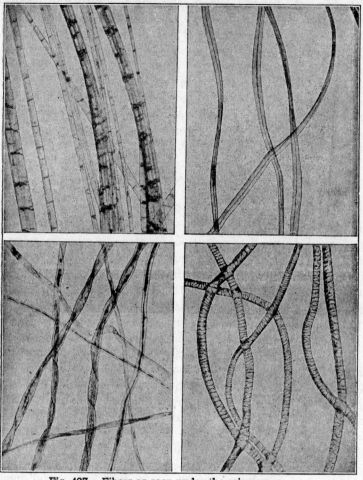

Fig. 427.   Fibers as seen under the microscope.

Flax	Silk
Cotton	Wool

yield only pulp wood.   We also import large quantities, chiefly from Canada.

The cellulose fibers of wood are used for the manufacture of paper.   If you tear a bit of blotting paper into shreds under water and examine the shreds under the microscope, you will see the fibers. Wood is ground to a pulp and treated with chemical reagents (chiefly compounds of lime, sulphur, and soda). Gums, resins, and hardening material are thus removed and the fibers are obtained. These fibers are then matted into a mass that makes paper.

Some other plant products. Nature's first aid to many wounded trees and bushes, as well as to some herbs, is a gummy substance that is exuded at the wound. Several of these gums are used in commerce, as gum arabic and gum tragacanth. Many shrubs and trees that grow on the edge of the desert in Asia and Africa furnish gums which are collected. They are used in mucilage, candy, water colors, and in stiffening fabrics.

Resins are exuded when pines and other evergreens are wounded. The rosin of commerce comes principally from the long-leaved pines of our southern states. Amber is a fossil resin from ancient trees. Since the days of the ancients, amber has been sent from the Baltic regions to other parts of the world. Copal consists of other hard resins, some of them fossil, which are collected in Africa, New Zealand, and the Philippines. Resins are used largely in varnishes.

Rubber is derived from a milky juice secreted by a number of plants. This juice, or latex, flows from a wound on the plant. The best grade is from the Brazilian rubber tree (Hevea), but the chief supply has come from the cultivated groves in Malaysia and the East Indies to which the plant was taken from Brazil. So far our supply of rubber has come from the tropics, but the Brazilian rubber tree is now cultivated in Florida. Science and industry are now studying temperate-zone plants, among them species of goldenrod and the Mexican and Texan shrub guayule (pronounced gwä-yōō′lä), and Russian dandelion as sources of rubber.

At some time when you have had a cold you have probably used soothing oils on the mucous membranes of your nose and throat. These light oils are often sweet-smelling or have a "medicinal" odor. They are called *essential oils* because they bear the essence or odor of the plant, or *volatile oils* because they evaporate readily. The essential oils are obtained by distillation of wood, leaves, flowers, seeds, or fruit of various plants. The substance to be distilled is sometimes mixed with water and distilled as you learned water is distilled, or it is heated dry and distilled as illuminating gas is distilled from coal (Experiment 59). Eucalyptol, often used on the membranes of the nose and throat, is from the eucalyptus tree. Other common essential oils are cedar, lemon, bergamot, and rose. Perfumes and flavorings use quantities of various oils. If you heat spruce needles in water, you will detect the odor of essential oils. You have smelled others when you peeled an orange.

On your hikes along a railroad you probably have noticed ties and poles treated with creosote to prevent decay. Heat some pine chips in a test tube, and you will detect the same odor as from the ties, and wood tar will collect on the cooler portions of the tube. Turpentine is distilled from the sticky juice of pine trees, which is not a true sap. Rosin is left behind when the turpentine is distilled. Camphor is distilled from a tree native to Japan and China.

EXPERIMENT 132 (OPTIONAL)

Question: How can you show the value of different clothing materials? Select pieces of cloth, of the same weight and shade, of wool, cotton, linen, rayon, and silk. Take five large test tubes, tin cans or other vessels of similar shape and size. Wrap a piece of cloth around each and tie it. Fill each vessel with the same amount of hot water at the same temperature. Put a thermometer in each. Record the temperature of each every ten minutes for an hour. Repeat, taking water from a pitcher of ice water, but without taking any ice.

Remove the cloths and throughly wet each piece. Squeeze out and lay aside to dry. Note the rapidity of drying of each kind.

EXPERIMENT 133

Question: How to test for various clothing fibers.
Materials: Pieces of wool, silk, rayon, celanese, cotton, mixed goods; potassium hydroxide; hydrochloric acid; nitric acid; olive oil; Bunsen burner; breakers; glass rod, etc.; microscope and slides.
Directions: (a) Pull out a thread from each specimen and examine under the microscope. Compare with Figure 427.
(b) Burn a little bit of each. Animal fibers burn with the odor of burning feathers. Plant fibers take fire more quickly, and burn more

rapidly and without the odor of burning feathers. Rayon from wood pulp burns like cotton. Celanese from cotton leaves an ash somewhat like the ash from silk, but the ash of celanese is firmer and harder.

(c) When dipped in nitric acid and then washed, wool and silk are stained yellow; cotton remains white.

(d) Silk dissolves quickly in hydrochloric acid.

(e) A hot potassium hydroxide (lye) solution quickly dissolves wool and silk.

(f) A drop of olive oil on linen forms a clear, translucent spot.

(g) Water is taken up more quickly and evenly by linen. Water weakens most silk substitutes so that they quickly pull apart, whereas silk remains strong when wet.

Results: Perform the tests above and record results in a table

EXPERIMENT 134 (OPTIONAL)

Question: How are essential oils obtained from plants? Heat pine chips in a test tube. Note the odor of creosote. Note the condensation on the upper, cooler parts of the test tube. This is wood tar. Boil spruce needles in a test tube. Note the odor of essential oils.

EXPERIMENT 135 (OPTIONAL)

Question: How are vegetable fibers prepared? Pick out some cottonseeds from their hairy coats. Spin the fibers between your fingers, twisting and pulling until you have spun an inch or two of thread. If you have no cottonseed, try some cotton batting. Try to do the same with fibers of milkweed, dogbane, dandelion, or other hairy seed. Examine the hairs under the microscope to find why some spin and others do not. Soak some flax stems in a glass of water for two or three days. Then strip or scrape the threads from the stems. The Indians had no flax, but they found among our native plants some substitutes. Break different kinds of weed stems until you find some with stringy inner bark, and treat them as for flax. Coarse, tough, old celery stems have fibers somewhat resembling the sisal used in "binder twine." Scrape some out with a dull knife.

QUESTIONS TO THINK OUT

1. Think of each article of clothing you wear. List the garment, the material, the source of supply. Does your clothing come mostly from plants or from animals?

2. Northern woodsmen often wear woolen clothing even on warm days. Why?

3. In the West they say, always wear a woolen shirt in the desert. Why?

UNIT ELEVEN

THE SCIENCE OF KEEPING FIT

The athlete skimming down the track, the young woman swimming the English Channel, the boy or girl flying over the ice or darting about the tennis court picture to us health and vigor. Sometimes we seem to have a feeling that health and vigor are gifts of nature that are withheld from some individuals. Nature withheld the gift from Theodore Roosevelt at first, for he was a weak child; but nature gave him a strong will, a will that determined to have a sturdy body. Year after year he studied and trained his body. In the years when he was President no man could tire him on the mountain trail; and afterwards his rugged health and strength carried him through the jungles of Africa and South America. Paralyzing disease struck Franklin D. Roosevelt, but intelligent use of his strong will trained his body to serve him and played an important part in raising him to the presidency of the United States.

To understand the laws of the living body is to understand the principles of health. In this unit we shall study the structure of the human body far enough to understand how it acts. We must know how it should act and what makes it act as it does. It is not something mysterious. It is an organism and obeys the laws that control other organisms. Chemical compounds form and change to other compounds in the body as in the test tubes. Energy is released and transformed from chemical energy to heat, motion, and electricity as in the laboratory. Life is complex, an exceedingly intricate and delicately balanced aggregation of the physical and chemical forces and substances that we find in the laboratory and in industry. The marvelous achievements of modern medicine show that we are learning how these forces act and react. We are learning to control the delicate balance of the living cells.

One of the most alluring studies in science is the study of mental life. What is the mind? How does it act? We know little of the answer to the first question, but we know a great deal about the second. We know that the cells of the nervous system respond to food, rest, control, as do other cells of the body. The scientist knows it, but often the business man and the worker do not know. Over half the beds in the hospitals of the United States are occupied by "nervous cases"; people who could not control their nerve cells or did not know how. In this unit we shall see a little of the operation of the laws of physiology and health in controlling these nerve cells.

Chapter L

FEEDING THE BODY

Life's fuel. You play, work, live because you burn up fuel. Though slow, the burning, or oxidation, is constant. The energy of life comes chiefly from burning.

Fuel and oxygen must be constantly supplied for the burning to continue. The fuel comes from food. Not all kinds of food are equally good fuel. For heating a house, oil is a good fuel, but what would happen if you poured oil on a burning coal fire? Wood is a good fuel, but you would not throw it into a coal fire. Perhaps you are making similar mistakes in your bodily fire. When you play tennis, hike, or saw wood you become warm. You burn faster. Then you get hungry. You need more fuel. What kind of fuel? Shall it be meat? potatoes? or neither?

FOOD AS WE BUY IT
BY
FRANK A. REXFORD
FOODS RICH IN FAT

BEST OLIVE OIL 1 lb.
PROTEIN .00 lb.
FAT 1.00 lb.
CARBOHYDRATES .00 lb.
CALORIES 4226

PROTEIN .00 lb.
FAT 5.00 lb.
CARBOHYDRATES .00 lb.
PURE LARD 5 lb.
CALORIES 20130

PRINT BUTTER 1 lb.
PROTEIN .00 lb.
FAT .85 lb.
CARBOHYDRATES .00 lb.
CALORIES 3605

PROTEIN .01 lb.
FAT .08 lb.
CARBOHYDRATES .02 lb.
CALORIES 430
KREAM 8 oz.

BACON 5 lb.
PROTEIN .65 lb.
FAT 1.80 lb.
CARBOHYDRATES .00 lb.
CALORIES 8700

OLEOMARGARINE 1 lb.
PROTEIN .01 lb.
FAT .83 lb.
CARBOHYDRATES .00 lb.
CALORIES 3525

Fig. 428. Fuel foods.

A group of college students, in order to save time while preparing for examinations, ate only concentrated and predigested foods. After the examinations all were in poor health and some were sick for months. Why?

In a Russian prison a group of political prisoners were so much disgusted with the filthy cabbage soup that they ate only bread. They all became sick, while the prisoners who ate the cabbage soup remained healthy. Why?

A stevedore or a lumberjack eats enough to put an office worker in the hospital. On the other hand, if a lumberjack or stevedore ate only the quantity of food sufficient for an office worker, he would be unable to do his particular kind of work.

If you eat slowly and chew a long time, your hunger will be satisfied by one half the amount that you might swallow hastily. When people eat just as much as they desire, the doctor sometimes finds that they are ill from too much food and sometimes from too little. How can you find out how much and what kind of food to eat?

What food does. In order to answer such questions as those given above, you need to know what food does in the body.

First, food must supply fuel.

Second, you are built of food. Food supplies the substances from which the tissues of your body are made.

Third, your burning and building must go on at a definite rate; neither too fast nor too slow. Each part of the body must grow and work at its own particular rate. The activity of each part is influenced by the activity of other parts. Substances in the food regulate the burning and building rates.

These very different operations in your body are due to very different food substances. To keep your body in health, you should know the common foods which contain each

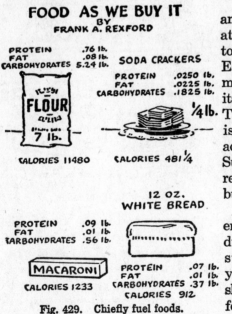

FOOD AS WE BUY IT
BY
FRANK A. REXFORD

PROTEIN   .76 lb.
FAT   .08 lb.
CARBOHYDRATES 5.24 lb.   **SODA CRACKERS**

FLOUR
7 lb.

CALORIES 11480

PROTEIN   .0250 lb.
FAT   .0225 lb.
CARBOHYDRATES .1825 lb.

¼ lb.

CALORIES 481¼

12 OZ.
WHITE BREAD

PROTEIN   .09 lb.
FAT   .01 lb.
CARBOHYDRATES .56 lb.

MACARONI

CALORIES 1233

PROTEIN   .07 lb.
FAT   .01 lb.
CARBOHYDRATES .37 lb.
CALORIES 912

Fig. 429. Chiefly fuel foods.

type of substance. Sometimes a careful mother is shocked when told by the doctor that her well-fed child is under-nourished. The child has had plenty of food, but some particular food substance has been lacking in the diet.

The fuel foods. Coal and oil, the chief furnace fuels, are largely carbon and hydrogen with other elements in smaller quantities. In our foods the elements that are burned are also largely carbon and hydrogen with others in smaller quantities. This similarity between furnace fuel and body fuel is not surprising when we remember that coal and oil both came from living things of ages past.

The fuel foods are chiefly of two kinds: (1) oils or fats and (2) carbohydrates. They contain three elements—carbon, hydrogen, and oxygen. The common carbohydrates of our food are sugars and starches. They form a large part of our food substances. Potatoes, grains, peas, and beans contain large quantities of starch. Fruits contain sugars. The sugar used on the table and in the kitchen comes from sugar cane and sugar beets. Butterfat and the fat of meat furnish most of the animal fats that we eat. Olives, corn, and nuts furnish oils that we use in salads and in our cooking.

The building foods. Protoplasm, the living substance inside the cells, is a complex of substances most of which are *proteins*. A protein (pronounced prō'tē-ĭn) always contains carbon, hydrogen, oxygen, nitrogen, sulphur, and usually phosphorus. Lean meat is

FOOD AS WE BUY IT
BY
FRANK A. REXFORD

FOODS RICH IN CARBOHYDRATES

3½ lb.
BEST
SUGAR
GRANULATED
CALORIES 6510

PROTEIN .00 lb.
FAT .00 lb.
CARBOHYDRATES 3.50 lb.

HONEY
CALORIES 1420

PROTEIN .00 lb.
FAT .00 lb.
CARBOHYDRATES .81 lb.

WHITE BREAD

12 OZ.
CALORIES 912

PROTEIN .07 lb.
FAT .01 lb.
CARBOHYDRATES .40 lb.

MOLASSES
24 OZ. NET
CALORIES 2338

PROTEIN .04 lb.
FAT .00 lb.
CARBOHYDRATES 1.25 lb.

BEST
TAPIOCA
14 OZ.
CALORIES 210

PROTEIN .00 lb.
FAT .00 lb.
CARBOHYDRATES .77 lb.

Fig. 430.   Chiefly fuel foods.

rich in protein as are fish and eggs. The white of egg is pure protein. Wheat, peas, and beans are also important sources of protein.

Proteins from all these sources are not equally valuable.

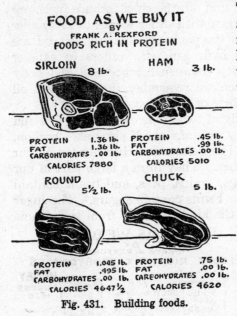

FOOD AS WE BUY IT
BY
FRANK A. REXFORD
FOODS RICH IN PROTEIN

SIRLOIN 8 lb.　　HAM 3 lb.

PROTEIN 1.36 lb.　PROTEIN .45 lb.
FAT 1.36 lb.　FAT .99 lb.
CARBOHYDRATES .00 lb.　CARBOHYDRATES .00 lb.
CALORIES 7880　CALORIES 5010

ROUND 5½ lb.　　CHUCK 5 lb.

PROTEIN 1.045 lb.　PROTEIN .75 lb.
FAT .495 lb.　FAT .00 lb.
CARBOHYDRATES .00 lb.　CARBOHYDRATES .00 lb.
CALORIES 4647½　CALORIES 4620

Fig. 431. Building foods.

The best protein foods are those that are most nearly like those of the human body. The vegetable proteins are not so valuable as those from animal sources. Vegetables lack, or have only in very small quantities, certain proteins that our bodies must have, especially when we are growing. Some animal proteins therefore must be included in the food or the child will not grow properly. These may be derived from milk, eggs, or, for older children, from meat.

The regulating foods. Our bodies need not only the fuel foods and the building foods, but also, for health and vigor, the substances to which the general name of *vitamin* has been given. Vitamins are known by their chemical names or, more often, as vitamin A, B, C, D, etc. The B vitamins are a group of differing chemical substances.

When Cartier was exploring the St. Lawrence, his men developed the wasting and painful disease known as *scurvy*. To cure it they drank an infusion of pine needles soaked in water, and the scurvy disappeared. When the Alaskan miners suffering with scurvy managed to reach the coast, they got potatoes and ate them raw. Scurvy was a scourge of the sailors in the old sailing days and also of the old-time Arctic explorers. To prevent it they used the juice of lemons or limes or, later, oranges. Now it is prevented by fresh and canned vegetables. Raw fruits and vegetables contain a certain substance which is called *vitamin C*. When vitamin C is present, scurvy does not appear.

During World War I when certain foods became scarce, eyes became sore and ulcerated, often resulting in blindness, due to lack of vitamin A. Night blindness is also due to this lack. Vitamin A is contained in butter, in egg yolk, and especially in cod-liver oil. Green vegetables and certain yellow vegetables, such as carrots, will also supply vitamin A.

Fig. 432. Eye disease due to lack of vitamin A in this rat's diet.

In the Orient, where the chief diet of a large number of people is white rice, the disease *beriberi* is common. At one time it was extremely common in the Japanese navy. In a prison in Java where the food was white rice, the disease was banished by adding washings of rice hulls to the diet. We now know that the group of B vitamins, which prevent beriberi, are found in a large number of fresh foods, but are lacking in the inner portions of grain such as rice.

Fig. 433. This rooster was fed a diet lacking B vitamins. You see the bird at the beginning of the experiment and eight months later.

Fig. 434. Measurements of height and weight at regular intervals are an aid in determining the kind of diet to be followed in building the body.

In the poorer sections of many cities of Europe and America, many children suffer with misshapen bones and bodies. This condition, called *rickets*, is due to lack of *vitamin D*. A rich source of this substance is cod-liver oil. Another source is butter, though butter contains much less. Our bodies can manufacture their own vitamin D if the sun falls upon our skins. Special kinds of lights giving out ultra-violet rays also produce vitamin D. A certain fatlike substance in our bodies absorbs some of the energy from the light and vitamin D is produced. When certain fats obtained from other sources are treated with ultra-violet rays (irradiated), vitamin D is developed. Such irradiated foods may be mixed with our regular food as our source of vitamin D.

Study of patients and animal experimentation has shown other diseases due to lack of vitamins. If vitamin E is lacking, animals fail to reproduce. If B vitamins are lacking, the disease *pellagra* develops. Pellagra is common among the poor of certain parts of our country during hard times when the diet is restricted to few articles with no fresh food.

When there is a variety of foods, including fresh vegetables, milk, eggs, and fresh meats, there is no trouble.

In addition to vitamins, *minerals* regulate many processes in our bodies. Some of them also build bones and teeth. Calcium and sometimes iron are the minerals that are most likely to be missing in our foods. Milk is our great source of calcium. Green vegetables contain it in lesser quantities. Iron occurs in green vegetables and in red meat.

How much to eat. The amount of gas that you burn in a car depends upon how fast and how far you drive, upon how hard you work the car. So it is with the body. A farmer, a stevedore, or a lumberjack needs much more fuel food than one who sits most of the day indoors. An active boy of fifteen needs more than a man in an office. The fuel value of a food is measured in calories. The table shows how many calories are needed by each of several kinds of workers.

HOW MANY CALORIES OF FOOD YOU NEED IN A DAY

At 12 years of age	about 1800
At 13 years of age	about 2100
At 14 years of age	about 2400
At 15 years of age, girl	about 2400
At 15 years of age, boy	about 2700 to 3000
Woman	about 2100
Man, sedentary occupation	about 2400
Man, light work	about 2700
Man, heavy work	about 3000 to 3500

How to choose your food. When you are hungry after a long hike and sit down to a good dinner, you are not likely to think about the number of calories you are consuming. With a little thought, however, you can select a good mixed and balanced diet. Select first your protein. One slice of meat or one chop will be about enough for dinner, if you have had eggs for breakfast and perhaps a meat sandwich for lunch. Now think of the fats. Unless you are working hard outdoors in a cold climate, you will not need much fat. A little with your meat, all the butter you want, and a glass of good milk will supply enough fats.

After the proteins, make sure of the vitamins, the protective foods. Fresh, raw fruits and vegetables contain one group of vitamins. Here are the salads, fruit cups, and fruit desserts. B vitamins are in fresh lean meats, liver, chicken, seeds (peas and beans, peanuts, whole cereals, whole wheat bread). Some of them must be eaten raw, for cooking destroys vitamin C, although canned tomatoes retain much of vitamin C. For vitamin A eat butter, yellow vegetables, such as carrots, and green leaves, such as spinach.

Now take a thought of the minerals. Calcium and iron are the only two that need bother you. Red meats and green leaves contain iron. Calcium is found in milk and milk products. In smaller amounts it is also in green leaves, but you would need to eat as much as a cow to get enough calcium from leaves alone. Dr. E. V. McCollum of Johns Hopkins University says that each of us needs to take a quart of milk a day or its equivalent in milk products.

The bulk of the meal may then be bread and vegetable, especially vegetable. You may eat these until your hunger is satisfied, but eat slowly and enjoy every mouthful. If you hurry your dinner into your stomach, the doctor may get you.

There are two general types of cooked vegetables. One type, such as potatoes and beans and corn, contains large quantities of starch. Beets contain sugar. Cooked vegetables of the second type are relatively bulky for the amount of nourishment they contain, but they are nonetheless valuable. The bulk element of food is called *roughage*. We need some bulk in our intestines to make them work properly. Bulky vegetables are parsnips, cauliflower, cabbage, and the like. These vegetables are valuable sources of vitamins.

Over half of your food (60 per cent) should furnish carbohydrates. About one quarter should be fat. About one eighth should be protein. When you are growing, you need more protein, about 14 per cent. At least half of the protein should come from animals—meat, eggs, milk.

Cooking. Although we need some uncooked food each day to supply vitamins, most of our food is cooked. Proper cooking makes food more appetizing and more easily digested. The substance cellulose, that composes the cell walls of plants, is indigestible in our systems. Cooking bursts these cell walls and allows the digestive juices to reach the foods stored inside the plant cells. The cells of meat, too, are bound together and enveloped by tough tissues that retard the digestive juices. Cooking destroys or alters these tough tissues so that digestive juices can reach the rich food inside. A further reason for cooking is to destroy disease germs and parasitic worms that are very often present in meat and sometimes in vegetables.

Just how each food shall be prepared is not entirely a matter of taste. Proper cooking is studied as a science. Scientific experiments to find the best methods for each food are being conducted by the United States Department of Agriculture, state departments, and universities, and by baking and other corporations which prepare foods.

Unspoiled food. Have you noticed in the butcher shop a "quarter" of meat bearing a violet stamp "Inspected and Passed"? Inspectors of the United States Government have examined the carcass and decided that the animal is fit for food. The inspectors stationed at the slaughterhouses search every carcass for evidence of tuberculosis, anthrax, and other diseases as well as for parasitic worms. Tapeworms in beef and pork and trachina worms in pork are common parasites. Any carcass showing evidence of parasites or disease is condemned and made into fertilizer.

You have probably read on a can label, "Guaranteed under the Pure Food and Drugs Act." This act of Congress requires that the label must state the presence of adulterants, inferior substances, coloring matter and preservatives, dyes, and flavorings added to conceal the adulteration. Borax, formaldehyde, salicylic acid, and benzoate of soda are sometimes added as preservatives. Some of these preservatives may be present in very small amounts, for instance, "benzoate of soda, one tenth of one per cent." Such a small amount in one meal may be harmless, but if many foods contain it and it occurs in meal after meal, it may finally poison the body.

Cheaper substances are sometimes substituted for more expensive ones. Glucose, which is a good food but cheaper than cane sugar, is used in jellies, honey, and maple sirup. Cereals replace meats in sausages. Dyes of various colors are sometimes used in candies, jellies, and adulterated fruits and meats.

Alcohol in drink. Alcohol will burn and is oxidized in the body, but it is not therefore a good food. It temporarily increases the flow of gastric juice, but in the end its efficiency diminishes and it may cause stomach disorders. It tends to produce hardening of the arteries, damaged heart muscles, and disease of the liver and the kidneys. It tends to narcotize the nerves (put them to sleep). That is the reason why automobile drivers under the influence of liquor are dangerous to traffic. Its narcotizing action also leads to dilation of the blood vessels at the skin and the flushing of the skin with blood. There results an immediate feeling of warmth, but the heat is soon lost from the skin and the body is cooler than before. A drink of liquor is, therefore, a poor means of warming up on a cold day. Experiments have shown that guinea pigs and white rats under the continued use of alcohol are more liable to the attack of disease germs. Insurance companies have found by actual experience that alcohol drinkers as a group die fifteen years earlier than abstainers.

Alcohol lessens the drinker's efficiency both physically and mentally. Vision is dulled, speed and accuracy are reduced, errors are increased, coördination (working of nerves and muscles in their proper order) is impaired, and memory is weakened. Most disastrous of all is the effect upon the mind. Reasoning power, self-criticism, self-control are seriously reduced and with continued use may be permanently lost. The continued and excessive use leads to the hopeless state of the habitual drunkard.

Drugs and patent medicines. Carloads of headache powders and other patent medicines are sold in the United States. It would seem that the country is suffering from a grand, continuous headache. A headache is a warning that something is wrong in the body. It is like a red light on the track. Hiding the red light will not remove the danger ahead. Headache powders are drugs that make you insensible to the ache without removing the cause. The headache is not the disorder; it is the result of some disorder. If headaches are frequent, the doctor should find what is wrong. The disorder must be corrected or there may be serious trouble ahead.

Some of the drugs commonly used in headache powders have damaging effects upon the heart. Drugs should never be taken except upon order of the physician who knows what they will do. Among the drugs used in remedies for headache and similar ills are phenacetin, acetanilide, chloral, morphine.

Fortunes have been made on the sale of patent medicines to the ignorant and the thoughtless. Some are simply frauds, bottles of water with flavoring and dye and a good percentage of alcohol to give them a "kick." Others contain drugs very dangerous when not properly used. The directions on the package cannot tell you when they should be used. The trained doctor who has learned how to find out what is wrong with a patient and how to correct the wrong is the person to prescribe the remedy.

Tobacco. There are poisons in tobacco. One of these is nicotine, a substance that gardeners use to poison insects on their plants. Tobacco smoke blown into the water of an aquarium will kill the fish. The human body is more resistant to some poisons when they are taken in small amounts through a long series of years, but that tobacco actually has a poisonous action upon the body is shown by the bad effects of the first smoke.

When coaches forbid athletes the use of tobacco, there is a good reason for it. Athletes cannot do well when poisoned with tobacco. In mental work also tobacco shows its poisonous effect. Experiments have shown that smokers are inferior as students to nonsmokers. The soothing effect of smoking upon smokers and their irritation without it are due to the narcotic poisoning.

PERSONAL FOOD TABLE

(© Frank A. Rexford)

FOODS AS WE EAT THEM	WEIGHT OF ORDINARY HELPING	Of This the Body Can Use			THIS PORTION CAN YIELD TO THE BODY IN ENERGY AND HEAT UNITS
		Muscle Builder	For Heat and Energy		
		Protein	Fat	Carbohydrates (Starch and Sugar)	
	Ounces	Ounces	Ounces	Ounces	Calories
Beef:					
Chuck...............	3.00	.57	.04	....	172.5
Corned...............	2.00	.31	.52	....	174.3
Dried...............	1.00	.26	.07	....	49.4
Flank...............	2.25	.44	.47	....	176.5
Heart...............	1.00	.16	.20	....	72.5
Liver...............	2.00	.41	.09	.03	75.6
Round...............	2.25	.43	.29	....	125.2
Sirloin...............	2.25	.37	.36	....	137.1
Sweetbreads..........	2.00	.33	.24	....	103.1
Tongue, pickled.......	2.00	.25	.41	....	138.1
Tripe...............	3.00	.38	.04	.01	60.4
Beverages:					
Cocoa...............	5.00	.11	.33	.19	123.0
Coffee, cream, and sugar only..........	.75	.01	.17	.27	53.0
Lemonade............	5.50	....	....	.66	78.1
Orange juice..........	5.00	....	....	.65	75.5
Bread:					
Biscuit, cream........	2.33	.20	.20	1.00	203.9
Homemade.........	2.00	.17	.05	1.10	162.5
Soda...............	2.00	.19	.27	1.05	216.3
Bread, corn..........	2.00	.16	.09	.93	150.6
Gluten.............	2.00	.18	.03	.99	145.0
Graham.............	2.00	.18	.04	1.04	151.3
Homemade.........	2.00	.18	.03	1.07	153.1
Plain rolls..........	2.00	.19	.08	1.20	183.7
Rye...............	2.00	.24	.01	.72	114.8
Whole-wheat........	2.00	.19	.02	.99	142.5
Zwieback............	1.00	.10	.10	.74	123.2
And butter	2.50	.22	.48	1.18	275.0
Buns, hot cross........	1.25	.10	.06	.60	99.6

PERSONAL FOOD TABLE (Continued)

FOODS AS WE EAT THEM	WEIGHT OF ORDINARY HELPING	OF THIS THE BODY CAN USE			THIS PORTION CAN YIELD TO THE BODY IN ENERGY AND HEAT UNITS
		Muscle Builder	For Heat and Energy		
		Protein	Fat	Carbohydrates (Starch and Sugar)	
	Ounces	Ounces	Ounces	Ounces	Calories
Crackers:					
Graham................	1.00	.10	.09	.74	122.2
Oatmeal.............	1.00	.12	.11	.69	123.1
Pretzels.............	1.00	.10	.04	.73	106.3
Saltines.............	1.00	.11	.13	.69	125.3
Soda................	1.00	.10	.09	.73	120.3
Toast, cream..........	5.00	.20	.56	.60	238.5
Toast, dry.............	5.00	.06	.01	.30	44.4
Cake:					
Charlotte russe........	4.25	.26	.56	2.39	395.2
Chocolate layer.......	2.50	.16	.20	1.60	257.8
Coffee................	2.00	.14	.15	1.26	203.1
Cookies:					
Molasses...........	1.75	.11	.13	1.32	209.0
Sugar..............	1.50	.11	.15	1.10	180.0
Doughnuts...........	1.75	.12	.37	.93	218.8
Frosted..............	2.00	.12	.18	1.30	211.9
Fruit.................	2.00	.12	.22	1.28	220.0
Gingerbread..........	2.00	.12	.18	1.27	208.8
Jelly roll.............	3.00	.15	.12	2.19	301.2
Lady fingers..........	.50	.04	.03	.35	52.7
Macaroons...........	1.00	.07	.15	.65	123.4
Nut.................	2.50	.20	.54	1.36	324.4
Sponge..............	1.50	.09	.16	.90	168.3
Cereals:					
Cornflakes	.75	.07	.00	.59	77.6
Farina...............	4.00	.44	.06	3.05	421.2
Hominy..............	4.00	.09	.01	.72	95.6
Oatmeal..............	4.25	.12	.02	.49	67.1
Puffed rice...........	.50	.04	....	.40	50.9
Rice.................	4.00	.11	.00	.98	127.5
Shredded wheat	2.00	.21	.03	1.56	212.5
Wheat flakes.........	.75	.10	.01	.56	79.2

PERSONAL FOOD TABLE (Continued)

| FOODS AS WE EAT THEM | WEIGHT OF ORDINARY HELPING | OF THIS THE BODY CAN USE | | | THIS PORTION CAN YIELD TO THE BODY IN ENERGY AND HEAT UNITS |
| | | Muscle Builder | For Heat and Energy | | |
		Protein	Fat	Carbohydrates (Starch and Sugar)	
	Ounces	Ounces	Ounces	Ounces	Calories
Dairy products:					
Butter...............	.50	.05	.43	....	112.7
Buttermilk...........	6.00	.18	.03	.29	61.9
Cheese:					
Cottage............	2.00	.42	.02	.09	63.8
Full cream.........	1.00	.26	.34	.02	121.9
Neufchatel.........	2.00	.37	.55	.05	191.3
Pineapple...........	2.00	.60	.78	.05	280.6
Swiss..............	1.00	.28	.35	.01	125.6
Condensed milk:					
Sweetened..........	.25	.02	.02	.14	23.8
Unsweetened........	.25	.02	.02	.03	12.2
Cream:					
Table..............	.50	.01	.09	.02	28.4
Whipped...........	.50	.13	.09	.05	31.1
Ice cream...........	2.00	.05	.10	.91	134.7
Milk, skimmed........	6.50	.22	.02	.33	69.1
Whole.............	6.00	.20	.24	.30	121.9
Oleomargarine........	.50	.01	.42	....	110.2
Eggs:					
Boiled (2)...........	3.75	.50	.45	....	179.1
Omelet..............	4.00	.48	.88	.03	296.0
Poached.............	1.25	.18	.15	....	60.4
On toast...........	2.50	.30	.17	.29	144.4
Scrambled...........	2.00	.24	.17	.03	78.5
Uncooked (2)........	3.75	.50	.39	....	168.8
Fish:					
Blue................	5.00	1.30	.23	....	209.4
Cod................	5.00	.32	.02	....	101.6
Halibut, steak........	3.00	.56	.16	....	105.9
Herring.............	.50	.56	.16	....	105.9
Salmon, canned.......	2.00	.44	.24	....	114.1
Sardines.............	1.00	.23	.19	....	78.1
Shad................	2.25	.42	.22	....	104.9
Trout, brook..........	1.75	.33	.36	....	135.9

PERSONAL FOOD TABLE (Continued)

FOODS AS WE EAT THEM	WEIGHT OF ORDINARY HELPING	Of This the Body Can Use			THIS PORTION CAN YIELD TO THE BODY IN ENERGY AND HEAT UNITS
		Muscle Builder	For Heat and Energy		
		Protein	Fat	Carbohydrates (Starch and Sugar)	
	Ounces	Ounces	Ounces	Ounces	Calories
Fowl:					
Chicken, broilers......	3.50	.75	.09	....	110.5
Fricasseed..........	3.50	.62	.40	.08	187.0
Goose...............	2.75	.43	.98	....	312.1
Turkey..............	1.25	.26	.26	....	104.0
Fruit:					
Apples, baked........	3.25	.02	.02	.78	98.5
Fresh.............	5.50	.02	.03	.78	99.7
Sauce............	3.50	.01	.03	1.20	159.7
Bananas.............	3.50	.05	.02	.77	100.6
Cherries.............	2.00	.02	.02	.33	45.6
Cranberries..........	3.00	.01	.02	.30	40.3
Currants.............	3.00	.05	....	.38	49.7
Dates...............	1.75	.04	.05	1.37	176.6
Figs................	2.00	.09	.01	1.50	184.4
Grapefruit...........	3.75	.03	.01	.37	49.5
Grapes..............	5.00	.05	.07	.96	140.6
Huckleberries........	3.00	.02	.02	.50	64.7
Lemons.............	1.00	.01	.01	.09	12.8
Olives, green.........	1.33	.01	.37	.15	116.3
Ripe..............	1.33	.02	.34	.06	100.2
Oranges.............	5.00	.04	.01	.58	75.0
Peaches, cooked......	3.50	.02	...	.39	48.2
Pineapple, canned.....	3.25	.01	.02	1.18	145.2
Fresh.............	4.00	.02	.01	.39	50.0
Prunes, cooked.......	3.75	.02	.00	.84	100.8
Raspberries, black....	4.00	.07	.04	.50	77.5
Red..............	3.50	.04	...	.44	55.8
Rhubarb.............	2.50	.01	.01	.57	67.0
Strawberries, fresh.....	4.25	.04	.03	.31	47.8
Jelly:					
Cherry..............	1.00	.01	....	.21	90.9
Cranberry...........	2.00	.01	.01	.85	102.2
Currant.............	1.00	.01	....	.77	91.3

32

PERSONAL FOOD TABLE (Continued)

FOODS AS WE EAT THEM	WEIGHT OF ORDINARY HELPING	Of This the Body Can Use			THIS PORTION CAN YIELD TO THE BODY IN ENERGY AND HEAT UNITS
		Muscle Builder	For Heat and Energy		
		Protein	Fat	Carbohydrates (Starch and Sugar)	
	Ounces	Ounces	Ounces	Ounces	Calories
Jelly (Continued):					
Orange...............	2.75	....	....	.85	100.1
Peach................	3.50	.02	.05	.74	98.4
Lamb:					
Chops................	2.00	.43	.59	....	210.0
Kidney stew..........	4.00	.72	.20	.08	150.0
Leg..................	3.50	.67	.44	....	194.3
Miscellaneous:					
Brown gravy..........	2.25	.03	.26	.07	81.2
Hash, beef...........	2.20	.26	.27	.32	114.3
Macaroni.............	2.75	.36	.02	2.00	286.2
With cheese........	2.75	.26	.16	.42	122.4
Mayonnaise dressing, cooked...............	1.25	.07	.32	.03	96.0
Olive oil, tablespoon...	.33	....	.33	....	88.0
Salad dressing, French.	.50	....	.74	.02	100.4
Mutton:					
Leg..................	2.50	.62	.51	....	108.0
Nuts:					
Almonds..............	.25	.05	.14	.04	47.3
Beech................	.50	.11	.29	.07	96.3
Brazil...............	.50	.09	.33	.04	102.0
Butter...............	.50	.14	.31	.02	98.9
English walnuts......	.50	.08	.32	.08	102.7
Filberts.............	.50	.08	.33	.07	103.1
Hickory..............	.50	.08	.34	.06	104.5
Peanuts..............	.50	.13	.19	.12	80.0
Pecan................	.50	.06	.36	.07	107.9
Pickles:					
Cucumber.............	1.25	.01	.00	.03	5.5
Mixed................	1.00	.01	.00	.04	6.9
Spiced...............	1.00	.00	.00	.21	24.7

PERSONAL FOOD TABLE (Continued)

FOODS AS WE EAT THEM	WEIGHT OF ORDINARY HELPING	Of This the Body Can Use			THIS PORTION CAN YIELD TO THE BODY IN ENERGY AND HEAT UNITS
		Muscle Builder	For Heat and Energy		
		Protein	Fat	Carbohydrates (Starch and Sugar)	
	Ounces	Ounces	Ounces	Ounces	Calories
Pie:					
Apple................	4.50	.29	.31	1.44	282.8
Blueberry............	3.87	.15	.19	1.50	237.0
Cream...............	4.00	.18	.46	2.05	380.0
Custard..............	4.00	.17	.25	1.00	207.5
Coconut cream.......	3.87	.23	.46	1.04	235.2
Lemon...............	4.00	.14	.40	1.49	297.2
Mince...............	5.00	.29	.62	1.90	417.1
Pumpkin.............	5.00	.15	.15	1.00	177.0
Raisin...............	5.00	.15	.56	2.36	439.5
Squash..............	5.00	.22	.42	1.05	262.5
Pork:					
Bacon...............	1.00	.10	.66	....	188.6
Chops...............	3.00	.47	.95	....	309.0
Ham croquettes......	2.00	.30	.24	.11	111.2
Ham, lean...........	2.25	.49	.55	....	203.2
Pudding:					
Blanc mange, chocolate	3.50	.10	.30	.49	148.8
Bread................	3.50	.19	.42	.57	131.6
Custard..............	3.25	.16	.16	.35	102.4
Date.................	2.50	.15	.23	1.40	243.0
Fig..................	2.75	.11	.17	.82	150.4
Floating island.......	3.00	.15	.05	.55	118.8
Indian-meal..........	3.25	.18	.16	.89	165.5
Rice.................	3.25	.12	.28	.55	149.5
Snow................	2.50	.10	.07	.35	75.9
Tapioca.............	3.25	.11	.10	.92	146.3
and apple	3.25	.01	.00	.95	112.7
Salad:					
Date-and-apple......	2.25	.05	.05	.87	121.7
Date-and-walnut.....	1.25	.63	.16	.62	124.1
Egg with mayonnaise.	2.25	.26	.25	.02	100.1
Fruit................	2.25	.04	.02	.52	70.4
Potato..............	2.25	.09	.22	.29	102.1

PERSONAL FOOD TABLE (Continued)

FOODS AS WE EAT THEM	WEIGHT OF ORDINARY HELPING	Of This the Body Can Use			THIS PORTION CAN YIELD TO THE BODY IN ENERGY AND HEAT UNITS
		Muscle Builder	For Heat and Energy		
		Protein	Fat	Carbohydrates (Starch and Sugar)	
	Ounces	Ounces	Ounces	Ounces	Calories
Salad (continued):					
String-bean..........	1.75	.01	.33	.04	95.7
Tomato, with mayonnaise...............	4.00	.06	.16	.15	67.6
Sandwiches:					
Cheese..............	3.25	.41	.49	1.20	314.2
Egg.................	4.00	.40	.37	1.19	279.7
Ham................	3.50	.33	.48	1.19	302.7
Jelly................	2.00	.01	.01	.85	102.2
Lamb..............	4.00	.53	.48	1.10	316.0
Lettuce-and-mayonnaise..............	3.50	.22	.24	1.21	214.2
Roast-beef...........	3.50	.39	.39	1.19	275.8
Sardine.............	3.50	.44	.35	1.19	279.6
Sausages:					
Bologna.............	2.00	.37	.35	.01	136.8
City................	2.00	.35	.48	....	172.5
Country.............	2.00	.56	.80	....	278.1
Frankfurters........	2.00	.39	.37	.02	141.6
Shellfish:					
Clams..............	3.75	.24	.02	....	32.2
Lobster.............	2.00	.32	.04	....	47.6
Oysters.............	3.50	.21	.04	....	36.4
Scallops.............	2.00	.29	...	.07	43.1
Soup:					
Bean................	4.75	.38	.07	1.00	182.8
Chicken.............	4.75	.19	.01	.10	31.3
Consommé..........	4.75	.10	....	.02	16.0
Clam chowder.......	4.75	.09	.04	.33	60.0
Cream of celery......	4.75	.11	.34	.17	124.8
Corn..............	4.75	.14	.33	.40	152.0
Lentil..............	4.75	.23	.25	.48	161.5
Oxtail..............	4.75	.20	.06	.20	65.0
Potato..............	4.75	.11	.03	.37	146.8

PERSONAL FOOD TABLE (Continued)

FOODS AS WE EAT THEM	WEIGHT OF ORDINARY HELPING	OF THIS THE BODY CAN USE			THIS PORTION CAN YIELD TO THE BODY IN ENERGY AND HEAT UNITS
		Muscle Builder	For Heat and Energy		
		Protein	Fat	Carbohydrates (Starch and Sugar)	
	Ounces	Ounces	Ounces	Ounces	Calories
Soup (continued):					
Tomato	4.75	.13	.12	.33	91.2
Vegetable (canned)	4.75	.13	....	.02	192.8
Sugars:					
Candy, Caramel	1.00	.05	....	.81	100.4
Chocolate	1.00	.01	.01	.73	90.0
Chocolate almonds	1.50	.06	.15	.95	160.0
Honey	1.63	.01	....	1.32	154.9
Maple sirup	1.25	....	....	.89	103.9
Maple sugar	1.00	....	....	.83	96.2
Sugar, granulated or loaf	.25	....	....	.25	29.0
Veal:					
Breast, lean	2.50	.38	.25	....	104.8
Cutlets	3.50	.70	.26	....	152.0
Leg	2.50	.65	.10	....	104.0
Liver	3.00	.56	.17	....	107.1
Vegetables:					
Asparagus, on toast	4.00	.18	.40	.64	202.8
Beans, baked	3.25	.31	.18	1.08	182.0
Kidney	3.25	.22	.65	.60	97.5
String	4.00	.09	.01	.29	48.7
Beets	2.25	.05	....	.17	26.1
Cabbage, boiled	4.00	.03	.09	.16	35.2
Carrots	3.75	.04	.02	.35	49.2
Cauliflower	4.00	.07	.02	.20	35.0
Celery	1.00	.01	....	.03	5.3
Corn, canned	2.75	.08	.03	.52	78.2
Cucumbers	2.00	.02	....	.06	10.0
Eggplant	1.50	.02	....	.08	121.9
Lettuce	1.00	.01	....	.03	5.6
Mushrooms	1.00	.04	....	.07	13.1
Onions, boiled	2.50	.03	.11	.13	26.3
Creamed	3.00	.04	.15	.15	65.7
Scalloped	3.00	.08	.27	.09	73.9

PERSONAL FOOD TABLE (Continued)

FOODS AS WE EAT THEM	WEIGHT OF ORDINARY HELPING	Of This the Body Can Use			THIS PORTION CAN YIELD TO THE BODY IN ENERGY AND HEAT UNITS
		Muscle Builder	For Heat and Energy		
		Protein	Fat	Carbohydrates (Starch and Sugar)	
	Ounces	Ounces	Ounces	Ounces	Calories
Vegetables (continued):					
Parsnips, creamed.....	3.00	.03	.07	.44	79.0
Browned..........	3.00	.05	.13	.29	75.6
Peas, canned..........	3.00	.09	.09	.54	66.6
Green..............	3.00	.13	.10	.20	103.2
Potatoes, baked.......	3.00	.10	.01	.68	98.1
Boiled.............	3.00	.08	.01	.73	82.8
Browned..........	3.25	.11	.06	.82	123.5
Mashed............	3.25	.09	.26	.68	100.4
Sweet..............	3.00	.09	.06	1.26	173.4
Radishes.............	1.00	.01	....	.06	8.4
Spinach.............	3.00	.06	.12	.08	16.3
Squash, winter, baked.	3.75	.05	.01	.33	50.4
Succotash............	3.00	.11	.03	.56	78.0
Tomatoes, sliced......	4.00	.04	.04	.18	26.8
Stewed.............	2.50	.03	....	.08	16.4
Turnips, mashed......	4.00	.02	.11	.11	24.4

EXPERIMENT 136 (HOME)

Question: (*a*) How many ounces of protein do I consume in one day?

(*b*) How many calories are yielded to my body by the food taken this day?

Materials: A list of all the different portions of food you eat for one whole day; the personal food table found on pages 482–490.

Directions: (*a*) Make a complete list of all the food eaten in one day. The best plan is to keep your list with you and keep it up to date as the day progresses. Do not omit anything. Note quantities eaten.

(*b*) Record the list of foods on a page of your notebook that has been ruled in the following manner:

FOOD FOR ONE DAY

NUMBER OF PORTIONS	FOOD EATEN	OUNCES OF PROTEIN	NUMBER OF CALORIES
....	....	....	....
....	....	....	....
....	....	....	....
....	....	....	....
....	....	....	....
....	....	....	....
....	....	....	....
....	....	....	....
Total............		....	....

(*c*) After you have completed your list, copy from the Personal Food Table on pages 482–490 the proper values of each food you have eaten into the protein and the calories columns, and add the two columns to find total ounces of proteins and total number of calories.

NOTE: Our main concern is with the building material (protein) and the heat and energy units (calories). The protein must be recorded in ounces, but since the fats and carbohydrates are chiefly responsible for the fuel values, it is only necessary to record the calories. The weights of the fats and carbohydrates are given in the food table in order that we may know which of the fuel nutrients is mostly responsible for the fuel value.

Diagram: None is needed other than the completed totaled list.

Conclusion: Answer the question.

Practical application: If we know the value of the food we actually eat, we can easily compare it with the food values we *should* receive daily, and modify our diet to meet our bodily needs.

EXPERIMENT 137 (HOME)

Question: How can I modify my daily diet so that my food will more nearly meet my body requirements?

Materials: Personal Food Table, pages 482–490; your own food list prepared in Experiment 136; a ruled form as in Experiment 136 for recording your results.

Directions: (*a*) Study the high-school student's dietary which is given below:

ORDINARY DAILY DIETARY OF A HIGH-SCHOOL STUDENT

NUMBER OF PORTIONS	FOOD EATEN	OUNCES OF PROTEIN	NUMBER OF CALORIES
	Breakfast:		
1	Oranges.................	.04	75.0
1	Coffee..................	.01	53.0
1	Bread and butter........	.22	275.0
1	Omelet.................	.48	296.0
	Lunch:		
3	Beef sandwiches..........	1.17	827.4
1	Oranges.................	.04	75.0
1	Chocolate candy..........	.01	90.0
	Dinner:		
1	Lamb chops..............	.43	210.0
1	Potatoes, mashed.........	.09	100.4
1	Peas....................	.09	66.6
1	Lettuce.................	.01	5.6
1	Pineapple cheese..........	.60	280.6
1	Crackers, soda............	.10	120.3
1	Apple pie................	.29	282.8
1	Milk...................	.20	121.9
	Total..................	3.78	2879.6

(*b*) Note what changes the student made in modifying the ordinary daily diet to conform more nearly to daily body requirements.

MODIFIED DAILY DIETARY

NUMBER OF PORTIONS	FOOD EATEN	OUNCES OF PROTEIN	NUMBER OF CALORIES
	Breakfast:		
1	Oranges..................	.04	75.0
1	Rice......................	.11	127.5
1	Cocoa....................	.11	123.0
1	Dry toast	.06	44.4
1	Butter...................	.05	112.7
	Lunch:		
1	Bean soup...............	.38	182.8
2	Lettuce-and-mayonnaise sandwiches.............	.44	428.4
1	Dates...................	.04	176.6
	Dinner:		
1	Cream of celery soup......	.11	124.8
1	Breast of veal............	.38	104.8
1	Baked potatoes...........	.10	98.1
1	Green peas...............	.13	103.2
1	Salad, string bean.........	.01	95.7
1	Bread and butter.........	.22	275.0
1	Pudding, floating island...	.15	118.8
1	Whole milk..............	.20	121.9
	3 O'clock Lunch:		
1	Lemonade...............	-------	78.1
	Total..................	2.53	2390.8

(c) Make such changes in your own dietary from Experiment 136 as will make it approximately what you should have daily in ounces of protein and number of calories.

Conclusion: Tell what changes in protein and in fuel value you have made.

Practical application: After a few days' practice in arranging your diet by the help of your knowledge and the personal food table, the habit of eating proper amounts of the right kinds of food will be easily acquired.

EXPERIMENT 138 (HOME)

Question: How can I select a balanced ration or dietary?

Materials: Personal Food Table; a page in your notebook ruled for use as in Experiment 136.

Directions: NOTE 1: It was determined by Professor Russell Chittenden in his laboratories at Yale University that an adult person doing moderate work should have in his food daily:

$\frac{1}{80}$ *of an ounce of protein for each pound he weighs*, plus enough fat and carbohydrate to provide 2500 to 3000 calories for heat and energy.

What would be the daily food requirement in protein and in calories for a man weighing 160 lb.?

NOTE 2: A growing child of high-school age, although he does not weigh so much, needs as much food as the 160-lb. man. Why?

(*a*) Taking into account that meals must contain attractive, palatable dishes and a sufficient variety, make up on your prepared form, with the help of the Personal Food Table, a dietary for one day which will approximately provide protein and calories as follows:

Breakfast.............	.75 oz. protein	750 calories
Luncheon.............	.75 oz. protein	750 calories
Dinner................	1.00 oz. protein	1000 calories
Total for day........	2.5 oz. protein	2500 calories

Conclusion: Tell what difficulties you have in making the proper balance. Does the protein tend to run high and the calories low? What foods were most helpful to you in making necessary changes in protein and in number of calories?

Practical application: While it is not expected or hoped that all high-school students will become expert dietitians, it is most important that everyone should become somewhat familiar with the uses of different foods and know how diet can be modified to meet individual requirements.

MARKETING FOOD TABLE

In the study of the Marketing Food Table a knowledge of the use and value of each of the different food stuffs, as given in the Personal Food Table, is presupposed. Up to this time our study of nutrition has been confined to the consideration of the needs of the individual and of *food as eaten*. When we come to *buying food*, the proposition is a little different. We do not buy food by the portion; we buy it as it is sold in the market. The analyses here given are, therefore, in most cases, computations from Government bulletins and are for quantities of different foods in just the condition we buy them. That is, meat with the bone, clams with the shells, peas with the pods, nuts with the shucks, etc.

For complete scientific data, study *Bulletin No. 28*, United States Department of Agriculture, Office of Experiment Stations.

MARKETING FOOD TABLE
(© Frank A. Rexford)

FOOD AS WE BUY IT	NOURISHMENT IN THIS FOOD			THIS FOOD CAN YIELD TO THE BODY IN ENERGY AND HEAT UNITS
	Muscle Builder	For Heat and Energy		
	Protein	Fat	Carbohydrates (Starch and Sugar)	
	Pounds	Pounds	Pounds	Calories
Beef:				
Chuck, roast or steak, 1 lb.....	.15	....	....	920
Corned, 1 lb..................	.14	.22	....	1195
Dried, 1 lb..................	.26	.07	....	780
Flank, roast or steak, 1 lb......	.19	.20	....	1185
Liver, 1 lb....................	.20	.03	.03	555
Round, roast or steak, 1 lb.....	.19	.09	....	745
Sirloin, roast or steak, 1 lb.....	.17	.17	....	985
Sweetbreads, 1 lb..............	.17	.12	....	825
Tongue, 1 lb..................	.14	.07	....	545
Tripe, 1 lb....................	.12	.01	....	270
Beverages:				
Cocoa, 1-lb. can..............	.22	.28	.38	2320
Coffee, 1 lb..................	....	....	....	....
Tea, 1 lb....................	....	....	....	....
Bread:				
Buns, 1 doz., 1 lb..............	.07	.08	.58	1515
Graham, 5¢ loaf, 1 lb	.06	.01	.39	908
Rolls, 1 doz., 1 lb.............	.10	.04	.60	1470
Rye, 5¢ loaf, 12 oz	.07	.01	.40	912
White, 5¢ loaf, 12 oz	.07	.01	.40	912
Whole-wheat, 5¢ loaf, 12 oz	.08	.01	.37	855
Cake:				
Charlotte russe, 1, 4.25 oz......	.02	.04	.17	395
Chocolate layer, 3½ lb..........	.20	.27	2.10	5500
Cookies, molasses, 1 doz., 12 oz.	.07	.15	.65	1975
Sugar, 1 doz., 12 oz..........	.05	.07	.55	1440
Doughnuts, 1 doz., 12 oz.......	.05	.16	.40	1500
Fruit, 1 lb....................	.06	.11	.64	1760
Gingerbread, 1 lb..............	.06	.09	.63	1670
Lady fingers, 1 doz., 4 oz.......	.02	.02	.18	422
Macaroons, 1 lb..............	.07	.15	.65	1975
Sponge, 1 lb..................	.06	.11	.66	1795

MARKETING FOOD TABLE (Continued)

FOOD AS WE BUY IT	NOURISHMENT IN THIS FOOD			THIS FOOD CAN YIELD TO THE BODY IN ENERGY AND HEAT UNITS
	Muscle Builder	For Heat and Energy		
	Protein	Fat	Carbohydrates (Starch and Sugar)	
	Pounds	Pounds	Pounds	Calories
Cereals:				
Farina, 1 box, 28 oz..........	.19	.02	1.34	2949
Hominy, 1 box, 28 oz.........	.15	.01	1.38	2888
Oatmeal, 1 box, 28 oz.........	.22	.10	.93	2558
Rice, 1 lb....................	.08	....	.79	1630
Shredded wheat, 1 box, 12 oz..	.09	.01	.56	1275
Wheat breakfast foods, 1 lb...	.12	.02	.75	1680
Crackers:				
Graham, 1 lb................	.10	.09	.73	1955
Oatmeal, 1 lb................	.12	.11	.69	1970
Pretzels, 1 lb................	.10	.04	.73	1700
Saltines, 1 lb................	.11	.13	.69	2005
Soda, 1 lb...................	.10	.09	.73	1925
Dairy products:				
Butter, 1 lb.................	.01	.85	....	3605
Buttermilk, 1 qt., 2 lb........	.05	.06	.01	330
Cheese, cottage, 1 lb..........	.21	.01	.04	510
American, 1 lb.............	.26	34	.02	1950
Cream, 1 bottle, ½ pt., 8 oz....	.01	.08	.02	430
Ice cream, 1 qt., 2 lb..........	.06	.18	.44	1808
Milk, 1 qt., 2 lb.............	.06	.08	.10	650
Condensed, 1 can, 14½ oz.....	.08	.07	.48	1323
Oleomargarine, 1 lb...........	.01	.83	....	3525
Eggs:				
Hens', 1 doz., 1½ lb..........	.18	.14	....	953
Fish:				
Bass, 1 lb....................	.08	.01	....	200
Blue, 1 lb....................	.10	.01	....	201
Butter, 1 lb..................	.01	.06	....	460
Cod, fresh, 1 lb..............	.18	.08	....	165
Salt, 1 lb....................	.22	.27	....	1020
Flounder, 1 lb................	.06	....	....	130
Halibut, steak, 1 lb...........	.15	.04	....	470
Smoked, 1 lb................	.21	.15	....	1020

MARKETING FOOD TABLE (Continued)

FOOD AS WE BUY IT	NOURISHMENT IN THIS FOOD			THIS FOOD CAN YIELD TO THE BODY IN ENERGY AND HEAT UNITS
	Muscle Builder	For Heat and Energy		
	Protein	Fat	Carbohydrates (Starch and Sugar)	
	Pounds	Pounds	Pounds	Calories
Fish (Continued):				
Mackerel, 1 lb................	.14	.06	....	525
Salmon, 1 can, 12 oz...........	.18	.07	....	638
Shad, 1 lb...................	.09	.05	....	380
Trout, lake, 1 lb..............	.09	.05	....	380
Flours, etc.:				
Buckwheat, 1 bag, 3½ lb........	.22	.04	.27	5607
Corn meal, 1 bag, 3½ lb........	.32	.07	2.54	5722
Graham, 1 bag, 3½ lb..........	.45	.03	2.50	5775
Macaroni, 1 box, 12 oz.........	.09	.01	.56	1233
Rye, 1 bag, 3½ lb.............	.24	.03	2.75	5705
Spaghetti, 12-oz. box...........	.09	....	.57	1245
Wheat, 1 bag, 3½ lb...........	.38	.04	2.62	5740
Wheat, 1 bag, 7 lb.............	.76	.08	5.24	11480
Wheat, 1 bag, 24½ lb...........	2.65	.27	18.32	40180
Whole-wheat, 1 bag, 5 lb.......	.66	.09	3.24	7956
Fruit:				
Apples, 1 qt., 28 oz............	.01	.01	.19	385
Bananas, 1 doz., 4½ lb.........	.04	.02	.64	1350
Cherries, 1 can, 30 oz..........	.02	....	.40	778
Cranberries, 1 lb..............	.01	.01	.10	215
Dates, 1 box, 12 oz............	.01	.02	.53	1088
Figs, 1 lb....................	.04	....	.74	1475
Grapes, 1 lb..................	.01	.01	.14	335
Lemons, 1 doz., 3 lb...........	.03	.02	.26	615
Oranges, 1 doz., 5¼ lb.........	.04	.01	.60	1200
Peaches, 1 can, 28 oz..........	.01	....	.19	385
Pears, 1 can, 28 oz............	.01	.01	.31	621
Pineapple, 1 can, 28 oz........	.01	.01	.64	1251
Prunes, 1 lb..................	.02	....	.73	1400
Jellies (average analysis):				
1 jar, 10 oz..................	.01	....	.50	950

MARKETING FOOD TABLE (Continued)

Food as We Buy It	Nourishment in This Food			This Food Can Yield to the Body in Energy and Heat Units
	Muscle Builder	For Heat and Energy		
	Protein	Fat	Carbohydrates (Starch and Sugar)	
	Pounds	Pounds	Pounds	Calories
Lamb:				
Chops, 1 lb	.14	.28	....	1445
Leg, 1 lb	.15	.15	....	900
Miscellaneous:				
Olive oil, 1-pt. bottle, 1 lb	....	1.00	....	4226
Mutton:				
Kidney, 1 lb	.17	.03	....	440
Leg, 1 lb	.14	.23	....	1235
Nuts:				
Almonds, 1 lb	.12	.30	.10	1660
Brazil, 1 lb	.09	.34	.04	1655
Filberts, 1 lb	.08	.31	.06	1575
Hickory nuts, 1 lb	.06	.26	.04	1265
Peanuts, 1 lb	.20	.29	.19	1935
Peanut butter, 1 jar, ¼ lb	.07	.12	.04	706
Pecans, 1 lb	.05	.33	.06	1620
Walnuts, 1 lb	.07	.27	.07	1375
Pickles:				
Cucumber, 1 bottle, 14½ oz	....	....	.02	61
Mixed, 1 bottle, 14 oz	.01	....	.04	96
Spiced, 1 bottle, 14 oz	....	....	.19	370
Pies:				
Apple, 1, 2¼ lb	.07	.22	.96	2857
Custard, 1, 2¼ lb	.09	.14	.58	1867
Mince, 1, 2¼ lb	.14	.28	.86	3003
Pork:				
Bacon, 1 lb	.13	.36	....	1740
Chops, loin, lb	.13	.26	....	1340
Ham, 1 lb	.15	.33	....	1670
Lard, 1 lb	....	1.00	....	4226
Poultry and Game:				
Chickens, broilers, 1 lb	.13	.01	....	295
Fowl, 1 lb	.14	.12	....	775

MARKETING FOOD TABLE (Continued)

FOOD AS WE BUY IT	NOURISHMENT IN THIS FOOD			THIS FOOD CAN YIELD TO THE BODY IN ENERGY AND HEAT UNITS
	Muscle Builder	For Heat and Energy		
	Protein	Fat	Carbohydrates (Starch and Sugar)	
	Pounds	Pounds	Pounds	Calories
Poultry and Game (continued):				
Goose, 1 lb	.13	.30	....	1500
Turkey, 1 lb	.16	.18	....	1475
Sausages:				
Bologna, 1 lb	.18	.20	....	1170
City, beef and pork, 1 lb	.19	.24	....	1380
Frankfurters, 1 lb	.20	.19	.01	1170
Shellfish:				
Clams, 1 doz., 5 lb	.10	....	.05	350
Lobsters, 1, heavy, 3 lb	.16	.02	....	400
Oysters, 1 qt., 2 lb	.12	.02	.06	460
Scallops, 1 qt., 2 lb	.30	....	.07	690
Soup:				
Asparagus, cream of, 1 can, 1 lb	.03	.03	.05	285
Bouillon, 1 can, 1 lb	.02	....	....	50
Celery, cream of, 1 can, 1 lb	.02	.03	.05	235
Chicken, 1 can, 1 lb	.04	....	.02	100
Consommé, 1 can, 1 lb	.03	....	....	55
Corn, cream of, 1 can, 1 lb	.03	.02	.08	270
Mock turtle, 1 can, 1 lb	.05	.01	.03	185
Mulligatawny, 1 can, 1 lb	.04	....	.06	180
Oxtail, 1 can, 1 lb	.04	.01	.04	170
Pea, 1 can, 1 lb	.04	.01	.08	235
Cream of, 1 can, 1 lb	.03	.03	.06	270
Tomato, 1 can, 1 lb	.02	.01	.06	185
Turtle, 1 can, 1 lb	.06	.02	.04	265
Vegetable, 1 can, 1 lb	.03	....	.01	65
Sugars and Starches:				
Candy, 1 lb	....	....	.96	1680
Cornstarch, 1 package, 1 lb	....	....	.90	1675
Sugar, brown, 1 lb	....	....	.95	1765
Granulated, 1 bag, 3½ lb	....	....	3.50	6510
Maple, 1 lb	....	....	.82	1540
Powdered, 1 lb	....	....	1.00	1860

MARKETING FOOD TABLE (Continued)

FOOD AS WE BUY IT	NOURISHMENT IN THIS FOOD			THIS FOOD CAN YIELD TO THE BODY IN ENERGY AND HEAT UNITS
	Muscle Builder	For Heat and Energy		
	Protein	Fat	Carbohydrates (Starch and Sugar)	
	Pounds	Pounds	Pounds	Calories
Sugar and Starches (continued):				
Molasses, 1 can, 29 oz..........	.04	....	1.25	2338
Tapioca, 1 package, 14 oz......	....	....	.77	210
Veal:				
Breast, 1 lb....................	.15	.09	....	645
Cutlets, 1 lb...................	.20	.08	....	690
Leg, 1 lb......................	.18	.06	....	585
Liver, 1 lb....................	.19	.02	....	575
Vegetables:				
Asparagus, 1 can, 28 oz........	.02	....	.05	149
Beans, string, 1 qt............	.04	.01	.12	315
Beets, 1 bunch, 2 lb...........	.02	....	.15	340
Cabbage, 1 head, 4 lb..........	.01	....	.17	500
Carrots, 1 bunch, 10 oz........	.01	....	.05	100
Cauliflower, 1 head, 2 lb.......	.04	.01	.09	280
Celery, 1 bunch, 10 oz.........	....	....	.01	44
Corn, 1 can, 19 oz............	.03	.01	.23	540
Cucumbers, 1, large, 12 oz.....	.01	....	.02	51
Eggplant, 1 lb.................	.01	....	.05	130
Lettuce, 1 head, 10 oz.........	.01	....	.02	51
Mushrooms, 1 lb..............	.04	....	.07	210
Onions, 1 qt., 28 oz...........	.03	.01	.16	359
Parsnips, 1 bunch, 24 oz.......	.02	.01	.16	360
Peas, canned, 1 can, 20 oz.....	.04	.01	.17	419
Green, 1 qt., 28 oz..........	.06	....	.17	446
Potatoes, Irish, 1 basket, 6 lb..	.10	.01	.88	1860
Sweet, 1 qt., 28 oz...........	.02	.01	.38	805
Radishes, 1 bunch, 5 oz........	....	....	.01	30
Spinach, 1 qt., 28 oz..........	.04	.01	.06	193
Succotash, 1 can, 19 oz........	.04	.01	.22	540
Tomatoes, fresh, 1 lb.........	.01	....	.04	105
Canned, 1 can, 38 oz........	.03	.01	.10	249
Turnips, 1, 3 lb..............	.03	....	.17	375

EXPERIMENT 139 (HOME)

Question: (a) How can I learn to buy food economically?
(b) How can I select an economical, balanced personal diet?

I. MUSCLE-BUILDING FOODS
© Frank A. Rexford

FOOD	COMPARATIVE COST
Oranges	41¢
Bananas	
Salt pork, fat	
Celery	
Apples	
Corn, canned	
Oysters	
Eggs	
Cabbage	
Beef, sirloin	
Pork, smoked ham	
Mutton	
Turnips	
Rice	
Milk	
Potatoes	3¢
Beef, dried	
Cod, fresh	
Pork, loin	
Beef, round	
Beef, flank	
Wheat bread	
Wheat breakfast food	
Cheese	
Salmon	
Cod, salt	
Beef, stew meat	
Corn meal	
Oatmeal	
Beans	1¢

NOTE: The two charts give an idea of the values of food from two standpoints. Chart No. 1 takes into account the cost of the *muscle-building food;* chart No. 2, the cost of the *energy food,* found in the different foods. Since most foods provide for us both building materials and energy, these charts should be studied together. It would be incorrect to attempt to get results from either chart to the exclusion of the other.

The amount of building material in each food in Chart No. 1, or energy material in each food in Chart No. 2, is the same. The only variations shown in these charts are in the *prices* which we pay for these materials, as represented by the black bars of different lengths.

Materials: Personal Food Table, pages 482–490; Marketing Food Table, pages 495–500; Food Economy graphs in this experiment; ruled forms for personal dietary and for family marketing list.

II. ENERGY FOODS

© Frank A. Rexford

FOOD	COMPARATIVE COST
Oysters	55¢
Celery	
Cod, dressed	
Oranges	
Eggs	
Halibut	
Beef, dried	
Bananas	
Beef, sirloin	12¢
Corn, canned	
Mutton	
Cabbage	
Cod, salt	
Beef, round	9¢
Beef, flank	
Pork, smoked ham	
Salmon, canned	
Pork, loin	
Milk	
Apples	
Cheese	
Turnips	
Beef, stew meat	
Butter	
Rice	
Potatoes	
Wheat bread	
Wheat breakfast food	
Pork, salt	
Corn meal	
Beans	
Oatmeal	1¢

Directions: (*a*) Select from the lower two thirds of the charts in this experiment a variety of foods to last your family a week; record, calculate and balance as to protein content and calories on the family marketing blank you have prepared; work it out from the Marketing Food Table.

(*b*) Make out a well-balanced personal dietary for yourself from this same list.

Diagram: None needed.

Conclusion: Answer the questions.

Practical application: A little perusal will bring out the fact that the foods found nearest the top of each chart are the most expensive and the more economical ones are found toward the bottom of the list.

Although the number and range of foods in this small table is necessarily limited, the lesson need be no less impressive. It must be remembered that only the financial side of the question is here considered and that digestion and personal peculiarities are individual problems; it is believed, however, that a family who cares to live economically can get enough variety and substance in the lower two thirds of these charts to nourish them palatably, economically, and well.

EXPERIMENT 140 (HOME)

Question: (*a*) How can I determine the amount of food value of the food represented by a given weekly marketing list?

(*b*) Does this list contain sufficient food value to nourish a family of seven?

(*c*) Has the food been purchased economically?

Materials: 1. Marketing Food Table, pages 495–500; a page of your notebook ruled as follows:

FAMILY MARKETING LIST FOR 1 WEEK FOR 7 PEOPLE

AMOUNT OF FOOD PURCHASED	POUNDS OF PROTEIN	NUMBER OF CALORIES	COST
. . . .			
. . . .			
. . . .			
. . . .			
Total.	-------------------	-------------------	-------------------

2. A family marketing list as follows:

FAMILY MARKET LIST

Amount	Price, Cents	Amount	Price, Cents
3½ lb. pork, loin chop.....at	24	1 head lettuce ....at	10
3 lb. lamb, leg...........	22	3 baskets potatoes........	20
½ lb. dried beef..........	25	2 qt. onions.............	15
1 lb. codfish, salt	18	3 bunches celery.........	12
2½ lb. beef, sirloin........	28	6 qt. spinach............	15
1 lb. bacon..............	26	1 head cabbage..........	6
1 lb. sausage.............	20	3 cans peaches...........	25
10 lb. beef, sirloin, roast..	25	2 doz. bananas...........	15
10 loaves bread, white....	10	4 qt. apples.............	16
5 loaves bread, graham...	10	1 doz. oranges...........	40
4 doz. rolls..............	10	1 lb. coffee..............	30
1 pkg. oatmeal...........	10	¼ lb. tea.................	50
2 lb. crackers, soda.......	15	1 can cocoa..............	40
1 pkg. tapioca...........	10	1 lb. walnuts.............	23
7 lb. sugar, granulated....	36	4 lb. butter..............	37
21 qt. milk..............	9	4 doz. eggs..............	40

Directions: (*a*) Record on the ruled form that you have prepared the items in a family weekly marketing list. Perhaps your mother would like to have you coöperate in the household buying so that you can make your own list and so gain practical experience. If that is inconvenient, use the one provided.

(*b*) By referring to the Marketing Food Table write the appropriate figures in the three columns headed "Pounds of Protein," "Number of Calories," and "Cost."

(*c*) Total the columns.

NOTE: 1.25 lb. protein plus enough fat and carbohydrates to make a fuel value of 15,000 to 25,000 calories will amply nourish one person doing moderate work one week, and can be bought for $2.50 or less.

Diagram: None needed.

Conclusion: Answer the three questions.

Practical application: This work has value only when it is applied. It is desirable that each family in the community work out a weekly market list and compare notes. This can be done by keeping account in each case of what is bought and the price paid. A tabulation of the results will show: (*a*) comparative cost of the same foods in different parts of the town; (*b*) whether or not the family is being approximately well nourished; (*c*) whether or not the family is getting good value in *nourishment* for the money expended each week.

EXPERIMENT 141 (HOME, OPTIONAL)

Question: How can I calculate the personal food needs for the different members of my family?

NOTE: Charitable institutions often have occasion to calculate the approximate food requirements for needy families.

This is done by taking the food requirements of a man at moderate work (2.5 oz. protein and 2500 calories) and multiplying these requirements by the factor which meets the condition, as in the following table:

	FACTOR		FACTOR
Man, period of full vigor:		Boy, 15–16 years	.9
At moderate work	1.0	13–14 years	.8
At hard work	1.6	11–13 years	.7
In sedentary occupation	.8	10–11 years	.6
Woman, period of full		Girl, 15–16 years	.8
vigor:		13–14 years	.7
At moderate work	.8	10–13 years	.6
At hard work	.9	Child, 6–9 years	.5
In sedentary occupation	.7	2–6 years	.5
Man or Woman:		Under 2 years	.4
In old age	.8		
In extreme old age	.7		

Example: A man at hard work needs 1.6 as much food as a man at moderate work. 1.6 times 2.5 oz. protein equals 4 oz. protein and 1.6 times 2500 equals 4000 calories.

Therefore, a man at hard work needs 4 oz. protein per day and enough fuel and energy foods to yield 4000 calories.

Materials: Ruled dietary blanks; Personal Food Table, pages 482–490; table given in this experiment.

Directions: (a) Calculate how much protein and how many calories each member of your family needs. Then, by using the Personal Food Table, you can proceed.

(b) Make up a suitable balanced daily dietary for each member of your family.

Caution: You must always remember that *variety, fitness, palatability,* and *balance* must be considered.

Diagram: None needed.

Conclusion: Answer the question.

Practical application: It has been found that, if you wish to effect the strictest economy, it is not necessary to plan 1.25 lb. of protein for each member of the family each week. By learning to calculate the requirements of your family, you can often save considerable money.

NOTE: *Remember always that the dietetic studies in this book are for the purpose of giving us a better knowledge of the requirements of our bodies and the nature of our food.   In case of digestive troubles, consult the expert, the family physician.*

EXPERIMENT 142

Question: How to test for nutrients in foods.

Materials: Starch; glucose or corn sirup; white of egg; a little butter; various foods such as bread, jelly, meat, ice cream, nuts; iodine solution; Fehling's solution; nitric acid; ammonia; test tubes; Bunsen burner.

Directions: (a) To a little water in a test tube add a little starch; shake; add a drop of iodine; note the color change.

(b) To half a test tube of water add a little glucose; then add some Fehling's solution; shake; boil; note color changes.

(c) Place the white of hard-boiled egg (protein) in a test tube; cover with nitric acid; warm; note color; pour off acid; add ammonia; note color.

(d) Smear a tiny bit of butter (fat) on a piece of absorbent paper and hold it for a moment over heat; then hold it toward the light.

(e) Perform the four tests on various foods provided.

Results: Draw up a table showing results.

Conclusions: Answer the question.

EXPERIMENT 143

Question: How can I tell whether an egg is fresh?

Materials: Eggs; 10 per cent solution of table salt; large bowl; candle; black cardboard or paper.

Directions: (a) Place the egg in the salt solution.   An egg that floats is not fresh.

(b) Cut a round hole in the cardboard just too small for the egg to go through.   Light the candle and darken the room.   Put the egg into the hole in the cardboard and hold toward the light.   A fresh egg will appear pink and evenly translucent.   Dark spots or too great opacity show that the egg is not fresh.

Results: Draw up a table of your results.

Conclusions: Answer the question.

EXPERIMENT 144

Question: How can some food adulterations be detected?

Materials: Ground coffee; butter; olive oil; cottonseed or other salad oil; milk; nitric acid; spoon; beaker; water; 2 test tubes; Bunsen burner; formaldehyde; hydrochloric acid; ferric chloride.

Directions: (*a*) Spread a little coffee over the surface of water in a beaker. Let it stand for 5 minutes. The coffee will float.

(*b*) Heat some butter in a spoon. If it sputters and has little foam, it is a butter substitute.

(*c*) Put about 5 c.c. of olive oil into a test tube and an equal quantity of cottonseed or other salad oil into another test tube. Add about 5 c.c. of nitric acid, and shake. Olive oil turns dark green in a few minutes.

(*d*) Formaldehyde, a poison, has often been used to preserve milk. The following test shows how it may be detected in milk. Place 10 c.c. of milk in beaker No. 1. Add a few drops of formaldehyde. Place 10 c.c. of milk in beaker No. 2. To 20 c.c. of hydrochloric acid add a drop of ferric chloride, and then add half of the mixture to each beaker containing milk. Mix thoroughly. Set beakers in a pan containing boiling water and heat for 5 minutes. A lavender color shows the presence of formaldehyde.

Observations: Draw up a table showing results.

Conclusions: Answer the question.

EXPERIMENT 145

Question: How does alcohol affect proteins and living protoplasm?

Materials: White of egg; a culture of paramecium; alcohol; 2 test tubes; microscope slides, cover glasses.

Directions: (*a*) Half fill test tube No. 1 with water and No. 2 with alcohol. Add to each a part of the white of egg. Note what happens in each test tube.

(*b*) Examine a drop of the paramecium under the microscope. With a glass rod or a medicine dropper place a drop of alcohol at one edge of the cover glass, and with a bit of blotter draw off a little of the water from the opposite side of the cover glass. Note the effect on the activity of the paramecium and on the protoplasm.

Results: In a table show results.

Conclusion: Answer the question.

EXPERIMENT 146

Question: Does our food contain carbon?

Materials: Test tube fitted with one-hole stopper bearing a glass tube; test tube of limewater; bread; Bunsen burner.

Directions: Place a bit of bread in the test tube. Fit in the stopper. Place the end of the delivery tube in limewater in the second test tube. Heat until the bread burns. Note what happens to the limewater. Compare the result with that obtained by exhaling (blow out your breath) through a glass tube into a second test tube of limewater.

Results: 1. What is the black substance left in the test tube?

2. Do you notice any deposit on the cooler parts of the test tube?

3. What happened to the limewater?

Conclusions: 1. A deposit of water on the cooler sides of the test tube would indicate the presence of what substance in the bread? 2. A milkiness in the limewater indicates what substance passing through the glass tube? 3. How could this substance be formed in the experiment? 4. What substance in the bread is responsible for the formation?

VITAMINS AND THE FOODS WHICH SUPPLY THEM

Best sources | Good sources

Vitamin A:

Butter, cheese from whole milk, egg yolk. Fish liver oils. Carrots, sweet potatoes (yellow vegetables). Spinach, turnip tops, beet tops, green lettuce, green peas, green beans (green vegetables). Apricots, prunes, peaches.

Kidney, red salmon, green asparagus, cantaloupes, olives, oranges.

The B Vitamins:

Thiamin:

Lean meats (pork, chicken, liver). Seeds (green peas and beans, whole cereals, wheat germ, whole wheat bread).

Lean beef, mutton, fish. Potatoes, tomatoes, green vegetables generally. Prunes, apples, pears, cantaloupes. Nuts.

Riboflavin (Vitamin G):

Liver, kidney, lean meats, eggs, cheese, milk. Wheat germ, peanuts, soybeans. Beet tops, greens.

Peas, beans, cabbage, cauliflower, carrots. Pears, prunes, peaches.

Niacin:

Liver, lean meats (beef, pork, chicken), salmon, eggs, milk. Green peas, soybeans, tomatoes, turnip tops, green cabbage. Whole grains, peanuts.

Vitamin C: (Easily destroyed by cooking.)

Tomatoes, oranges (and other citrus fruits), salad greens generally (green in color). Fruits in general (raw), especially currants, strawberries, raspberries, cantaloupes.

Fruits and greens generally when fresh and raw.

Vitamin D: Sunshine develops this vitamin in our bodies.

Fish liver oils, egg yolk.

Butter, salmon.

CHAPTER LI

DIGESTING AND DISTRIBUTING

Why digestion. Suppose that you could find no bricks with which to build a new house except those in an old house. You would need to tear down the old house to get the bricks and then build your new house. In building our bodies we are in a somewhat similar position. We can find no food except that which is part of the bodies of plants, or animals. We eat parts of plants and animals. Our digestive systems tear down the plant and animal bodies and get out the building material for our own use. Our bodies and cows' bodies are made largely of proteins but not of exactly the same kinds of proteins. Our digestion takes the cow proteins to pieces, and our bodies build up again human proteins out of the pieces. Digestion thus reduces complex substances to simpler substances in order that they may be used in the body.

Digestion must also turn food into a liquid. A solid in the intestines cannot get into the blood stream to go around in the body. Only liquids can be absorbed. Proteins are insoluble (will not dissolve), but the simpler substances made from them in digestion will dissolve. Similarly starch will not dissolve, and therefore it cannot be absorbed. Digestion changes starch into grape sugar which does dissolve and is absorbed from the digestive organs. Fats, too, do not dissolve in water, but digestion changes them into glycerine, fatty acids, and soaps which will dissolve, and they are absorbed by the walls of the intestine. By digestion is meant the process of chemically changing and dissolving the food.

How foods digest. The first step in digestion is breaking up the food into small pieces so that the digestive fluids can easily reach the material. This is the work of the teeth. When you bolt your food with a chew or two, you force the work of the teeth upon the stomach, which has its own work to do.

The chemical changes of digestion, as from starch to sugar, are produced by certain substances called *enzymes*, or ferments. There are several kinds of enzymes in the digestive system. Each enzyme acts on one kind of food.   Thus an enzyme in the mouth acts upon starch, another in the stomach on proteins, others in the intestine act on starch, proteins, and fat.   The enzymes are manufactured in glands which pour their secretions into the digestive organs.

[The saliva poured into the mouth by three pairs of glands contains the enzyme *ptyalin*.   This is the enzyme that changes starch to glucose, or grape sugar.   Chewing the food well gives the enzyme a chance to penetrate the mass of food and do its work.   When the food has been rolled into balls by the teeth and tongue and thoroughly wetted by the saliva, it passes through the esophagus and into the stomach. With every swallow the windpipe closes up against a little lid, the *epiglottis*, keeping the food out of the air passage.

The walls of the stomach have layers of muscle which keep the food slowly churning around.   Minute glands in the stomach walls pour in *gastric juice*, which contains the enzyme *pepsin* and *hydrochloric acid*.   The proteins are changed to simpler substances called *peptones*, but are not completely digested.   When the food has been liquefied and acidified, a small opening (the pylorus) at the lower end of the stomach opens for a moment and a little of the liquid food passes into the small intestine.

In the small intestine the food receives further treatment. A great gland, the *pancreas*, pours in *pancreatic juice* and the *liver* pours in *bile*.   The bile makes the food alkaline.   An enzyme in the pancreatic juice completes the digestion of proteins.   Another digests starch, changing it to glucose.   A third enzyme in the pancreatic juice digests the fats.   Other minute glands along the intestines pour in intestinal juices which aid in the digestion of all three kinds of food.   An enzyme (invertase) in these intestinal juices digests cane sugar, making grape sugar from it.]

Absorption. The small intestine is especially fitted for the absorption of food. It is much longer than the body, about 20 feet long in a man. Its inner surface is raised in folds and has innumerable minute projections known as *villi*. The great length, the folds, and the projections increase the surface through which the digested food may be absorbed. Absorption is accomplished by the process of osmosis.

The digested starches, the sugars, and the proteins are taken up by the minute blood vessels in the walls of the intestines and carried away by the blood. The digested fats are taken away from the intestines by a different set of vessels, the *lacteals*. They unite to form a great vessel, the thoracic duct, that empties into a large vein near the heart.

The large intestine is chiefly a place of temporary storage for indigestible portions of the food. Here the refuse is retained until expelled from the body. It is very necessary that elimination take place regularly from the large intestine. If it is too long delayed, water is absorbed from the large intestine and the elimination is much more difficult. Decay also takes place, releasing poisonous substances that are carried by the blood throughout the body. A feeling of fatigue, headache, and general debility (weakness) is often due to such poisons.

Taking care of digestion. To judge from the display of advertising in street cars and store windows, the country has a stomachache along with its headache. Except in rare cases digestive complaints are the result of abuse through ignorance or indifference. Nature has made some defective digestive systems, and these need the attention of the doctor. The other cases, the large majority of cases, are nature's punishment for abuse.

The care of digestion begins with the selection of food. We have studied the general principles for the choosing of foods. They need to be adapted to individual cases. If strawberries cause a rash on your skin, choose some other kind of raw fruit. If tomatoes cause a disturbance, then omit tomatoes. Pies, sweet cakes, and candy in large quantities sometimes upset the digestive system. If so, they must be reduced or omitted from the diet.   The taste is not always a good guide for selection.

A common cause of digestive disturbance is too much food. "Stuffing" at a dinner until you feel uncomfortable is sure sooner or later to bring its punishment of damage to your system.   Too much not only overloads the digestive organs but leaves a mass of material in the intestines as food for the bacteria of putrefaction and fermentation.   The decay of food by these bacteria produces gas and poisonous substances that are absorbed and carried through the body.   The feeling of sluggishness and fatigue that sometimes comes over one may be due to these poisons.   Cleaning out the intestines makes one feel full of life again.

Evacuation of the intestines regularly every day is absolutely necessary for health and good spirits.   Fresh fruits and vegetables are great aids to the intestines in this respect.   Concentrated foods, such as cornstarch, rice, bread, are less stimulating to the intestines.   Exercise in the open air every day is an excellent stimulus.   Hiking, swimming, and all the games that make one breathe deeply and work the large muscles of the abdomen are the best.   Occasionally a cathartic medicine may be necessary, but if there is occasion to use it often, one is not living properly or there is some defect that needs medical care.

Care of the teeth.   Civilization seems to be hard on teeth.   Few indeed are the persons among us who have not defective teeth.   Not only poor digestion, but illness of various kinds results from diseased teeth. Bacteria in abscesses about the gums poison the whole body. Rheumatism, aches of various kinds, fatigue, and ill health may arise.   Removal of diseased teeth has brought prompt relief from such ills.   The first care of the teeth involves the diet, especially

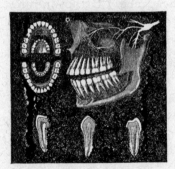

Fig. 435. You must brush every crevice between your teeth on both inside and outside.

in young children. Deficiency of minerals and vitamins results in defective teeth and future suffering. The next care involves the proper and frequent use of the toothbrush.

Teeth should be scrubbed twice or three times a day, preferably after each meal. Never go to bed with dirty teeth. Bacteria will have a good chance to do their evil work before morning.

Fig. 436. The points on this tooth-brush will reach the crevices between the teeth.

The toothbrush and tooth powder should be of the right kinds. The toothbrush should be made so that it will reach the crevices between the teeth on both the inside and the outside surfaces (Fig. 436). A brush of medium hardness is best. Tooth powder is as necessary for cleaning the teeth as soap for the hands. Soap is one of the ingredients of tooth powder. Of the great number of tooth pastes and tooth powders on the market, some are good and some harmful to the teeth. Your dentist will advise you which to use.

In brushing your teeth think about what you are doing. You are trying to reach every crevice and scrape out the remaining bits of food. Brush the upper teeth downward, starting the brush stroke on the gums. Brush the lower teeth upward, starting on the gums. Brush both the outer and the inner faces of the teeth.

The body's delivery system. Water transportation carries the food and other substances around the body. The blood is mostly water. Over a gallon of blood (about 5¼ quarts) goes through a man's heart every

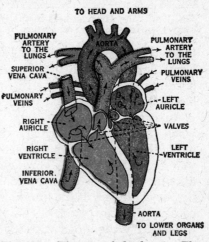

Fig. 437. Diagram of the heart. The right side is in blue and the left in red. Why? Does any blood pass directly from right to left side?

quarter of a minute during rest and twice that or more during exercise. The liquid part, the *plasma*, carries red corpuscles and white corpuscles and many dissolved substances.

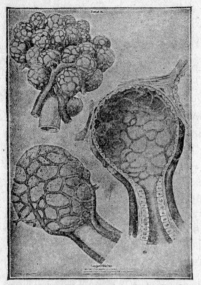

Fig. 438. The air chambers in the lungs surrounded by capillaries.

The *white corpuscles* are carried to places in the body where bacteria have entered and there they do their work of eating bacteria. The *red corpuscles* carry the oxygen to the cells that demand it. Food is carried dissolved in the blood. Waste matters also are carried dissolved to the organs that cast them out of the body. Moving from the deep-seated organs to the surface, the blood serves also to carry out heat to the skin and extremities.

The power house of the transport system is the *heart*. It is a great hollow muscle that at regular intervals contracts and squeezes the blood suddenly out into the arteries. Little flaps of tissue form *valves* that prevent the blood from flowing the wrong way. Figure 437 shows the route of the blood through the four chambers of the heart.

An *artery* leaving the right side of the heart carries the blood to the lungs. The artery branches and branches again until the blood flows through minute blood vessels, the *capillaries* (Fig. 438). Through the very delicate walls of the lung capillaries, carbon dioxide passes out from the blood to the air chambers of the lungs. From the air chambers oxygen passes into the blood. The capillaries unite to form *veins* which carry the blood with its oxygen back to the heart.

Once back in the heart, this time in the left side, the blood gets another vigorous pump that sends it out through the greatest artery of the body, the *aorta*, on its journey through the body.   On its way out some of the blood is sent on a side journey through the kidneys to deliver waste material for casting out of the body.   The rest of the blood passes on to deliver the oxygen and food to the cells throughout the body. The arteries branch and rebranch until once more the blood is flowing through delicate-walled *capillaries*.   These walls are so thin that the hungry cells outside readily draw away the oxygen from the red corpuscles and the food dissolved in the blood.   Carbon dioxide and other wastes are taken by the blood away from the cells.   The capillaries unite again to form veins that carry the blood back to the heart. The circulation from the left side of the heart to the body cells and back to the right side of the heart is called the *systemic circulation.*

Some of the blood goes to the *intestines* to gather up the dissolved food.   Circulating through capillaries in the intestinal wall the blood receives the food as it passes through the walls of the intestines.   Leaving the intestinal wall the blood bearing the food goes first to the liver.   There the veins break up into capillaries.   Liver cells draw out sugar from the blood and store it away for future use.   Liver cells also aid us by drawing from the blood certain poisonous substances.

Once out of the liver the blood rushes on back through great veins to pour into the right side of the heart.   The entire journey around the body from the heart through the lungs and back, and then out to feed the tissues and back again, takes less than a quarter of a minute.

[The circulation of the blood through the lungs is known as *pulmonary circulation*.   The pulmonary artery carries the dark-colored blood bearing carbon dioxide to the lungs.   The pulmonary veins bring back the red, oxygenated blood to the heart.   The oxygen unites with a substance in the red corpuscles called *hemoglobin* to form a chemical compound, and as such is carried to the cells that are hungry for oxygen.

The circulation through the kidneys is often called the *renal* (kidney) *circulation*.   The cells of the kidneys take from the blood a number of different waste compounds.

Among them are nitrogenous wastes from broken-down protoplasm and from protein of the food.

The circulation through the liver is the *portal circulation.* Liver cells take from the blood glucose or grape sugar that is not needed by the cells in other parts of the body. They change the glucose to a new kind of sugarlike substance called *liver sugar,* or *glycogen.* When the cells of the body have used up their supply of sugar, the liver cells change the liver sugar again to glucose and the blood carries it away to the cells that need it. The liver cells also take away poisons, changing them to harmless wastes which the blood then takes and carries to the kidney cells].

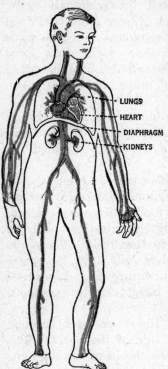

LUNGS
HEART
DIAPHRAGM
KIDNEYS

Fig. 439. Circulation of the blood. Where does the blood change from blue to red? where from red to blue?

EXPERIMENT 147

Question: How does saliva change starch?

Materials: Starch; iodine; Fehling's solution; test tubes; Bunsen burner.

Directions: (a) Boil some starch for a minute. Then test portions with iodine and with Fehling's solution. See Experiment 142.

(b) Collect some saliva from the mouth. Test with Fehling's solution.

(c) Mix a little boiled starch with saliva in a test tube. Set aside for 10 minutes in a beaker of water at about 90° F. Then test with Fehling's solution.

Results: Draw up a table showing each step, the reason for it, and the results.

Conclusion: Answer the question.

Plants also digest food. Sprout some grains of corn in wet sawdust. Test some other grains of corn for starch and for glucose. Then test the sprouted grains for each substance.

DEMONSTRATION

Microscopic Appearance of Blood

Sterilize the tip of a finger and a needle with alcohol. Prick the finger tip and squeeze out a drop of blood. Smear thinly along a microscope slide and examine under a microscope.

DEMONSTRATION

Circulation

Wrap a goldfish or a tadpole loosely in wet cotton. Lay it on a microscope slide and examine the tail under the microscope. The red corpuscles may be seen traveling through the capillaries. Do not keep the fish or tadpole too long wrapped in the cotton. Return it to the aquarium and use another.

THINK AND RECALL

What freight is loaded and unloaded at each station of the body's transportation system?

1. Head
2. Lung
3. Kidney
4. Intestine
5. Liver
6. Feet

CHAPTER LII

CONTROL OF THE BODY

How the body cells are governed. Did you ever accidently touch a hot pipe? You did not stop to reason out that it was wise to move away. You jumped first and thought about it afterward. If a dentist hits a "hot spot" in your tooth, you probably start in spite of all your will power. There is a part of your nervous system always on duty. Even in your sleep you will move into a more comfortable position without waking. Such actions are *reflex actions*, responses that are made to irritation or other stimuli before the sensation rising from them reaches consciousness.

A part of your nervous system keeps your heart beating, your chest expanding and relaxing to take in air and expel it, and your glands secreting—all without your taking thought. This part is called the *sympathetic* or *autonomic system*. It is fortunate that a part of the nervous system takes care of these bodily actions. Without such unconscious control, human minds would never have found time to study out the laws of science and invent machines that put nature's forces under our control.

Most wonderful of all is the operation of that part of the nervous system by which we think. We do not understand what thought is or by what processes it arises, but we know much about the organ in which it occurs. We know that its cells oxidize foods as do other cells, and in their activity electric changes take place as in other cells. Because of their own peculiar constitution, they act in their own peculiar way just as muscle cells act in their own peculiar way.

Nerve cells and nerves. Like other cells, nerve cells are composed of protoplasm, part of which is the nucleus. But nerve cells have a very peculiar shape (Fig. 440). Long

(518)

branches stretch out from the body of the cell. By means of the branches nerve cells connect with other nerve cells and with cells of other kinds, such as muscle and gland cells. Bundles of branches make up the nerves.

The sensitive parts of our sense organs—our eyes, ears, tasting and smelling organs, and organs of touch—are branches of nerve cells. Each sense organ has cell branches with end organs that are sensitive only to its own type of disturbance in the outer world: those in the eye are stimulated by waves of energy that we call *light;* those in the ear by vibrations in the air; certain cells in the tongue by substances in solution; certain cells in the nose by substances floating in the air; certain cells in the skin by touch and others by heat or by cold. The nerve cells send long branches through the nerves until by joining with other nerve cells they eventually reach the brain. By

SHORT BRANCHES (DENTRITES)
NUCLEUS
CELL BODY

DENTRITES
AXON
CELL BODY
TINY BRANCHES
A NEURON FROM THE BRAIN

LONG NERVE (THE AXON)
FATTY SHEATH SURROUNDING NERVE
TINY BRANCHES TO MUSCLES
MUSCLE
A MOTOR NEURON

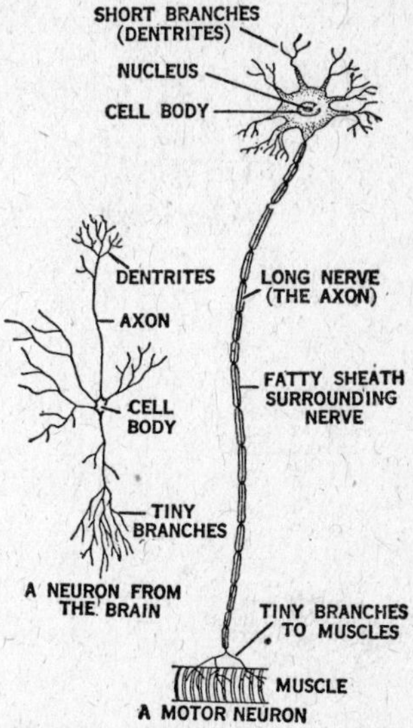

Fig. 440. Nerve cells. The branches pass the stimulus to other nerve cells. Bundles of long branches make up the nerves.

such arrangements we learn what goes on in the world. Knowledge depends upon response of nerve cells to stimulus from without.

The brain. The brain is made up of nerve cells and their branches. Nerve cells lie on the outer surface of the brain, and their branches to other brain cells and to cells in other parts of the body make up the interior of the brain (Fig. 441).

The brain has several main parts. The biggest part of the brain of man is the *cerebrum*, the thinking part. Its cells receive messages from the outside world that come by way of the sense organs. By the activity of its cells, we decide what is sending in the messages and what we shall do about it.

The *cerebellum*, or "little brain," relieves the thinking part of much unnecessary work. The cerebellum keeps us balanced, and it makes the muscles act in the right order when we do things; that is, it coördinates movements. Try to think of how many muscles must contract and relax in their right turn when you walk. Perhaps you have seen what happens when these cells are poisoned with alcohol. The *medulla oblongata* takes care of actions within our body that keep us alive: breathing, the beating of the heart, swallowing, digestion, and the other phenomena of life.

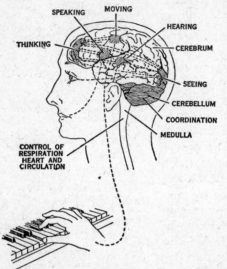

Training the nervous system. If you do not remember how difficult it was to learn to write, perhaps you remember how difficult it was to learn to skate, swim, or play tennis. Having once learned, you can think of other things while you do these. They have become habits. Habits are great time savers for the brain. Habits also relieve you of much annoyance. When washing the teeth after a meal or taking a morning bath has become a habit, it is no longer an annoyance that takes an exercise of will power to go through with. Habits are easy to form. It is simply necessary to do a thing over and over again until the nerve cells have become accustomed to do it. To develop skill in doing things, it is necessary that the act be done in exactly the right way each time. A good swimmer or a good driver has forced his nerve cells to act in exactly the right way until they act without thought. To become skilful one must prevent every slovenly per-

Fig. 441. Nerve pathways: (1) the person is balanced on the piano stool; (2) heart, lungs, and other internal organs work without thought; (3) the person sees; (4) thinks; (5) plays; (6) hears. Locate the centers and the pathways involved in each activity.

formance of the act.   Do it exactly right each time.   Even school work can be made easier by doing a thing right the first time.

Body messengers. The giants in the circus have grown to be giants because a little gland under the brain made too much of a certain chemical substance that stimulated their growth.   If it makes too little, a dwarf is produced.   If there is too little iodine going into the body, a gland in the neck (the thyroid) works overtime to produce more secretion that also controls growth and bodily functions.   The enlargement of this gland is "goiter."   When the thyroid gland fails to work properly in babyhood and early childhood, the child becomes an idiotic dwarf, known as a *cretin*.

If you get thoroughly scared or "fighting mad," a tiny gland just above the kidneys pours a substance into the blood that takes the blood away from your stomach and sends it to your heart and lungs so that you have more power to fight or to fly.   There are others of these chemical substances produced in the ductless (or *endocrine*) glands that control processes of the body.   All such "chemical messengers" are called *hormones*.

Taking care of the eyes. The eye is one of the most delicate organs of the body.   We have seen how it is constructed (pages 277–278).   We depend so much upon our eyes in school and in modern life that we need to take thought for their care.   The blaze of lights in the city and on the highways at night, the constant demand for reading and close work, and even the "movies" are temptations to abuse the eyes.   We have seen the general causes of defective sight and their remedies (page 279).

An examination of the eyes for defects of nature is necessary for everyone who uses the eyes for close work.   Neglect may ruin the sight.   Often indigestion, nervous and other disorders are due to faulty vision left uncorrected.   A pair of glasses has relieved a farmer or a woodsman of stomach trouble.   In modern school systems the eyes of pupils are examined, and often ways are found to provide glasses for those who cannot afford it from the family income.

In reading and writing one must always take thought of the lighting and position of book and paper. There must be sufficient but not too intense light. Try out the positions of

book and light until you get conditions "just right," with no glare. (See also page 263.)

How to stay well. Unless you feel bursting with vigor, you are not getting the most out of life. The feeling of an excess of good health comes only with good, healthful living. If you are an indoor worker, you need to take thought of health or you will not be superb in health. It is not difficult to stay in health and vigor if you know how and have will power enough to do as you know you should do. If health slips away from you, it is often exceedingly difficult to get it back.

Through unnumbered generations man lived out of doors. Today a large part of mankind spends its days shut away from the winds and the sun. Man's body through the ages of savagery became adjusted or adapted to face sun and wind. In the few centuries that he has lived buried in cities, man's body has not changed sufficiently to maintain

Fig. 442.   This little fellow suffered with knock knees and inbent ankles because of improper shoes.

vigorous health indoors. We must get out where the sun and wind beat upon us, and we must work the great muscles that make up the biggest parts of the body. Exercise in the open air is the first requisite for superb, vigorous health.

The next requisite is rest, sleep, and plenty of it. Nine hours each night is demanded by the body cells of the boys and girls of high-school age. Rest the moment that you feel tired and rest until you feel rested. Fatigue is due to poisons gathering in the body. If you rest, the body gets a chance to throw off these poisons, oxidizing them and sending them out through the organs of excretion. A fatigued body is a poisoned body.

When the body is fighting the poison of fatigue, it has less strength left to fight disease germs that are continually entering through the nose and mouth. You are much more liable to colds and other diseases when you are fatigued. If you are cold in addition to being fatigued, the body has

Fig. 443. Look at the natural shape of his foot and of the proper shoe.

still less strength to fight the germs. A tired, cold, wet person on a winter day is easy prey for germs of colds and pneumonia.

The next precaution is food. No body can be vigorous if not well fed. Filling the stomach several times a day is not a guarantee that the body is being well fed. The principles of diet that we have studied are the guide in choosing food.

One should have any defects in the body corrected. Eyes, teeth, digestive organs, limbs, and other parts of the body often have defects (Fig. 442). Perhaps the defect is trifling, not at all painful, but in time it may bring on serious illness. Defects left by nature in the body are not always corrected by nature. The doctor must correct them. When examination by your school physician or your family physician reveals a defect, see that it is corrected at the first possible moment and see that the possible moment comes soon.

Fig. 444. And look at the knees and ankles of the same little fellow when wearing proper shoes.

The greatest triumph in modern medicine is the conquest of infectious disease. Science has learned how to protect us from many germ diseases. Vaccination and other preventive treatments have banished most of the dreadful plagues of the Middle Ages. We study the methods of prevention in Chapter LV.

One system in our bodies still remains a weak spot for hostile germs to attack, the lungs and breathing passages. Colds, pneumonia, and tuberculosis are among the greatest causes of illness and death. To fight them we rely on the vigor of our bodies maintained by good food, exercise, and plenty of rest. Besides these measures we must do what we can to avoid the germs. The germs are thickest in crowded, ill-ventilated places, street cars, poorly ventilated theaters, and other places of assemblage. When there is an epidemic of

colds and penumonia about, stay out of such places.   A
coughing person will load the air near by with germs.

The skin must be kept clean.   It is our first line of defense
against the germs of disease.   Some skin disease and irrita-
tions are due to lack of cleanliness.   Even in winter our
bodies perspire.   As the perspiration evaporates, it leaves
behind the waste products it held in solution.   They eventually
become ill-odored and may cause irritation of the skin, which
is then liable to attack by germs.
The prevention is soap and water, a
bath each day, and frequent changes
of underwear.   Aside from the health
measures, your seat mate and indoor
associates will like you better for
your cleanliness.   A cold plunge in
the lake or a cold souse in the tub is
also a valuable stimulant.   If persons not in vigorous health find a
cold plunge too great a tax, they
should not take it.

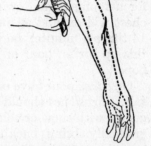

First aids.   Suppose on a hike in
the woods a knife slips and slashes
the leg, or someone in swimming
steps on a broken bottle.   There are
two dangers from a cut, great loss of
blood and infection by bacteria.

Fig. 445.   How to make a
tourniquet to stop a bleeding
vessel.   In a short time the
tourniquet should be loosened to see if bleeding has
stopped.

Even a trifling cut may be infected.   Clean every scratch by
squeezing it out and bathing with clean water, preferably
water that has been boiled to kill bacteria.   Then touch
the cut with iodine or other antiseptic.   If the cut is of any
size, lightly bind on a piece of gauze wet with iodine.

If the wound is large, the bleeding must be stopped.   A
wad of sterile gauze (gauze that is free of bacteria) or of
cotton may be tied on.   The gauze or cloth may be sterilized
by boiling or by wetting with iodine.   If the blood comes out
in spurts, an artery has been cut.   If it does not stop with
binding, make a tourniquet (Fig. 445).   Tie a handkerchief
around above the cut and twist it tight with a stick.   This

34

will compress the artery and stop the blood. In a short time loosen the tourniquet a little and, if the blood has stopped, take it off promptly. If the tourniquet is kept tightened too long, it may cause serious injury.

A *sprain* or *bruise* may be treated by cloths soaked in cold water. A doctor had better see a sprain that is at all severe.

By all means learn how to revive a person by *artificial respiration*. It is simple to learn. Lay the patient face down, with the face turned to one side. Kneel astride the body (Fig. 447). Place your palms on the short ribs with your thumbs nearly touching over his back. Swing your weight forward and force the air out of the lungs (Fig. 448). Press for a moment and swing back to your first position. The chest will expand again and draw in the air. Repeat 12 or 14 times a minute; be very careful not to go too fast. Keep this up for an hour or two, if necessary, before you give up hope.

On *burns* pour olive oil, vaseline, or cream, or any oil without salt. *Frostbites* should not be treated with hot water. Rub gently with snow or cold water to increase the circulation and gradually bring back to normal temperature. Too rapid warming may have serious results.

Sometimes you get something in your eye. Do not rub it. If the eye is closed, tears will sometimes wash out the object. Try lifting one lid over the other several times. If this fails, stand before a mirror or get someone to help you. Pull down the lower lid, and with the corner of a clean handkerchief or a tuft of cotton remove the object. If it is under the upper lid, roll up the lid over the edge of a toothpick to look for it. After the object is out, bathing the eye in either cold or hot water may soothe it, or a drop of a solution of boric acid may help if the eye or its lid are scratched.

Fig. 446. Do not move the patient until you have put a splint on a broken arm or leg to prevent the bone cutting through the flesh. A padded board or even a heavy sweater will do.

Fig. 447. Artificial respiration: (1) beginning position.

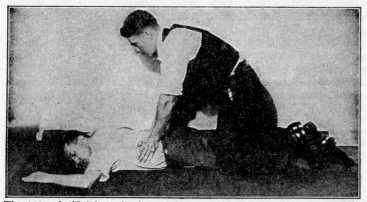

Fig. 448. Artificial respiration: (2) arms stiff, full weight pressing down on the small ribs.

QUESTIONS TO THINK OUT

1. What is food?

2. Why does a city man sometimes count his calories while a lumberjack worries only about getting enough to eat?

3. Why are birds and children always hungry?

4. Why is the Eskimo's diet notable for the amount of fat?

5. Why does hiking make you hungry? Why do you breathe hard when you run or skate?

6. Why is food better than a stimulant? Does food stimulate?

7. If you are overweight, what foods should be used sparingly? If underweight, what food should be used abundantly?

8. From the tables make up a day's diet as it should be.

9. Make up a balanced diet that will give you the most calories for your money.

10. Why is it unwise to work or play violently immediately after a meal?

11. Make a microscopic examination of milk, cream, and butter.

12. If you step on a tack, you probably jump before you know it. Why?

13. List your reflex actions that you detect in one day.

14. With a fine needle, touch various spots on the back of your hand to determine spots sensitive to pain and those relatively insensitive. Make an enlarged drawing to show the class.

15. List the habits that you use in a day.

16. Select a useful action that you wish to become a habit and practice it day after day until it no longer is irksome.

17. Note some action or lack of action that shows that you have not learned to control your mind. Note some that show that you have mental control at least in part.

18. Draw up ten rules of health that you are following sufficiently.

19. Can you study well immediately after dinner or after a football game? Make a study of your play and study habits. Consider study at home and at school. Take into account mealtime, play, mental and physical fatigue, temperature of room, ventilation, distraction, lighting, etc. Plan improvement in conditions and in the day's program that will make you more efficient at study time.

20. Examine your posture in walking and sitting. Does it interfere with circulation, digestion, or other bodily function? Are the chairs at home and at school built to keep the body comfortable yet in a healthy posture? How should they be changed?

21. Why do athletic coaches forbid the use of tobacco?

22. Demonstrate to the class methods of first aid given in the Scout Manual, the Red Cross First Aid, or other good book.

23. Is a man's health his own business to preserve or neglect as he sees fit? Argue it in class.

24. If you cannot pay for dental treatment or treatment to prevent smallpox, diphtheria, typhoid fever, and other preventable diseases, how can this treatment be provided?

UNIT TWELVE

HOW WE CONTROL AND USE THE MICROSCOPIC WORLD

There is a swarming world all about us, and indeed within us, that no man knew until the microscope was invented. Leeuwenhoek (1632–1723), a Hollander, in 1683, saw bacteria with little microscopes he made himself. In the two and a half centuries that followed, our knowledge of the microscopic world has grown until no one man pretends to know intimately more than a small part of the field (Figs. 449 and 450).

The microscopic world is peopled with both plants and animals. We had a glimpse of them in Chapter XXXIX, when we studied those that live in pond water. Others live in the soil. From our skins, mouth, intestines many more kinds

Fig. 449. One of Leeuwenhoek's microscopes. One lens was used. The object was mounted on the point.

may be extracted. Many are harmless, but many cause disease to ourselves and to our domestic plants and animals. Many are beneficial, helping to rid the earth of refuse and dead bodies of plants and animals, and some aiding in the preparation of our foods and other materials of civilization. Some bacteria must be cultivated to enrich the soil. In this unit we shall study some common kinds that we can easily find, some that aid us in our battle for life and comfort, and some that we must battle constantly if we would stay alive. We shall see some of the most

brilliant triumphs of science in man's effort to understand
and control the forces of the earth.

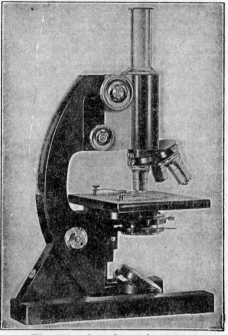

Fig. 450. A modern microscope.

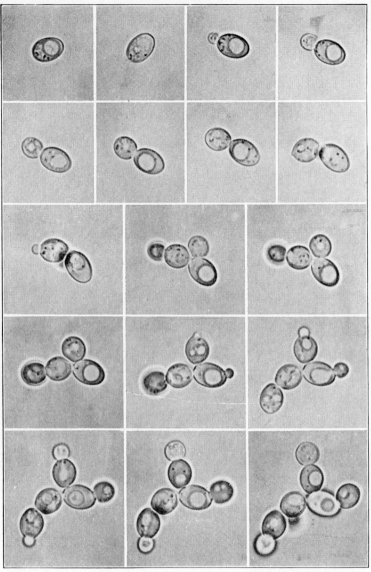

Development of yeast cells. This series of photographs, magnified 1000 times, shows the development from a single yeast cell at fifteen-minute intervals for a period of four hours.

Chapter LIII

MOLDS AND YEASTS

Plants called fungi. Toadstools and mushrooms have many relatives. You can recognize many of them about the woods, fields, and refuse heaps where things are rotting. None of them have that peculiar green substance, chlorophyll. Most of them are colorless. They cannot make their own food. They take it, therefore, from ready-made stores. Like bacteria, they find their food in that which we have laid up in storehouses, in the manure that the farmer spreads upon his fields, in the dead bodies and dead leaves in the forest, and in living bodies of plants and animals. Like bacteria, some remove refuse and add to the fertility of the fields. At the same time there are others that the farmer instructed by the

Fig. 451. Common fungi.

pathologist (scientist who studies disease) must battle to protect his animals and crops from disease and death. The physician and public health officer battle those that attack our own bodies.

These groups of plants all belong to the fungi, common kinds of which are toadstools and mushrooms, yeast and molds (Fig. 451).

The nature of molds. Every housewife is familiar with the gray and black molds that grow on a forgotten piece of bread. She probably regards molds as an unmitigated nuisance, not realizing that although some spoil her bread and preserves, others do many useful things. The mold that

(531)

spreads over a piece of bread is not microscopic but it starts from microscopic bodies that float through the air.

Leave a slice of moist bread uncovered in the room for

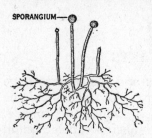

SPORANGIUM—

a day. Moisten slightly and cover it with a bell jar or a dish to prevent the bread from drying. Let it stand in the laboratory for several days. You will probably see develop a soft fluffy mass, usually white, although it may be bluish or gray (Fig. 452). A number of coarse threads will run all through the mass of bread. (The thread tangle is known to botanists by the term *mycelium*.)   At first it is a white, loose mass, but as it grows older, it branches and becomes denser.

Fig. 452.   Bread mold under the microscope.   Dustlike spores from the sporangium are the reproductive bodies.

After a few days the surface of the mold becomes colored. Short stems grow up. These terminate in numerous black balls the size of a small pinhead, containing microscopic bodies which correspond roughly to the seed of a plant. These microscopic bodies are called *spores*. As these spores become ripe, the ball containing them bursts and the spores float off into the air. When one of them falls on food material, it starts to grow and in a few days produces spores of its own. So many of these spores are produced and float about the air that food material exposed to the air almost always receives some of them. They are slightly heavier than air and after floating awhile, they sink to the floor. When you sweep or dust, you throw them again into the air and increase the probability that the food in your kitchen will spoil. Wiping up dust with a damp cloth is better than using a dry duster. Carpet sweepers are better than brooms and a vacuum cleaner is better than either.

What molds must have to grow. Expose a bit of banana, a slice of apple, and a piece of bread to the air in your kitchen for a half hour. Then put all three upon a plate and cover the plate with a bell jar. Put it aside for several days. You will probably find molds on all these foods.

Lay a small piece of bread in the oven until it is thoroughly dry. Then put it on a plate, cover it with a tumbler, and set it aside. You will find that no mold develops. Moisture, then, is necessary for the growth of molds.

Put on a plate of glass some mold that is ripe and is producing spores. Cover this mold with a tumbler and set it aside. In a few days you will see that the mold has dried up. Food is necessary for the growth of molds.

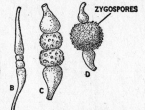

Fig. 453. A second kind of reproduction in bread mold— conjugation. Two cells from different plants join to form one reproduction body.

Smear some mold spores upon a piece of banana. Cut it in halves. Place each half upon a plate and cover with a tumbler. Put one plate in the refrigerator and the other in a warm room. In a few days you will see that the mold placed in the warm room has grown luxuriantly while the mold in the refrigerator has not grown at all. Warmth, then, is necessary for the growth of mold.

Where molds grow. You perhaps have seen molds not only on forgotten foods put away carefully, but on old shoes in the corner of the cellar, on an old coat that has hung in a damp place, on decaying wood and on manure. Mildews that we see on rosebushes and lilacs as well as other plants are relatives of the common mold.

Not all molds are harmful. You perhaps have seen a green mold on Roquefort cheese. That is not a harmful contamination. It is planted there in the preparation of the cheese. Molds are used in the preparation of several other cheeses. These cheeses are partially digested by the molds and therefore more readily digested when we eat them. The molds are carefully cultivated by the cheese makers to keep them in a healthy condition and free from harmful molds and bacteria.

Our debt to yeast plants. Did you ever eat hardtack, ship's biscuit, or matzoth, the unleavened bread of the Bible? They are rather tasteless, but they keep indefinitely. They are not much like the soft white bread from the baker or from mother's oven. They are dense and hard, because no yeast plants have grown in the dough.

Fig. 454. To show fermentation by yeast.

Alcohol, too, we owe to yeast plants. Alcohol is one of the most valuable industrial products we get from the plant world. We shall see presently some of its many uses. In addition to its valuable properties it is a poison. It is a valuable poison to kill lower forms of life. Unfortunately, it is poisonous also to human tissues, and when used in drinks, it slowly poisons the body.

Fermentation and its use. Yeasts feed upon sugar and from it produce carbon dioxide and alcohol, which leave the yeast plants as wastes. This process is fermentation. A simple way to illustrate fermentation is to make a dilute solution of molasses or sugar. Add $\frac{1}{4}$ of a yeast cake to a tumbler of the mixture, stir well to distribute the yeast through the sugar solution. Fill a large test tube with the yeast and molasses mixture and invert it in a tumbler of the solution. Put the tumbler and test tube in a warm place (Fig. 454). In a few hours, or even in a half hour, you will see that a gas is driving the liquid out of the test tube. When the test tube has filled with gas, remove it and pour some of the gas into a clean, dry test tube. Add limewater and shake. The limewater turns milky, a test for carbon dioxide. If you add a small bit of potassium hydroxide and a crystal of iodine to the molasses-yeast mixture, you may detect the "hospital smell" of iodoform. This is a test for alcohol. Or you may place 100 c.c. or more of the liquid in a distilling flask connected with a condenser and distil a few drops. You will find that your distillate has the odor and taste of alcohol and that you can set fire to it.

Fermentation is the principle of the production of all alcoholic beverages. The spores of wild yeast are present in the air. When you press apples to obtain cider, some of these yeast spores pass from the skin of the apple to the cider. In a short time the sugar of the cider undergoes the same change that the molasses did in our experiment. We say that the cider has become hard. That is, its sugar has largely disappeared because it was used up as a food for the growing yeast. Alcohol and carbon dioxide are produced from it.

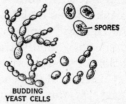

SPORES

BUDDING
YEAST CELLS

Fig. 455. Yeast cells under the microscope.

Alcohol, in the chemical indus- try, is surpassed in importance only by sulphuric acid. Alcohol is used as a solvent, that is, to dissolve other substances. It is used to dissolve resins, as shellac in making varnish, and many other substances used in industry. It is used in the manufacture of soaps, collodion, celluloid, smokeless powder, drugs, perfumes, and many other products too numerous to mention. Ninety per cent of commercial alcohol is prepared as in our experiment, by the action of yeast on molasses. After fermentation the alcohol is distilled off.

The carbon dioxide produced in the fermentation is also a valuable product. It is used as a preservative for foods. Pumped into water under pressure, it makes soda water "fizz." Cooled and compressed, it becomes a solid, the "dry ice" that is becoming so familiar. Dry-ice refrigeration is much simpler and cleaner than refrigeration with ice. Dry ice does not melt but passes away as a gas, carbon dioxide.

A baker makes use of yeast for its production of carbon dioxide. He adds to his bread dough some yeast plants, and then places the dough in a warm place. The growing yeast produces carbon dioxide inside the dough. As these bubbles of gas cannot escape, they make the bread light. In the fermenting bread dough you can smell alcohol. You need not hesitate to eat the bread on that account, however, for the heat of the oven drives off the alcohol.

What are yeasts? Yeasts are microscopic oval plants that reproduce by a process called *budding*. Each plant is very small, being about $\frac{1}{3000}$ of an inch in diameter. Take a drop of the cloudy liquid formed in your fermentation experiment and examine it under the microscope. You will find it filled with these yeast cells (Fig. 455). A small knob forms on one end of the plant. This knob grows larger and the cell wall pinches in, dividing the knob from the original plant until finally the two may break apart. The multiplication of yeast plants is a very rapid process.

Commercial yeast. There are many varieties of wild yeast. Some produce a much better tasting bread than others. By selection, bakers have found the best variety to use for bread. This cultivated yeast is grown commercially in large tubs. When yeast is provided with food, moisture, and warmth, the plants grow and multiply rapidly.

Compressed yeast is a soft, somewhat soggy, material obtained by adding starch and sometimes other materials to the growing yeast plants. The mass of yeast and starch is pressed to squeeze out the excess water, and then cut up into cakes; the cakes are covered with tin foil to protect the yeast plants. Compressed yeast has one disadvantage, it does not keep long.

A second type of commercial yeast is the dry yeast cake. This is prepared by adding starch to the growing yeast, pressing into cakes and drying it at a low temperature. The yeast plants in this case are in an inactive (resting) condition. They remain alive for a long time. When the dry yeast is added to the moist dough, the yeast starts to grow and acts just as the fresh yeast does, but somewhat more slowly.

Experiment 148

Perform the experiments with mold described in this chapter. Write a report of the experiment in the usual form.

Study the mold with a lens and under the microscope and make fully labeled drawings showing the various parts of the mold.

Experiment 149

Perform the experiment with yeast described on page 534. Write a report in the usual form.

Study the yeast cells under the high power of the microscope. Make a drawing of the cells.

EXPERIMENT 150 (OPTIONAL)

Question: How does yeast affect bread dough? Mix two cups of dry flour with two teaspoonsful of sugar and add sufficient water to make a stiff dough. Mix thoroughly. Separate the dough into halves. Mix a yeast cake with a quarter of a glass of water and work the yeast mixture into one half the dough. Set both halves aside in a warm place till next day. Cut into each mass of dough and compare results.

CHAPTER LIV

USING BACTERIA AND FIGHTING THEM

Bacteria. Bacteria are our smallest plants. Even under the microscope it is difficult to see much of their structure. An unusually large kind of *bacterium* may have a diameter of $\frac{1}{1000}$ of an inch, but many have a diameter of only $\frac{1}{50,000}$ of an inch. Their extremely small size and their simplicity under the microscope often make it impossible to tell one kind from another by looking at them. We learn their habits by studying how they behave when they exist in large masses called *colonies*. In shape, bacteria are usually spherical, rodlike, or spiral (Fig. 456).

They multiply by simple division. The rod, which is one bacterium, lengthens, divides in the center, and so produces two plants. This process is called *fission*. It is often very rapid, occurring sometimes every half hour. At this rate, in 24 hours, one of these tiny plants would produce 281,000,000,-000,000 and in a few days would cover the earth. Fortunately, most of them are destroyed almost as soon as they are formed.

Study of bacteria. To study the conditions under which bacteria grow, we must provide a suitable food for them. This we do by making a gelatin or agar-agar (seaweed) jelly and adding beef extract or other food substances. This

bacterial food (nutrient jelly) is poured into test tubes or flasks and these are plugged with cotton. They are then heated with steam, sometimes under pressure, to kill any life that might be present. This killing process is *sterilization*. On the sterile food after it has cooled the bacteria which we wish to study are

Fig. 456. Several different kinds of bacteria.

planted. Very often the sterile food substance is poured into sterile covered dishes called *Petri dishes* (Fig. 466).

We determine that bacteria are present in milk by spreading the milk on the sterile nutrient jelly, covering it with a sterile cover, and placing it in a warm place. The bacteria in the milk grow and soon show as spots (colonies) on the jelly. By counting these colonies, each of which developed from a single bacterium, we can tell the number of bacteria present in a drop of milk. By the shape of the colonies and their general appearance, we can recognize some different kinds of bacteria.

In studying bacteria which cause disease (pathogenic bacteria) we must go to the patient for the germs. Tuberculosis germs are obtained from the sputum (material coughed up by the patient). A sterile swab of cotton will collect many bacteria from noses of most healthy persons—often those bacteria that are associated with sore throats and colds. Typhoid bacteria may be obtained from the excrement from the intestine. Discharges from abscesses often furnish the germ of infection.

Each germ must be grown on the kind of food material upon which it will thrive. The necessity of getting just the right food makes the growth of some in the laboratory exceedingly difficult. Some will not grow in a test tube or flask. The scientist then tries to find an animal in which they will grow. White mice, white rats, guinea pigs, and rabbits are often used. These animals have enabled scientists to save millions of human lives. Sometimes no animal can be found which will support the disease germs. Then progress in conquering the disease is slow. The germs of the terrible plague of childhood, infantile

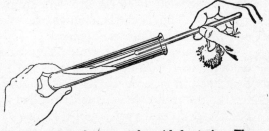

Fig. 457. Inoculating a tube with bacteria. The wad of sterile cotton held between the fingers is used to plug the test tube after inoculation to keep out germs from the air.

paralysis, resisted attempts to grow them artificially until after many failures a method was found of giving the disease to monkeys. There is now hope of finding a way of saving thousands of children from suffocating death or permanent deformity.

Vinegar. Bacteria make vinegar. When we press apples, we obtain sweet cider. Yeast cells on the apple skins, or yeast settling from the air, ferment the sugar of the cider, changing it into alcohol and carbon dioxide. If, then, the mass of bacteria commonly known as "mother of vinegar" falls into the hard cider, the bacteria change the alcohol into *acetic acid* or vinegar. It is for this reason that it is almost impossible to keep cider sweet for any length of time. If it is stored in barrels that have been previously used to contain cider, the old barrels will almost certainly contain both yeast and those bacteria that make acetic acid so that the sweet cider will change to vinegar. In this manner *cider vinegar* is made on the farms. The alcohol of wine is similarly changed to *wine vinegar*.

In the making of *malt vinegar* a layer of grain six to eight inches deep is moistened and allowed to sprout. As the seed starts to grow, the stored starch is changed to sugar. The grain is then heated, killing the young plant. The sprouted grain is called *malt*. Crushed malt is placed in large vats with yeast. The yeast feeds upon the sugar, producing carbon dioxide and alcohol. The alcoholic liquid is allowed to trickle over beechwood shavings or pumice stone on which the acetic acid bacteria are left from previous passage of vinegar. The bacteria change the alcohol into acetic acid and produce a white *malt vinegar*.

Other uses of bacteria. You have studied the use of bacteria in returning to the soil and air the food elements contained in organic wastes and dead bodies. If it were not for their activity, the elements needed by living bodies would be locked up in a vast rubbish heap. You have studied also the nitrogen bacteria that grow in the soil and in the roots of legumes, such as peas, beans, clover, and alfalfa. By their activity, nitrogen of the air is added to the soil. The prepara-

Fig. 458. A modern milking stable, the rotolactor.   Each cow is bathed before milking by machine.

tion of many products involves bacteria.   The characteristic flavors of butter, cheese, and meats are due largely to the action of bacteria.   In cheese and butter factories the desirable kinds of bacteria, largely bacteria that make lactic acid (the acid that sours milk), are kept under constant scientific care to protect them from contamination by harmful organisms.   The preparation of linen uses bacteria at one stage of the process.   After the flax plant is pulled, the soft parts are allowed to rot away through the action of bacteria. Bacteria aid also in the tanning of leather.

Food poisoning.   Bacteria as well as yeasts and molds are destroyers of our food.   Yeasts and molds attack especially sugars and starches.   Some bacteria attack these and other carbohydrates, and some attack proteins.   Meat, fish, milk and its products are favorite foods of many bacteria. Violent upsets of stomach and intestines due to food poisoning sometimes have followed picnics, circuses, county fairs, and church suppers, for which foods have been prepared a long time in advance and have not been properly cared for.

The poisons or toxins are produced by bacteria that grow upon the food both before eating and in the intestines.   Food that is at all tainted should be discarded, but sometimes the poisoning bacteria may be present without tainting the food enough for us to be aware of it.   Most attacks of food poisoning pass off after a period of violent distress.   One type, however, called *botulism*, or *sausage* or *meat poisoning*, is

Fig. 459. In a large milk distributing plant. Milk pasteurized at 143½° for thirty minutes, then cooled to 38° in 2 seconds, then bottled and capped by machines, and stored at 40°.

usually fatal unless a serum is promptly administered. The bacterium (*Bacillus botulinus*) that causes this poisoning lives on vegetable as well as meat proteins. Speed is necessary to save the patient. The doctor should see promptly all cases of violent digestive disturbances.

Keeping foods. We preserve foods by attacking the food-spoilers in their weak spots. As bacteria do not grow readily in the cold, refrigeration is the common way of keeping foods. Meats for shipment to far countries are often frozen immediately upon killing. Meats and fish frozen quickly and kept frozen retain their flavor. Large quantities of fruits and vegetables are now prepared by the frozen-pack method. Many kinds of bacteria are not killed by low temperatures, but they do not grow vigorously. If the foods are contami-

Fig. 460.   The machine that washes the milk bottles.

nated by bacteria of food poisoning before being placed in
the ice box, the bacteria may survive the cold and revive
upon return of more favorable conditions.   The temperature
of refrigeration must be low, below 45° F.   A leaky ice box
is a dangerous place to keep food.

The success of canning foods depends upon killing all
bacteria that are on the foods or vessels and then sealing
them tightly so that no more can enter.   Drying and smoking
foods are common methods of preservation discovered by
savages around the world and still in use in modern life.
Bacteria cannot thrive without water, and smoke contains
substances that are fatal to them but of no apparent harm to
man.   Certain kinds of food are preserved by vinegar, salt,
and spices, all of which prevent the growth of bacteria without harming the food for use.

The milk supply is one of the big food problems of the
cities.   Rigid enforcement of regulations to protect the
supply has removed one great source of disease.   Cow barns
are inspected for cleanliness and sanitary conditions.   The
farmer must deliver the milk to the collecting stations below

a certain temperature. Samples of milk delivered by each farmer are examined for butterfat and bacteria. It is impossible to obtain milk free from bacteria, but the bacterial count must be below a specified limit. Some cities require milk to be pasteurized (Fig. 459). Pasteurization destroys or renders harmless most bacteria of disease but not all bacteria. Bacteria of tuberculosis and some others that are dangerous are destroyed. Although pasteurized milk does not sour so readily because the lactic-acid bacteria are killed, one cannot be careless with bottles of pasteurized milk. They should be kept in the refrigerator. In *pasteurization*, milk or other liquid is heated to about 140° F. for twenty to thirty minutes.

EXPERIMENT 151

Question: How do germs come?

Materials: Several Petri dishes or other round, flat dishes with plates to cover them; a pan to boil them in; 4 ounces of gelatine or agar; a half ounce of beef extract or a glassful of beef broth; a little salt and a little baking soda; a pair of forceps.

Directions: Boil the dishes for an hour to kill all germs. Melt the gelatine or agar. Add beef extract or broth, a pinch of salt and a pinch of soda. Heat the gelatine until it melts. Hold the points of the forceps in the gas flame. Remove the dishes from the boiling water with the forceps and lay them flat on a table. Pour the gelatine into the dishes and promptly cover. Allow to cool.

(a) Open the first dish and leave exposed to the air for a half hour. Then cover.

(b) Touch your finger to the gelatine in the second dish and cover.

(c) Wash the hands with soap and water. Then touch the third.

(d) Pour a little drinking water on the fourth.

(e) Cough at one dish.

(f) Touch a dish with a slice of bread cut with a knife heated in the flames.

(g) Touch another with a pretzel bought at the curb.

(h) Continue testing various substances with the remaining dishes.

(i) Leave one dish unopened as a control. Then put all dishes away in a warm place for two or three days. Examine each day.

Observation: Each spot or colony that you observe came from a bacterium. Keep a record of the colonies in each dish.

Conclusion: How do bacteria reach you?

NOTE: Slices of cooked potato may be substituted for the gelatine or agar mixture.

EXPERIMENT 152

Question: What is the effect of temperature and of antiseptics on bacteria?

Materials: As in the last experiment.

Directions: Prepare the dishes as in the last experiment. Hold a needle or wire in a flame to kill all bacteria that may be on it; then hold it in the air until it cools. Touch it to a colony on one of the dishes. Touch a fresh dish with the same wire, thus planting the bacteria on the new dish. Do this to each dish. Set one dish in the refrigerator, one in a warm place, one in a hot oven, one in the laboratory.

On a second set of dishes similarly planted, try various antiseptics in dilute solutions, such as carbolic acid, formaldehyde, a strong salt solution, a sugar solution. Set these plates in a warm place.

Observations: As in last experiment.

Conclusions: Answer the question.

EXPERIMENT 153

Question: What do bacteria do to meat?

Materials: A wide-mouthed bottle and a cork; a piece of meat that will go into the bottle.

Directions: Expose the meat in the laboratory for an hour. Then cork it tightly in the bottle. Examine daily for some days by looking through the bottle and removing the cork and smelling it.

Conclusions: Answer the question.

EXPERIMENT 154

Question: Why and how is milk pasteurized?

Materials: Raw, or unpasteurized, milk; three beakers; a thermometer; tripod and Bunsen burner.

Directions: Pour milk into each beaker; set No. 1 aside untreated; warm No. 2 gently to 145° F., no higher, for 20 minutes; boil No. 3. Set all aside for 48 hours. Then with pipette put a drop from each into a dish of culture medium (Experiment 151) and set in warm place.

Observations: Record appearance and taste of each. Examine the culture dishes for number of colonies.

Conclusions: Answer the question.

CHAPTER LV

WINNING THE BATTLE WITH DISEASE

Defending a cut. Did you ever have a sore on the finger that discharged pus ("matter")? That discharge was evidence of your ignorance or neglect. Bacteria had entered through a break in the skin. Tucked safely inside, away from the danger of sunlight, amid warmth and food, they multiplied until there were millions. The white blood cells rushed to the scene of invasion. Each white blood cell ate bacteria till it could eat no more. More white cells came. They came faster than they could be carried away with their load of eaten bacteria to be cast out of the body. Then they broke out

Fig. 461. Robert Koch (1843-1910), a German physician. He discovered the germs of tuberculosis and cholera. A founder of the study of bacteria.

through the skin as the ill-smelling, creamy pus. Perhaps then you went to the doctor's or to the hospital to have the painful finger lanced and treated with antiseptic dressings to kill the bacteria. Pain, soreness, time, and expense might have been saved by a trifling attention to the cut or splinter at first. The great surgeon Joseph Lister (1827–1912) taught us that about seventy years ago.

Lister, in a hospital at Edinburgh, Scotland, saw men dying of diseased wounds as surgeons of all time had done. But Lister sought a way to stop the tragedy. Pasteur had shown that there could be no fermentation and spoiling of food without micro-organisms. Lister thought that disease in wounds might be due to micro-organisms. He did what surgeons had not done before. He insisted that instruments and everything else that touched the wound be cleaned as rigorously as soap and water would clean them, then washed with carbolic acid to kill bacteria. The world laughed at Lister until the recovery of his patients without

Fig. 462. Louis Pasteur (1822-1895). French chemist and bacteriologist. He proved that fermentation and decay are due to microscopic organisms. He showed that several diseases are due to microscopic germs and may be controlled by vaccination and antitoxin treatment.

out suppurating sores of diseased wounds showed that he was right. Now we look upon little cuts and flesh tears as a source of possible danger. A daub of iodine on every cut may prevent a dangerous infection.

There are a great variety of substances that poison bacteria (antiseptics and germicides). In addition to those just mentioned, formaldehyde, bichloride of mercury, solutions of chlorine, and many others are used. These are all dangerous chemical poisons and they should be used exactly as directed by experts.

Insect allies of disease. As late as 1878 thousands of people died of *yellow fever* in the United States. Up to 1900 thousands were dying each year in Cuba. Up to 1905 thousands were dying in Panama. Now yellow fever has been driven to its last stronghold on earth in parts of Africa and parts of South America. The danger that it may spread again is hanging over us, but it never will spread if we remain alert to the danger. We may not banish it forever from the earth. The bravery of the little group of United States Army doctors and their assistants among the soldiers taught the world how this scourge might be conquered.

In 1900 a commission under Major Walter Reed of the Army Medical Corps was sent to Cuba to find the cause of the deadly disease. A few suspected a kind of mosquito, but it had not been proved to be the carrier of the disease. A grave difficulty arose. No animal was then known that was susceptible (would carry the disease). Only man could be used in experiments to learn the cause. Two of the doctors offered to allow themselves to be bitten. Both developed yellow fever. Dr. James Carroll recovered; Dr. Jesse Lazear died. The world was not yet convinced. A call was sent out among the soldiers of the medical department for volunteers to be bitten by the mosquitoes that had already caused two cases of yellow fever among the commission and one death. A soldier named Kissinger and an army field clerk, Moran, volunteered, and allowed themselves to be bitten by mosquitoes that had been fed on yellow-fever patients. Both went down with the fever, but both recovered. Other soldiers volunteered for further experiments. The bravery, suffering, and death of

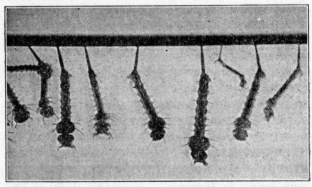

Fig. 463.   Larvae or wrigglers of the common mosquito, *Culex*.

those who offered their lives for the benefits of humanity made it possible to prove that one kind of mosquito (*Aëdes*) carried the yellow fever, and that the disease can be controlled by controlling the mosquito.

But the battle against this disease is not yet over. In 1932 Doctor Noguchi of the Rockefeller Foundation died on the coast of Africa from fever contracted in the laboratory erected there to study the African form of the disease. Other scientists have since given their lives in Africa and America. The battle goes on. By daring and sacrifice it will be won.

Fig. 464. The pupa stage in which the mosquito changes to adult.

Malaria, a disease that has given the tropics the name of the white man's grave and kills hundreds of thousands of natives yearly, is carried by another kind of mosquito (*Anopheles*). Our knowledge of the mosquito's part is due chiefly to the English doctor, Colonel Sir Ronald Ross (1857–1932), working in India. The final poof of the part played by the mosquito came when two English doctors, Manson and Warren, allowed themselves to be bitten by infected mosquitoes sent to them from Italy.

Our battle to prevent these two devastating diseases is directed against the mosquitoes. To kill them the marshes and pools where they live are drained or coated with oil. Little fish (*Gambusa*) that eat the young mosquitoes (larvae) have been sent around the world to feast upon them. People are being taught to live in screened houses. The drug quinine kills the malaria germ, a minute animal of only one cell, that lives in the blood

Fig. 465. The adult of the common mosquito.

of the patient, where it destroys the red corpuscles.   Persons who must enter a region infected with yellow fever may be protected by vaccination.   The conquest of both

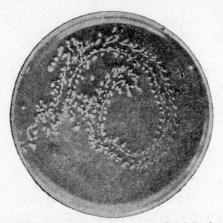

malaria and yellow fever, however, has been made by attacking the mosquitoes. As the result of the campaigns, Havana, once dreaded, has become a winter resort. The Panama railroad cost the life of a man for each tie laid; but now the Panama Canal is on the regular tourist route. In the United States, each year sees further progress in stamping out malaria, but the battle must still go on.

Fig. 466.   A fly walked over the jelly in this Petri dish.   Colonies of bacteria grew in its footsteps.

During the fourteenth century over twenty-five million were killed in Europe by *the plague*.   Rats are hosts to fleas that carry this terrible disease, the *bubonic plague*.   Rigorous campaigns against rats, ground squirrels, and other small animals that are attacked by these fleas are carried on in certain plague danger spots in the United States.   *Typhus fever* is carried by lice; under the name of jail fever, camp fever, and ship fever, this disease has killed men by the thousands where they have been concentrated.   Bedbugs carry the germs of *relapsing fever*.   The tsetse fly of Africa has depopulated large areas of that continent through *sleeping sickness* and diseases that kill cattle and horses.

Even the common house fly is a carrier of disease.   It lays eggs in manure and other filth where the larvae (young) may feed.   The adult fly feeds upon filth and upon food exposed in stores or in our homes.   Its feet have moist pads which enable it to walk upon walls.   These moist pads easily transfer bacteria from a filthy gutter or outbuilding to

Fig. 467. In a week and a half the house fly passes from egg through larva and pupa stages to adult.

uncovered food. Cleaning away all filth, screening all homes and food stores, covering all food

Fig. 468. Moist pads on the foot of the house fly carry bacteria. Do not let it walk on your food.

with screen or glass when displayed for sale are important measures in reducing the evil work of flies. *Typhoid fever* is especially liable to be spread by the house fly, but germs of *tuberculosis* and many other diseases may easily ride on the fly's feet (Figs. 467 and 468).

The last few years have added to our knowledge of the depredations of insect diseases transmitted to domestic animals and to farm and orchard crops. We have learned much and accomplished something, but seem to be only at the beginning of our campaign against insect-borne diseases that cost man dear.

Helping the body fight disease. A milkmaid told the English physician, Edward Jenner (1749–1823), about 1798, that she could not get *smallpox* because she had had cowpox. Those were the days when 95 per cent of the adults of Europe bore the disfiguring scars of smallpox. One can only guess the number of deaths each year, there being no reliable records. Jenner took some of the material from a sore on a cow and used it to vaccinate persons. A slight sore developed on the person's arm and thereafter he was immune to smallpox (would not take it). Smallpox vaccine is now grown upon healthy calves and prepared under scientific supervision, but the principle is that which Jenner discovered. In new experimental processes the smallpox organism is grown upon eggs or on living cells in test tubes instead of upon calves.]

In those states where vaccination is compulsory very few physicians have even seen a case of smallpox. In those states where it is not compulsory, smallpox is of much more frequent occurrence.

Another brilliant conquest is that of *typhoid fever*. This

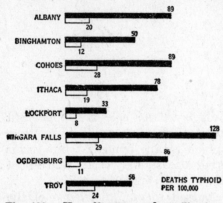

disease has been the scourge of cities and army camps for centuries. In our Spanish War we lost 1500 men from typhoid and had 20,000 cases of the disease, in an army of about 100,000 men. In World War I with an army of about 4,000,000 men, we had only 300 cases and 23 deaths. The disease in the World War was fought by vaccination and by care of the food and water supply to see

Fig. 469. How filtration and sterilization of water changed the death rate from typhoid fever. Black line, before water was treated; white line, afterwards.

that the germs were not carried into the mouth. The bacteria of typhoid attack the walls of the intestine, causing ulcers. The poisons (toxins) they produce are carried throughout the body. A *vaccine* is made by growing the bacteria—originally from a person having the disease, but now grown on cultures in laboratories. The bacteria are killed and the poisons from the bacteria make the vaccine. Small quantities are injected under the skin. The protection seems to last a few years, then vaccination must be repeated.

We do not know exactly how vaccines protect against disease, but it seems to be about as follows: The body tries to destroy any poison that enters it. The power to destroy poison is increased by slow additions of the poison. By small doses of the poison of certain disease germs the power of the body to destroy those poisons is vastly increased. The vaccine contains those poisons. After they have been injected, the blood contains some unknown substances which destroy the poisons. The unknown substances are called *antibodies*.

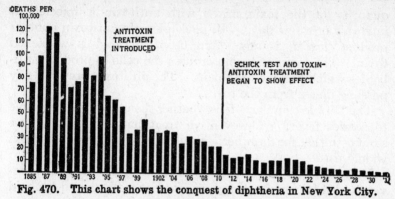

Fig. 470.   This chart shows the conquest of diphtheria in New York City.

Using horses in our battle with disease. If small but increasing doses of the toxin (poison) of diphtheria are injected into a horse, the horse's blood soon contains antibodies that destroy the toxins. If we draw a small quantity of the horse's blood and take the watery part, called the *serum*, we can use it to destroy diphtheria germs. This is the *antitoxin* used to fight diphtheria. When a child is attacked by diphtheria, if the antitoxin is promptly injected, the child recovers. Before the discovery of antitoxin, the child very often died. "Membranous croup," as it was called, killed hundreds of thousands of children each year.

Science has produced similar serums for some other diseases. Lockjaw (tetanus) is due to germs that grow when they are jabbed deep into the tissues away from the contact with air. It is deadly, but can definitely be stopped by prompt injection of the proper serum. Serums have also been used successfully to combat scarlet fever, pneumonia, yellow fever, dysentery, and a few other diseases.

Can you get disease? Many children have now been given the *Schick test* to see if they can get diphtheria. A small quantity of diphtheria toxin is injected under the skin. If an irritation occurs, the child is susceptible (liable to the disease), and should be treated to prevent it. Many persons are naturally immune to this and many other diseases. If they are not immune to diphtheria, they may be made artificially immune to this disease by the *toxin-antitoxin treatment*. A small quantity of the toxin mixed with antitoxin is injected at intervals of a few days. In place of toxin-antitoxin another product, *toxoid*, is now often used. Toxoid is weakened toxin. The toxin or toxoid arouses the cells to produce antibodies which destroy the toxins. The antitoxin prevents any possible illness from the toxin.

The *Dick test* similarly tells whether the person is susceptible to scarlet fever. A preventive treatment for scarlet fever similar to that for diphtheria is still experimental but has been widely used.

Unfortunately we do not have such simple tests and preventive treatment for many diseases. Smallpox and typhoid may be prevented by vaccination, and their devastation where preventive measures are not taken shows that practically every person is susceptible.

Vanquishing tuberculosis. "The great white plague," tuberculosis, is a curse of civilization. Savages living a vigorous life in the open air do not have it. It comes with crowded life in cities and houses that shut out the stimulating rigors of nature. It has been estimated that some 5,000,000 people now living in the United States will die of tuberculosis. Yet this need not be. The death rate has been reduced 50 per cent in about 30 years. It is possible to banish the disease from earth, provided men can be educated to know, to do, and to lend a hand to those unable to do for themselves.

The germ of tuberculosis attacks almost any tissue in the body, but is most common in the lungs. There it causes the breaking down and hardening of the tissue. The masses of diseased tissue and mucus loaded with disease germs are coughed up by patients. This sputum should be received into such receptacles as paper bags and destroyed in the fire or in germicidal solutions. On the sidewalk or in the gutter it may be fed upon by flies which will next walk upon a pretzel or cake exposed for sale at the curb or in an unscreened store.

Tuberculosis is also carried by cows, and may be transmitted to man through milk and milk products. A convenient test will show the tuberculous cow. If *tuberculin,*

Fig. 471. An open-air class to restore health.

a preparation of toxin from the tuberculosis germ, is injected into a tuberculous cow, it causes a rise of temperature. Many states now provide inspectors who test every cow supplying milk to the trade, and State officers kill every cow found to be tuberculous.

In treating the patient, we need only the simple ways of nature, if the disease is not too far advanced. The best remedies are rest in bed or in easy chairs, good food, air, and sunshine. Such simple means may cure the disease. It may take a long time. If the home is slovenly, the patient should be removed to a sanitarium where care is provided. Many sanitariums are supported at public expense. Whether at home or in a sanitarium, the patient needs to be under the care of a physician.

To prevent tuberculosis, we have the means of nature and the safeguards of our public-health officers. Protection of our food supplies from flies, filth, and tuberculous handlers is the work of the health authorities. We can all help them by guarding our individual habits. Beyond these measures our great protection is a vigorous, healthy body.

Keeping the body in fighting trim. There are many other diseases, and legions of germs ever attacking our bodies. Common colds cause vast loss to workers and to industry. Against them, as against tuberculosis, pneumonia, and a great many so-called minor ills, we must turn the vigor of our fighting cells. Warm clothing in the winter helps to prevent the drain upon our resistance powers. Rubbers and raincoats or umbrellas help the body in its battle against the ever-present germs, and wet feet and extreme fatigue often throw the battle to the germs. No body can carry on its battle without proper feeding. Care of the diet is one of the first thoughts in guarding against disease. Exercise and rest are of equal importance. Vigor demands both. A person under-fed, fatigued, and chilled is often easy prey for bacteria. A person in abundant vigor, "in the pink of condition," can resist germs.

Health battalions. Living as we do in communities, we cannot individually carry on the battle against germs. Each one of us is a source of danger to his neighbors, and each neighbor is dangerous to each of us (Fig. 472). Yet in our battle for health, each adds strength to each, provided each understands and does his part. The great diseases cannot be fought single-handed. Laboratories, hospitals, and trained men and women are absolutely necessary.

Departments of public health protect our milk, meat, and other food supplies. Infected, adulterated, and misbranded goods are driven from the market by the united action of health officers, police, and courts. Under the National Pure Food and Drugs Act some kinds of unfit goods can be seized and dealers prosecuted. Our meat supply is protected by United States inspectors who are stationed in slaughter-houses where they inspect every carcass and stamp it as fit for use or condemn it as fit only for the manufacture of fertilizer.

Water supplies are sources of danger until properly con-trolled. Fifty years ago many a city in the United States was a pest hole for typhoid because of contaminated water. Now the large cities are the safest places to obtain drinking water when traveling. In Chapter VII you studied how water is made safe.

In the control of epidemics the health department advises how the individual may best live to avoid the danger. By quarantine, sufferers from infectious diseases and those who have been in contact with them are isolated until danger of their infecting others is past. Patients are treated in hospitals, often free of charge. Vaccines and serums are often supplied and administered free

Fig. 472. Germs may be spread many feet by a cough. Cover the mouth with a handkerchief.

of charge. At our ports the United States maintains quarantine stations where entering ships and their passengers are inspected, and patients and other sources of disease are cared for by hospitalization, vaccination, disinfection, or such other treatment as is needed. It is to the vigilance of health officers at the ports that we owe our freedom from many diseases. The plague, for example, rages in the East where ships constantly clear for American ports; without the care of our health officers many cases would certainly land on our shores.

Our success in control by health officers depends upon giving them sufficient authority to enforce regulations that science has proved necessary. The magnificent work of the Army Medical Department under General Gorgas and his successors in Panama is a brilliant example of how health may be restored and improved when health officers are given authority.

ADDITIONAL QUESTIONS TO THINK OUT

1. Bread wrapped in wax paper or cellophane costs more than unwrapped bread. Is it worth the extra cost?

2. Why does bread mold easily and package breakfast foods seldom?

3. Why should the bread box be periodically scalded and sunned? why should the garbage pail?

4. When a campaign against flies was well under way in a certain city, the sickness of infants was reduced. Do you see any connection?

5. Watch how bread, meat, and milk are handled before they reach you. Is there danger of infection? What can you personally do about it?

6. Survey your neighborhood for sources of flies, mosquitoes, rats, and mice. How can each be removed? Can you yourself do anything about it? If not, who has control and what recommendations can you make for the correction of the condition?

7. Report to the class a survey of a food store or a lunch counter. Note all foods liable to contamination and the defect in care, and make recommendations for improvement.

8. Note for a day every action that might introduce disease germs into your body.

9. Look up the causes of death in your community. Which have been reduced by the control of disease germs? How?

10. Laws in many states prohibit the common drinking cup. Why? How does your school solve the problem? Is the arrangement satisfactory?

11. What conditions in your community and state hinder the work of the health officers? What should be done about it?

12. If "colds" are due to germs, why are you more liable to colds and sore throats in winter time?

13. How does your body defend itself against disease germs?

14. Suppose your brother or sister had a bad cold, what could you do to avoid catching it? What precautions should you recommend in school when there is an epidemic of colds?

15. Medical inspection of school children is costly. How is it justified?

UNIT THIRTEEN

THE BALANCE OF NATURE

Someone dropped a water hyacinth from South America into a river in Florida, and soon the streams were choked so that boats could hardly force their way through. Someone threw a piece of Canadian water weed into a stream in England and the streams were choked. Someone introduced the mongoose, the killer of snakes from India, into Jamaica, and soon it became a terrible enemy of the poultry raiser. A box of gypsy-moth eggs from Europe blew out a window of an experimenter in Massachusetts, and now the Government is battling to save the forests from destruction by gypsy moths.

Man destroyed the vast herds of buffalo that sometimes covered the plains as far as the eye could see. Then he introduced cattle. Wolves, mountain lions, and bears turned from buffalo to cattle calves. He poisoned, shot, and trapped the beasts of prey; and rabbits, prairie dogs, and ground squirrels swarmed. So the story could be repeated throughout the world, of man's introducing a creature or destroying a creature and creating a pest. Rats, mice, and, worst of all, insects and weeds have followed the white man around the globe, everywhere preying upon the fruits of his labors.

Farmer, forester, stock man, and scientist now are studying methods of control of these creatures of nature that have escaped from the control of nature. When methods of destruction as by poison and trap have failed, they have turned to study the processes of nature that have to do with the increase and decrease of living things in nature. The vast stores of grain, fruits, meats, cotton, and other products that fill trains, ships, and storehouses show that man has learned some of the laws of increase. Yet crops and herds sometimes dwindle and waste away before his despairing eyes.

Our chapters on microscopic organisms show how such organisms increase and how man controls their increase. Our chapters on plant life, forest, and farms have shown some of the processes that increase the plant population of the earth. This unit will tell how animal populations increase and decrease and how the changing populations of plants and animals affect each other. An understanding of the laws of increasing and decreasing populations is pointing the way to the scientific control of pests and beneficial animals and plants. Man having upset nature's balance is finding that he must play nature's game to reëstablish another balance. Pests are due to lack of such a balance of some kinds of plants and animals against others.

CHAPTER LVI

HOW LIFE IS BALANCED

Fitness for living. Eat but do not be eaten. That is the first law of animal nature. The search for food and safety has led creatures to the depths of the sea and into the desert, to the ice fields and to the steaming jungles. Scarcely a space or a cranny on earth is without its living things. Every animal living upon the earth has found a way to get food and to escape from its enemies for a time.

The clam secretes a hard shell for itself and digs into the mud, and sends up a long neck or "siphon" containing two tubes. Through one of these it draws down water containing microscopic food and oxygen; through the other it sends out water carrying waste matter. Contrast this sluggish life with that of the

Fig. 473. The skull of a squirrel. The sharp front teeth gnaw nut shells. The back teeth grind the nuts.

squirrel that clings with agile limbs and sharp claws to the swaying twigs while he bites off buds, pine cones, and nuts. His sharp teeth are fitted to clip off woody twigs and gnaw away hard shells of nuts (Fig. 473). Alert and quick, at the sign of an enemy he scampers up the trunk and lies flat

Fig. 474. How is the cat adapted to steal upon its prey? to spring? to grasp? to eat the meat?

Fig. 475.   Skeleton of a cat.   Compare the arrangement of leg bones with your own.   How are the cat's legs fitted for its life and how are yours better fitted for your life?

against a branch, his gray-and-brown coat hiding him from many an enemy.

The deer goes bounding over the fallen trees at the first suspicious sound or smell to hide in the depths of the forest. Wolves, keen of smell, quiet of foot, crafty and fleet, creep up under the shelter of grass and bushes until they can make a united rush at the deer.   The hawk, keen of sight, swoops down suddenly to a grass field and grasps a mouse in its deadly talons.   The pheasant lies low in the grass or flashes into the brushy thickets, its color in either surrounding hiding it from hawk or gunner.

Notice how a cat is built to catch its dinner in the wild. It has padded feet on which it can creep silently upon a feeding bird.   Its limbs are built for the sudden spring (Fig. 474).   Its extended claws grasp the prey.   Its teeth are adapted for its diet of meat.   The front teeth, unlike those of the gnawing squirrel, are small and weak.   Its long canine teeth plunge into its prey.   Its sharp back teeth shear away the flesh like a pair of scissors (Fig. 476). The cat is an excellent example to show how the bodies of carnivorous (flesh-eating) animals are adapted to their way of life (Fig. 475).

Consider the cow, a herbivorous (plant-eating) animal (Figs. 477 and 478). Look at those big back teeth with their hard ridges. They are adapted to their work of grinding the hard cellular walls of grass and corn, so that digestive juices can reach the starch and protein stored inside the cells. Front teeth are lacking on the upper jaw. The cow wraps its long tongue around a bunch of grass, gives it a pull, and cuts it off with the front teeth of the lower jaw. Watch them the next time you see cows grazing in a field. The legs and feet of the cow, too, are adapted to a grass eater's life. In the protected life of our dairy cows their fitness for speed is not so important as it is to their wild relatives, deer, antelope, and buffalo (Fig. 479).

Fig. 476. Skull and teeth of a cat. Note big canine teeth for holding prey, and sharp back teeth for shearing flesh. Compare front teeth and others with squirrel.

Fig. 477. Skull and teeth of a cow. What teeth are lacking? Why has the cow no use for them?

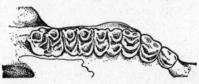

Fig. 478. The back teeth of a cow. What are they fitted for? Compare with cat and squirrel, and your own.

Upsetting the balance of nature. The antelope, struck down by the lion, and the deer, torn apart by a pack of wolves, excite our sympathy. Is the work of the lions and the wolves all evil? In some of our national game preserves in the West, wolves and mountain lions were exterminated to save the deer. Afterward deer multiplied until they are so numerous that there is not food enough to supply them. When winter comes and food is scarce, they die by the hundreds. Many more die of starvation than were killed by

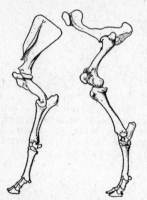

Fig. 479. Cow's leg bones. In the wild state the cow trusted largely to its legs for safety. How are they fitted for speed?

the wolves and mountain lions, and the survivors are weakened with hunger. On some of the preserves hunters are sent in to kill enough deer to prevent all from starving to death. The herds of elk in the Yellowstone region, driven by hunger, sometimes attack the stacks of hay that ranchers have laid up for their cattle. The Government has sent in feed, but the protected herds are so large that supplying them is out of the question. Disposing of surplus buffalo on the Yellowstone range has become a serious problem. On the Canadian buffalo range enough animals are shot annually to keep the herd within the capacity of the range.

Similarly in the insect world, man's interference with nature's population has brought on hordes of hungry animals. When potato fields replaced the grass and wild plants of Colorado, a little striped beetle left certain wild relatives of the potato and took to the great feasts that man had unwittingly spread for it. It multiplied till it swarmed out of Colorado, and marched and flew eastward until it reached the ocean. Then after a time it took passage for the fields of France. This is our common potato bug.

You have probably heard of the rabbits that someone introduced into Australia. With none of their native enemies, they multiplied until they ate the sheep country bare of grass. Later someone introduced the American cactus into the Australian dry lands, and now it is a curse crowding out the native plants that furnished fodder for cattle and sheep. America, too, has had its share of animals and plants that have been introduced intentionally or by accident and later become pests. The English sparrow and the starling were introduced here in the same manner as the rabbits in Australia. These introduced animals and plants have become pests because their enemies have not been introduced with them.

Nature in the long run keeps her creatures balanced. Food and enemies are two of nature's means of balancing the populations of plants and animals in any country. Increased food brings increased population. But increase of any animal in a country means food for its enemies. The increase of enemies brings down the number of the food animals. If man has killed all the enemies, or if he has carried an animal to a new country where it finds no enemies, it may increase until it becomes a pest.

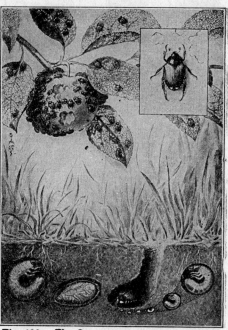

Fig. 480. The Japanese beetle came into our country without its enemies. It has destroyed miles of vegetation. Biologists are importing its enemies from Japan to reëstablish the balance of nature.

Regaining the balance. Our worst pests are imported insects. The Japanese beetle came into New Jersey on some nursery stock. It eats almost every plant that grows, and is spreading farther and farther each year. The European corn borer was introduced on broom corn from Italy and Hungary. Now it threatens the vegetation of our great corn belt, for it feeds on many plants besides corn. The Mediterranean fruit fly came uninvited into Florida and threatened to destroy the fruit industry in all our warm-climate states.

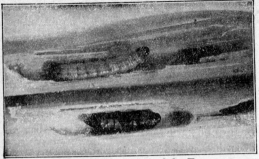

Fig. 482.   The larva and pupa of the European corn borer.   The caterpillar threatens to destroy corn and many other crops.

Fig. 481.   This little moth is the parent of the destructive corn borer, accidently imported into the United States.

Biologists are fighting these hordes of insects by introducing their enemies from their native homes.   One of the most successful attempts to reëstablish nature's balance in this way was by fighting a scale insect that threatened to stop orange growing in ·California.   In faraway Australia our biologists found that the scale was living but was not a serious pest.   They found out why.   A lady beetle fed upon it.   These lady beetles were introduced into California.   With an abundant supply of their favorite food, they multiplied until the scale was brought under control. Insect enemies of many other insect pests are being studied and introduced to restore the balance that was upset.

Our animal allies.   If you have watched a mother bird feeding a nest of young, you will see the old bird return to her nest every few minutes with a beak filled with food.   That food for the young is largely insect larvae (young).   Even seed-eating birds feed their young on animal food.   Young birds grow at an extremely fast rate.   They must have protein to make tissue.   Animal food supplies the tissue-building food.   The animal food that is available in abundance is insects.   A wren was seen to feed its young six hundred times in one day.   Vast quantities of weed seeds are also eaten by birds, notably by our native sparrows, juncos, bobwhites, grouse, and ducks. The diagram, page 568, shows the food of some of our common birds.

Fig. 483. Nature maintaining a balance. A little wasp lays eggs on the tomato worm. The young wasps eat the worm and spin their cocoons that you see here.

SOME BIRDS THAT HELP MAN

Birds that catch insects on the wing:
 Swallow
 Swift
 Martin
 Nighthawk
 Whippoorwill
Fly catchers:
 Kingbird
 Phoebe
 Pewee
 Other fly catchers
Warbler:
 About 30 species
 Bluebird
Birds that search trunks and branches for insects and insect eggs:
 Creeper
 Nuthatch
 Woodpecker
Birds that search twigs and foliage for insects and insect eggs:
 Vireo
 Kinglet
 Chicadee
 Titmouse
 Cuckoo
 Wren
 Thrush
 Catbird
 Oriole
 Tanager
 Robin
 Bluejay
 Goldfinch
Birds that search low plants and ground for insects:
 Thrush
 Wren
 Flicker
 Meadow lark
 Robin
 Killdeer
 Snipe
 Blackbird
 Catbird
 Starling
 Crow
 Gull
 Sparrow
Birds that eat weed seeds:
 Song sparrow
 Chipping sparrow
 Field sparrow
 Tree sparrow
 White-throated sparrow
 White-crowned sparrow
 Vesper sparrow

Grasshopper sparrow
Fox sparrow
English sparrow
Many other sparrows
Goldfinch
Purple finch
Other finches
Indigo bunting
Grouse
Pheasant
Quail
Chewink
Dickcissel (black-throated
  bunting)
Horned lark
Meadow lark
Blackbird
Red-winged blackbird
Cowbird

Cardinal
Robin
Duck

Birds that eat rats and mice:
Owl
Hawk
Crow
Raven
Heron
Jay
Gull

Birds that eat dead animals:
Turkey buzzard (turkey vulture)
Black vulture
Crow
Magpie
Eagle
Gull

The damage that birds do to our orchards and fruit gardens
is more than offset by their destruction of insects and weed
seeds.   Where birds are encouraged, the insect hordes are
diminished.   Nesting sites, including boxes for those that
will use them, bird baths, and food induce them to stay about
houses and gardens.   The enforcement of existing laws will
afford protection from men with guns.   Treaties with Canada

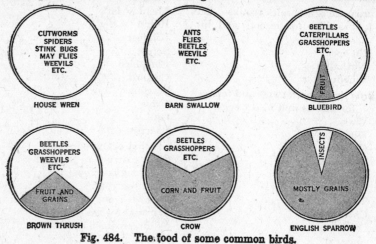

Fig. 484.   The food of some common birds.

have protected migratory birds in these two countries. We now need treaties that will secure protection of those that spend the winter season in South America.

The worst enemy about our houses and gardens is the house cat. The practice of clipping the claws of cats has been tried with good results. It is true

Fig. 485. For what use is each of these beaks adapted?

that it prevents cats from climbing trees, but it also prevents them from catching birds. The simple procedure of keeping cats indoors in the morning until they have been well fed helps to reduce their activity in bird catching.

In our battle with insects, some other animals are on the side of man. Frogs and toads feed chiefly on insects. A toad in the garden is said to be worth twenty dollars a year. Snakes, which most people kill without thought, are valuable destroyers of our chief competitors, the insects as well as of mice and rats. Skunks, too, and other furry animals pick up many insects in their nightly nosings about the ground. All these animal friends need our protection and encouragement in the battle to keep the balance of life in our favor.

A thoughtless man with a gun usually kills hawks and owls on sight, yet we probably have no more valuable allies than these birds of prey. Their chief food is rats and mice. Examination of

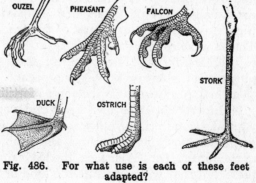

Fig. 486. For what use is each of these feet adapted?

Fig. 487. Big toads were imported into Puerto Rico to eat insects that were destroying sugar cane. Compare with common toad, one of our valuable animals.

the stomach contents and of droppings of these birds has shown only now and then a small bird and rarely a chicken. Only two or three out of our many species of hawks and owls sometimes kill chickens. If an individual of one of these species forms a habit of searching for young chickens on a farm, there is nothing to do but to get the gun. Usually, however, the hawk circling about the fields is searching for field mice. Where hawks have been killed off, plagues of field mice have sometimes developed.

Balancing the food elements. Plants and animals are also balanced against each other. Plants are continually drawing their carbon and oxygen from the air and their hydrogen and other elements from the soil. Animals are continually drawing their food elements from plants. Is there any limit to the supply of the food elements on earth? The experience of farmers seems to show that there is a limit to it on the farm. There comes a time after continual cropping when the farm is no longer profitable unless some of these elements are returned to the soil as fertilizers.

Nature fertilizes her own fields and woods. The next time you take a walk through a woods, try to find where the leaves go when they die. Examine the dead leaves on the floor of the forest. On the surface, the leaves are generally so well preserved that you can name the kind of tree. A little below the surface they are broken into bits. Still farther down they are merely small parts, and below this is just dark-colored soil, humus.

Perhaps you will find white threads winding through the decaying leaves. These are the threads of toadstools and other fungi. You may find beetles, and the young or larvae of many kinds of insects. Perhaps you will find worms and other small animals. With a microscope you may find bacteria.

The fungi and the little animals feed on the dead leaves. All the dead leaves and broken twigs and branches contain the elements that the trees get from the soil. Having served the tree they serve the bacteria, fungi, and little animals of the forest floor.

Even when the worms and insects are done with these elements, nature is not yet done with them. The wastes of the animals and their dead bodies still contain food elements. They serve then as food for bacteria and fungi. When bacteria are through with them, the elements are again in condition for feeding green plants.

Thus, through the long ages of life on earth, nature has used the same elements again and again. The green plants continually build the simple elements up into more complex compounds. Animals and colorless plants, the bacteria and fungi, continually tear them down into simpler compounds. The building process begins with photosynthesis (food-building by means of light). The tearing down is chiefly oxidation. Thus carbon dioxide from the air and water from the soil are united to form carbohydrates. Other elements from the soil, such as nitrogen, sulphur, and phosphorus, are added to make proteins. Green plants build these foods, using the energy of the sun in the process of photosynthesis. Then living cells in plants and animals oxidize the foods to get the energy of life. The elements return to soil and air. Figures 488 and 489 shows in diagrams the cycles through which carbon and nitrogen pass.

Not all the nitrogen however returns to the soil directly. The foul odors of decaying bodies are often due to nitrogen compounds that are passing off as gas into the air. **Green plants cannot use the gaseous nitrogen of the air.** Only certain lowly plants can, chiefly certain kinds of bacteria that

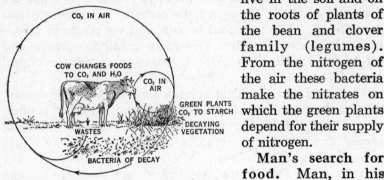

live in the soil and on the roots of plants of the bean and clover family (legumes). From the nitrogen of the air these bacteria make the nitrates on which the green plants depend for their supply of nitrogen.

Fig. 488. Much of earth's supply of carbon keeps moving around a cycle.

Man's search for food. Man, in his search for food, finds that nature provides for him just as she provides for other living things. The raw minerals are in the soil where he cannot use them for food. Like other animals and plants without chlorophyll, he must turn to green plants for the first combination of the elements into food. Man's conquest of the earth has been

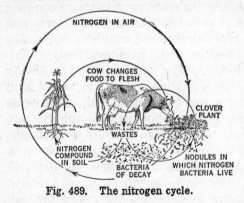

made possible by his control of those plants which serve him as food factories. He has learned that the control of the crop plants, however, requires the control of many other living things—insects, rats and mice, birds and other animal allies, bacteria and fungi. Successful farming is

Fig. 489. The nitrogen cycle.

thus a very intricate process, requiring study of many kinds of plants and animals, of their feeding, their home life, their breeding, and the disposition of their wastes.

Fig. 490. White man upset the balance of nature by almost exterminating the buffalo. Now this protected herd in Yellowstone must be reduced to keep it in balance with its pasture.

The new balance of life. Before the white man came into this country, there was a balance of life that fitted the Indian living in his wild environment. The Indians were not numerous. There are probably more Indians in the United States today than when Captain John Smith first met them in Virginia. Their main food supply was the wild animals of the country. Corn, beans, and a few other crops were raised in a small way by some Indians, but in the main they were hunters, not farmers. The forest and the prairies fed their food animals. Deer, buffalo, elk, and moose were kept in balance with their supply of winter fodder by wolves, mountain lions, and Indians. The country was supporting about as much life as it could in the wild state.

Fig. 491. The wolf is one of nature's agents in keeping the number of plant-eating animals in balance with their food supply. What keeps down the number of wolves?

Fig. 492.   Man attempting to regain control of the balance of nature he upset.   Spraying to protect orchard from insects.

Then the white man spread through the country.   He cut down the woods and planted corn, wheat, and other crops. He killed off the deer from most of the country and almost exterminated the buffalo.   At the same time he wiped out the bear, wolves, and mountain lions.   The white man's invasion of his hunting ground and the destruction of his game was the chief cause of the wars with the Indian.

The upset of natural life at first favored the settlers' crops and farm animals.   The rich land that had never been tilled yielded large crops.   More white men came in and developed farms in the wilderness.

Gradually came a change.   The age-long balance that had been upset was readjusting itself.   The soils, no longer receiving their yearly return of dead forest leaves and suffering from the yearly removal of food elements in the crops, showed signs of exhaustion.   Reduced yield was nature's readjustment.   Many kinds of insects had also increased with the increase of food supplied by the settler's crops.   New insects without their enemies were introduced from foreign lands. Insects further reduced the yield. Many farms, no longer profitable, as in New England, were abandoned. Then the forest began to return over the abandoned fields.

On the better lands man has set out to battle nature as she set about readjusting the balance. Reduced yields are fought by fertilizing the fields. Scientific farming feeds the soil bacteria with organic food and cultivates the soil to give them air, warmth, and proper moisture. Better seed, better varieties of crop plants, and better systems of farming are introduced to secure increased yield. Insects are fought by poison sprays and their natural enemies. Man has learned to protect the birds and wild animals that feed on insects. He protects also the birds and beasts of prey that keep down mice and other gnawing animals so destructive to his crops and stores.

FIELD STUDY

To study the adaptations of animals and plants. As you studied briefly the adaptations of the cat and the cow in this chapter, study other animals at home, on the farm, in the woods, at the zoo. Note where the animal lives, how it escapes its enemies, how it gets its food, etc. How is the animal adapted or suited to attain these ends? Note coloration, skin covering, legs and feet, jaws and teeth. Among common animals you may see: frogs and salamanders; snakes, turtles, and lizards; birds; bats; fish; oysters; starfish; bees, moths, and other insects.

Similarly study the adaptations of some common plants including roots, stem, leaves, flowers, and fruit. Study some of the following: a tree, a vine, an herb, seaweed, pond scums, mushrooms.

EXPERIMENT 155

To establish a balanced aquarium. You may buy suitable plants and animals for an aquarium, but it is more fun to find them out of doors. Put some sand and a few rocks on the bottom. For plants try various submerged plants until you find those that thrive in your aquarium. Anchor the plants in the sand by tying to rocks or other weights. To capture the animals, use a dip net covered with mosquito netting. Try minnows, frogs, tadpoles, salamanders, snails, aquatic insects. Do not put too many animals into your aquarium. Two or three minnows or tadpoles, a salamander, and four or five snails are enough. Try them with various foods and see what they take. For frogs try worms and live insects. Watch the snails find their own food in your aquarium. Do not overfeed, and remove promptly any food not taken before it begins to decay. Learn how each plant or animal in the community helps others and is helped.

ADDITIONAL QUESTIONS TO THINK OUT

1. Is man as well adapted as a dog to run; to find food in the wild; to endure cold? Name some acts that man performs with his hands that a dog does in another manner. Which does them better? What parts of man's body have given him the advantage so that he has destroyed the wild dogs?

2. Is man as well adapted to life in the wild as are wild animals and plants? Before you answer, consider the lives of the Eskimo, the African savage, and our own pioneers in the days of Daniel Boone.

3. Prepare a list of wild animals that are harmful to garden and forest and another of those that are helpful. Indicate the influence of each.

4. How does a tree protect itself against enemies?

5. How do wild things protect themselves against the rigors of winter? Think of the oak tree, the lilies, annual plants, squirrel, bee, groundhog, and bear.

6. A horned toad has been known to live for six months without eating. Why could not a cat do so?

7. Why have birds higher bodily temperatures than furry animals? Why are snakes more active in hot summer?

8. Why are communities of plants and animals made of various and diverse kinds?

9. Brown rats have followed the white man around the world. How could they upset the balance of nature in a new country?

10. Compare the Eskimo and the polar bear as to their places in the Arctic community. Sealers from farther south have destroyed seals and walruses in many parts of the Arctic. How would such destruction affect the Eskimo and the bears?

11. Siberian reindeer were introduced into Alaska to support the natives after white men had made serious inroads upon the game and fish. How are reindeer adapted to live in the Arctic winter? How are the Eskimo? How would the introduction change the lives of other animals and men?

12. Explore a vacant lot; a park; a field; a brook; a wood. Dig about the roots of plants, search the dead leaves and mud. List the living things and tell how each gets food and shelter.

13. What wild and half-wild animals live about the city—sparrows, insects, mice, stray cats, etc.? How does each get food, water, protection?

14. Sometimes disease kills large numbers of wild rabbits. How would such disease affect plants and animals, including man?

15. What would you do to encourage birds in your neighborhood?

16. Make a collection of common weeds. Name them from books in the library.

17. Collect and identify some common insects. Identify 20 birds.

UNIT FOURTEEN

EARTH SCIENCE

Have you stood on a hill overlooking a valley with a stream winding through it or a lake gleaming in the summer sun, and asked what made that valley? Have you stood on a rocky headland looking at the great bays reaching into the land and the little bays or coves cut in the hard rock? Have you ever wondered what carved out the bays, the sea cliffs, and the rocky islands? Have you gazed down a sandy beach or over a plain till the land met the sky and asked why they are there? Have you watched from your camp fire in the valley and wondered as the moon peeped over a great granite mountain?

In our present study we shall try to answer these questions and many others. How old are the mountains? Why do New England and Canada sparkle with thousands of crystal lakes and Maryland and Ohio have comparatively few? Why does the earth shake and the mountains belch forth fire? How do geologists, the students of earth science, know that the mighty Andes Mountains are moving eastward five feet a century?

We shall study still other questions perhaps nearer home for some of our students, and less dramatic but no less fatal in their importance to man. Why must harbors be dredged? Why does hard rock crumble away? Why does glacial soil in New England, where there are no glaciers, send men to sea and to the factories? Why does the glacial soil of the Middle West make farmers rejoice over bumper crops?

Then we shall ask what is *inside* the earth. We shall see how the scientist tries to find out what is there, though he cannot go there. Does it seem fantastic to think of the continents as floating? We shall see why such an idea has

been proposed in science.   How is rock made?   How do we
know that ocean waves once rolled where now there are waving
fields of grain, and sharks chased other sea creatures where
now cattle graze on a thousand hills?

When man appeared on the earth, he fitted into things as
he found them, just as the wild creatures did.   Today, though
he has changed the face of the earth, yet he takes advantage
of nature's work, where he can, in locating his railroads and
harbors where the forces of earth have prepared places for
them.   He spreads his fields of grain where ocean, lake, or
river has spread level blankets of fertile soil.   He finds in
the rock material for construction of machines by which he
controls the forces of earth.   Man is still a creature of the
earth, but he is studying and using the material and
the forces of the earth to increase his control steadily.

After studying the solid parts of the earth, we shall turn
to the sea.   Have you ever sat on the sands or the rocks,
gazing out where sea and sky meet, and longed to see what
lay beyond?   The call of the sea led daring adventurers
around the globe to the tropical coral islands and to the seas
and shores of eternal ice.   The sea today calls the scientist,
and science is finding there great stores for the comfort and
wealth of mankind.   We shall study the sea, what it is, how
it moves, what lies beneath.   Perhaps we shall understand
how man's power has grown through the ages with his science
of the sea.

Chapter LVII

EARTH'S CHANGING FACE

The vanishing hills. The ancient psalmist might sing of the everlasting hills and the American poet of hills ancient as the sun, but to the geologist the hills are fleeting things. It is true that it may take a million years for a hill to wear away, but in the history of the earth, "a thousand years ... are but as yesterday when it is past." If you learn to look with a seeing eye, you may observe that the granite hills dissolve away. The geologist learns the past of the earth by studying the present. If you will picture the hills in your imagination, as the geologist does, a million years ago, and the same hills a million years in the future, you will be able to understand the history of our hills and valleys. You will see mighty mountains as high as the Rockies where the low hills of New York, Philadelphia, and Baltimore now are.

These flights of imagination are based on such little acts as picking up bits of rock at the foot of a solid cliff and crumbling them between the fingers (Fig. 493). What makes the cliff and the rock crumble? Water seeps into the tiny cracks in the rocks and freezes. In freezing it expands and breaks off pieces of the rock.

Heating and cooling help to break up rocks. The heat of the summer sun expands the rocks and helps to crack them just as heating a china plate cracks the plate. In hot deserts the outer shell of boulders sometimes breaks off with a report like a pistol shot. In more temperate climate, expansion and contraction also helps to break rocks to pieces, but the process is slower. In dry regions wind-driven sand forms a natural sand blast that grinds away solid rocks, and along our sandy shores it wears away stone lighthouses and other buildings.

(579)

Fig. 493. A canyon is a young valley. The stream and the weather have worn away the valley. Why is there loose rock at the foot of the cliffs? Bryce Canyon, Utah.

Other processes of nature play their parts in the wearing process. Oxygen of the air unites with some constituents of the rock and thus releases others. When carbon dioxide from growing plants is dissolved in water, it forms carbonic acid, and eats away limestone. The great caves of Kentucky, Virginia, and elsewhere were eaten away by the dissolving action of underground streams and dripping water containing carbon dioxide. Other acid substances given off from the roots of plants help crumble the rocks. Expanding roots also push them apart. The penetration of the soil by roots lets in the rain water from the surface. Burrowing creatures, such as ants and ground hogs, help in the destruction.

Rocks to soil. All these agencies are slowly reducing solid rock hills to smaller and smaller bits. Eventually all are reduced to soil. The fineness of the soil varies with the length of time that reduction has been going on, the agencies that have worked, and the resistance of the rock. Some soils are little more than broken rock mixed with finer soils. Sandy soils are composed of angular bits of rocky material that can be seen under the microscope. Extremely fine particles form clay.

Fig. 494. An old valley. The hillsides are worn away to gentle slopes.
Valley of the Susquehanna River, Pennsylvania.

What made the valleys. If you have taken a walk beside a brook in a meadow, perhaps you have noticed that the brook lies in a diminutive canyon or little valley below the level of the meadow. You will readily guess that the brook cuts its little canyon into the meadow. Given high land, proper climate, and time the little canyon might become a rival of the Grand Canyon of the Colorado or Bryce Canyon, Utah (Fig. 493). With more time the walls of the canyon will crumble away and a broad, open valley will be made. In the moister climates the widening of the valley goes on more rapidly as the rain washes down the valley sides. A broad, open valley is an older valley than a canyon (Fig. 494). In very old age the hills that formed the valley walls have been eaten away till the country is almost or quite a plain. If you live in a hilly country, look over the land from a hilltop and decide the relative ages of the valleys you see.

How water cuts valleys. Did you ever wonder why pebbles and cobblestones are round? Perhaps you have waded in a swift stream and have felt the pebbles roll under your feet. Every roll grinds away a little bit of the pebble and a little of the other stones and rocks it meets. Pebbles and rocks are the stream's grindstones. Sand is its sand-

Fig. 495. Stones and sand are tools with which a river digs.

paper (Fig. 495). With these tools it gives the stones of its bed their characteristic shape.

You have probably seen a creek speed up after a rain. If the creek could roll along a one-pound cobblestone before the rain, it can roll along a 64-pound boulder after its speed has been doubled by the rain. (The carrying power of a stream varies as the sixth power of its velocity.)

Rain that runs down the bank of a creek carries mud with it. That is why creek water is muddy after a rain. This mud is part of the hills that formed the valley walls. Every rain washes some of the hills into the stream to be carried away. It is only a question of time until the hills will all go down the stream. The land is being continuously carried away. The surface of the United States is being slowly lowered by rain and streams one inch in 1400 years in Mississippi, one inch in 760 years in the Sierra Nevadas. If nothing interfered, the whole country would ultimately be worn down to a plain. The wearing away of rocks or of land is called *erosion*. A plain that is so formed is called a *plain of erosion*.

How streams build land. You have probably seen a fan-shaped spread of mud at the foot of a rain gully (Fig. 496).

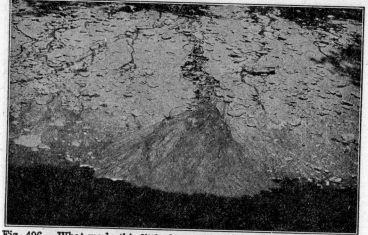

Fig. 496. What made this little fan-shaped deposit of mud at the foot of the small gulley?

The rain running swiftly down the gully in the steep bank or hillside might carry its load, but when it ran on to the more level land at the foot of the hill, it lost speed and therefore was not able to carry its mud. When a river flows into a lake or sea, its current loses speed in the same way, and it drops its load of mud and sand. It drops its heaviest materials when its speed is first slackened. As it loses more speed, down goes the sand. Finally in the deeper water, often far out from the mouth where the current is very slow, the mud is laid on the bottom of the lake or sea.

The Mississippi carries each year 7,500,000,000 cubic feet of sediment to the sea. This would make a pile of mud a mile square and 268 feet high. In addition it carries 2,850,-000.000 cubic feet of dissolved material.

When a flood spreads the river out over its banks across the adjoining land, its speed over the flooded land is slackened. Much of its mud is dropped over the land. This builds up a plain called a *flood plain*. Great rivers flowing through level land have great flood plains. You may have seen smaller flood plains along level stretches of creeks and brooks (Fig. 497). Flood plains are rich farming soils, and in regions where

Fig. 497. The Animas flood plain along the stream, Colorado. What dug the valley?

the climate is not too severe, they are densely populated. Every overflow of the streams enriches the land. It is this yearly overflow that has kept the soils of Egypt productive for over 3000 years. The floods, however, are often destructive to life and property, as we have frequently seen along our own Mississippi; those on the Hoang-ho have caused the

Fig. 498. A delta built by a creek. Watch for them on your hikes.

Fig. 499. The plains around the Great Lakes were lake bottom when the lakes were much larger.

river to be named *China's Sorrow*. Flood plains at the mouths of many rivers develop *deltas* (Fig. 498). Look for little deltas as you hike along streams.

What made the great plains? When a river lays down its load over the bottom of a lake, it fills in the hollows of the lake bottom and makes it level. During the great ice age, when our Great Lakes were much larger than at present, vast areas were leveled off on the bottoms of these lakes. When the ice melted, the lakes decreased in size and laid bare much of their former bottoms. Those ancient lake bottoms are the plains along our Great Lakes where now orchards, grain fields, and vineyards are to be seen (Figs. 499, 500).

Once the ocean rolled down the middle of what is now North America from the Arctic to the Gulf. The land rose gradually on both sides from the sea. The smooth old sea bottom as it emerged became covered with grass and other vegetation, and now is the great plain in the interior of North America. How do we know? The sand along our Atlantic coast from Long Island to Florida stretches out under the water for fifty to one hundred miles. When clams, oysters, sea snails, and fishes died in similar sands of the ancient sea, their shells and skeletons were buried with the shifting sands. In time the sand became sandstone in ways we shall presently study, and the shells became fossils. We find sandstone with fossil sea animals in the interior plains of the United States. What does this tell us? Limestone is formed below the deeper sea. Through large areas of the interior country we find great stretches of limestone containing fossils of animals that inhabited deeper seas. What does that tell us?

What made the seashore. If you have been along the beaches where the waves are breaking, you perhaps have seen and heard the stones pounding on the rocks, or have felt the sand dragged over your bare feet. The sand and stones are ground finer and finer, and the sand is thrown out in bars and then beaches by the waves. In this way the long sandy islands on our coast from Long Island to Florida were made (Fig. 501).

Perhaps you live on, or have visited, the rough, rocky coast of New England (Fig. 502). How can geologists tell how it came to be as it is? Look at Figure 503. Suppose this land sank and the sea came into the valleys. You would find then a coast like Figure 504. The waves then would gnaw away at the sides of the hills until cliffs were formed like those in Figure 502.

Our eastern coast is just such a coast. The bays and harbors are drowned valleys. The gorges cut by the streams when the shore was farther east can be traced now under the sea from the St. Lawrence, the Hudson, the Delaware, and through the capes of the Chesapeake. The undersea gorge of the Hudson is 125 miles long and that of the St. Lawrence is 300.

The coasts with long ranges of mountains and very few harbors are lands where mountain ranges are rising parallel with the coast. Such coasts stretch from Oregon to Chile. How do geologists know that these coasts are rising? In rare instances they have seen it happen. In Alaska parts

Fig. 500. The valley of the Red River of the North is the bed of a great lake that existed at the close of the Ice Age.

Fig. 501. The flat, sandy beaches from Long Island to Florida were once sands below the sea.

Fig. 502. The bays of the Maine coast are sunken valleys. What made the cliffs along the shore?

Fig. 503.   An area along a coast before the land sank.   Locate the valley, higher hills, lower hills, the distant ocean.

Fig. 504.   The same area after the land had sunk.   What produced the bay? the small island?   the point of land?

of the seacoast rose nearly 50 feet in 1 month of 1899.   In 1822 and 1835 part of the Chilean coast rose 2 feet and more.   High on the mountains, old sea beaches with sand, pebbles, and seashells tell that the land rose in ages past. The thick layers of sandstone and limestone above sea level also tell that the land has risen, for these rocks were formed under the water.

Young mountains and old.   Mountains that are rising rapidly, such as the Coast Range, the Rockies, the Andes, the Alps, and the Himalayas, are rough mountains.   As soon as mountains thrust their tops above the sea, rain and frost and other agents attack them.   The higher they rise, the fiercer are the rains and the winds, and the more severe

Fig. 505.   Sharp, high peaks are young mountains.   The Matterhorn, Switzerland.

the frosts.   Glaciers form from the year-long snows and grind out their valleys.   High mountains with jagged, jutting peaks are young, rising mountains (Fig. 505).

As the rate of rise slackens, erosion, with its work of destruction, gains the upper hand.   The jagged peaks are gradually tumbled down the mountain sides rock by rock; valleys broaden, and the mountains are reduced to the stage of those of New England and New York, and the Appalachians (Fig. 506).   In extreme old age the mountains have been worn down to hills such as may be seen in our eastern region from New York to Washington and farther southward.

How mountains arise.   Have you ever noticed layers of rock on the sides of a gorge or a railroad cut (Fig. 507)?   Such layers are called *strata* (singular, *stratum*).   Often the strata are folded or wrinkled.

We know that the material that composes stratified rock was originally laid down in water in level layers.   When we find the strata wrinkled and folded, we know that the rocks were altered after the material was laid down and probably long after it hardened into rock.

38

Before the stratified rock was wrinkled, it covered much more area than afterward, as you can see by spreading a hand-

Fig. 506.   The Ozark Mountains, Arkansas. These low, rounded mountains are among the oldest mountains on the earth.

kerchief on the desk and then wrinkling it by pushing the sides toward each other. If we should reconstruct the folded strata of the Appalachian Mountains and spread them out flat, they would spread over twice as much area. The Alps would spread over four times as much area. It is, therefore, reasonable to suppose that the land where these mountains now stand was once level, and that later the stratified rocks were wrinkled up in gigantic folds to form the mountains.

Fig. 507.   Folded layers of rock.   What history do they tell?

Fig. 508. These layers of rock were horizontal. They are now part of the huge wrinkles in the earth's crust that form the Sierra Nevadas.

Perhaps the material below the strata shifts its position. The strata then resettle to fit. An old theory, not now satisfactory to scientists, explained the wrinkling by a shrinkage of the earth. The interior part of the earth, down toward the center, is becoming denser and more compact. It takes less space and the crust wrinkles up to fit (Fig. 508).

Splitting and slipping rocks. As the folding goes on, the layers of rocks are under terrific strain. Sometimes a layer of rock breaks across, and the broken sides slip one against the other. Such a break in the rocks accompanied by a movement of the broken sides is called a *fault* (Fig. 509).

When the rocks slip in the fault, the earth trembles. This is an *earthquake*. Geologists have mapped the great faults of earthquake regions, and have even measured the amount of slipping in various earthquakes (Fig. 510). In the Japanese earthquake of September, 1923, there was an up-and-down slip of four feet. In the California earthquake of 1906 there was a horizontal movement of twenty feet. Through the slipping of faults, the mountains of California are moving one foot northward in five years, and the Andes one foot eastward in twenty years.

Fig. 509. A fault. Rock layers split and slipped, causing an earthquake.

Fig. 510. The crack a half mile long was formed when a fault slipped in the Great Salt Lake desert. The accompanying earthquake registered in Maryland.

Why rocks melt. The great pressure in the interior of the earth prevents the heat from melting the rocks. When the pressure is relieved through folding and faulting, the rocks melt. The molten rock oozes in and under the folds. There it hardens again. Ages later, when the folded rocks above are eroded away, these great central areas are exposed as masses of granite. This process accounts for the granite peaks of the Rockies, and of the older and more rounded granite mountains in the East.

Fig. 511.   Mount Lassen, California.   The only active volcano in
the United States.

Lava flows. Sometimes the molten rock flows out through
the great cracks or fissures in the rocks and spreads out over
the land surface.   In this way were formed the lava coverings
of great parts of the states of Montana, Idaho, and
Washington.

Sometimes the molten rock flows out through more definite
holes.   Such flows build up volcanoes like those of Hawaii.
Water seeping down through the ground until it meets hot
rock becomes steam.   The expansion of the steam and hot
gases may be held in check by the rocks for long periods of
time.   Finally the force of steam and gases breaks away,
tears the rocks to pieces, and blows the molten lava into
volcanic ash that rains down on the surrounding country.
Such are the explosive eruptions like that of Vesuvius in
79 A.D., that buried the cities of Pompeii and Herculaneum,
and of Mont Pelée in 1902 that destroyed 30,000 people in a
few minutes on the island of Martinique in the West Indies.
Such explosions shoot fine dust into the upper air.   The

Fig. 512. Nisqually Glacier, Rainier National Park.

terrific explosion of Krakatoa in the sea west of Java in 1883 sent dust around the world. (Fig. 511).

How glaciers are made. Did you ever make a very hard snowball? You made it by repeated pressing of snow in your bare hands. The heat of your bare hands and the pressure melted the ice a little. The little water formed was immediately frozen again by the surrounding snow. Roughly that process might be compared to the making of a glacier.

Fig. 513.   Icebergs break from a glacier that enters the sea.

When snow falls in the high mountains where the melting and evaporation are very slow compared with the rate of snowfall, the snow accumulates in a great snow field.   The pressure and possibly the slight melting by the sun gradually convert it into ice.   Under the great pressure of the accumulated mass of snow and ice, it is forced slowly down the valleys.   Such is a glacier (Fig. 512).

What glaciers do to land.   Ice is heavy.   A layer of ice a thousand feet deep, as in the Muir glacier, Alaska, has great power to wear away land.   Everything loose on the rocks is carried away.   Rocks frozen into the bottom of the ice grind away the solid rocks as they are carried along. Valleys are gouged out.   Sharp crags are smoothed down. Hills are rounded off.

There is no mistaking a glacial country.   It has rounded hills, rounded valleys, scratches in the rock made by the embedded rocks carried in the ice (Fig. 514).   All the material carried by the glacier is left when the ice melts. Boulders, gravel, sand, and clay are piled in mixed heaps, not sorted out as water sorts it (Fig. 515).   At the end of the glacier are left long ridges of mixed materials.   These ridges are called *terminal moraines*.   The débris left by the glacier often dams up streams, producing lakes (Fig. 516).

Fig. 514.   Glacial scratches in the rocks.

All these marks of a great glacier are found in the northeastern United States from northern Pennsylvania northward, and from Missouri to Montana, and all over Canada.   Most of Europe also shows the same evidence of glaciation.   These markings tell the geologist that a great sheet of ice, several

Fig. 515.   Glacial till, unsorted rocks, gravel, and clay left by the glacier. Clinton, Massachusetts.

Fig. 516. Kettle-hole lake in gravel and sand left by glacier. Clinton, Massachusetts.

hundred to several thousand feet thick, once covered these lands. This great glacier covered the land for many thousands of years, and the last of it disappeared from the mainland of Europe about 15,000 years ago. The land during the ice age appeared as the interior of Greenland appears today— ice as far as the eye can see, with only here and there at long intervals a jut of rock through the white coating of ice (Fig. 517).

How man fits into nature. Ever since the Old Stone Age man has adjusted himself to nature's work, utilizing the land and nature's products as best he could. Nature

Fig. 517. The Greenland Ice Cap. How northern United States appeared in the ice age.

Fig. 518.   How do the two jetties force the river to improve navigation?

furnished stone-age man with a ball of rock which he chipped roughly against other stones and fitted with a rough handle. It furnished him with a young tree which he broke and hacked into a stout staff and perhaps pointed and hardened in the fire.   For food it furnished roots and shellfish, cave bear and mammoth.   The skins he threw over his shoulder in his battle with cold and rain.   His drink he found in a stream and his shelter in a cave.

As he learned to plant and reap, man sought the open places, the flood plains where yearly overflow kept vegetation under control, and the grassy hills where forests were unable to live.   He learned to make boats, and voyaged along the streams and close to the shores of lakes and seas.   Then he made a great discovery that gave him implements with which to cut down forests so that he could use the soil in which they grew, to dig effectively in the earth for its treasure, to build far better than ever before.   He discovered that when certain rocks were mixed and heated in the fire, out would come a new substance, metal.   Iron has been the most valuable discovery in man's struggle to control his environment.

Even today, however, when man has changed the faces of continents, he still fits himself into the work of nature.   He uses plains, valleys, and low hills as farm lands.   He pastures cattle and sheep on lands where there is not rain enough for crops.   He uses drowned valleys as harbors, he avoids shores bordered by rising walls of mountains as unfit for towns. He dredges out the silt that rivers bring into the harbors, or he builds jetties to increase the speed of the current, and thus forces the river to do its own dredging (Fig. 518). His roads and railroads follow the passageways dug by streams through the hills (Fig. 519). Many lakes and streams have been serving as routes of travel and sources of food since before the days of written history. Others are sources of water supply for distant cities (Fig. 79). Sandy beaches furnish recreation. Mountains unfit for agriculture furnish valuable timber, minerals, and places of recreation.

Even volcanoes and glaciers are serving man. Volcanic soils are often very rich (Fig. 520). Glaciers have been powerful agents in reducing rocks to soil. These great grinding mills of nature ground the rock to a fine flour.

Fig. 519. Man takes advantage of nature's work. How is it shown here?

Glacial streams carried it out to lake bottoms and to outwash plains where the water rushed out from the end of the glaciers. Often this glacial-prepared soil has been picked up again by the winds and carried long journeys to its present resting place where man farms it. A peculiar, rich soil called *loess* (pronounced lō'ĕs) is composed of material brought by the winds from glacial deposits and desert areas to more favorable regions. Great areas of loess are found along the middle course of the Mississippi and the Missouri, along the Rhine, and in northern China. Loess, like sand, is a loose soil and does

Fig. 520. Volcanic soils are often very rich. Harvesting pineapples, Hawaiian Islands.

not hold water well, but where there is rain enough, it produces good soils.

Glaciers have not always benefited the farmer, but have served other men. Much of New England is covered with the coarse mixture of boulders and gravel dropped by the great ice sheet. This land has kept many a New England farmer poor. The streams dammed by the glacial débris, however, furnished abundant water power that made New England the first great manufacturing region of the United States. The excellent harbors and the shallow waters offshore where fish feed and breed gave New England a race of mariners. Her sunken coast made it a commercial center for the shipping of manufactured goods and the receipt of foreign products.

FIELD STUDY

Crumbling rocks. Find an old quarry, a cliff, or a railroad cut. Note the size of the fragments that have fallen to the base of the cliff. Look on the cliff or exposed rock surface for cracks that water might penetrate. Note plants growing on the rocks—mosses and lichens grasses, weeds, and bushes. Do plants help or hinder the crumbling process? How? Take a picture of the cliff or make a sketch or diagram. On the face of the cliff or of the railroad cut, note the bed rock below, the looser rock, the subsoil, and the topsoil.

Work of running water. Look for brooks and creeks that show the result of weathering action: steep banks, worn banks, pebbles and rounded rocks that are the tools of the stream, "potholes" (Fig. 521) and pools cut by the stream. Look for gullies cut by rains in open fields and banks. Along the sea or lake shore look for cliffs made by the waves, level "benches" under the water, rounded stones worn by the water.

If you are in a glaciated country, look for typical U-shaped glacial valleys, for boulders and smaller stones unlike the rock of the country roundabout, for glacial scratches on smoothed rocks.

Valleys and hills. Study the pictures illustrating young, mature, and old hills and valleys and try to find them on your hike. Take your camera or sketchbook along. Often

Fig. 521. Potholes made by the cobble-stones in a swift stream.

you can find them in miniature along the brooks.

Visit a creek in fair weather and after a rain. Note the current and the cutting.

Deposition by water. Look for little deltas where brooks enter ponds and slower streams. Look for flood plains along rivers, creeks, and brooks. Look for alluvial fans at the foot of banks and sloping fields. Examine the deposits to see the position of larger stones, pebbles, and mud. Look for places where streams have filled up their channels and cut others. Can you determine why the deposition took place? Try the experiment of building a little jetty in a brook to increase its speed.

Rock strata. Look for rock layers exposed in a gorge. Are the rocks folded, tilted, or horizontal? Can you account for the condition? Look for faults in the layers of rock where one side has slipped up or to right or left.

How man has used land surfaces. Note the kind of land that is farmed. Is it on hillsides, valley floors, or flood plains? What use is made of steep hillsides? of rocky cliffs? Do the railroads follow any natural feature? do the roads? Where has there been dredging? Why was it necessary? Why were there deposits at that point? Examine contour maps and look down on harbors from hills and determine why harbors are there. Where are cities and towns situated? Why?

FIELD AND LABORATORY STUDY

Question: What is meant by the weathering of rocks?

Materials: The rocks to be found in any field; hammer and knife.

Directions: Go to any field or lot where you can find a number of rocks exposed. Select a good-sized rock. Examine the outside. Scrape it with your knife to determine how hard it is. Break off a piece and repeat your observations on the inside rock. What is the difference between the outside and inside rock as to color and hardness?

Repeat your observations on several rocks, choosing different kinds as far as possible. What, in general, is the difference between the inside and outside? What do you think is the cause of this difference? Examine the soil of the field. Can you find any evidence that the soil is broken rock (weathered rock)? How do you account for the fact that while freshly broken rock has sharp edges the grains in the soil are rounded?

Conclusion: Answer the question.

Practical application: Why is the weathering of rock of importance to you? You will find it interesting to make a collection of the various rocks found in your neighborhood.

EXPERIMENT 156

Question: How does the action of water affect rocks?

Materials: A teaspoonful each of ocean-beach sand and of inland sand from a sand bank; silt from a stream deposit; hand magnifier; cobblestones or gravel; stones with ragged surfaces.

Directions: (a) Dry the silt until it is like dust.

(b) Spread your samples of sea sand, inland sand, and dried silt each on a piece of white paper about 6 inches square. Spread them thin, so that individual grains may be examined with the hand magnifier.

(c) Examine through the magnifier. Which samples have rounded, smooth surfaces? Which have sharp, jagged surfaces? Which of the samples are you sure have been acted upon by water? Which sample has not been exposed long to water action?

(d) Compare the surface of a cobblestone or gravel stone with that of a jagged stone. Which of these stones or rocks has been acted upon a long time by water? How do you know? If you should walk in a field covered with cobbles what conclusion should you draw concerning the probability that this land had at some former time been under water for a long period?

Conclusion: Answer the question.

Practical application: By studying the rocks on the surface of the earth, we can get an idea of what the conditions there were in past ages.

EXPERIMENT 157

Question: How does water affect rocks when it freezes in cracks?

Materials: Small narrow-necked bottle; freezing mixture of salt and ice; water and bucket.

Directions: (a) Break a lump of ice into small pieces. Mix with it one third its volume of salt.

(b) Fill the small narrow-necked bottle with water, and cork tightly. Wire the cork in so that it is held firmly. There must be no air in the bottle. To prevent this, put a wire in the neck of the bottle before inserting the cork. This allows the air to escape when the cork is put in place. Then pull out the wire.

(c) Put an inch of the ice and salt mixture in the bottom of the bucket; next put in the bottle, and then pack the salt and ice on all sides of the bottle. Allow the whole to stand until the water inside the bottle is frozen. This will require about twenty minutes. The exact time cannot be stated, as it will depend upon the size of the bottle and the amount of salt and ice used.

(d) Remove the bottle and examine it. How do you account for the fact that is is cracked?

Conclusion: Answer the question.

Practical application: Why are water pipes buried? Why are autoists so careful to prevent the water in their radiators from freezing? What happens when water freezes in the crevices of rocks?

EXPERIMENT 158 (OPTIONAL)

Question: How can you show the effects of heat and cold in erosion? The splitting of rocks in the desert may be imitated by heating a heavy glass bottle in a gas flame. Try also heating a glass tube and cooling it suddenly by plunging it into cold water.

EXPERIMENT 159 (OPTIONAL)

Question: How are rock particles kept in suspension in water? How does water transport soil and rocks? What causes deposits of suspended materials?

Materials: Large pitcher or pail; water; a handful of fine dirt; large oblong dripping pan or long tin pan with a quarter-inch hole in one end; two or three stones or pieces of lead and some grass or sod to form obstructions; a piece of wood $1\frac{1}{2}$ inches thick; a stick to stir with.

Directions: (a) Pour water into the pitcher or pail until it is about two-thirds full. Place the dirt in this water and stir until the dirt is evenly distributed throughout the water. Describe the appearance of the water after the soil has been stirred into it. What happens if you let the water come to rest? What keeps the soil suspended in the water?

(b) Using the $1\frac{1}{2}$-inch piece of wood to block up one end, place the large pan with the hole in one end so that it is inclined, the hole in the lower end resting over the sink.

(c) Place the plug in the sink drain.

(d) Place some square-edged stones or pieces of lead in the bottom of the dripping pan. You have made an imitation of a river bed.

(e) Make sure that the dirt is in suspension, and while stirring it, pour the muddy water *gently* and *slowly* into the higher end of the pan, allowing it to run down the incline over the obstructions and out of the hole in the lower end into the sink. Keep stirring the water in the pitcher or pail while you are pouring it and pour *slowly*.

(f) Examine the obstructions in the bottom of the pan. Where did the fine soil on their upper sides come from?

(g) Examine the bottom of the sink after the water has come to rest. What do you find?

Conclusion: Answer the questions.

Diagram: Make an outline sketch of the apparatus.

Practical applications: Rapidly flowing streams carry much soil and rock in suspension. This rock is deposited wherever the current of the stream is impeded. Lands which are covered with vegetation tend to slow up the force of streams and to allow a comparatively small amount of soil to be carried away. The great delta of the Mississippi River is an example of how a river deposits its suspended particles when the current is slowed.

EXPERIMENT 160

Question: How does water sort dirt or soil into layers?

Materials: Soil containing fine gravel, sand, and clay; water; 1-quart fruit jar.

Directions: Put two inches of soil into the fruit jar, fill it with water, and put on the cover. Shake well. Allow the jar to stand quietly while the contents settle. Which part of the dirt settles first? After the jar has stood quietly for a few minutes, look at the material that has settled and at the water. What was the second part of the soil to settle? What remains suspended in the water? Examine the jar after it has stood long enough for the water to become clear. What has become of the fine material (clay) that was suspended in the water? Is the material in the bottom of the jar mixed together or it is in layers?

Diagram: Show how the water has sorted the soil into layers.

Conclusion: Answer the question.

Practical application: This is the process by means of which dirt is sorted into the layers that form rock. If you can find a hillside one side of which has been cut away, notice the layers in which the dirt exists.

Chapter LVIII

WHAT THE SOLID EARTH IS MADE OF

Rock, water, air, and living things make up the earth. Some of these we have been studying, their action and interaction. In the present chapter we shall continue our study of the solid rock substance of earth. We shall learn what the rock is like some thousands of miles underground and some two or three miles under the sea. We shall find out how the scientist studies the rock buried deep under miles of other rock and sea water. We shall learn what rocks are made of, and how they are made in nature's laboratory. Finally, there will be a brief word on how man, an intelligent part of the earth, has sought to use other parts to advantage. Man first used rock by seeking shelter in a cave or by seizing a crude chunk of flint as a weapon or a tool. Science now takes from the same bare rocks, amid which the cave man lived, the materials for a great airship and an ocean liner that could carry around the globe the population of many an ancient city.

Inside the earth. Our deepest mines penetrate the earth for about a mile and a half. That is a small fraction of the 4000 miles to the center of the earth. The rocks of the mines are not very different from the rocks that we see on the surface. Since we cannot learn what the deep interior of the earth is like from direct observation, we arrive at our knowledge indirectly. Let us see what the scientist has actually observed and what are his conclusions about the earth's interior.

As we go down into the earth, the temperature increases about one degree Fahrenheit for each 55 feet of descent. At this rate the temperature would be sufficient to melt every known kind of rock at only a small fraction of the

Fig. 522. Seismographs. The heavy balls stand still as the earth shakes. Writing points projecting from the balls write the record of the earthquake.

distance to the center of the earth. But the rock probably does not melt.

Rock is heavy. The pressure of a mile of overlying rock can be calculated but hardly imagined. The deeper down the greater the pressure. This enormous pressure prevents the heated rocks from melting. The interior of the earth is probably more rigid than steel. The rock, however, is plastic (capable of being molded) under the pressure in which it lies.

The denser, heavier materials of the earth's substance are pulled by gravity down toward the center of the earth. The plastic condition of the hot rocks would allow the continuous sinking of heavier material. The deeper part is probably largely iron and iron mixed with stone. Outside of the iron parts are the flowing or plastic rocks. Finally we come to rocks of the outer crust, the rocks that we see about us on the earth's surface. This crust is a very thin shell about the interior, proportionally thinner than the shell of an egg.

Evidence from several sources leads to the view that the deep interior of the earth is very solid. One of the most convincing observations is the speed of travel of earthquake waves. Earthquake waves from Japan are felt by seismographs around the world (Fig. 522). They have been timed in their travel from Japan to England (Fig. 523). Their speed is that of waves traveling through a solid body, not through a liquid.

The continents float. Why have the continents risen above the level of the sea bottom? A recent theory is based on the different density of the rocks of the land and of the sea bottom. We cannot see rocks under the depths of the sea, but their pull of gravity has been measured. It shows that the rocks under the sea are heavier than those of the land. The lavas also from volcanoes of the ocean are denser than those from land volcanoes. All the rocks of the crust, under the sea and on the land, lie upon the plastic heated rock below. The heavier rocks of the sea bottom have sunk deeper than the lighter rocks of the land. The continents have been floated up on the denser rock.

Fire rocks and water rocks. Even the rock of the continents has been at some time heated and plastic. Some of it has come to the surface as fluid lava. More of it has cooled below the surface. Once on the surface, as we have seen, rock eventually crumbles away to form soil. This soil again may collect in the beds of lakes and oceans and become rock, but it is a very different kind of rock from that which was formed by cooling from the molten state.

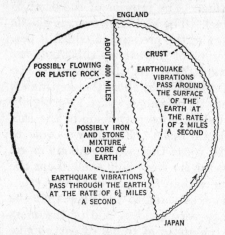

Fig. 523. The speed at which earthquake waves travel around the earth and through it tell that the interior is solid and heavy.

Rocks from earth's melting pot. Rocks that have been molten and have hardened are called *igneous rocks* (Latin *ignis*, fire). The lavas from volcanoes and fissures are examples. Sometimes the lava cools very fast and produces volcanic glass or *obsidian*, once prized by the Indians

Fig. 524. A granite quarry in Minnesota.

for the making of sharp arrowheads. Often the molten rocks have cooled below a surface still covered by overlying rocks. They then cool very slowly and their various minerals form crystals. Such a crystalline rock is *granite*. It is a very hard rock that stands up as mountain peaks when other rocks have been eroded away. Because of its resistance to the weather, it is a very valuable building stone. *Basalt* is a darker colored, fine-grained igneous rock. *Pumice* is formed by explosive volcanoes that blow the molten lava full of bubbles of gas. Pumice is often found floating on the surface of the sea after violent eruptions.

What rocks are made of. If you should examine a piece of granite, you will readily see that it is made of several different constituents, or *minerals*. One of these is a glistening white mineral that is very hard. You cannot scratch it with a knife point. This is *quartz*. A duller white or flesh-colored mineral in the granite is *feldspar*. It often is glistening, but can be told from the quartz by its flat faces and duller color. A third mineral in the granite you can recognize by its thin sheets and black color. This is *mica*. When granite weathers away, the mica and quartz make a soil that often glistens as with tiny bits of glass. In some rocks, sheets of mica can be dug out with a knife. Though granite is composed chiefly of three minerals, some rocks are formed of only one mineral, as sandstone or quartz.

Rocks from water. The material which drops to the bottom of streams, lakes, and oceans is *sediment*. As it settles, it is pressed together into layers or *strata*. Since the sediment gathers and the water continues to deposit additional soil on the layers already there, the fine materials are pressed together firmly by their own weight and that of the water above them. The grains of sand are often cemented together by compounds of lime, iron, and other substances. Pressure and cementing make solid rock. Rocks formed in this way are called *sedimentary rocks*.

About four fifths of the land surface of the earth is composed of sedimentary rock. It covers such a great part of the earth because water, which deposited it, has always been working in most parts of the earth in the form of springs, brooks, rivers, seas, or oceans. Sedimentary rock is still being formed, as it has been through the past centuries.

Sandstone. You have noticed how particles of sand cling together when they are wet. If sand is pressed together for centuries by water and by an enormous load of rock and soil, while cement-laden water trickles through it, strata of sandstone are formed. Sometimes gravel and pebbly sand and mud have thus become consolidated into rock. Such rock is called *pudding stone* or *conglomerate*.

Shale. Have you ever made figures and small houses of modeling clay? It is so pliable that it can be molded into any shape you wish. Clay is composed of the finest soil particles. You may find it at the bottom of brooks and in other places in thin, sticky layers.

When deposits of clay are pressed upon for centuries by millions of tons of rock, or when water containing cement seeps through, *shale* is formed. It is found in brittle layers

Fig. 525. Chalk cliffs on the coast of England. Chalk is made of the skeletons of microscopic sea animals. How long was the chalk accumulating on the sea bottom?

of flat, smooth rock, and may sometimes be found in the walls and roofs of mines and along the sides of ravines.

Limestone. In sedimentary rocks which were formed at the bottom of bodies of water, we often find other materials in addition to soil. Water supports millions of large and small animals. Some of them, such as snails, clams, and oysters, are inclosed in shells. All these shells, and the bones of fish and other sea animals contain lime. When the animals die, the softer parts of their bodies disappear. The solid parts, including the shell and bone skeletons, sink to the bottom. There they pile up and are subjected to the same pressure and conditions as other particles at the bottom of the water. Eventually they form *limestone*, a variety of sedimentary rock. A great part of the limestone is composed of the skeletons of microscopic animals that live floating at and near the surface of the open oceans. The famous chalk cliffs of Dover and the chalk beds of our own country are softer rocks made of the skeletons of such microscopic animals of ages past. (Fig. 525.)

Dead plants make rock. A small portion of sedimentary rock is formed from partially decayed plant matter such as leaves, logs, and twigs which have dropped to the bottom of lakes and swamps and have been buried by the later sediment. *Bituminous* or *soft coal* is a variety of sedimentary rock formed from such accumulations.

Transformed rocks. The folding that rocks undergo in mountain-making heats them.   Contact with hot molten rocks often adds to the heat.   Such heating changes the rocks.   Hence they are called *metamorphic*, meaning "having to do with change in form."   Limestone is changed to marble, shale to slate, bituminous coal to anthracite.   Metamorphic rocks are often found in volcanic regions and in low hills, such as those east of the Appalachians, that are the worn-down remnants of ancient mountains.

New rocks from old. Sand, pebbles, and clay are made by nature from the rocks and are built into rocks again.   The geologist can sometimes locate the older rocks that were weathered away to furnish the material for the newer.   This helps him to draw a map showing how continents and seas looked millions of years before man appeared on the earth. The older rocks mark the land surface.   The newer rocks mark the sea where the sand, pebbles, and clay were being laid down as sediment.   Nature thus uses the same materials over and over again, tearing down old structures and building new with the materials.

What fossils tell. Animals that lived in the ancient mud and sands, and others that swam in the waters, left their remains in the sedimentary rocks.   Land animals that made an unwary step into oozy mud or quicksand have left record of their existence in the rocks.   Plants, too, have fallen and been engulfed.   Mud and sand that covered them have preserved their remains.   The bodies, bones, or shells are gone, but in their place is stone that preserves their form, sometimes even to the microscopic structures.   In the Arizona desert is a forest of stone trees.   The living forest was overwhelmed by volcanic ash.   The trees died.   Water oozing through deposited the substance of which sand is made, silica, in place of the wood cells.   When the volcanic ash was weathered away in later ages, the hard silica was exposed.   These remains of plants and animals are the *fossils* that tell the history of past life on the earth.   It is a fragmentary history.   Sometimes a complete skeleton remains, but more often a part or even a footprint or an impression of a leaf. The scientist pieces together the various bits of evidence that tell of past life. Thus he learns the long story of the development of life on the earth. The evidence of fossils with evidence from the origin of rocks helps also to reconstruct the maps of land and sea millions of years ago.

Using the rocks. In his search for the means of living comfortably, man has found the rocks a rich treasure house. Stone is the most durable building material he has found. Granite is selected for durability and beauty. Massachusetts, Vermont, and Maine have supplied a large section of the country. North Carolina and California are also granite states.

Sandstone was once widely used for building stone, but some sandstones crumble badly. As grindstones certain sandstones have served man well in an age of iron. Limestone is more valuable as a building stone and often more beautiful. It is also the greatest source of lime. When limestone is heated, carbon dioxide is driven off, leaving lime. Limestone also plays a necessary part in the age of iron and steel, for mixed with coke it enables man to extract iron from its ore. Marble is the stone of special beauty for works of art and buildings. Slate because it is easily split into thin slabs has long served for roofing.

The search for ores of iron, copper, lead, aluminum, and other metals has taken the white man to the jungles and the frozen north. Which metal is of most value would be hard to say. Without iron we should have no modern machinery. Without copper our electrical development would be slow, for copper is the best conductor of electricity. Aluminum, because of its lightness, is of increasing value in air travel. Alloys of aluminum with other metals are proving so valuable in construction that aluminum may some day surpass iron. Gold and silver are useful not only as currency, but in the industrial arts in a multitude of ways.

The three chemical substances most needed for fertilizers on our farms are obtained from rock deposits. Beds of phosphate rocks are found in Florida, Tennessee, and Wyoming, and elsewhere. Some of these phosphate rocks were

Fig. 526. A forest of the coal age. How do we know the trees looked like this?

made from the deposits of bones which were composed of calcium phosphate. Nitrogen fertilizer has been imported by millions of tons from Chile, where it is found in great beds of sodium nitrate. Beds of rock in Germany have supplied our third important fertilizer, potassium.

Coal, the base of our energy supply for industry, is a rock formed from plant remains (Fig. 526). Petroleum is probably also the accumulation of materials from living things of bygone ages, but scientists have not yet proved the source beyond dispute.

EXPERIMENT 161

Question: What is a test for limestone?

Materials: Hydrochloric acid; glass rod; limestone; several other rocks.

Directions: Using a glass rod, put a drop of the hydrochloric acid on each of the rocks. Notice in each case whether the rock fizzes. What is the only rock on which the acid acts?

Conclusion: Answer the question.

Practical application: This is the test used to distinguish between limestone (or marble) and other rocks.

EXPERIMENT 162 (OPTIONAL)

To make an imitation seismograph. Attach a bristle to the bottom of a heavy pendulum bob so that it projects downward. Support the pendulum so that the tip of the bristle just touches the top of a table. Now smoke a strip of paper over a candle or other smoky flame. **Draw** the smoked paper slowly under the bristle tip with the bristle just making a line on the smoked paper. While the paper is being drawn under the bristle, have someone thump or strike the far end of the table. The record on the paper is an imitation of the seismographic record of an earthquake.

EXPERIMENT 163

Question: How can you imitate the formation of one type of rock?

Materials: Plaster of Paris or Portland cement; sand or pebbles; cardboard or wood frames.

Directions: Mix up the cement or plaster of Paris with water, and mix in the sand or pebbles. Use 1 part cement, 3 parts sand, and 6 parts pebbles. Use just enough water to make it pour slowly. Pour into the frames and set aside to harden until the next day. You can then imitate one kind of erosion by dripping dilute hydrochloric acid upon it.

Results: Report condition next day and result of dripping acid.

Conclusion: What kinds of rock may be formed in similar manner? What takes the place of the hydrochloric acid in nature? In what sort of country should you expect to find similar erosion? What structures which you know of are formed in similar manner?

EXPERIMENT 164

Question: How may imitation fossils be made?

Materials: A pint bowl; an old spoon; a pasteboard-box cover about 3 inches square and $\frac{1}{2}$ inch deep; Portland cement; water; a small fern leaf or other object with which to make an impression. Plaster of Paris may be used instead of Portland cement.

Directions: (a) Mix the plaster of Paris or cement as in the preceding experiment.

(b) Lay the fern leaf on the surface of the cement paste in the box cover and gently press it into the cement so that the upper surface of the leaf is even with the surface of the cement.

(c) Set it away for 24 hours with the leaf lying embedded in the cement surface.

(d) Examine the cement and the fern leaf. What has happened to the pasty cement?

(e) Lift the leaf out of the cement block. It may be necessary to use the point of a knife or a pin to remove it neatly.

(f) What do you find where the fern was embedded?

Diagram: Make a line drawing of the cement or plaster block with the fern impression in the surface.

Conclusion: Answer the question.

Practical application: The experiment that you have performed with pure cement or plaster in a few hours represents what happens over long periods, perhaps thousands of years, in the earth where cement is impure and mixed with other substances.

FIELD AND LABORATORY STUDY

Make a collection of rocks of your region. Identify them from books on rocks and minerals borrowed from the library. A school museum can be built up in this way.

CHAPTER LIX

THE SCIENCE OF THE SEA

Through the centuries men have loved and feared the sea. Science is banishing the terror of it. Down through the Middle Ages sailors, daring as they were, feared unseen monsters and demons of the open ocean. The scientific vision of Columbus and other men in the days of the reawakening of science banished the terror demons. Science has now made the sea as safe as the land and is ever increasing its value. Weather bureaus have reduced the danger from storms. The international ice patrol by the ships of the U. S. Coast Guard keeps track of advancing Arctic ice. Currents that bring ice from the polar oceans, and others that bring warm waters to temper colder lands, the tides, waves in calm and storm, fish and other life of the waters, the content of sea water, the bottoms of the ocean and their changes—all these and more are subjects of study included in the science of *oceanography*.

The depth of the ocean. The ocean reaches its greatest depth at a point between the Philippine Islands and Japan, where it is 7 miles deep. Mount Everest in the Himalaya Mountains of Asia, the highest mountain peak in the world, rises about $5\frac{1}{2}$ miles above sea level. The highest point of land in the world is vertically only about 12 miles higher than the deepest known part of the sea. The average elevation of the land above sea level is about $\frac{1}{2}$ mile, and the average depth of the ocean is about $2\frac{1}{2}$ miles. The height of the highest mountains is trifling compared to the diameter of the earth. It would be represented in about the right proportion by some slightly crinkled tissue paper pasted on the outside of an ordinary school globe.

Plummets, pieces of lead attached to long wires, let down from the sides of the ships, were the first means of learning the depths. The echo method, which depends upon the time it takes for sound to be reflected from the ocean bottom, is used extensively now for measuring ocean depths. Temperature is measured with registering thermometers, and water bottles that open and close at definite depths bring up samples of water. Dredges and other apparatus are used to drag the floor of the ocean and bring up specimens of the materials covering it (Fig. 527).

How does the ocean bottom look? Our knowledge of ocean geography is far from complete, but in the opinion of most authorities, it varies greatly from that of dry land. In comparison with the land, the bed of the sea is flat, with relatively few definitely pronounced hills, valleys, and mountains. There are many elevations, but they rise with gentle slopes. There are many sloping volcanic cones, not so steep as land volcanoes. Thousands of these cones exist in the South Pacific Ocean. Usually they are too low to rise above the surface of the sea, but occasionally they are high enough to form small islands. Then they are sometimes topped by coral islands or reefs, particularly in the tropics.

Systems of mountain ridges under water sometimes emerge above the surface, as in the case of Cuba and the islands surrounding it. There are also broad plateau lands under the ocean somewhat similar to those on land.

What is on the ocean bottom. When you are bathing in shallow water and pick up a handful of material from the bottom, you will find that it is largely composed of pebbles, sand, or mud. This material was deposited by rivers in shallow water near the shores, or washed directly down from the shores and further ground up by the pounding breakers.

Over most of the deep ocean is an ooze composed of the skeletons of microscopic animals of the sea which when consolidated forms limestone. In greater depths is an ooze composed of silica, the substance of sand. The microscopic limy skeletons are dissolved as they slowly settle through the sea and fail to reach the greater depths. Some microscopic sea animals have skeletons of silica which is very much more difficult to dissolve.

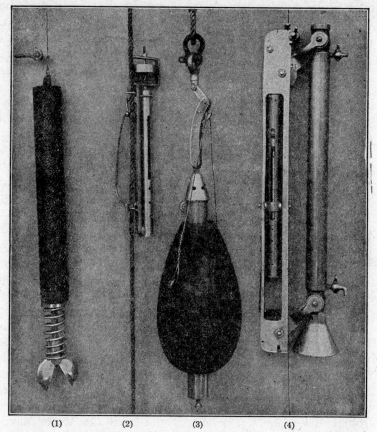

(1)   (2)   (3)   (4)

Fig. 527. Apparatus for studying the sea bottom. (1) For collecting specimens from bottom. (2) Registering thermometer. (3) Cylinder with sinker for collecting water. (4) Thermometer with reversing case.

At still greater depths, a type of material is found which is unlike any ever found on land. It is red clay of powderlike consistency and it accumulates in water at a depth of about 18,000 feet. This red clay covers more than a third of the entire sea bed and is believed to have formed to a large extent from volcanic dust and from dust blown from the land. It contains insoluble portions of limy skeletons and shells, such as the teeth of sharks. Because similar red clay material has never been found on land, scientists are led to believe that no part of the present land was ever covered by what is now the very deep sea.

Ocean currents.　The currents of the oceans, or some of them, are like mighty rivers of the sea, rivers flowing between banks of stiller water.　The Gulf Stream is like a thousand Mississippis combined, large enough to carry the water from all the great rivers of the world.　Ships from New York bound for Europe can recognize the Gulf Stream when they enter it.　It has bluer and warmer water and often carries living things of the tropic seas (Fig. 528).　Somewhat similar currents occur in other oceans (Fig. 529).　Cold currents steal down from the polar seas —for example the Labrador current along the eastern American coast, and the Humboldt current along the west coast of South America.

Fig. 528.　Portuguese man of war.

We learn in another chapter that the difference in the heating power of the sun's rays at the Equator and in the polar regions accounts for a circulation of water over the globe. The precise course of the current is affected by other forces.　Blowing westward toward the Equator are the trade winds.　They would tend to send ocean waters in a circle around the globe.　The continents turn the water aside. The westerly winds in the temperate zones drive the currents toward the east again until the opposite coast again turns them Equatorward.　Thus the great eddies or whirls move in the northern sphere in the direction of the hands of a clock, or clockwise; in the southern hemisphere, they move counterclockwise (see Fig. 529).

What makes the waves?　The ocean is never still. Waves are formed when the wind blows over the surface of the water.　You perhaps have seen waves on the ocean or on a lake when you felt no wind.　The waves run on when the wind has ceased, and spread hundreds of miles beyond the

Fig. 529. The ocean currents of the earth. What makes the water move and what determines the direction it shall follow?

place of disturbance. On a pond there may be only gentle ripples lapping the shore. In violent ocean storms they may be forty or more feet high. Usually the ocean wave is not more than ten feet high.

Have you ever watched wind blowing over a field of wheat or hay? There you see wave motion. The grain bows in a long trough and rises in place again, while the movement passes on.

In spite of the fluidity of water, it hardly moves with the waves. You can prove this for yourself by throwing a large cork into a rough sea. It will bob up and down but will move forward only because of the currents of water, not because of wave motion. In wave motion chiefly the form goes forward, not the water itself, as you can see in the field of grain, although there is some forward movement of the water.

If you have been bathing in the breakers, however, you know that they will tumble you along toward the shore. The Hawaiian natives ride ashore on surf boards through the breakers. When waves run into shallow water, they reach a depth where there is not enough water to form a full wave. The front of the wave is lacking and the top curls over and forms a breaker. The water then shoots forward.

40

The sea is a great solution. Sea water is a solution of many chemical substances. We learned in another chapter why the sea is salty. (See page 122.) Salt is brought by the rivers from the land. The rivers bring in a great variety of other chemical compounds in addition to common salt. Many of these are intensely bitter to the taste.

Practically all the substances that we find in the rocks we find also in the water. Even gold is there, although in such minute quantities that it would not pay to extract it.

The concentration of salt and other dissolved substances makes it easier to float in the sea than in fresh water. Perhaps you have noticed it when bathing. Some parts of the sea are saltier than others. Where great rivers pour in fresh water, the salt is more diluted. In inclosed seas like the Mediterranean where the sun is warm and the air clear, greater evaporation takes out more water but leaves the salt behind.

Life in the sea. All the elements that plants and animals need in their bodies are in the sea. It is not surprising, therefore, that the sea is teeming with life. Along the shallower waters larger life is more abundant for there the feeding is better. Plants must live where the sun reaches them, and light does not penetrate more than a quarter of a mile and is weak below 200 feet. In the sea as on land, animals depend upon plants for food and so live where plants can get light. In the middle of the ocean there is a dearth of larger life, but the microscope shows myriads of living things, both plant and animal. Sometimes this microscopic life is so abundant as to give the sea for miles a pink or a shining brown color. The living things that spend their lives down below in the dark waters must depend for their food on the things living and dead that drop down from the surface waters. Down in the greatest depths no life has ever been found by the dredges that explore those hidden places. Perhaps no oxygen penetrates to those depths or the food substances are all dissolved in the miles of water above them. These great deeps are life deserts.

The pressure on deep-sea animals. Did it ever occur to you to inquire why animals under a mile or more of water were not crushed to death? When deep-sea animals are brought to the surface, sometimes their stomachs and intestines are forced out through their mouths. Their internal pressure is much greater than the pressure of the atmosphere. The pressure inside an animal's body balances the pressure of the water at the depth at which the animal lives, just as the internal pressure of a man's body balances the atmospheric pressure at which he lives. A man's body must sustain a pressure of 15 pounds to the square inch (see page 22). The body of an animal living at a depth of three miles of sea water must sustain a pressure of over two tons to the square inch.

The sea serves man. Like many lower creatures man has fitted himself to make use of the sea. Life was long in the sea before it had fitted itself to the land, but once fitted to land it became very difficult to return to the sea. Men of the Old Stone Age were land creatures, perhaps getting a little food along the sea's edge. All through the centuries of ancient history man in his voyages upon the sea clung close to the shores. In ancient times the sea separated peoples; now it unites them. The sea is man's greatest pathway from one part of the earth to another.

The sea also furnishes supplies. Fish were responsible for many ancient coast settlements. Fisheries took men across the Atlantic to the Newfoundland Banks. Tropic waters and Arctic alike are fished. Sea plants, too, furnish products. Iodine was long obtained only from seaweeds and part of our supplies still comes from that source. Even the water furnishes supplies. Salt is obtained by evaporation in the sunnier climates (see page 123).

EXPERIMENT 165

Question: Is anything dissolved in ocean water and in fresh water?

Materials: Ocean water, fresh water, Bunsen burner or stove, two 8-ounce evaporating dishes.

Directions: (a) Fill the evaporating dishes half full, one with ocean water and one with fresh water.

(b) Place them on the stove or over the flame and allow them to boil until the water is gone. What becomes of the water?

(*c*) After allowing the dishes to cool, examine the substance which is left in them.

(*d*) Roll between your thumb and forefinger a pinch of the powder which you find. Taste it. What do you decide it is?

Diagram: Make a drawing of the evaporating dishes over the flame.

Conclusion: Answer the question.

Practical application: Water contains dissolved rocks and minerals. Certain rocks dissolved in water make it "hard." We can separate the water from the substance dissolved in it by boiling and allowing the water to evaporate.

ADDITIONAL QUESTIONS TO THINK OUT

1. If the earth had no atmosphere, it would probably have no soil. Why?

2. What evidence is there that the earth's surface in past ages was worn down by the same processes that we see today?

3. Do forests aid or retard soil-making?

4. If rain is always wearing away land, how is it that there is any land left?

5. Why do you find round rocks in the bed of a stream but angular rocks at the foot of a cliff?

6. If you found a section of a hill made up of rounded stones mixed with gravel, what should you conclude as to its past history?

7. In Nova Scotia coal mines run out under the sea. How do you account for coal under the sea?

8. Why are the chief fishing grounds found in shallow waters, or banks?

9. Why does mud settle when a river flows into a lake?

10. Why does a stream usually deposit more material at the sides than in the center?

11. In some places off the coast of Florida fresh water rises in the midst of the sea in such quantities that sailing ships formerly filled their water casks there. Where does the fresh water come from in such quantities?

12. Why do not the bottom waters of the deep sea show the heating effects of the interior heat of the earth?

13. Are fossils found in volcanic rock? in granite?

14. Why is there granite in New England and New York but none in the peninsula of Florida?

15. Why is it believed that the interior of the earth is hot?

16. In what direction do the chief mountains of Europe trend? of America? How does the trend affect man's use of the continents?

17. How do the shapes of the continents affect man?

18. Why was there a glacial period? First write down a hypothesis (guess) of your own. Then write down all the evidence for and against

your hypothesis.   Finally look up the hypothesis of scientists in a large encyclopedia or in books on geology or physiography.

19. Look up the question whether mountain and polar glaciers are now advancing or retreating.

20. If the southern states had been glaciated, how would their present surface appear?

21. Why do some lakes have salt water?

22. If there are lakes or swamps near your home, visit them and decide why they are there.

23. If you have seen salt marshes near the coast, try to explain why they are there.   Form your own hypothesis and then look up the scientists' explanation in the library.

24. Why do you suppose there are so many small islands dotted over the map of the South Pacific?

25. Where does the sea get its sand? its lime deposits?

26. What becomes of all the water that rivers pour into the ocean?

27. Why is the sea water not limy as it is salty?

UNIT FIFTEEN

WHAT DETERMINES WEATHER

A ball game or a picnic spoiled by a rain makes one wish for a way of knowing in advance what the weather will be. There is a way of knowing, although predictions sometimes go wrong because our knowledge is incomplete. In spite of an occasional wrong prediction, we rightly have faith in weather forecasts. Mariners delay the sailing of ships when the storm signals fly at the ports. Fruit growers make ready to light fires in the orchards when frosts are predicted. River men and dwellers along the large rivers watch carefully when flood warnings are announced. Aviators get the latest weather advices before flying. By predicting weather conditions, the weather bureaus save us millions of dollars each year.

We can easily understand the general principles of weather science, and from whatever information we can collect we can make predictions of our own. The government has information collected from thousands of miles and may be in better position to make a prediction, but it is interesting to compare the government prediction with our own. Science still has much to learn before every prediction will come true and before the weather man never will be in doubt. The coöperation of the different nations, such as the establishment of weather stations in the Arctic, the broadcasting of radio messages from ships on the high seas to the government bureaus, airplane flights for observation of weather conditions at high altitudes, and the study of the sun which is the fundamental cause of our weather are all helping to make weather prediction more nearly perfect.

In this unit we shall study what makes storms and fair weather, why it rains and hails and snows, why we have hot spells and cold waves, what a thunderstorm, a tornado, and a hurricane are, why and where the wind blows. We shall see how government weather maps are made and how the forecaster uses them to make his predictions of the weather for our vicinity. We shall show how you can make your own weather prediction with or without the government weather maps.

CHAPTER LX

CONDITIONS GOVERNING WEATHER AND CLIMATE

Why the wind blows. If you pour water on a table top, it will spread out in all directions. When air pours down on the earth's surface, it spreads out in the same way. There are certain areas, not always the same places, where the air is pouring down and spreading out.

The air pours down because it is colder and therefore heavier than the adjoining air. We can locate the areas of heavy air with the barometer. The heavy air forces the mercury to rise in the barometer. Therefore these areas are called *high-pressure* areas or simply *highs*.

There are also *low-pressure* areas or *lows* that we can locate with the barometer. In the lows the air is warmer and therefore lighter than the surrounding air. The warmer, lighter air is floated up by the colder, heavier air around it, just as a cork lying in a basin is floated by the heavier water.

The air in motion on the surface of the earth is wind. The wind always blows from a high to a low pressure. The greater the difference of pressure, and the nearer highs and lows are together, the more violent the wind.

Wind blowing from high to low is diverted by the motion of the earth. If the earth were standing still, the air pouring down in a high-pressure area would flow straight out. By the motion of the earth, however, it is turned steadily to the right and so blows out spirally, in the direction that the hands of a clock move (Fig. 531). Blowing into low-pressure area, it is similarly turned to the right and blows in a counterclockwise spiral (Fig. 531). In the Southern Hemisphere the winds are diverted to the left so that the winds around a high form

Fig. 530. Studying upper air currents with a pilot balloon. A radiosonde, an automatic radio transmitter, sends back weather information.

a counterclockwise spiral and the winds around a low form a clockwise spiral.

Why it becomes cloudy, and rains. Air dries the soil and carries away the moisture. Similarly it takes water from lakes and oceans. It receives large quantities by transpiration from plants. Air dissolves water as water dissolves sugar.

Warm water dissolves more sugar than does cold water. If you make a saturated sugar solution (a solution containing all the sugar the water will dis-

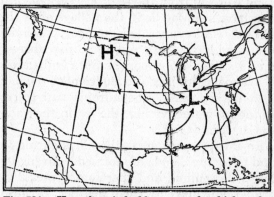

Fig. 531. How the winds blow around a high and a low pressure area.

solve) in warm water and then allow the solution to cool, some sugar will be dropped out of solution and will appear in the bottom of the dish. Similarly if warm air dissolves all

the water it can hold, and then the air is cooled, water will drop out of the air. Cooling leads to condensation of water. We have seen in the unit on air that an ice-water pitcher "sweats" because of the condensations of atmospheric moisture.

At night the air near the ground cools, and, if it contains much dissolved water vapor, some of this water is deposited as *dew*.

Fig. 532.   An anemometer for measuring wind velocity.

Grass cools faster than rocks and soil so that early in the evening it may soak your shoes with dew. If the night is cold, *frost* may form. When the sun comes up, the air is warmed and the dew dissolves in the air and disappears.

Perhaps you have seen *fog* collect in the harbor as the cool wind came in from the sea. Or perhaps in the early morning you have seen fog lie in the valleys after the sun has warmed the hills and evaporated their fog. Driving along a road in the evening you may often find fog where the road dips into a cool valley and none where it climbs the warmer hill.

Whenever air is cooled sufficiently, the moisture is condensed into fine droplets. These droplets are the mist on the outside of the ice-water pitcher, the fog in the valley, and the clouds in the sky.

In low-pressure areas the air is steadily cooled as it rises, and therefore clouds are formed. In high-pressure areas the air is descending and therefore is steadily warmed. Highs are accompanied by clear weather, because the warming air will hold all its moisture without condensation into clouds or rain.

If cooling continues long enough and there is sufficient water vapor in the air, the tiny droplets of the clouds steadily grow in size. Finally they reach a size when the air will no longer support them and the condensed moisture comes down as rain. If condensation occurs below freezing point, snow crystals are formed.

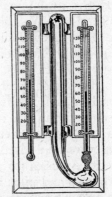

Fig. 533. Wet and dry bulb thermometers. Used to measure the humidity of the air.

Water in the air. The amount of water dissolved in air determines its *humidity*. The weight of water in a cubic foot of air is the *absolute humidity*. If we want to know whether it will rain, we are more interested in knowing the *relative humidity*—that is, the amount actually present compared with the amount that would saturate the air at whatever temperature it has. The capacity to dissolve water varies with the temperature. For any temperature, a relative humidity of 100 means that the air is saturated with moisture, and precipitation will follow a drop in temperature.

Did you ever see a little doll that would indicate coming rain by the changing color of her skirt? The skirt has been dipped in a solution of cobalt chloride. When the air is dry, the skirt is blue. When the humidity increases in the air, the cobalt chloride absorbs moisture and turns pink. Sometimes the rain indicator is a painted landscape with a sky painted with cobalt chloride.

The scientific instrument for measuring humidity is a *hygrometer*. In one type, a human hair lengthens as it absorbs moisture from the air and allows a pointer to move over a dial. In another type two thermometers are mounted as in Figure 533. The bulb of one is surrounded by a wet wick. If the air is dry, the evaporation from the wet bulb will be great and the evaporation cools the thermometer. The humidity can be ascertained for the various readings of wet and dry bulbs by referring to prepared tables.

Highs and lows travel. Look at a weather map issued by the U. S. Weather Bureau (Fig. 534). Find the high and the low. Now look at the weather map of the next day (Fig. 535). You see that the high and the low have moved eastward. In this manner the highs and lows follow one another across the United States. Predicting the weather is based in part on the movements of highs and lows with their accompanying rain and fair weather.

How the weather map is made. At regular hours trained observers read instruments at several hundred stations from Arctic America to the West Indies and on ships at sea. Airplanes and pilot balloons also report. These observations are on air pressure, temperature, humidity, rainfall or snow-fall, cloudiness, wind direction, and velocity. The observations are speeded by wire and radio to central stations. With these data the central stations make the weather map.

When a storm is coming. Select a place on the weather map in Figure 534, just to the east of a low. Suppose you are living at that spot. You awake in the morning to find the wind blowing from the east (an east wind). As the day goes by, clouds increase. If you look at the barometer, you will find that it is falling. At sea level it may read about 29.4. It is not very cold, but if it is winter, it may be chilly, and if summer, it may be warm and "sticky." Probably by the next day the rain is falling (see weather map). You are in the midst of a *cyclonic storm* or *cyclone*. The rainy weather may last for a day or two, or even three. By that time the wind has set in from the west or northwest (see weather map). The sky gradually clears, the barometer rises, it gets cool. The storm has passed. You are then in an anticyclone (see weather map) or high-pressure area.

Cyclones, or storms, follow one another across the country at intervals of a few days. The *cyclone*, as the term is used by the scientist, must not be confused with the violent "twister"

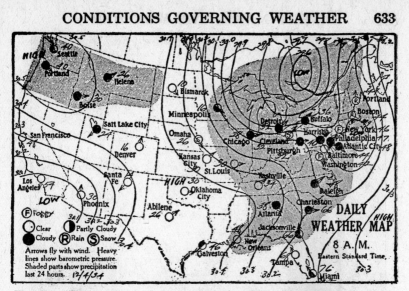

Fig. 534. The weather map for December 4, 1934. The LOW is the storm center. Where did it move to during the next 24 hours? Learn the meaning of each kind of marking.

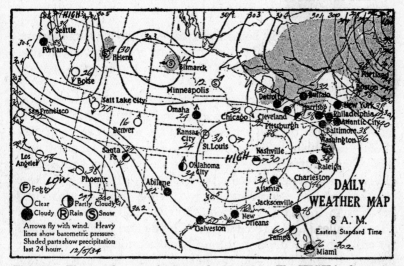

Fig. 535. The weather map for December 5, 1934. The HIGH is the center of fair weather. Where has it moved from in the last 24 hours? See also Experiment 168.

Fig. 536. Clouds and winds have a meaning in predicting weather.
This is a cumulus cloud. Watch for them to see what follows.

or tornado which is sometimes called by the same name.
Cyclones are our usual rainstorms, and may be very gentle.
Each storm extends over a large area, sometimes several
hundred miles.

Air masses and air fronts. Sometimes a great mass of
air covering thousands of square miles of Arctic Canada
moves southward and eastward. This air is cold and dry
(Polar-Canadian). The edge of the advancing air mass is a
cold front. It pushes under the warmer air to southward,
chills it, and produces clouds and rain. Then cold, clear
weather follows. Sometimes a warm, wet mass of air moves
north from the Gulf of Mexico (Tropical-Gulf). A *warm front*
advances against the colder air. Clouds and rain are formed
by chilling. Then warm, humid weather follows. Other air
masses advance from the Pacific and from the Atlantic. The
weather forecasters map such advancing fronts to predict
the weather.

Fig. 537. A thunderstorm at Pensacola, Florida. Note the high pile of clouds, a thunderhead, due to uprush of air. Locate the rain.

Thunderstorms.   On a warm summer day you often may see bright, white clouds like piles of wool toward noon or afternoon.   They are called *thunderheads*.   The air below them is warm and rising.   As it rises to the cooler regions, it expands and cools and its moisture is condensed into clouds. If the rising continues, the droplets increase in size.   The rising of the air may become a violent rush upward that piles the white clouds into a sharp pyramid.   Finally, the raindrops become too heavy for even the violent upward rush of wind to support, and they come down as a deluge of cold rain with a great draft of cold wind from the high places.

In ways that are not fully understood, the condensing of moisture into raindrops, their movement and breaking into smaller drops charges the clouds with electricity.   Giant sparks leap from cloud to cloud and from cloud to ground as flashes of *lightning*. The passage of the spark through the air heats it and the air expands and contracts violently with the vibrations that are *thunder*. Often the whirling air carries the drops up till they

Fig. 538.   A tornado or twister, a violent whirling storm.

freeze, lets them fall part way, and carries them up again and again, each time adding a new coating of ice, until they are too heavy to be again blown upward.   Thus *hailstones* are formed.

"**Twisters.**"   In parts of the United States, there are sometimes violent whirling storms with a black funnel of clouds that suck up or blow about anything that is loose on the ground—woodpiles, wagons, horses, chickens, cows, men. These storms are called *tornadoes* by the weather man, but are often called "cyclones" by the people whose land they tear through.   If a tornado passes over a house, the walls of the house may shoot outward and the boards whirl away. Boards and objects of like weight have been carried along for a mile.   In a Louisiana tornado a rooster was picked up on a farm and landed safely in the next parish.

These storms occur in spring and summer when the air suddenly starts to rise with the inrush of the surrounding cooler air.   The rush is so violent, estimated at 500 miles an hour, that a partial vacuum is created in the "eye" of the storm, which accounts for the "sucking" action and the tumbling outward of house walls due to the pressure of the inside air.   Tornados advance from the southwest to the northeast at 20 to 50 miles an hour.   In the open country they may be seen coming a long way off, so that it may sometimes be possible to get out of their reach by speeding to the northwest.   The storms are small in diameter, a few hundred yards across.   The early settlers on the plains dug "cyclone" cellars in which to retreat when one appeared to the southwest.

The earth's scheme of climate.   Great belts of high and low pressure divide the earth into climatic belts.   The hot equatorial regions form a low-pressure belt around the globe.   From each side wind blows in as the northeast and southeast trades

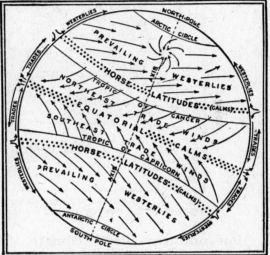

Fig. 539.   The wind belts of the earth.

(Fig. 539).   This incoming wind raises the hot air of the equatorial belt.   As it rises, it cools and produces abundant rain.   The equatorial low forms a belt of fitful winds and calms which the sailors called the "doldrums."   High aloft the rising air moves north and south toward the poles until it cools sufficiently to descend in another belt of calms at about 30° north and south latitude.   These calms are the "horse latitudes," so named, it is said, because ships carrying horses to Australia were becalmed there so long that the horses died and were thrown overboard.   Beyond the horse latitudes are the belts of westerly winds, "the prevailing westerlies," with their cyclonic storms that make our weather.

41

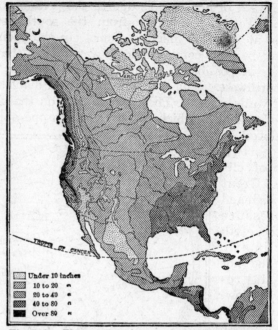

Fig. 540. The rainfall of North America. State the
reasons for the wet regions and for the dry regions.

How continents modify climate. The winds and calms
do not have it all their own way in making climate. Seas are
slow to heat and cool so that they modify the climate of the
land within their influence. The interiors of continents are
hotter in summer and colder in winter than the coasts. The
coldest spot on earth is not at the North Pole but in the interior of Siberia. The average winter temperature of the
Arctic is about 40° F. below zero, while the "cold pole" in
Siberia is 60° F. below zero. Western Europe and western
America are much tempered by the prevailing west winds
from the oceans (Fig. 540).

Mountains, also, upset the world climatic scheme. The
Cascades and the Sierras force the wind from the western
oceans to drop their moisture on the west side by chilling the
ascending winds. East of the mountain crests the air descends

Fig. 541. How has the climate influenced the Papuan's activity and civilization?

and is warmed. Therefore, east of the mountains are regions of dry lands (Fig. 540).

Land and sea breezes. Perhaps along the sea or lake shore you have noticed that by day there is generally a breeze from the sea—a sea breeze. Then about sundown there is often a calm. After that the breeze sets in from the land toward the sea—a land breeze.

When the sun shines on land and water, the land warms up faster than water. When the sun sets, the land cools off again faster than the water. Water is slow to gain heat and slow to lose it. The warmer surface makes the air above it warmer and therefore lighter. As long as the land is warmer, the cooler air above the sea flows in and displaces the warmer land air, thus forming a sea breeze. As long as the air above the land is cooler, the cool land air flows out and displaces the air above the sea, thus forming a land breeze.

Changing climates. Have you heard your elders tell of the cold winters we used to have? After we make allowances for the poor heating arrangements they had in their homes and the tricks memory may play them, there may still be something to their stories. Perhaps they remember some

Fig. 542.   How has the Siberian used the resources of his stern land for clothing, shelter, and weapons?

very cold winters and forget the milder ones.   For weather runs in cycles.   For a period of years the seasons increase in severity and then moderate for another period.   Besides the records of the weather bureaus, we have much older records of such changes.   The rings of growth in tree trunks (see page 386) show how much growth is made in a season. Tree trunks in Europe and America show series of better growing years alternating with periods of poorer years.   Some of these periods seem to be influenced by the periods of sun spots (see page 656).

There are longer periods, too, in which the climate varies. The ruins of cities dot the deserts of Asia where now no city could exist.   There are irrigation works where now there is no water.   An army would now die of thirst on the route on which Alexander's army marched to India.   Caesar's army found a wetter, colder climate in France than the French live in today.

If we go back to earlier ages in the earth's history, there is evidence of still greater changes.   An ice age covered northern Europe and America.   Still earlier warm-country trees grew in Greenland.   Coal in the Antarctic, where now is the bleakest land on the globe, tells of a climate warm enough to support dense vegetation. There are records in the rocks of earlier ice ages alternating with periods of mild and even hot climates. Earth's climates change as do the continents and oceans. All on earth is change. Even the positions of the North Pole and Equator seem to change.

What climate does to us. The progressive nations of earth live in regions of varying storms and sunshine. The changing weather stimulates human brains and muscles. When we have monotonous weather for several days, the work done in factories and in schools is poorer until a change comes. In climates where there is no change, progress lags. Some climates are too good to our bodies; they furnish food and shelter too easily (Fig. 541). Other regions are too severe, exhausting all human energies just to find food and shelter (Figs. 542 and 543). Between the extremes lies the ideal climate where farms yield surplus and cyclones and anticyclones stimulate man to labor and invent.

Fig. 543. The climate of northeast Siberia is so severe that all of man's energy is needed to obtain food and shelter.

EXPERIMENT 166

Question: How can I determine the relative humidity of the air in the classroom, using a hygrometer (wet- and dry-bulb thermometers)?

Materials: A hygrometer.

Theory: Read the two thermometers and determine from the table the relative humidity of the room. *Optional.* A committee from the class will find the relative humidity every day for a week, or longer, as directed by the teacher. From their results plot a *graph* for your notebook.

Diagram: Draw a hygrometer.

Conclusion: Answer the problem.

Practical application: What practical value is there to your results? See the weather map.

TABLE SHOWING RELATIVE HUMIDITY

DIFFERENCE BETWEEN DRY-AND WET-BULB THERMOMETERS

DRY THERMOM-ETER, °F.	1°	2°	3°	4°	5°	6°	7°	8°	9°	10°	11°	12°	13°	14°	15°
50	93	87	81	74	68	62	56	50	44	39	33	28	22	17	12
52	94	88	81	75	69	63	58	52	46	41	36	30	25	20	15
54	94	88	82	76	70	65	59	54	48	43	38	33	28	23	18
56	94	88	82	77	71	66	61	55	50	45	40	35	31	26	21
58	94	89	83	77	72	67	62	57	52	47	42	38	33	28	24
60	94	89	84	78	73	68	63	58	53	49	44	40	35	31	27
62	94	89	84	79	74	69	64	60	55	50	46	41	37	33	29
64	95	90	85	79	75	70	66	61	56	52	48	43	39	35	31
66	95	90	85	80	76	71	66	62	58	53	49	45	41	37	33
68	95	90	85	81	76	72	67	63	59	55	51	47	43	39	35
70	95	90	86	81	77	72	68	64	60	56	52	48	44	40	37
72	95	91	86	82	78	73	69	65	61	57	53	49	46	42	39
74	95	91	86	82	78	74	70	66	62	58	54	51	47	44	40
76	96	91	87	83	78	74	70	67	63	59	55	52	48	45	42
78	96	91	87	83	79	75	71	67	64	60	57	53	50	46	43
80	96	91	87	83	79	76	72	68	64	61	57	54	51	47	44
84	96	92	88	84	80	77	73	70	66	63	59	56	53	50	47
88	96	92	88	85	81	78	74	71	67	64	61	58	55	52	49
90	96	92	89	85	82	78	75	72	68	64	62	58	56	53	50

EXPERIMENT 167

DAILY WEATHER RECORD

This record should be started about one month before the topic of weather is taken up. You can read the instruments even though you may not understand the principles upon which these instruments depend. You will learn the principles later when you study the weather.

In addition to this record, you would do well to start a collection of clippings, pictures, and weather maps.

Date	Air Pressure (Barometer)	Temperature (Thermometer)	Humidity (Hygrometer)			Wind Direction (Weather Vane)	Weather (Use Map Symbols)
			Wet Bulb	Dry Bulb	Relative Humidity		

EXPERIMENT 168

Question: How is rain produced?

Materials: Large beaker; alcohol; asbestos mat; cardboard; piece of glass to fit top of beaker.

Directions: Pour a little alcohol in the beaker and cover with the cardboard. Heat alcohol gently for a few minutes. Remove lamp. Replace cardboard with cold glass. 1. What appeared inside the beaker as soon as the glass was put on? 2. After a short time, what did you notice on the surface of the alcohol? This a rain of alcohol instead of a rain of water.

Conclusion: 1. What causes rain? 2. Why doesn't it always rain when we see clouds? 3. Why are raindrops sometimes large and sometimes small?

CAUTION: The vapor of alcohol readily catches fire. There is a safe way to boil the alcohol. Heat a pan of water to the boiling point. Turn out the light and set the beaker of alcohol in the boiling water. Alcohol boils at a lower temperature than water, and you can watch it boil in safety in the pan of water.

EXPERIMENT 169

Question: How should I read a weather map and predict the probable weather conditions for tomorrow?

Materials: United States weather maps covering a period of about one week.

Directions: 1. Examine the map so that you may become familiar with its main features and then answer the following questions about it:

   (*a*) In what city was your map made?
   (*b*) On what day was your map made?
   (*c*) At what time of day were the observations taken?
   (*d*) By what government department was the map made?

2. Answer the following questions about the continuous black lines:

   (*a*) What are the numbers at the ends of these lines and what do they mean?
   (*b*) Why are the lines not straight?
   (*c*) What name do we give to these lines?
   (*d*) With what lines are the words *high* and *low* connected?
   (*e*) To what do these two terms refer?

3. Examine the dotted black lines and answer the following questions about them:

   (*a*) What numbers are at the ends of these lines and to what do they refer?
   (*b*) What name is given to these lines?
   (*c*) Why are the lines not straight?

4. Find the small circles some of which have arrows attached and answer the following questions:

    (a) How do the circles differ?

    (b) What do the shading and letters on the circles mean?

    (c) Find the arrows attached to the circles. What do these arrows mean and why do they not all point in the same direction?

5. What facts are given in the columns in the lower corner of the map that are not given on the map itself?

6. Examine a high. What is the direction of the winds around it and how does the barometer reading change as you pass outward from the center of the high?

7. Examine a low. What is the direction of the winds around it and how does the barometer reading change as you pass outward from the center of the low?

8. Trace from your weather map an outline map of the United States. Mark on this map the position of the most westerly high as shown in the first of your week's maps.

Mark the daily position of this high as it moves across the country. Connect these marks with a line and you will have the path of the high.

Repeat this procedure with a low. These lines will give you an idea of the direction and speed of the storms and fair weather as they pass over the country from west to east.

Diagram: Insert your diagram in your outline map with your notes.

Conclusion: Of what use is a weather map?

EXPERIMENT 170 (OPTIONAL)

Question: How does expansion affect the temperature of air? Hold a thermometer at the valve opening as you release the air from a tire. How does the temperature of the expanding air from the tire compare with the air round about?

EXPERIMENT 171 (OPTIONAL)

Question: How can I form a cloud? Wet a flask inside, close it with a stopper, place it under a bell jar of an air pump and exhaust the air. As the cork blows out, note the cloud in the flask. How do you account for the cloud?

EXPERIMENT 172 (OPTIONAL)

Question: How would you show that heated air is lighter than cool air? Balance two unstoppered "empty" flasks suspended from a meter stick. Heat one of the flasks gently with a Bunsen burner. The air inside expands as it heats and overflows from the neck of the flask. What then happens to the two flasks?

ADDITIONAL QUESTIONS TO THINK OUT

1. Why does the sun lose heating power in the late afternoon? Why is it usually cooler at 8 A.M. than at 4 P.M.?

2. Why is the south slope of a hill warmer than level land in the springtime?

3. Why is it that in the warm days of spring the ocean is often cool for a bath, and in the cool days of autumn it is often warm?

4. Why do lakes and oceans warm more slowly than land? You will find a suggestion in the section How Water Heats, page 204. For further explanation consult a textbook on physics.

5. Why are mountains cool in summer? why is the seashore?

6. Why are the Banks of Newfoundland foggy?

7. Why is the air clear after a cyclonic storm?

8. Sometimes you see upper clouds drifting to the east and lower clouds to the west at the same time. How can this happen?

9. Why are thunderstorms more common in the afternoon?

10. Why does a thunderstorm cool the air?

11. There are four principal kinds of cloud. Watch the sky until you distinguish and describe them. Note down the kind of weather that is associated with each. Look up their names in a book on weather (meteorology).

12. Is snow frozen rain?

13. What makes a desert?

14. Why do deserts get cold at night?

15. Mountain climbers often blacken their faces to prevent sunburn. Why does the sun burn more fiercely in the high, cold mountain?

16. If the mountains along the west coast of North America disappeared, how would it affect the climate of the interior?

17. In the dry lands of the West the traveler goes up the mountain to search for water. In the Appalachians the mountaineer descends. Explain.

18. Why do morning fogs usually disappear as the sun climbs?

19. When you sleep under the open sky, you may find in the morning that your hair and shoes are wet with dew but your face is dry. How do you explain?

20. A night without dew is a "sign" of rain. Why? Watch to see if the sign is dependable.

21. Why is there more danger from frost on a clear night than on a cloudy night?

22. Write down on your weather record the days when you feel full of life, when work goes easily, and the days when work is irksome. Is there any connection between work and weather? After you have investigated for yourself, consult the books of Ellsworth Huntington to see what he found.

UNIT SIXTEEN

OUR PLACE IN THE SKY

Fig. 544. A priest of the New Stone Age greets the rising sun. At Carnac, in Brittany, France, two miles of these great stone columns still stand, where the Stone Age people worshiped the sun.

Picture to yourself an ancient druid priest facing the rising sun on the first day of spring (Fig. 544). The ancients knew that day of the calendar as our astronomers know it. They built temples to mark that one day of the year by allowing the rising sun to look down an aisle of columns or to peek for a few minutes into a dark chamber where the rays of the rising sun could penetrate at no other time in the year. They commemorated with festivals the return of the sun after its journey to the southern sky. They knew that the good things of the earth come from the sun. They looked upon the sun as a god, and attributed its benefits to his good will. Knowledge of natural bodies and natural forces has grown since those days, and now we seek the explanation in laws of energy.

We have studied man's use of energy at home, in industry, in supplying his cities, and in protecting his nation. We have seen how energy produces life in his body. We have seen man battling, studying, then controlling the forces of nature. We have seen the same fundamental forces in the microscopic cell, in the living body, and in the earth, water, and air—the energy of heat, sound, light, electricity. Within the cell and in its environment, energy is changing from one form to another. The ceaseless change is action, life. Science is steadily advancing man's control over the changing earth.

Now we shall study man amid the vast changing universe. The same forms of energy that we have studied produce the changes on the earth, the sun, and the stars. Do we expect man to control the stars? Hardly; but he makes use of the stars. They are part of his environment, distant but valuable. The scientist studies those distant parts of the universe and controls to some extent the energy that comes from them. We can measure in part their influence upon us. Let us plunge into that study that has fascinated man since the days of the ancient priests and is proving more astounding the more we learn.

Chapter LXI

EXPLORING THE SKY

What is in the sky. When shepherds kept watch over their flocks by night, they had time and opportunity to study the stars (Fig. 545). The citizens of ancient cities, unblinded by the glare of electric lights, saw the beauty of the heavens. From those ancient gazers upon the night skies have come down to us the names of stars and of constellations, or groups of stars. With a star map like that of Figure 546 spread out before you on a clear night, you can trace the constellations named by the ancient watchers of the skies in Babylon and Athens.

Find the North Star (Polaris), the star that guided the ancient mariner, the desert traveler, and the runaway slave in our own country. Figure 565 and Experiment 177 tell how to find it. Trace out the Big Dipper or Great Bear (Ursa Major), the Little Dipper, the Twins (Gemini), the

Fig. 545. The Los Angeles planetarium where one may observe the stars and see their movements reproduced.

(648)

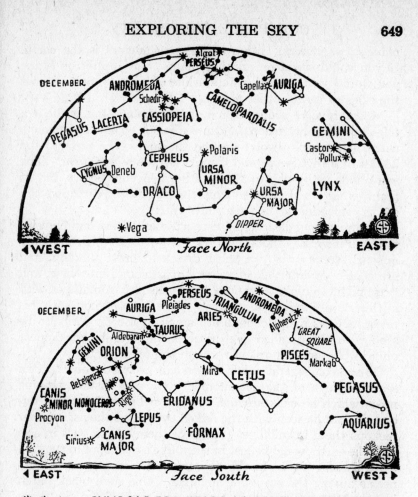

✿ ✳ ○ • SYMBOLS FOR STARS IN ORDER OF BRIGHTNESS

Fig. 546. Take these maps outdoors and trace out the constellations.

Seven Sleepers (Pleiades), the Bull (Taurus), Orion, the mighty hunter who threatens the Bull with his club, and other constellations about which the ancients told their myths.

The ancients saw, as you may see, that most of the brilliant, starlike objects in the heavens keep their relative positions unchanged, but that a few move slowly among the fixed ones as you watch them from night to night. These are the

planets (wanderers).   One of these wanderers is the earth.
If you could stand on another planet, say Jupiter or Mars,
you would see the earth as a starlike object advancing across
the skies as we see other planets.

Moons revolve around some of the planets, but without a
telescope the only moon we can see is our own.   The planets
with their moons revolve around the sun.   The sun and the
bodies that revolve around it make up the *solar system*.   The
sun blinds us by day to all the other heavenly bodies, but at
night, when we are hidden from the sun by the earth, we can
see the splendor of the vast multitude.

On almost any clear night, especially in August and November, you may see "shooting stars," or *meteors*, which suddenly
appear, streak swiftly a short distance across the sky, and
are gone.   At intervals of years a *comet* comes into view, and
from night to night advances across the sky, sometimes with
a thin "tail" stretching away.   The astronomer with his
telescope sees many comets too small or too far away to be
seen with the unaided eye, some so faint that they appear
only in photographs taken through the telescope.

Objects of several other kinds can be made out by the
searching eye of the astronomer.   He sees distant shining
mists which he calls *nebulae*.   A few nebulae, faint and uncertain, can be seen with the naked eye.   But the astronomer
reckons them in millions.   Some of them are so vast in size
that the earth would be lost in them like a dust spot in the sky.

At certain places in the sky there are mysterious black-
nesses among the stars and nebulae.   One such black patch
in the Milky Way near the constellation of the Southern
Cross is called the *Coal Sack*.   The astronomers interpret
the black areas as masses of dark material that shut out the
light of the stars beyond.   Of these dark areas we know
nothing except that there they are.

And where are these bodies, some of them measured
in millions of miles in diameter?   in the sky?   But what
is the sky?   The only answer that we can give at present is
that it is *space*, a great void or emptiness stretching away in
every direction.   At vast distances here and there through

Fig. 547. The great forty-inch refracting telescope of the Yerkes Observatory, Williams Bay, Wisconsin.

this great, cold, dark emptiness are brilliant hot bodies and fiery mists—the stars, comets, and nebulae. There may be millions of bodies unlighted, and therefore unknown, and others too far away to be seen.

In the chapters which follow you may learn something of the fascinating study of astronomy. You may learn a little of all the bodies that have just been mentioned, of what they are, of how they act, and what makes them act as they do. You may see how the astronomer tries to solve the problems of his science. You may see some ways in which the distant bodies affect our lives. It is to be hoped that there will remain other questions in your mind not answered in this book, for science is still seeking answers and it is the search for answers that makes science alluring.

How astronomy grew. It was natural for the men of the ancient world to think that the earth was the center of the universe. The sun, moon, and stars seemed to move over the earth. Some of the explanations made by the ancients seem childish to us, but they were made in the childhood days of our civilization. To the Greeks the sun was the chariot of the sun god who drove across the heavens once a day. Some of the ancient thinkers, however, taught that the earth moved around the sun. That view was not approved by their great philosopher Aristotle (384–322 B.C.). All through the Dark Ages men continued to believe that the earth was the center and the most important part of the universe. To teach differently was dangerous. As late as 1600 Giordano Bruno was burned at the stake for thinking "there are endless particular worlds similar to the earth."

In 1543 Copernicus, a Polish churchman, published an astronomy showing the sun as a center with the earth and other planets moving around it. A Danish astronomer, Tyco Brahe (1546–1601) spent a lifetime making accurate observations of the positions of heavenly bodies, and from these observations Johann Kepler (1571–1630), a German mathematician, drew up laws showing how the planets moved around the sun. Still the world doubted. It was much easier and safer to repeat what men had been saying since the days of Aristotle.

But a new day had dawned in science. Men turned to nature instead of to books, and forced nature through experiments to answer their questions. Modern science was born then. Galilei (1564–1642), an Italian astronomer commonly called by his Christian name *Galileo*, proved that a statement that had come down from Aristotle, that heavy bodies fell faster than light bodies was untrue. Galileo dropped light bodies and heavy bodies from the leaning tower of Pisa, and showed that they reached the ground in the same time. In 1608, Lippershey, a Flemish spectacle maker, discovered that

Fig. 548. The great one-hundred-inch reflecting telescope at the Mount Wilson Observatory, California.

two lenses placed in a tube brought distant objects close to view, and so made the first telescope. Two years later Galileo turned on the sky a telescope made with his own hands and proved that Copernicus was right in saying that the earth and other planets moved around the sun. Then modern astronomy was under way. Galileo saw that the Milky Way was made of stars. He saw for the first time the mountains on the moon and the shadows that they cast on the plains of

the moon. He saw four moons revolving around the planet
Jupiter, and, as Copernicus had predicted, saw the face of
the planet Venus increase in size and diminish again as the
moon does in its change of phases.

Astronomy has made a long journey from the watchful
shepherd on the Asian hills to the modern astronomer at the
100-inch telescope on Mount Wilson, California.   And the end
is not yet. A 200-inch telescope is being constructed. New
worlds as yet unknown will come into view when it is in
operation (Fig. 548).   Instruments of other kinds help out
the astronomer. The photographic
plate, for example, is more sensitive
than the eye and has revealed much
that we know of the heavens that
the eye could not see. The spectroscope tells what stars are made of,
and how fast they travel and in what
direction, and makes possible the
calculation of their sizes and weights.

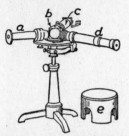

Fig. 549. A spectroscope. A
lens in tube *c* makes the rays
of light parallel before they
strike prism *b*. The spectrum is viewed through telescope *d*.   The image of a
scale in tube *a* is reflected
into the telescope. *e*, The cap.

The spectroscope breaks up the
light as a simple glass prism or
chandelier glass breaks up the sunlight into the colors of the rainbow.
It spreads these colors out in a band,
each color always in the same posi-
tion.   Such a band is a spectrum (Fig. 264).   Each element,
when heated till it glows, gives off its own peculiar colors
arranged in definite order.   Its spectrum is its color map.
By the spectrum the astronomer learns the elements in the
stars and nebulae.   By the spectroscope a gas was discovered
on the sun before it was discovered on the earth. This gas
now fills the great dirigibles and the "blimps."   It is the sun
gas *helium* (*helios*, the sun).

Chapter LXII

GOVERNED BY THE SUN

The sun. The sun is hot—terrifically hot, far hotter than anything that we can imagine. It is about 7000° C. on the surface and about 40,000,000° C. in the center. We have no idea how hot that is, but we might try to make our imaginations stagger by seeing what that much heat would do. Suppose that we had a column of ice two miles in diameter stretching from here to the sun, 93,000,000 miles. If the heat of the sun could be concentrated on it, the ice would melt in one second and disappear in vapor in eight seconds. Sir James Jeans, the English astronomer, tries to give an idea of the sun's heat as follows. A coin the size of a quarter dollar heated to the temperature of the interior of the sun would shrivel up every living thing within a thousand miles by its heat.

The sun is so hot that it is all gas. Even iron on the sun is gaseous. The spectroscope reveals also the gases of silver, platinum, lead, and other heavy metals. Light gases are there, too—helium and hydrogen, the lightest substance known. Of the elements that we have on earth over half have been found on the sun. All the others may be there buried deep in the interior where we cannot see their light. The sun seems to be made of the same materials as the earth, but they are all so hot that they are gases.

If one looks at the sun through a smoked glass, the surface looks calm and motionless, but through the instruments of the astronomer, its surface appears like a seething, boiling mass, shooting fiery tongues and clouds of gases hundreds of thousands of miles above its surface. At total eclipse we can see these fiery tongues, called *prominences*, like brilliant red flames shooting up from the edge of the sun

(Fig. 550). They are composed largely of hydrogen gas, not burning but heated to intense brilliance.

Great whirlpools of gases on the surface of the sun mark

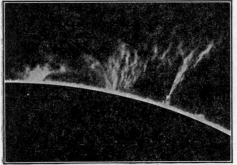

where hot gases are seething upward to the surface. We call these whirlpools *sun spots* (Fig. 551). We can often see them by looking at the sun through heavily smoked glass. They look like black spots because the gases spread out when they come to the surface and their expansion cools

Fig. 550.   Prominences of the sun, 80,000 miles high, August 21, 1909.

them a little. They are, however, much hotter and more brilliant than anything that we know on earth. Some sun

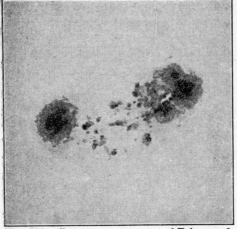

spots are of such size that the earth would drop into one like a baseball into a bucket. The sun spots come and go, lasting from several days to several months.

The sun is of immense size compared with the earth. It is 866,000 miles in diameter; the earth is 8000. Over a million earths could be packed inside the sun (Fig. 552). This great ball of gases is turning around on its

Fig. 551.   Great sun-spot group of February 8, 1917.

axis as the earth does, but it takes 25 of our days to make a turn. Because of its immense size and the vast amount of matter in the sun, things on its surface would weigh much more

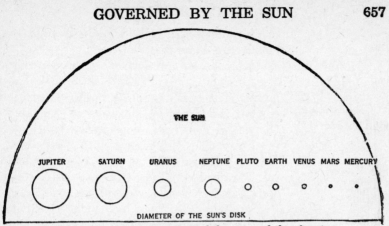

Fig. 552. The relative sizes of the sun and the planets.

than on the earth. A stone that weighs 10 pounds on the earth would weigh 280 pounds on the sun, and a baseball would be so heavy that a pitcher could never put it over the plate. A 100-pound boy would weigh over a ton, and he would be crushed to death by his own weight. This does not mean that there would be any more matter in the boy's body, but that the sun has 28 times as much pull as the earth. Weight is a measure of the pull of gravity.

	Mean Distance from the Sun in Millions of Miles	Diameter	Period of Rotation on Axis	Period of Revolution Around the Sun
Sun.........		864,390		
Mercury....	36.0	3,030	88 d.	87.9 d.
Venus.......	67.2	7,600		224.7 d.
Earth.......	92.9	7,918	23 hr. 56 m.	365.25 d.
Mars.......	141.5	4,200	24 hr. 37 m.	1.88 yr.
Planetoids ..	200–300	20–300		3–7 yr.
Jupiter......	483.3	87,000	9 hr. 53 m.	11.86 yr.
Saturn......	886.1	72,000	10 hr. 14–38 m.	29.46 yr.
Uranus.....	1,782.8	31,000	10.7 hr.	84.02 yr.
Neptune....	2,793.5	33,000	15 hr. (?)	164.78 yr.
Pluto.......	3,800	4,000(?)	(?)	249.17 yr.
Moon.......	238,840*	2,160	27 d. 7 hr. 43 m.	27.7 hr. 43 m. around earth

* Distance from earth.

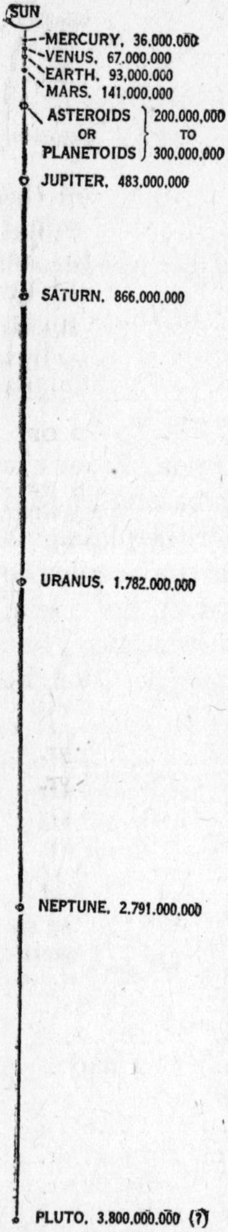

SUN
---MERCURY, 36,000,000
--VENUS, 67,000,000
-EARTH, 93,000,000
MARS, 141,000,000

ASTEROIDS } 200,000,000
OR   TO
PLANETOIDS } 300,000,000
JUPITER, 483,000,000

SATURN, 866,000,000

URANUS, 1,782,000,000

NEPTUNE, 2,791,000,000

PLUTO, 3,800,000,000 (?)

Fig. 553. The distances of the planets from the sun.

The sun's family. Moving around the sun in the same direction as the sun spins on its axis but millions of miles away are the planets, globes of gases, liquids, and rocks. The earth is one of the planets. We can see the largest and closest of them with the naked eye, but some are so small or so far away that a telescope is needed. The planets have no light of their own but shine by the reflected light of the sun. Figure 553 shows their names and positions. (See also Fig. 552).

Why the planets revolve. Why do the planets go round and round the sun through the endless ages? For the present let us not try to explain how they started, but only why the planets do not wander off in space and lose themselves.

If anything starts moving, anywhere on the earth or out in space, it tends to keep on moving. That tendency to keep on going is what makes the crash when an automobile hits a pole or a meteor hits the earth. On the earth something always gets in the way of a moving object; if nothing else, the surface of the earth stops it. A ball rolled across a level field is stopped by friction with the surface of the field. Beyond the earth's atmosphere there is no friction, nothing to rub against. You might think that anything once started out in space would just keep on going forever, unless, of course, it hit a heavenly body. Nothing gets in the way to stop the planets. Indeed they are millions of miles from anything except small meteors such as occasionally hit the earth.

Now why do they not wander away? This secret was discovered by the English scientist and mathematician Sir Isaac Newton (1642–1727), about the beginning of the eighteenth century. According to tradition the idea came to him when he saw an apple fall to the ground in his garden. The secret is that every body in the universe attracts every other body. Ordinarily we see only the attraction of the earth for smaller bodies on its surface. But by delicate experiments scientists have measured the attraction of other bodies for one another. This attraction is called *gravitation.* From his observations Newton formulated his laws of

Fig. 554.   A total eclipse of the sun. The bright glow is the corona, which extends millions of miles but is seen for only the few minutes of total eclipse.

gravitation. The attraction, he found, depends upon the amount of matter in the bodies and the distance between them.

The reason why the planets do not shoot off in a straight line out into space is that the gravitation of the sun holds them. The pull of the sun is not strong enough to draw them straight into the sun because of their tendency to keep going on their way. As a sort of compromise between the tendency to go straight and the tendency to fall into the sun, they keep in courses around the sun.

The way around the sun. The astronomers measure and plot the courses of the planets around the sun, their *orbits.* The position of the planets at any hour for a million years can be found. This understanding of the orbits

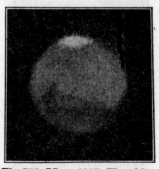

Fig. 555. Mars, 1907. The white spot is probably a polar ice cap.

has enabled astronomers to discover two new planets that the ancients never saw.

A hundred years ago the planet Uranus was believed to

Fig. 556. Saturn. The rings are composed of tiny moons. Saturn also has eight large moons.

be the farthest from the sun. But its observed orbit did not exactly agree with the orbit that had been calculated for it. The astronomers Adams, an Englishman, and Leverrier, a Frenchman, calculated independently that a planet outside and in a certain position would have gravitational pull enough to draw Uranus into its observed position. Then Leverrier wrote to a German astronomer named Galle, telling him to turn his telescope to a definite position in the sky. There the new planet Neptune was found.

Still Uranus did not go where it was expected. Lowell, at the observatory at Flagstaff, Arizona, calculated the position for still another planet farther outside. After Lowell's death and after several years of search, it was found in 1930 in photographs of the regions of the sky where Lowell had predicted. This planet was named Pluto.

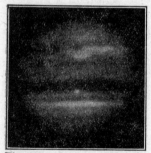

Fig. 557. Jupiter. Note the belt and the "great red spot" in the upper left part.

Moons. Around all but the smaller planets revolve other bodies, their satellites or moons. Jupiter has eleven moons and Saturn has nine. (Figs. 556 and 557.) Uranus, the next planet in size, has four. Saturn, in addition to its nine moons, has three rings moving around it. The rings are made up of a vast number of tiny moons. These tiny moons have not been seen, but the way the rings move shows the astronomer that they are made of small bodies. Mars has two moons.

Our moon is our nearest neighbor (Fig. 558). It is only about 240,000 miles away. It is rather a small neighbor, only

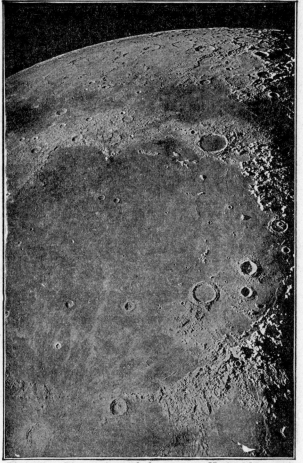

Fig. 558. The surface of the moon. Notice the great plains and the mountains. The circular rims look like volcanic craters but may not be.

2,163 miles in diameter, about the distance from New York to Spokane, Washington. Because of its small size, the force of gravity on its surface is small. A man weighing 180 pounds on the earth would weigh only 30 pounds on the moon, and an athlete could jump 25 to 30 feet straight up.

The moon is a cold, dead neighbor. Nothing lives there. It has no air. Its temperature also would prohibit life. In

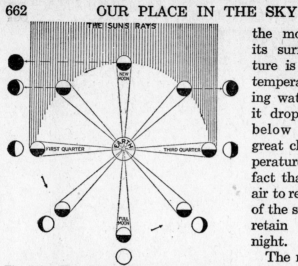

Fig. 559. The phases of the moon. The outer figures show the face of the moon. The inner figures show the position of the moon at each phase.

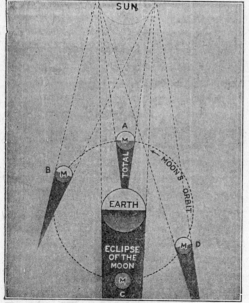

Fig. 560. When does an eclipse of the moon occur? an eclipse of the sun?

the moon's daytime its surface temperature is 212° F., the temperature of boiling water. At night it drops to 220° F. below zero. This great change of temperature is due to the fact that there is no air to reduce the blaze of the sun by day and retain the heat by night.

The moon revolves around the earth in $27\frac{1}{3}$ of our days. It rotates on its axis also in $27\frac{1}{3}$ of our days, keeping the same face always toward the earth. No man has seen the other side of the moon.

Because the moon moves in an orbit around the earth, the visible face changes from new moon to full moon and back again. These changes are the *phases of the moon* (Experiment 174 and Fig. 559).

At certain times the moon gets directly between us and the sun and we have an *eclipse*

Fig. 561.   Halley's Comet.   In the long exposure necessary, the motion of the earth carries the camera under the stars, producing the small streaks.

of the sun (see Experiment 175) (Figs. 554 and 560). At other times it moves into the earth's shadow, and we have an *eclipse of the moon.*

Comets and meteors.   Comets are often many times as big as planets.   They are composed chiefly of thin matter, gas, but in addition they may have solid matter in small pieces.   Some of them have been described as traveling gravel banks.   Their tails, when they have tails, are so thin that the waves of the sun's radiant energy keep them pointed away from the sun.   From calculation of their orbits, astronomers conclude that some are members of the sun's family but rather wayward members, circulating in orbits very different from those of the planets.   Some comets return regularly.   Halley's comet appears every 75 years, and Encke's comet appears every $3\frac{1}{4}$ years.   (Fig. 561.)

Some comets have disappeared, but in their places we now encounter swarms of meteors like those of April and August, which are the remains of comets that disappeared in 1861 and 1862.   Apparently the meteors are broken-up fragments of the comets.   Meteors are generally small objects, perhaps the size of walnuts.   We do not see them until they have entered the earth's atmosphere. They take fire as they tear through the air at terrific speed. They usually burn up before striking the ground. Occasionally one strikes before it is entirely burned up. These fallen meteors are called *meteorites*. They are usually of stone and iron, with a little nickel (Fig. 562). In Arizona is a great hole in the ground like the crater of a volcano that is supposed to have been made by the fall of a gigantic meteor in prehistoric times. In 1908 a huge meteor fell in the wilderness of Siberia. A party of scientists a few years later found the forest for 10 miles around leveled as if by a scorching wind.

Fig. 562. This meteorite, weighing 820 pounds, fell at Paragould, Arkansas, February 17, 1930.

EXPERIMENT 173

Question: How to make a model of the solar system.

Materials: A globe a foot in diameter to represent the sun; a ruler divided into sixteenths of an inch; a tape measure of 25 or 50 feet; some clay.

Directions and observations: 1. Using the table on page 657, make balls of clay representing the planets and the moon. Let $\frac{1}{16}$ inch represent 1,000 miles. 2. Place the sun at one end of the playground. Then place the planets in their proper positions, letting $\frac{1}{16}$ inch represent 1,000,000 miles. 3. The nearest star is 25,000,000,000,000 miles from the earth. How far from the globe in your school yard would you need to place this star?

EXPERIMENT 174

Question: Why does the moon's face change?

Materials: A candle to represent the sun; a white ball to represent the moon.

Directions and observations: Set up the light to represent the sun. Your head represents the earth. Hold the ball out at arm's length and rotate your body (turn around) so that the ball representing the moon makes a circle around you. The circle is the revolution of the moon around the earth.

Now darken the room. Hold the ball out at arm's length on the side of your head opposite to the light and just high enough to avoid the shadow ot your head. The moon and the sun are now on opposite sides of the earth. How much of the moon's face is lighted? Draw a picture of this face. This is the full moon.

Move the moon ⅛ of its journey around the earth (your head). Draw a picture of the lighted portion of its face. This is a crescent phase.

Move the moon another ⅛ of its journey. This is first quarter of the moon. Draw its lighted face. Continue moving ⅛ of a revolution until the journey is complete.

When the moon is between the earth and the sun, it is new moon. How much of its face can be seen from the earth? Three fourths of the way around is last quarter.

Make a diagram of the position of the three bodies in each phase. Mark the phases from new to full, waxing (growing), and those from full to new waning (diminishing).

Practical applications: Where does the moon get its light? If you examined the moon's light with a spectroscope, what spectrum would you expect to find?

The planet Venus also shows phases. Demonstrate the phases of Venus as you did for the moon. Remember that Venus revolves around the sun.

What other planet shows phases as seen from the earth? Which could not?

Would the moons of Jupiter show phases to an observer on Jupiter?

EXPERIMENT 175

Question: What causes the eclipses of moon and sun?

Materials: Small white ball to represent the moon; larger ball to represent the earth; a flashlight or electric lamp to represent the sun; two supports with clamps.

Directions and observations: Set up the apparatus similar to the arrangement in Figure 560. Darken the room. 1. Pass the moon suspended on a string between the earth and the sun so that the moon's shadow falls on the earth. What body disappears from view (is eclipsed) as seen from the earth? What is the shape of the moon's shadow as it moves across the earth? 2. Pass the moon on the side of the earth opposite the sun so that the moon goes completely into the shadow of the earth. What body is eclipsed when the earth is between the moon and the sun? 3. Pass the moon through the earth's shadow so that the moon is partially eclipsed.

Diagrams: Draw the apparatus in each position. Draw pictures of the sun's face during the solar eclipse (1) when the eclipse has just started, (2) when the moon is halfway across, (3) at total eclipse, (4) when the moon is three quarters of its way across, (5) when it is just leaving the sun's disk.

Conclusion: 1. What causes an eclipse of the sun? 2. What causes an eclipse of the moon? 3. What causes a partial eclipse?

Practical applications: At what phase of the moon does an eclipse of the sun occur? eclipse of the moon?

Why can you not see an eclipse of the sun at night?

The passage of Venus across the face of the sun is called the *transit* of Venus. Demonstrate and draw a diagram of the transit of Venus. The transit corresponds to what eclipse?

As viewed from the earth, which other planet could have a transit across the sun similar to that of Venus? which could not?

To see a transit of the earth across the sun where would an observer have to be?

Suppose the moon were twice as far away from the earth as it is. Could there be a total eclipse of the sun? See Experiment 176.

In an eclipse of the moon, what shape is the earth's shadow? What does that show as to the shape of the earth?

If the moon revolved around the earth on exactly the same plane as the earth revolves around the sun, how many eclipses of the sun would there be each year?

EXPERIMENT 176 (OPTIONAL)

Question: How may I demonstrate an annular eclipse?

At a total eclipse of the sun the moon is just the right distance from the earth to hide the sun completely. At some eclipses the moon is farther away. What, then, is the appearance of the sun during eclipse?

Proceed as follows: Set up the sun several feet away. Take a marble or a small ball, smaller than the diameter of the flashlight, to represent the moon. Your eye will represent the observer on earth.

Hold the marble on the level of the eye and light at such a distance from the eye that the marble just shuts out the sun. What kind of eclipse is that?

Now hold the marble farther away so that it does not hide the sun. Move it just in front of the center of the sun's disk. Draw a picture of the sun at this eclipse. It is called an annular eclipse (*annulus*, little ring).

Chapter LXIII

BEYOND THE SUN

How many stars? How many stars can you see on a cloudless night? Millions and millions of them? No, not at all. The best you could do with the naked eye on a cloudless and moonless night, away from city lights, would be considerably less than 3000. These stars are named and charted by the astronomers. The great 100-inch telescope at Mt. Wilson, California, reveals about 1500 million stars. Many that are too faint to be seen with the human eye, even through the giant telescope, are photographed. Even so, it is certain that we know only a small part of the stars. Astronomers have estimated between 30,000,000,000 and 40,000,000,000 in our part of the sky (Fig. 563).

What are the stars? The stars are suns, or better the sun is a star. To a person away off in space, the sun would appear as the stars do to us. Many stars are about the size and brightness of our sun. One little fellow is about the size of the earth but much heavier and hotter. A few are much larger than our sun. Betelgeuse, the big star in the constellation of Orion, is so big that if our sun were placed in the center of the star, the earth would have room to travel around its orbit inside the star.

Like the sun, the other stars are hot balls of gas, boiling and seething in their fierce heat. They give off light because they are so hot. We know the stars by their light. Their light enables the astronomer to calculate their sizes, temperatures, and weights.

No planets can be seen revolving around any of the stars. They are much too far away for any planets to be seen, if any are present. Astronomers have shown that it is probable that very, very few of the stars have planets.

Fig. 563. A part of the sky in the constellation of Orion, showing the vast number of stars.

The Milky Way. On a cloudless, moonless night, in a place where lights on the earth do not interfere, you can see a cloudlike band stretching across the sky. Part of the way it is divided into two clouds somewhat parallel. This is the Milky Way, or *Galaxy*. It is composed of stars so numerous, faint, and far away that their light blends into a luminous cloud.

Our sun, with its planets, belongs to the Galaxy. It is our little part of the stupendous stretches of celestial space, our little corner of the sky. The stars that we see on a nighttime stroll in the country or a row on the lake all lie in this Galaxy. There are millions upon millions more stars in the Galaxy, too faint for the naked eye. In fact, the Galaxy appears like a luminous band, the Milky Way, only because of the vast number of stars that lie, not scattered indiscriminately, but in a group. The whole group is shaped like a disk or watch. Our sun and its planets lie in the midst of the Galaxy. The brightness of the Milky Way is due to our

Fig. 564. A spiral nebula in the constellation Ursa Major.

looking out from the center through the great breadth of the group, so that the stars appear closer together than when we look at right angles to the plane of the disk.

How far to the stars. Try to picture in your mind the vastness of our Galaxy. Our sun is 93,000,000 miles from us. An airplane traveling 250 miles an hour in nonstop flight would take $42\frac{1}{2}$ years to reach the sun. To reach the nearest star, about 25 thousand billion miles away, the airplane would take over a billion years.

When we talk in these figures, miles mean little. A billion miles is beyond our mental grasp. Instead of miles we measure celestial distances in light years. A *light year* is the distance that light travels in a year. In one second light travels 186,000 miles. Light comes to us from the sun in about $8\frac{1}{2}$ minutes. In a year it travels 5,880 billion miles. The nearest star is 4.3 light years away. The North Star is about 400 light years away, and Betelgeuse, the giant star you may easily find in the constellation of Orion, is 273 light years away. When you look up at the North Star at night, you are seeing light that left the star 400 years ago and is just getting to you. The astronomers know of stars in our galaxy that are 30,000 light years away. The light that is received in the telescope from these stars left the stars 30,000 years ago and has been traveling ever since. The disk of our galaxy may be 100,000 light years in diameter, although some astronomers estimate much less and some double the estimate.

Island universes. Remember that the stars we see, except through the greatest telescope, are all in our own galaxy. Beyond our Galaxy is space, empty space, for millions of light years; but then, at that long interval, millions of light years away, are other galaxies. The nearest of these outer galaxies is 850,000 light years away. The farthest that we know of are 140,000,000 light years away. There are probably millions of galaxies more beyond the reach of our telescopes. Each galaxy is a great gathering of stars separated by stretches of space as immense as those which separate the stars of our own.

These galaxies are so far away that they appear, so far as we can see them at all, as faint, shining clouds or mists. Even in the 100-inch telescope the individual stars in the galaxies can be seen in only a few. Some are too far away to show the stars, and some may be composed not of stars but of glowing gas. These distant galaxies are often called *nebulae*. (The term nebulae is also used for luminous mists within our own Galaxy.) (Fig. 564.)

A model of the universe. To gain some faint idea of the immensity of the universe, Jeans, the English astronomer, proposes the following model. Represent the orbit of the earth about the sun by a pinhead. The sun is a microscopic bit of dust in the center of the pinhead. The earth is a second bit of dust a millionth part of the volume of the first. This second bit is traveling around the circumference of the pinhead. To put into the model, in the proper scale, the 40,000,-000,000 stars of our galaxy, we need an area the size of North America. To put in the "island universes," the distant galaxies that the astronomer can actually see, we should need to extend the edge of the model 4,000,000 miles, 14 times as far away as the moon.

Jeans compares the number of stars to the number of specks of dust in London. The sun would be a single dust speck, and the earth a speck only one millionth as large.

Now let us ask a question that we shall not attempt to answer. How important is man in the universe? Physically, the human race occupies a small part of the surface of a microscopic dust spot. But let us remember that man has been able through the genius of Copernicus, Galileo, Newton, Einstein, and others to explore the mighty universe and to understand something of its structure and its laws.

EXPERIMENT 177

Question: How can I locate the position of the North Star (Polaris)?

Materials: A compass; the sky at night; a star map.

Directions: (a) On a clear night look to the north and locate the

Fig. 565. The Dipper and the North Star. A and B are the pointers.

Great Dipper in the constellation of the Great Bear (Ursa Major). (See Figures 546 and 565.) You can easily recognize this group of stars. The stars composing it are bright, and their arrangement makes them easily found.

(b) When you have found the Great Dipper, in imagination draw a line through the two stars that form the outer end of the bowl. These two stars are called the *Pointers*. This name is given to them because they point almost directly toward Polaris. Your imaginary line if continued will almost pass through Polaris, which will be found at a distance from the Pointers about five times as great as the distance between them.

(c) Polaris is part of the constellation named the Little Bear (Ursa Minor). It is at the end of the handle of the Little Dipper. The position of all these stars is shown in Figure 546.

Diagram: Show the Great and Little Dippers, the Pointers, and Polaris.

Conclusion: Answer the question.

EXPERIMENT 178 (OPTIONAL)

Question: How can I learn the cause of the daily motion of the stars?

Materials: Umbrella, globe, star map, paper, mucilage, scissors.

Directions: Open the umbrella. Cut out small disks of paper to represent stars. These are to be pasted to the under side of the umbrella. Paste one of these as near as possible to the point where the rod passes through the cloth covering of the umbrella. This represents the North Star. Using a star map to guide you, paste the other disks of paper so as to represent the other stars in their relative positions with respect to each other. Remove the handle from the rod of the umbrella. Insert the rod through the globe so that the globe can rotate on the rod as an axis. Replace the handle.

(a) Hold the globe motionless while you rotate the umbrella. This represents the way the stars *seem* to move from hour to hour (called the *apparent motion* of the stars).

(b) Hold the umbrella motionless while you rotate the globe. As the globe rotates, imagine yourself standing on it and at the same time watching the stars.

(c) On the next clear night, locate the North Star and a few other bright stars. Observe the position of these stars at hourly intervals.

Observations: (a) When you rotate the umbrella: 1. Which star does not move? 2. In what kind of path do the others move? 3. Compare the path made by a star near the North Star with one at a greater distance from the North Star.

(b) When you rotate the globe: 4. How do the stars *appear* to move? 5. How long does it take each star to get back to its original position? 6. Compare the movements in (a) with the *apparent* movements in (b).

(c) When you have watched the stars at night: 7. Compare your observations with those in (a). 8. Are the hourly movements of the stars real or apparent? 9. Which star does not appear to move? Why is this true? 10. What causes the other stars to appear to move?

Practical application: What use can be made of a star that does not move? Why are the stars not visible at all hours of the day?

NOTE: Although the nightly rising and setting of the stars is due to apparent, not real, motion, the stars do really move. We cannot see this real motion, however, because the stars are so far away from us. See page 690.

EXPERIMENT 179 (OPTIONAL)

Question: How can I learn the cause of the yearly motion of the stars?

Materials: A candle and a dark room in addition to the materials used in the previous experiment.

Directions: Using the apparatus of the last experiment in a dark room, light the candle and place it a short distance from the constellation umbrella, where it will illuminate the globe. Remember that you cannot see the stars when you are on those portions of the earth that are illuminated.

(a) Rotate the globe on the umbrella handle so that the city in which you live is in darkness. Which constellations can be seen from your city?

(b) Revolve the globe halfway around the candle, that is, carry it around to the other side of the candle. Be careful not to rotate the umbrella around its handle. The new position represents the earth half a year later than (a). Again rotate the globe so that your city is in darkness. Again be careful not to rotate the umbrella. Which constellations can be seen from your city now that were invisible in (a)? Which stars can be seen now that were also visible in (a)?

Conclusion: Are the yearly movements of the stars real or apparent? What causes the yearly movement of the stars?

Practical application: Which are the winter constellations? spring? summer? autumn? In which portions of the earth are the constellations that you can see invisible?

NOTE: The stars do not revolve with the earth around the sun as this experiment may seem to indicate. However, the stars are so far away that the effect produced is the same as if they did.

CHAPTER LXIV

HOW THE HEAVENS INFLUENCE US

Influences from afar. Without energy from space we could not live. The radiant energy from the sun makes plants grow. Plants feed animals and men. Sun energy is the energy of life. It is also the energy that runs our trains and factories, for coal is the energy of the sun stored in plants of ages long past. Petroleum, too, it seems, is the remains of life long gone. The winds and currents are also the result of the sun's activity. In brief, the sun's energy supplies our bodily and industrial life.

Energy that is not light also comes to us and affects our lives. When sun spots are unusually active, our magnetic compasses and radios are affected, and the aurora, or northern light, is brilliant. There is a magnetic storm. Periods of sun-spot activity coming every eleven years are connected with changes of climate on the earth; stormy years come in cycles that correspond with great sun-spot storms on the sun.

Even the outermost stars and nebulae are sending energy to us. By their energy alone we know them, chiefly by the energy of their light. When the scientist spreads the light of these bodies out in its spectrum, he can measure the energy of each band of light. Beyond the red rays at one end of the spectrum are other rays that we cannot see but can measure. They are called the infra-red rays. Beyond the violet are the ultra-violet that seem to have great power to tan our skins and to prevent the wasting disease called rickets.

In the last few years scientists have been actively studying rays that seem to come to us from the depths of space, the *cosmic rays*. They seem to start either from the space between the stars or from the stars themselves. Some scientists interpret them as energy that is released when matter is made or when a new element is formed from others. How the cosmic rays affect living things we do not know.

Gravitation, also, of heavenly bodies has effects upon the earth. We have seen how it keeps the earth from wandering away and freezing in the depths of space. The tides that sweep our bays and coastal rivers regulating bathing hours, fishing, and often the passage of ships are due to the gravitational pull of the moon and sun.

The movement of the earth around the sun changes our seasons, and sets the limits of the habitable climates. The daily weather changes are the doings of the sun. The positions of the sun and other heavenly bodies tell us where we are on earth. Without such information from the heavens, we could not find our way across the Atlantic, nor could we find the boundary line between the United States and Canada. The rotation of the earth measured by the passage of the stars across the sky sets our clocks and so makes possible the exact adjustments of modern transportation by which our modern civilization lives.

Why days vary in length. We can understand why days vary by performing Experiment 180. The earth's axis is tilted instead of upright. It is always tilted the same amount ($23\frac{1}{2}°$), in the same direction. It always points toward the North Star. As the earth revolves around the sun, the North Pole inclines toward the sun in June and away from the sun in December. Because of the inclination toward or away from the sun, the distribution of sunlight varies and the days vary in length. We shall study the distribution of sunlight on four special days in the year.

1. June 21 or 22, the date on which the North Pole is most inclined toward the sun. This is the longest day in the year in the Northern Hemisphere; it is called the summer *solstice* (sun standing). At the time of the summer solstice the North Pole is bathed continuously in sunlight; and the South Pole is continuously in the dark. The sunlight reaches only to the Antarctic Circle. In the Northern Hemisphere the days have been growing longer until this date. Now they

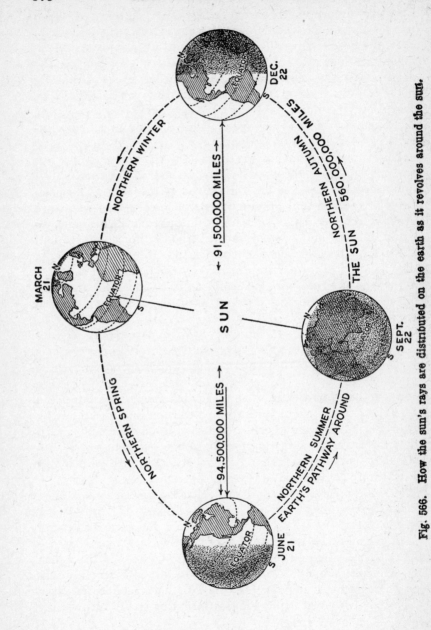

Fig. 566. How the sun's rays are distributed on the earth as it revolves around the sun.

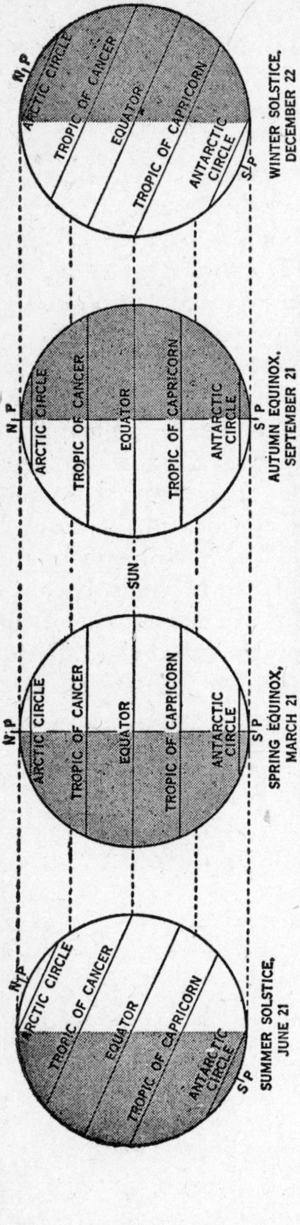

Fig. 567. The distribution of sunlight on the earth at each season.

immediately begin to shorten. In the Southern Hemisphere the situation is reversed: the nights are long, and the days are short.

2. September 23, three months later, the North Pole is not inclined toward the sun any more than the South Pole is. On this day the sun is directly overhead at noon on the Equator, and day and night are equal all over the earth. This is the time of the *autumnal equinox* (equal night). The sunlight stretches exactly from pole to pole.

3. December 21 or 22, the *winter solstice*, or the shortest day of the year in the Northern Hemisphere, the North Pole is inclined farthest away from the sun. The North Pole is in darkness 24 hours a day. The sunlight reaches northward only to the Arctic Circle. Up to this date the days in the Northern Hemisphere have been getting continually shorter but now they begin to lengthen and the sun is shining continuously on the South Pole.

4. March 21, the spring or *vernal equinox*, when, as at the autumnal equinox, day and night are equal.

The two points of special interest are thus the two solstices. At the winter solstice the days of the Northern Hemisphere, which have been getting shorter and shorter for six months, begin to lengthen. At the summer solstice the days of the Northern Hemisphere, which have been lengthening for six months, begin to shorten.

Why winter is colder than summer.   There are several reasons why winter is colder.

1. Longer days in summer give longer time for the earth to heat up.   More heat is received.

2. Experiment 181 shows that slanting rays cover more ground than direct rays.   Figure 568 shows it more briefly.   The same amount of heat is spread over more ground and therefore does not raise the temperature so high.

3. Slanting rays travel through more air than do direct rays.   As they pass they give up some of their heat to the particles of dust, moisture, and the air itself.   When they strike the earth's surface, therefore, they have less heat to give.

The sun makes ocean currents.   The slanting rays on the poles give less heat than the direct rays on the tropics. Cold water near the poles contracts, becomes heavier, and sinks.   The warmer water near the equator expands, becomes lighter, and is floated up.   The downward movement of the water at the poles and the upward movement at the Equator

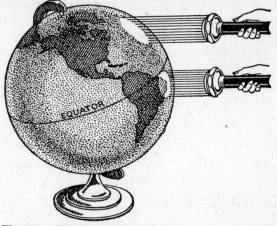

Fig. 568.   Why do the sun's direct rays give more heat
than the slanting rays?

causes a drift of water along the surface toward the poles and a drift of deep water toward the Equator.   Thus the sun's rays falling unequally on the earth causes the continuous circulation of the ocean waters.

The heavens tell where we are.   Think of a place on a smooth, spotless sphere and try to tell a classmate where the spot is.   You cannot locate a spot on a sphere.   You may say the top, but where is the top when you turn the sphere over?

Now suppose that you are in the middle of the Atlantic Ocean.   How do you find where you are and where the nearest harbor is?   You must turn your eyes to the heavens to find where you are on earth.

Scientists have put a system of two sets of lines on globes to enable us to tell where we are on earth.   If you mention two intersecting lines in this system, you locate the spot of their intersection on the earth exactly, down to the foot and inch.

One line of reference is the Equator, drawn around the earth midway between the poles.   Lines parallel with it are parallels of latitude.   To say that Philadelphia and Madrid are on the fortieth parallel north latitude, or 40° N. Lat., tells exactly how far north of the Equator these cities are.

To locate any spot we must also tell how far east or west it is.   Lines are drawn from one pole to the other, called *meridians of longitude*.   For convenience the nations have agreed to call the meridian that goes through the famous observatory at Greenwich, England, the prime meridian, or the meridian of zero degrees longitude.   If you say that a certain spot is 40° N. Lat., 75° W. Long., that place is 40° north of the Equator and 75° west of the meridian of Greenwich.

A degree is $\frac{1}{360}$ of the distance around the circle.   A degree is divided into 60 minutes (indicated by '), and a minute into 60 seconds (indicated by ").

How the heavens set our time.   When is it noon on any given day?   When the sun is as nearly overhead as it can get that day.   Remember that the sun never gets exactly

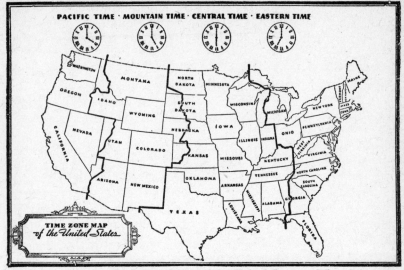

Fig. 569. The Standard Time Zones of the United States. When it is noon in Washington, D. C., what time is it in your town?

overhead for points more than $23\frac{1}{2}°$ away from the Equator. The spot directly overhead is called the *zenith*. When the sun is on the meridian that passes through the zenith in our town, is it on the meridian in a town 100 miles to the west of us? No, not yet. In a town 10 miles west of us? No, not yet. What time is it in a town 100 miles east of us? Afternoon, for the sun has passed that meridian. Then if each town set its clocks when the sun was on its meridian, the clocks would show correct time, but each town would have a different time. You could never run a railroad with that jumble of times. Therefore, when railroads spread over the country, *standard time* was adopted.

The United States is divided into four standard time belts (Fig. 569). Every place in the belt of Eastern Standard Time uses the time of points on the meridian of 75° west longitude. The Central Time belt has its time set by 90° west longitude. Mountain Time is the time of 105° west longitude, and Pacific Time the time of the 120° west longitude. When it is noon on the 75th meridian, it is 11 A.M.

on the 90th, 10 A.M. on the 105th, and 9 A.M. on the 120th. The sun travels 15 degrees of longitude each hour (360 ÷ 24 = 15). For convenience the change from one time to another is not made exactly midway between the time meridians but at convenient cities along the railroad. Therefore the time belts are bounded by irregular lines on the map.

Where the day begins. When Magellan's ship arrived in Portugal after the first voyage around the world, its calendar was one day wrong. Every day the mariner puts down the happenings of the day in a record which is called the ship's log. Although Magellan's log accounted for every day, it was one day out. Let us try to understand why.

Suppose an aviator had a plane that would fly as fast as the sun—around the earth in one day. Suppose that he left Greenwich at noon Monday and flew westward on a nonstop flight. If he traveled as fast as the sun, he would have the sun always overhead. It would always be noon on his plane. When he arrived back at Greenwich after encircling the globe, it would still be noon. The people of Greenwich would say that it was noon Tuesday, for a night would have elapsed since the aviator left. The aviator might say it was still noon Monday for he had seen no night. To keep his calendar right with the rest of the world, he would need to add a day to his calendar.

Every time one moves westward, he gains a little on the sun, that is, the sun after encircling the earth must move a little farther west to catch up with him the next day. When he moves 15°, the sun takes an hour longer to catch him. When he moves 360°, the sun takes 24 hours longer to catch him.

To keep the calendar right as we go west around the world, a day must be added. The nations have agreed to add this day when their ships cross a line drawn down the Pacific Ocean where no one lives. When a westbound ship crosses the *International Date Line*, it adds a day. When an eastbound ship crosses the line, it subtracts a day. Thus if the line is crossed at 8 A.M. on September 10, the westbound ship will enter in its log: 8 A.M. September 11. An eastbound

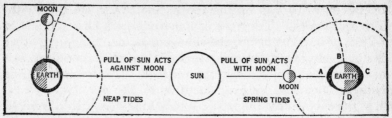

Fig. 570. Diagram to show how the moon and the sun cause the tides on the earth. Why are the tides greater in position on the right than on the left?

ship would enter 8 A.M. September 9, and the passengers will appear to live September 9 over again.

How moon and sun make tides. Probably few people who watch the tide creep into a harbor or up a winding creek think that here is a demonstration of a mighty power 240,000 miles away and another 93,000,000 miles away. The pull of the moon draws the water of the ocean upward into a swelling, or wave. As the earth turns around, this wave comes into the harbor as the tide.

About twelve hours later another tide comes in. It is not quite so easy to see the cause of this high tide. The moon actually pulls the solid earth as well as the water. In Figure 570 the parts of the earth at b and d are nearer to the moon than the part at c by about 4000 miles. They are therefore pulled more strongly. They are pulled away from the water at c, leaving an area of high water.

The gravitational pull of the sun also is felt, but as the sun is so much farther away, its tides are less noticeable. When the sun is on the same side of the earth as the moon or on the opposite side, the sun helps the moon's tide, then high tides are higher and low tides are lower than at other times. These are called *spring* tides. They have nothing to do with the spring of the year. When the sun is pulling at right angles to the pull of the moon, the difference between high tide and low tide is not so great. These are called *neap* tides. Two spring tides and two neap tides occur every $27\frac{1}{3}$ days, for the moon goes around the earth in $27\frac{1}{3}$ days.

Where is north? The stars and the sun were the early seaman's guides. The navigator uses them still. But they cannot give him his direction when clouds cover the sky. The magnetic compass was a great discovery for the seaman. This compass does not always point north, however, as we learned in the chapter on magnetism, and furthermore, it may be deflected by the steel on the ship.

Science has produced another instrument, the *gyrocompass,* to supplement the magnetic compass. The gyrocompass is now used on ocean liners and submarines. The principle is seen in the spinning top. If you set a top spinning on a piece of board, you can move the board around without changing the direction of the spinning top. The *gyroscope* is such a spinning top that maintains its position (Fig. 571). The gyrocompass is a gyroscope spinning with its axis parallel to the axis of the earth and hence pointing north. It is kept spinning by a motor. It maintains its direction no matter in what direction the boat turns (Fig. 572).

[**How the mariner finds where he is.** Suppose that you are on a ship somewhere out in the Atlantic. All that you can see is ocean and sky. Where are you and where is your harbor?

If you knew your latitude and longitude, you could pick out your spot on the map. How could you find your latitude amidst the gray waste of sea and the blue waste of sky?

Suppose it is September 23 or March 21. Then the sun is over the Equator. If you were on the Equator, you would find the sun at noon exactly 90° above the horizon. If you were 20° north of the Equator, the sun would be 20° lower or

Fig. 571. The gyroscope is a top. When spinning, a top keeps its axis pointing in the same direction.

70° above the horizon. If you know the number of degrees the sun is above the horizon—its altitude—you can find your latitude. In order to find the sun's greatest altitude on the given day, you may

have to take several observations of the sun at about noontime, and select the reading which shows the sun highest. The time of this reading will give you noon. Figure 573 shows the instrument which the mariner uses to find the sun's altitude.

If it is not March 21 or September 22, you must know exactly how far north or south of the Equator the sun is on the day in question. Tables showing the position of the sun every day in the year are published in the **Nautical Almanac.** From the information

Fig. 572. The gyrocompass. What advantage has this compass over the magnetic compass?

in the tables and observation of the sun's altitude, the mariner gets his latitude.

The mariner must also know his longitude. Suppose that when it is noon on our ship somewhere in the Atlantic, it is 2 P.M. in Greenwich. We know that the sun travels 15° an hour. We must be, therefore, 30° west of Greenwich, that is 30° W. Long.

The mariner finds out when it is noon on his ship every day by observing the sun, and he tells what time it is in Greenwich by carrying a clock which keeps Greenwich time. Such a clock is called a chronometer (meaning time measurer). Radio time signals now enable the mariner, wherever he may be, to see that his chronometer continues to keep accurate Greenwich time.]

EXPERIMENT 180

Question: How can I show that day and night are caused by the rotation of the earth on its axis?

Materials: Darkened classroom, electric-light bulb, and a small earth globe.

Directions: (*a*) Light the electric-light bulb and place it on the center of the table. This represents the sun.

(*b*) Hold the globe with its axis parallel to the table top so that the light shines directly on the equator and neither north pole nor south pole points toward the sun. Rotate the globe. Notice how much of the globe is lighted by the sun. This part of the globe would be in daylight. 1. If the axis of the earth really had this position, what would be the relative length of our days and nights?

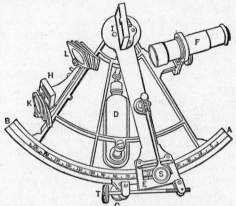

Fig. 573. The sextant, used to find sun's altitude. The sun is reflected from mirror I to H, half of which is mirror and half clear glass. The observer looks through the telescope F at H, and moves the arm IE until the sun appears to rest on the horizon in the clear glass of H. Then the altitude is read from the scale AB.

(*c*) Hold the globe with its axis perpendicular to the table top. Again observe what portion of the globe would have daylight. Rotate the globe and observe whether the position of the daylight changes. 2. If the axis of the earth really had this position, what would be the relative length of our days and nights?

(*d*) Hold the globe with its axis inclined at an angle of $23\frac{1}{2}°$ from the perpendicular. This is the true position of the earth relative to the sun. Again rotate the globe and note how the positions of daylight and darkness change. Mark the position of your city on the globe. 3. Why does your home have day and night?

Diagram: Show the position of the globe and sun in *d*.

Conclusion: 4. What is the cause of day and night? 5. Why is the inclination of the earth's axis of great importance to us?

44

EXPERIMENT 181

Question: How can I show that slanting rays bring less light and heat to the surface of the earth than vertical rays?

Materials: A square tube 2 inches in cross section and at least 12 inches long. An electric lamp that can be placed inside the tube (a flashlight will do).

Directions: (a) Place a sheet of paper on the table. Light the bulb inside the tube. Hold the tube so that the rays coming from it strike the paper vertically (direct rays). Mark the area that is lighted by these rays.

(b) Holding the tube at the same distance from the paper incline it so that the rays strike the paper at an angle of 30° (slanting rays). Again mark the area on the paper that is lighted by the rays.

(c) Repeat b, making the angle of the rays 60°.

Diagram: Show the apparatus giving direct rays and slanting rays.

Conclusion: The rays coming from the tube represent the light and heat reaching the earth from the sun. The paper represents the surface of the earth. The actual amount of light coming from the tube is the same in a, b, and c. 1. How does the amount of light received on each square inch of the paper vary in a, b, and c? 2. Why do slanting rays of sun give us less light and heat than direct rays? 3. Give one reason why it is warmer in summer than in winter.

NOTE: Some of the sun's light and heat is lost (absorbed) when it passes through the air. The more slanting the rays, the greater the amount of air that they must pass through and the greater, therefore, will be the loss. This is another reason why slanting rays give us less heat and light than vertical rays. ·

Practical application: Why is it that in the winter, when we are nearer to the sun, it is colder than in summer when we are farther away from the sun?

EXPERIMENT 182

Question: How can I show that the seasons are caused by the revolution of the earth on an inclined axis?

Materials: A globe so mounted on a stand that it can be rotated and inclined 23½°. Mark your city with a cross, and through it draw a circle, everywhere equally distant from the North Pole. This represents your parallel of latitude. An ellipse drawn with chalk on the tabletop may represent the earth's orbit. Draw the ellipse with its long axis running approximately north and south. Mark the south end of the long axis A and the north end C. Mark the east end of the short axis B and the west end D. Place an electric light on the long axis just north of the middle. The light is the sun.

Directions: (a) Hold the globe at *A* with the North Pole inclined toward the bulb and toward the north end of your room. Light the bulb. Note where the vertical rays and the slanting rays fall and where no rays fall. Rotate the globe once. This represents the position of the earth and sun in June. 1. What kind of rays does your city receive? 2. What season is it there?

(b) Hold the globe at *C* with the North Pole pointed away from the sun, but still toward the north end of the room. Rotate the globe. Note where the vertical rays fall, the slanting rays. 3. What part of the globe receives no rays? 4. What rays does your city receive? 5. What season is it there? This represents the position of the earth and sun in December.

(c) Hold the globe at *B* and *D* with the North Pole still toward the north and hence with neither North nor South Pole pointing toward the light. These represent the positions of the earth and sun in September and March respectively. Make observations as suggested in directions marked (a) and (b).

Diagram: A page drawing is required showing the earth at each of the four seasons. Draw rays of light showing how they strike your city in summer and in winter.

Conclusion: 1. What causes the seasons? 2. Why does your home receive different kinds of rays? 3. Upon what do the seasons depend?

Practical application: 1. Give two causes why the summer is hot in your home. 2. Why is our hottest season after June 21, instead of on that day? 3. If the earth's axis were not inclined, but vertical, what would be true of the length of days and nights? 4. Hammerfest, a town in Norway, is located at 71° N. From May 13 to July 8 the sun never sets. From November 18 to January 23 it never rises. Explain how this is possible.

NOTE: It is difficult to explain the direction in which a rotating body is moving. When the top of a rotating wheel is moving from left to right, the bottom is moving from right to left. The best way of describing such motions is to compare them to the hands of a clock. If the wheel is rotating in the direction in which the hands of a clock move, it has a *clockwise* movement. If it is moving in the opposite direction, it has a *counterclockwise* movement. Remember these two words. They will often help you out of a difficulty. *The earth moves counterclockwise in its orbit.*

Observe that the varying distance of the earth from the sun has little effect on the seasons. It is summer with us when the earth is farthest from the sun. The activity of plants and animals including man is largely determined by the seasons.

Practical application: Put the four tables below into your notebook, filling in the vacant spaces:

1. During a day of 24 hours there are:		Hours of Sunlight	Hours of Darkness
On December 21	At the North Pole		
	At the South Pole		
	At your home town		
On March 21	At the North Pole		
	At the South Pole		
	At your home town		
On June 21	At the North Pole		
	At the South Pole		
	At your home town		
On September 23	At the North Pole		
	At the South Pole		
	At your home town		

2. The sun's rays strike the earth's surface at your home town:
   On December 21 at an angle of
   On March 21 at an angle of
   On June 21 at an angle of
   On September 23 at an angle of
3. When it is:
   Winter in the Northern Hemisphere, it is .... in the Southern.
   Spring in the Northern Hemisphere, it is .... in the Southern.
   Summer in the Northern Hemisphere, it is .... in the Southern.
   Autumn in the Northern Hemisphere, it is .... in the Southern.
   At 10 P.M., in New York City, on December 21, what are the conditions in London, England? in Constantinople?
   At noon in New York City, on June 21, what are the conditions in Australia? in Brazil?
4. Effects of seasons on plants, animals, man in your home town.

(Some entries are made to show you the kind of answers intended)

	Plants	Animals	Man
Spring:	Seeds and trees start to grow.		
Summer:		Horses cannot do as much work as usual because of the heat.	

	Plants	Animals	Man
Autumn:			
Winter:			*Snow makes travel difficult. Cold freezes water pipes.*

How the plants adapt themselves to climate:
  Torrid Zone
  Temperate Zone
  Frigid Zone

How animals adapt themselves to climate:
  Torrid Zone
  Temperate Zone
  Frigid Zone

How man adapts himself to climate:
  Torrid Zone   *Heat makes white, light-weight clothing desirable. Men need little meat and more fruit and vegetables. Men become lazy, etc. Houses? Business hours? Sleeping hours, etc.?*

Temperate Zone
Frigid Zone

Chapter LXV

HISTORY AND LIFE IN THE HEAVENS

The speeding stars. Things in space are moving, moving fast, about a thousand times as fast as an express train. The earth is traveling around the sun at 18½ miles a second. Other planets are going at comparable speeds. The sun, too, is moving through space, taking the whole solar system with it. The other stars that seem so still, fixed about where the first man saw them, are also moving. Our whole Galaxy is rotating furiously. Other galaxies are doing the same.

Because of their vast distances away, we cannot see the stars change their places. Only the instruments of the scientist can tell us of their motions, of the direction, and the rate. That invaluable instrument, the spectroscope, again comes into service. Light rays from a fixed source are refracted a known amount by a prism; if the lines of the spectrum made by the light from a given star do not fall where we should expect them, but are displaced toward the red end of the spectrum, it tells us that the star is moving away from us; if they are displaced toward the violet end, it is moving toward us. By mathematical computation, the rates may be learned.

The beginning and the end. The structure of stars, nebulae, and planets likewise is changing. Measured in terms of human life the change is infinitely slow. The records of science are much too recent to tell the history of a star directly, but the astronomer sees nebulae and stars that seem to show stages in the history of a celestial body. With the aid of mathematics he can write the history. Our knowledge is still a little uncertain. There is a difference of opinion about the details of the history, but there is an agreement on the general story.

Fig. 574. A globular cluster of stars. One stage in the
history of stars.

Let us imagine that at first all matter was evenly distributed
in a thin cloud or gas throughout the universe. It does not
stay in that state. Every particle attracts every other
particle. Movement of particles begins. Where several
particles approached one another, their combined pull of
gravitation would tend to bring together still others. So the
accumulation would grow.

Because of the tendency of things to keep on moving, the forces of gravitation would make the accumulations go round and round as the planets move around the sun. Great balls of thin gas would be formed. Many nebulae are just such balls of gas. With continued rotation and increased speed, the balls would flatten at the ends. Such nebulae are also in the skies. Still further flattening would make rotating disks. Such nebulae are also common.

Meantime within the nebulae the gas gathers in denser spots separated by thinner areas (Fig. 564). These denser areas are the young stages of the stars. A nebula becomes a globular cluster of stars (Fig. 574).

Does a star once formed last forever? No, not so. The ball continues to condense and lose heat. Gas becomes liquid and liquid becomes solid. The heat gradually passes into space. There is left a cold, hard ball of rock much like our moon. We have not actually seen such dead stars. They would have no light of their own and would be too far away to be seen by reflected light. Astronomers have reason to believe that such dark stars exist. Certain stars vary in brightness in such a way as to suggest that a dark star may revolve in front of them, shutting off part of their light.

Such then is the life history of a star—a fiery mist, a rotating ball, a rotating, flattened nebula, a cluster of stars, then gradual darkness and cold. And shall such death last forever? There is some reason to suspect a resurrection. The star material may be dissipated again to start the cycle over. But that is a matter of deep mathematics which we shall not attempt to follow. The idea that the stars and the solar system originated in a nebula is the *nebular hypothesis*.

How the earth began. In rare instances stars meet with accidents by which planets are born. At one time a big star went sweeping past, close to the sun. Such near approach of two stars must be extremely rare, for stars are millions upon millions of miles apart. As it approached, the gravitational pull of the star increased. When it was very close, the gas on the sun was drawn up in a great tidal wave; when it was still closer, only three times the star's diameter away, the gas was actually pulled away from the sun, out into space. But the big star rushed on past, and the gas was left in space as the gravitation of the star decreased with distance. The initial pull of the star set the gas circulating around the sun. Gradually the gas condensed into balls as steam condenses into drops of water. These balls were the young planets, one of which was the earth. The earth has grown since that time by the addition of various small bodies which, like meteors, were attracted to it. These small bodies are called *planetesimals* and the idea of such growth is called the *planetesimal hypothesis.*

Perhaps the earth did not pass through a liquid stage. Its center now is not liquid, but denser than its crust. Perhaps it gathers gas now as it gathers solid meteors from space.

How old is the earth? The actual figures that scientists have arrived at are not important. They do not agree, and they are too big to mean much to us anyway. The methods used to obtain the figures are important, for they show how scientists use facts, and why the results disagree when different methods are used.

An old method of estimating the age of the earth is based on the salt in the sea. Sea salt is land salt that the rain has dissolved from the rocks, and the rivers carried to the sea. When the water evaporates from the sea, the salt remains behind. We can estimate the quantity of salt in the sea and the quantity brought in by the rivers each year. Thus we can arrive at an age for the sea.

Another method is based on the sand and mud carried down by rivers. In Egypt we have the record since the days of Rameses II three thousand years ago.

The latest method is based on the change in radioactive rocks. Uranium gives off rays resembling X rays and in so doing changes into lead. The rate of change is known. The amounts of uranium and lead in a radioactive rock will tell how long the process has been going on.

As a compromise of the results from the various methods, it would seem that the earth has been in existence for about 2,000,000,000 years.

Life in the heavens. After the seas had formed on earth and had cooled to a comfortable temperature, a strange new event took place. Life arose. Scientific guesses as to how life arose are too vague to bother about. Perhaps it took place about 300,000,000 years ago, but that is also too uncertain to remember.

Is there life outside the earth? Let us reason it out from the facts known to science. The moon has no oxygen to support life and therefore no life. Mercury, the planet nearest to the sun, has a daytime temperature of 660° F. That temperature melts lead. There can be no life on Mercury. Venus, the next planet, has only $\frac{1}{10}$ of 1 per cent as much oxygen as has the earth. No life is there.

Mars has 15 per cent as much oxygen as has the earth. Much of earth's life could not exist there. Its daytime temperature is about 50° F. at Equator, but it falls below freezing before sunset. The outer planets are all too cold for life: their temperatures are 150° to 220° below zero or even lower. Mars is then the only possibility for life in the solar system, and life there is doubtful.

We have seen that few of the stars are likely to have planets. If planets exist outside of the solar system, the chances of one's having just the right temperature and just the right amount of oxygen and other substances for life as we know it are few indeed. Science has found no evidence of earthly life beyond the earth.

ADDITIONAL QUESTIONS TO THINK OUT

1. If you were at the North Pole, where should you see the North Star?

2. If you were in the Southern Hemisphere where the North Star is not visible, could you tell your direction from the stars?

3. How could you tell time at night without a watch?

4. With an ordinary camera you can take an interesting picture of star tracks. Find a place outdoors away from electric lights. Point the camera to the north if possible. Set the shutter for "time." Open the shutter and leave the camera for as many hours as convenient. You will find that the star tracks on the film are curved. Why?

5. Could you jump higher on Mercury or on Jupiter? Why?

6. Some of the asteroids are only 10 miles in diameter. Do you think such a body would have a dense atmosphere?

7. Why do we believe that the earth revolves around the sun?

8. How do you know that the moon shines only by reflected light?

9. Why is it said that the other side of the moon is made of green cheese?

10. If the moon were suddenly covered with an atmosphere, it would promptly lose it. Why?

11. For several nights watch the moon rise or note when it reaches the top of the house. Does it rise earlier or later each night? Why?

12. How long does it take light to travel from the moon to us?

13. Do you see the new moon in the west or in the east? Why?

14. If you saw a crescent moon in the early morning, would it be a new moon or an old moon? Demonstrate with a globe and light.

15. Sometimes when the moon is a narrow crescent, you can see the whole face dimly. Where does the dim light come from? This is the condition called "the old moon in the new moon's arms."

16. Why do the mountains of the moon cast no shadows when the moon is full?

17. Why can there not be an eclipse of the sun at full moon?

18. Why do ships crossing the Atlantic follow steamship lanes?

19. How can the size of the earth be determined without measuring all round?

20. To use your watch as a compass, point the hour hand toward the sun. Halfway between the hour hand and twelve o'clock is south. Do you see why?

21. How was time measured before clocks were built? Look up in the library.

22. Make a rough sundial. Draw a north-and-south line on a board. Set a large pin or knitting needle upright on the line. Place the board in the sun and each hour rule a line on the shadow of the pin.

23. On what day, at what hour, is your shadow shortest?

24. Is there a spot on earth where the noon shadow is always the same?

25. Does the earth as a whole receive more sun energy in our summer or in our winter?

26. In Alaska many plants such as tomatoes grow faster than farther south. Why?

27. What evidence is there that the moon causes tides?

28. Why are the tides an hour later each day?

29. Why do you suppose there is little or no tide in lakes?

INDEX

Absolute: humidity, 631; zero, 196
Absorption, of energy, 188–189; of food, 511
Acetic acid, 540
Acetylene, 184
Acid, 313; defined, 118
Aëdes, 549
Aëration, 82
Aërial, radio, 346, 348
After image, 287
Age: of earth, 693; of trees, 386
Air: 16–58; and combustion, 51–52; as a gas, 17, 39; as matter, 17; compressed, 32–37; conditioning, 16; currents, 628–629; hot, 215–216; in body, 24; in high altitudes, 22; in soil, 23; in water, 24; liquid, 17; motion, 628; pollution of, 16; pressure, 18–32, 241–242; solid, 17; water in, 631; weight of, 17–18
Air brakes, 33
Airplanes, 30, 31, 32
Air pump, 17, 23
Alcohol, 200, 534–535; as solvent, 101
Alfalfa, 435
Alkali, 118
Allies: animal, 567; bird, 566
Alloy, 100
Altimeter, 21
Alum, 79
Ammeter, 316
Ammonia, 208, 209
Amperage, 315–316
Anchor roots, 434
Anemometer, 630
Animals, 366–369, 402–415; allies, 566; deep sea, 622–623; famous breeds, 411; reproduction, 403–404, 412
Anode, 311–312
Anopheles, 549
Antarctic Circle, 675
Anther, 391, 392
Antibodies, 552, 553
Anticyclone, 636, 641
Antifreeze, 200
Antiseptics, 547
Antitoxin, 553
Aorta, 513–514
Aqueduct, 75, 76

Arc, electric, 322
Archimedes' principle, 67
Areas, barometric, 628, 632–633
Argon, 44, 323
Aristotle, 652
Armature, 331, 333, 337–338, 340
Artery, 514, 525
Artificial respiration, 526, 527
Asexual reproduction, 399
Asphyxiation, 28
Astigmatism, 279
Astronomy, 646–695
Atmosphere, 19, 29
Atmospheric pressure, 623
Atom, 304; defined, 105
Atomizer, 37
Attraction; electrical, 303; magnetic, 299
Auditory nerve, 241
Autoclave, 61
Automobile, 174, 175, 176
Autonomic system, 518
Autumnal equinox, 677
Axis, of earth, 675

Bacteria, 23, 41, 43, 49, 81, 114, 369, 512, 525, 529, 546, 547, 550, 552, 556; colonies of, 538; inoculation with, 539; in soil, 421; kinds of, 538; multiplication of, 538; plant, 538; poisoning by, 541, 542; protection against, 542, 543
Bacterium, 538
Balloon, 29, 30, 31
Bark, 386
Barometer: aneroid, 21; Torricellian, 19–20
Bast, 385
Basalt, 609
Base, 118–119; defined, 118
Battery jar, 64
Bearing: ball, 156; roller, 156
Bee bread, 396
Bees, relation to flowers, 396
Beet, sugar, 446
Bell, electric, 328, 333–334
Bell jar, 20, 23
Belts, wind, 637
"Bends" (caisson disease), 24
Beriberi, 475

S